D1177369

PSYCHOLOGICAL STRESS

THE CENTURY PSYCHOLOGY SERIES

Richard M. Elliott, Gardner Lindzey & Kenneth MacCorquodale
Editors

Psychological stress

Issues in research

Edited by

MORTIMER H. APPLEY
York University

RICHARD TRUMBULL
Office of Naval Research

1967

Appleton-Century-Crofts
Division of Meredith Publishing Company

New York

PRINTED IN THE UNITED STATES OF AMERICA
E03395

To the subjects, both human and animal, without whose service in psychological stress studies no understanding of the issues involved would be possible, this book is gratefully dedicated.

Preface

This book is based on an interdisciplinary Conference on Psychological Stress held at York University, Toronto, Canada, May 10–12, 1965, under contract Nonr 4612-(00) between the Group Psychology Branch, Psychological Sciences Division, U.S. Office of Naval Research and the Department of Psychology, York University.

The idea for the conference developed out of earlier ONR-sponsored research on Motivation and Psychological Stress (Contract Nonr 996(02), Project NR 172-228), conducted by M. H. and Dee G. Appley and George Moeller at Connecticut College, New London, from 1953 to 1958, and discussions with Luigi Petrullo and Richard Trumbull of the Office of Naval Research.

Actual arrangements for the conference were made through and with Abraham S. Levine, then Assistant Head, Group Psychology Branch, Office of Naval Research, and the editors wish to express their sincere appreciation to Dr. Levine for his helpful cooperation and advice throughout the project. Drs. Sheldon J. Korchin and Richard S. Lazarus formed an initial steering committee, with Dr. Levine and the editors, which determined the form of the conference and the invitation list. We should like to thank them for their useful assistance in planning. Obviously, not all those invited were able to accept, nor, for reasons of economy and efficiency, was it possible to extend invitations to all who could profitably have contributed to the conference. The editors believe, however, that they were most fortunate in being able to gather together a distinguished group of active workers in the field of psychological stress research and that the edited proceedings contained in this volume are a reasonable sampling of the spectrum of opinions and of research in the areas covered by this concept.

The conference was arranged for a three-day period, each day devoted to hearing and discussing four papers on physiological, psychological, and social factors, respectively. Although slightly reorganized for purposes of this volume, the reader may well observe the clear shifts in emphasis and in concern for detail as one moves from considerations of physiological to social factors and from microcosmic to macrocosmic units of discourse.

It was by deliberate design that the conference proceeded as a single session through its three days, with anthropologists, sociologists, and social psychologists participating in discussions of endocrine and physiological factors in stress, and neuropsychiatrists, physiological psychologists, and physiologists contributing to discussions of social and cultural factors in stress. Clearly, there was enough input from any one of the twelve papers to have formed the basis for three days of discussion and for an informative volume. The decision to limit discussion and stay "on schedule" was regretted each time, but in retrospect it has produced an overview of the significant issues in stress research that might not have been possible with more extended discussions of a smaller range of topics.

A word should be said about the editing of this volume. Each author and discussant was given an opportunity to reexamine and edit his own contribution as transcribed from recorded conference tapes. The more polished language and the greater clarity of expression of ideas that resulted compensates, we feel, for the occasionally disjointed interactions between discussants caused by changed wordings here and there. Two other decisions made by the editors should be communicated to the reader. The first editorial decision was to leave unchanged the idiosyncratic styles of the individual contributors and their preferences for particular forms of words and expressions. Thus, *physiologic* and *physiological, adrenaline* and *epinephrine, conditioned* and *conditional,* and several other sets of terms with essentially the same meaning will be used in different chapters. Considering the range of disciplines represented by the contributors to this volume and by potential readers as well, the editors took the more cowardly approach of retaining the differences and hoping that the reader can make the necessary translations himself without too much difficulty.

A second editorial decision was to leave, in the introductory remarks of the twelve papers, the authors' definitional treatments of the concept of *stress* and the particular uses made of the term. In Chapter 1, we attempt to deal with the problem of definition and the ranges of use and meaning of the term *stress.* Comparisons across chapter introductions provide useful examples of this variation and set the frame for each author's further remarks. Again, our decision was the "easy way out," but it was taken consciously and in keeping with the intention of the volume to display the *issues* in psychological stress research, not the least of which is to focus on a common meaning and use of the concept itself.

The editors wish to acknowledge their sincere indebtedness to David Homer, audio-visual aids coordinator of York University, for his invaluable assistance in faithfully preserving the entire conference on tape. Without these tapes the discussions contained in this volume would have been lost forever. Thanks are also due to Dr. L. R. Boulter and Messrs.

Grant Coulson and Boyd Richards for assistance in conference arrangements; to York University Chancellor Air-Marshall W. A. Curtis for his thoughtful words of greeting in officially opening the conference; and to Mrs. Margery E. Adamson, Miss Joan Hancock, and Mrs. Verna Hunt who assisted in the typing and proofreading of the manuscript for this book. A special word of thanks must go to Miss Donna Hughes for her most faithful and conscientious help in the transcriptions of the conference tapes.

The editors wish to acknowledge the splendid cooperation of the contributors in agreeing to participate in the conference in the first place; in editing their own materials so carefully; in providing corrections, tables, figures, and references so quickly upon being asked; and in allowing the editors sufficient liberty, in most cases, to get on with their task in reasonably short time.

We wish further to record our appreciation to our wives, whose enduring patience during the long hours this task has taken made it possible at all.

Finally, to Mrs. Lillian Kindree, without whose dedication neither the conference nor this volume would have been possible, we acknowledge our greatest debt. As project secretary she assisted in the complex arrangements for and during the conference, to its great benefit, and from transcription to final revised manuscript gave continuity to this volume.

M. H. A.
R. T.

Participants

ALTMAN, Irwin, Ph.D., Project Director, Behavioral Sciences Department, Naval Medical Research Institute, Bethesda, Maryland.

APPLEY, Mortimer, H., Ph.D., Professor of Psychology and Chairman of the Department and Dean, Faculty of Graduate Studies, York University, Toronto, Canada.

ARNOLD, Magda, B., Ph.D., Professor of Psychology, Loyola University, Chicago, Illinois.

AX, Albert F., Ph.D., Head, Psychophysiological Division, Lafayette Clinic, Detroit, Michigan.

BACK, Kurt, W., Ph.D., Professor of Sociology and Anthropology, Duke University, Durham, North Carolina.

BAKER, George W., Ph.D., Staff Associate, Division of Institutional Programs, National Science Foundation, Washington, District of Columbia.

BIDERMAN, Albert D., Ph.D., Senior Research Associate, Bureau of Social Science Research, Inc., Washington, District of Columbia.

BOVARD, Everett W., Ph.D., Associate Professor of Anatomy, Albert Einstein College of Medicine, Yeshiva University, New York, New York.

COHEN, Sanford I., M.D., Professor of Psychiatry, Head, Division of Psychophysiologic Research, Duke University Medical Center, Durham, North Carolina.

HAGGARD, Ernest A., Ph.D., Professor of Psychology, Department of Psychiatry, College of Medicine, University of Illinois at the Medical Center, Chicago, Illinois.

HAYTHORN, William W., Ph.D., Director, Behavioral Sciences Department, Naval Medical Research Institute, Bethesda, Maryland.

KORCHIN, Sheldon J., Ph.D., Professor of Psychology and Director of Clinical Training, University of California, Berkeley, California.

KUBZANSKY, Philip E., Ph.D., Associate Professor of Psychology and Assistant Dean, Graduate School, Boston University, Boston, Massachusetts.

LACEY, John I., Ph.D., Chairman, Department of Psychophysiology and Neurophysiology, Fels Research Institute, Yellow Springs, Ohio.

LANZETTA, John T., Ph.D., Professor of Psychology, Dartmouth College, Hanover, New Hampshire.

LAZARUS, Richard S., Ph.D., Professor of Psychology, University of California, Berkeley, California.

LEVINE, Abraham S., Ph.D., Program Research Branch, Division of Research, Office of the Commissioner, Welfare Administration, Department of Health, Education and Welfare, Washington, District of Columbia.

LUCAS, R. A., Ph.D., Professor of Sociology, University of Toronto, Canada.

MANDLER, George, Ph.D., Professor of Psychology and Chairman of the Department, University of California at San Diego, La Jolla, California.

MECHANIC, David, Ph.D., Associate Professor of Sociology, University of Wisconsin, Madison, Wisconsin.

NOTTERMAN, Joseph M., Ph.D., Professor of Psychology, Princeton University, Princeton, New Jersey.

NOWLIS, Vincent, Ph.D., Professor of Psychology, University of Rochester, Rochester, New York.

OKEN, Donald, M.D.,[1] Associate Director, Institute for Psychosomatic and Psychiatric Research and Training, Michael Reese Hospital and Medical Center, Chicago, Illinois.

OPLER, Marvin K., Ph.D., Professor of Social Psychiatry (Department of Psychiatry) and Professor of Sociology and Anthropology (Graduate School), State University of New York at Buffalo, Buffalo, New York.

PEPITONE, Albert, Ph.D., Professor of Psychology, University of Pennsylvania, Philadelphia, Pennsylvania.

PRESCOTT, James W., Ph.D., Assistant Head, Physiological Psychology Branch, Office of Naval Research, Department of the Navy, Washington, District of Columbia.

RUFF, George E., M.D., Associate Professor of Psychiatry, School of Medicine, University of Pennsylvania, Philadelphia, Pennsylvania.

SELLS, Saul B., Ph.D., Professor of Psychology, and Director, Institute of Behavioral Research, Texas Christian University, Fort Worth, Texas.

STERN, John A., Ph.D., Professor and Head, Medical Psychology, Department of Psychiatry, School of Medicine, Washington University, St. Louis, Missouri.

TRUMBULL, Richard, Ph.D., Director, Psychological Sciences Division, Office of Naval Research, Department of the Navy, Washington, District of Columbia.

WEYBREW, Benjamin B., Ph.D., Head, Personnel Research Branch, U.S. Naval Submarine Base, New London, Groton, Connecticut.

WILKINS, Walter L., Ph.D., Scientific Director, U.S. Navy Medical Neuropsychiatric Research Unit, San Diego, California.

[1] Present address: Clinical Research Branch, National Institute of Mental Health, Bethesda, Maryland 20014.

Contents

PSYCHOLOGICAL STRESS

MORTIMER H. APPLEY

RICHARD TRUMBULL

1

On the concept of
psychological stress [1]

The concept of *stress* was first introduced into the life sciences by endocrinologist Hans Selye in 1936 and elaborated in successive papers, leading to a full theoretical statement in book form in 1950. The wide appeal of the concept was evidenced by the fact that the literature on its primarily physiological aspects alone was close to six thousand publications per annum by the early 1950's, when Selye began his *Annual report of stress* series (see Selye, 1951 on). The use of the term in psychological research had an accelerated growth curve following Selye's invited address to the American Psychological Association in 1955. Initially, as Harris et al. (1956) have suggested, this interest developed "because of the importance of physiological variables as independent measurable indicators of a stressed organism" (p. 3). However, the use of the concept has spread through many facets of psychology (cf. Appley, 1957a, b; Cofer & Appley, 1964, pp. 441–465) and has been applied even where no physiological or endocrine factors were subject to study.

There are at least three reasons for the apparent popularity of stress as a psychological concept. The first might be called a bandwagon effect. Since the term gained some attention, and apparently some status, as a research topic, it has been used as a substitute for what might otherwise have been called anxiety, conflict, emotional distress, extreme environmental conditions, ego-threat, frustration, threat to security, tension, arousal, or by some other previously respectable terms. Secondly, because of its wide use in the biological field, the use of the term suggested both apparent and real possibility of correlating psychological events with

[1] This chapter combines and extends the introductory remarks made by the two authors to the Opening Session of the Conference on Psychological Stress, May 10, 1965.

physiological substrata, a prestigious and hopeful pre-occupation of psychologists these days. Thirdly, of course, is the genuine interest in stress phenomena, stimulated in part by concern with the effects of the unusual environments in which men are being placed these days in military and space operations, and in part by the exciting possibilities of real links being established between areas of clinical, psychosomatic, and various types of traditional experimental research.

That the use of common language might lead to the establishment of relationships is surely an advantage. That the use of common terms in different ways may lead to confusion, however, is quite apparent to anyone studying or confronted by the burgeoning stress literature.

The present volume provides an opportunity to examine the concept of stress across a wide spectrum of situations, levels, and views. Its ultimate usefulness as a psychological concept will depend upon the adequacy with which differentiations can be made among stimulus-, organismic-, and response-elements of stress situations, and whether stress researchers can avoid the inviting trap into which many personologists, for example, have fallen, namely that of treating their subject as though it were a unitary, all-or-none phenomenon. The papers and discussions which compose this volume will make clear some of the difficulties which are unique to the field of stress research as well as show how some of these problems are common to psychological investigation and scientific research generally.

Systemic stress

To begin at the beginning one should look at Selye's original conception of systemic stress. In arriving at this concept, Selye made much of the point that although different disease syndromes have unique attributes and symptoms, they have many features in common, and it is those features that are common among them that constitute stress. He wrote:

. . . if we abstract from these specific reactions, there remains a common residual response that is non-specific as regards its cause and can be elicited with such diverse agents as cold, heat, X-rays, adrenalin, insulin, tubercle bacilli, or muscular exercise. This is so despite the essentially different nature of the evocative agents themselves and despite the coexistence of highly specific adaptive reactions to any one of these agents. (1959, pp. 406–7)

. . . the stereotypical response, which is superimposed upon all specific effects, represents the somatic manifestations of non-specific "stress" itself. (1953, p. 18)

And in further elaboration in another context, Selye explains:

Among other things . . . stress is not necessarily the result of damage but can be caused by physiologic function and . . . it is not merely the result of a non-specific action but also comprises the defenses against it. (1955, p. 626)

Selye found antecedents for his work in the concept of Hippocrates that disease not only includes suffering (pathos) but a reaction of the body seeking restoration through toil (panos) as well. Claude Bernard's (1859) description of and evidence for the necessity for maintenance of the "constancy of the internal milieux" was an acknowledged base for Selye (1956), as well as for Cannon (1932) in the development of his concept of homeostasis. This general notion of systemic equilibration had still another early advocate in Herrick, who wrote:

The material and energy of the living body are in constant flux, yet the pattern of their manifestation persists. When this pattern is deformed by external violence or by changes of internal state it is said in current biological descriptions that there is a tendency to return to the typical condition. This restoration of the original pattern after deformation is termed regulation. . . . In view of the fact that the ordinary conditions of life involve constant changes in the relations of the body to its environment, regulation in the broad sense means simply the continuous readjustment of the organism to the flux of surrounding conditions. (1924, pp. 279–280)

It would be impossible to do justice to Selye's concept of stress (or to its precursors) in a few paragraphs here. His own work on this subject has extended over thirty years and resulted in a thousand publications (Institut de Médecine et de Chirurgie Expérimentales, 1964). But as background for the papers which follow, we shall try to indicate a few of the salient emphases in his development of the stress concept.

Systemic stress is manifested by a *General Adaptation Syndrome* (*GAS*). The first stage of this syndrome, or the *alarm reaction,* includes an initial *shock phase* (in which resistance is lowered) and a *counter-shock phase* (in which defensive mechanisms become active). A second *stage of resistance* follows, during which maximum adaptation occurs. Should the stressor persist, however—or the defensive reaction prove ineffective—a *stage of exhaustion* is reached in which adaptive mechanisms collapse.

The *alarm reaction* is typically characterized by autonomic excitability, adrenaline discharge, heart rate, muscle tone and blood content changes, and gastrointestinal ulceration. Adrenocortical enlargement and hyperactivity are ordinarily observed in the countershock phase.[2] Depending on the nature and intensity of the stressor and the condition of the organism at the time of exposure, the periods of resistance may be

[2] For a more detailed description of characteristic symptoms see Selye (1950, 1952, 1959). General schemata of the stress syndrome have been offered elsewhere by Appley (1961); Cofer and Appley (1964).

foreshortened or prolonged and the severity of symptoms may vary from mild invigoration to what Selye has called the "diseases of adaptation." [3]

Throughout his extensive writings, Selye emphasizes the fact that a variety of circumstances gives rise to a highly stereotyped bodily reaction, as well as reactions peculiar or specific to the nature of the insulting agent. It is the general (or common) rather than the specific reaction of the organism which constitutes stress as we have earlier noted. Both the events in the environment which induce stress and certain concomitant and resultant responses may be quite varied. The *systemic stress* response, however, is invariant.

This pattern might be described in terms of an hourglass model, feeding from a wide source of stimuli through a narrow *common* element to a spectrum of responses. Although psychologists do not usually measure changes in terms of adrenal weight or stomach ulcers, preferring such indices as the galvanic skin response (GSR) or changes in heart rate, they nevertheless have assumed and sought to identify *common* elements of body change to index the stress response. In other words, something like this hourglass model underlies much of the prolific research which is carried on by psychologists on the physiological changes accompanying emotion. This belief in a *common* state in aroused organisms follows from a conviction of psychosomatic unity and from a desire to have at least one stable anchor in their descriptive system. It seems most likely, however, as research findings accumulate, that such a conception will turn out to be an oversimplification of the facts. Individual differences, styles, patterns of response, and prepotent tendencies appear to be the rule rather than the exception in studies of psychological stress. As laboratories in universities become more affluent and can afford to add channels to their psychophysiological recording equipment, as measurement techniques become more sophisticated, and as computers permit more exacting and exhaustive data analysis, we may find a common response pattern. It seems more likely, however, that the study of idiosyncratic psychobiological patterns will emerge as a major area of stress research.

Turning now to psychological stress more specifically, and looking at how people have dealt with the concept, we see that it is in fact an inference from either manipulations of the environment (external and/or internal) or from measurements of change in response (internal and/or external).

[3] *"Diseases of Adaptation* are those in which imperfections of the *GAS* play the major role. Many diseases are actually not the direct result of some external agent but rather the consequences of the body's inability to meet these agents by adequate adaptive reactions. Maladaptation plays a major role in diseases of the heart and blood vessels, diseases of the kidney, eclampsia, rheumatism and rheumatoid arthritis; inflammatory diseases of the skin and eyes, infections, allergy and hypersensitivity, nervous and mental diseases, sexual derangements, digestive and metabolic diseases, and cancer" (Institut de Médecine et de Chirurgie Expérimentales, 1964, p. 23).

Psychological stress

1. On the *stimulus* side, the term has been used to describe situations characterized as new, intense, rapidly changing, sudden or unexpected, including (but not requiring) approach to the upper thresholds of tolerability. At the same time, stimulus deficit, absence of expected stimulation, highly persistent stimulation, and fatigue-producing and boredom-producing settings, among others, have also been described as stressful, as have stimuli leading to cognitive misperception, stimuli susceptible to hallucination, and stimuli calling for conflicting responses. Any one of these procedures has at some time actually been used as an operational means for defining and producing stress.

2. On the *response* side, the presence of emotional activity has been used *post facto* to define the existence of stress. This usually refers to any bodily response in excess of "normal or usual"—states of anxiety, tension, and upset—or for that matter any behavior which deviates momentarily or over time from normative value for the individual in question or for an appropriate reference group. Indices used include such overt emotional responses as tremors, stuttering, exaggerated speech characteristics, and loss of sphincter control—or such performance shifts as perseverative behaviors, increased reaction time, erratic performance rates, malcoordination, error increase, and fatigue.

3. The existence of a stress state *within* the organism has alternatively been inferred from one or more of a number of partially correlated indices, such as a change in blood eosinophils, an increase in 17-ketosteroids in the urine, an increase in ACTH-content or gluco-corticoid concentration in the blood, or changes in any number of psychophysiological variables, such as heart rate, galvanic skin response (GSR), change in critical flicker fusion (CFF) threshold, inspiration:expiration $\left(\frac{I}{E}\right)$ ratio, and so on. (These are response measures, of course, but they can be usefully distinguished from responses which are of the order of overt performance changes or observable symptoms of emotionality, such as those noted above.)

The problem of definition

Investigators have usually sought both a condition which produces stress and a measure which indicates its presence as the most frequent combination of circumstances in which to study the phenomenon. Unfortunately, the choices have been selective—as often governed by the convenience or tradition of a given laboratory as by rational considerations. There are, then, clearly wide variations in specific uses, specific definitions, and specific purposes with which the term *stress* has been associated. However, one is reminded of Whitehorn's comments:

We may be able to get some use out of the term stress, even if it is left vague and not very clearly defined, provided we succeed in specifying fairly sharply some of the aspects of the biological reactions to stress.

If we were dealing with inanimate objects, the conceptual and terminological problem would be greatly simplified, because in physics action and reaction are equal, and stress can be expressed in dynes per square centimeter; but in biology this is not so. Living organisms are specially organized to accumulate and spend energy on their own discriminately, and not in exact equality to the forces acting upon them. We take this one step further and recognize the psychological factors which further influence this discriminating function and appreciate that our difficulties of description and evaluation have been geometrically expanded. (1953, p. 3)

Without a doubt, this geometrical expansion has served as a deterrent to exploring the psychological complex which produces the inequality of response to the forces acting.

Let us look next at the pattern of stress experiments. Typically, the experimenter manipulates the environment in a manner intended to produce a response, and then measures the extent and/or direction of the behavior change produced. (This is, of course, the pattern of all psychological experiments. Stress studies are usually distinguishable primarily in the selection of stimulating conditions).

Experimenters in these studies choose environmental manipulations which would, in their consideration, serve to produce not just change in the direction of on-going behavior—which after all is what any response must be, and would not distinguish stress studies—but a disruption of behavior, or its disorganization. Accompanying such disorganization one expects to find certain physiological changes, and it is here that much of this research is concentrated. In fact, the most widely accepted types of operational definitions of the existence of stress are changes in physiological indices. Unfortunately, one investigator relies on the GSR, a second on blood volume changes, a third on pulse rate or heart rate, a fourth on muscle action potential, and so on. In animals, the presence of stress is often inferred from feces counts, trembling, "freezing" or washing behavior, and so on. The use of these measures rests on the simple assumption that certain environmental conditions induce not only overt behavioral effects but common autonomic and other internal effects as well.

We would not so much disagree with the logic of this argument as with the facts it has produced. In the studies with which we have acquaintance there are marked individual differences, as has already been noted. All subjects apparently do not respond to given environmental conditions as a given experimenter expected or intended. We may either conclude that the conditions were not stress-producing or, if we insist that they were, we must face the problem of explaining why some subjects were thereby *not* put into a stress state. We surely needn't labor this point which could be made in connection with most psychological studies. It is of particular importance here, however, because of what we have described as the assumption of the commonality of intervening responses in stress situations. Further, the dependence on the stimulus to define a situation as stressful is obviously too limiting.

If we accept that a physiological index is a proper monitor of the presence of stress, which may be reasonable in some respects, we must nevertheless parallel our studies of these responses with investigations of those conditions which precipitate stress in the individuals under study. It is clear that if we cannot rely upon the stimulus we must look for some pattern of stimulus-organism interaction to understand why stress occurs in some exposed organisms and not in others.

With the exception of extreme and sudden life-threatening situations, it is reasonable to say that no stimulus is a stressor to all individuals exposed to it.[4] The earlier assumption of a common all-or-none psycho-physiological stress state is untenable in the face of evidence to the contrary. James Miller and his associates (1953), after surveying the available stress-sensitive tests more than a dozen years ago, concluded that "in a specific situation it becomes necessary to recognize the many different kinds of stress" (p. A-4). Lazarus, Deese, and Osler (1952), after reviewing the literature on the effects of stress on performance, concluded that these effects are not general, but "will depend upon what the individual expects or demands of himself" (p. 296). In a more recent paper, Lazarus (1964) suggested what he called "cognitive appraisal" as a mediating condition for such determination,[5] and Appley (1962) has placed emphasis on the importance of "threat perception" as a mediator of stressfulness. A similar point was made earlier by Pascal (1951) in defining stress "in terms of a perceived environmental situation which threatens the gratification of needs . . ." (p. 177).

Basowitz, Persky, Korchin, and Grinker (1955), in an elaborate study of anxiety and stress in paratroopers, started with a situational definition but concluded that "in future research . . . we should not consider stress as *imposed* upon the organism, but as its *response* to internal or external processes which reach those threshold levels that strain its physiological

[4] An interesting contrast can be made within the category of life-endangering situations. Attempted strangulation, for example, may be a psychological stressor of great import, whereas significant levels of irradiation (which may be near fatal but are not "detected" by the organism) may have no discernible effect on behavior at all.

[5] See Lazarus, this volume, for an elaboration of this point, and related concepts in Arnold's chapter and in discussion elsewhere in the volume.

and psychological integrative capacities close to or beyond their limits" (pp. 288–289).

Cofer and Appley (1964) defined stress as "the state of an organism where he perceives that his well-being (or integrity) is endangered and that he must divert all his energies to its protection" (p. 453). In all of these instances we see an emphasis on individual determination of when stress will or will not occur.

It is further evident from the definitions cited that another area in which separation of psychological from physical aspects is required is that of "threat." In reports of studies involving physical "threat" we sometimes do not know and cannot determine if the "threat" is really "perceived" by the subject as such. Often the experimenter merely assumes that the situation *should have been* threatening or would have been threatening had he been the subject. The point to be made is that the first necessary step in such studies is to determine how the subject perceives the stimulus or situation presented. We know many ways to change deliberately his perception of the situation, but seem often to ignore other subtle forces which may be present and acting to change the value of an "objective" stressor. The extreme stimuli which some experimenters have used—such as electric shock or pistols fired close to the ear—indicate their awareness of this point. However, the very use of such strong stimuli probably obscures the influence of intervening perceptual factors, the understanding of which is so important. Obviously, it would be unreasonable to insist that the experimenter know what constitutes a stressor for his subject before beginning an investigation, when often that is to be its end point. However, the implications of this are found in Haggard's (1949) discussion of emotional stress:

An individual experiences emotional stress when his over-all adjustment is threatened, when his adaptive mechanisms are severely taxed and tend to collapse. Some of the factors which influence an individual's ability to tolerate and master stress include: the nature of his early identifications and his present character structure, and their relation to the demands and gratifications of the present stress-producing situation; the nature of his reactions to the situation; his ability to master strong and disturbing emotional tensions; the extent to which he knows about all aspects of the situation, so that he is not helplessly unaware of the nature and source of threat; his available skills and other means of dealing effectively with it; and the strength and pattern of his motivations to do so. (p. 458)

It would take months if not years to know a subject well enough to meet these demands. However, this does delineate those interests which are primarily psychological in nature, and we will briefly note a few studies which emphasize them. Lazarus et al. (1952) summarize their extensive review in the following terms:

Very little information has been obtained about the relationship between various measures of personality and reaction to stress. The problem has theoretical as well as practical importance. On the one hand, while great individual differences in response to stress have been recognized, few fruitful attempts have been made to discover their nature. On the other hand, it would be most useful to be able to predict which people will be adversely affected by a stressful situation. (p. 307)

Essentially, this boils down to a consideration of interactions between persons and types of stress. It would be interesting to know what kind of individual develops anxiety reactions to task-induced stress. We might guess that such people are highly motivated to perform well. The successful understanding of any individual's performance under stress depends upon some way of measuring the kinds and strength of his motivations and relating them to the characteristics of the situation in which he must perform. The fulfillment of this aim is, indeed, no simple affair. (p. 314)

If measurement of performance is the criterion, there would have to be decrement but one would never be certain as to why. The teasing out of truly psychological factors would appear to be the major contribution to come from psychologists.

Once again, literature reviews show us how pursuit of these many psychological factors without system has produced little or nothing.

Some investigators have studied the effects of subject variables upon performance under short-term stress situations. Stopol (1954) tested twelve hypotheses involving Rorschach responses . . . and found no relationship between such responses and performance under stress. Lofchie (1955), however, found that subjects who scored high on a Rorschach index of perceptual maturity performed better on a psychomotor task under distraction stress than did subjects who scored low on the index. Katchmar (1953) selected anxious and non-anxious subjects by the Taylor Manifest Anxiety Scale. Under failure stress conditions, the anxious subjects did worse than the non-anxious subjects on a form-naming and substitution task, although the performance of both groups showed a decrement over control conditions. Hutt (1947) found that maladjusted children did better than well-adjusted children on the Stanford-Binet Test under failure stress conditions. Further studies on the personality correlates of behavior under stress are cited by Lazarus et al. (1952). (Harris, Mackie, and Wilson, 1956, p. 34)

These definitions and comments generally suggest that stress is a response state and that its induction depends on the mediation of some appraising, perceiving, or interpreting mechanism. As was suggested earlier, certain universally adequate stimuli may be expected to lead to stress more rapidly than others—as, for example, cutting off the air supply.[6] This should lead to a stress state in *all* persons, with little variation in the rate of its development. However, any less severe stimulation—and

[6] See *n. 4*, p. 7.

particularly where the effectiveness of the stimulation is dependent on prior conditioning (as in the case of social stimuli)—will give rise to response patterns that vary greatly from person to person and may induce anxiety or stress much more rapidly in one person than another.

What must be taken into account is not only the objective reality of any given situation, as perceived by an independent observer, but the series of subtle, subjective equations comprising the individual's own assessments of possible success or failure in motive satisfaction. Simultaneous equations must be solved for the multiple motives, multiple response modes (as these are evaluated in terms of situational feasibility), and for motive-mode interactions. We must also recognize *time* as an important additional factor, altering both absolute and relative strengths of motives and the efficacy of different response modalities. We have not even mentioned the to-be-expected effects of stress, as these feed back into the subjective equations which modify the thresholds for threat perception from moment to moment.

Stress and individual vulnerability

We have emphasized the personal equation in assessing reactions to stress. It is consistently found that these reactions vary in intensity from person to person under exposure to a same environmental event. (This has been shown when the conditions studied were combat, oppressive leadership, internment, threat to life, threat to status, threat to livelihood, and others.) It has also been noted that, with few extreme exceptions, the *kind* of situation which arouses a stress response in a particular individual must be related to significant events in that person's life. Many people have used the terms "ego-strength," "stress-tolerance," and "frustration-tolerance." It is perhaps doubtful that there is such a thing as a general stress-tolerance in people. There is more likely to be a greater or lesser insulation from the effects of certain kinds of stress-producers rather than others. The common idea of a threshold of tolerance for stress implies that stress-producing agents must reach a given strength in order to arouse this response. It seems more likely that there are differing thresholds, depending on the kinds of threats that are encountered and that individuals would be differentially vulnerable to different types of stressors. In other words, *not only must a situation be of a given intensity to lead to stress, it must also be of a given kind for a particular person.* To know what conditions of the environment are likely to be effective for the particular person, the motivational structure and prior history of that individual would have to be taken into account. Where the particular motives are known—where it is known what a person holds important and not important, what kinds of goals he will work for and why, what kinds of situations have for him been likely to increase anxiety or lead to aversive or defensive behavior,—a reasonable prediction of stress proneness might be made. It is clear that what we would then have is a *vulnerability profile*, perhaps analogous to the industrial psychologist's job-profile, but based on strengths of motives and of motive-satisfying possibilities in situations rather than on strengths of skills and of skill requirements in particular jobs.[7]

If one tries to gain some overall perspective on what stress studies have so far revealed, and especially on their relation to studies of frustration, conflict, and anxiety, one is led to these kinds of general observations.

1. Stress is probably best conceived as a state of the total organism under extenuating circumstances rather than as an event in the environment.

2. A great variety of different environmental conditions is capable of producing a stress state.

3. Different individuals respond to the same conditions in different ways. Some enter rapidly into a stress state, others show increased alertness and apparently improved performance, and still others appear to be "immune" to the stress-producing qualities of the environmental conditions.

4. The same individual may enter into a stress state in response to one presumably stressful condition and not to another.

5. Consistent *intra*-individual but varied *inter*-individual psychobiological response patterns occur in stress situations. The notion of a *common* stress reaction needs to be reassessed.

6. The behaviors resulting from operations intended to induce stress may be the same or different, depending on the context of the situation of its induction.

7. The intensity and the extent of the stress state, and the associated behaviors, may not be readily predicted from a knowledge of the stimulus conditions alone, but require an analysis of underlying motivational patterns and of the context in which the stressor is applied.

8. Temporal factors may determine the significance of a given stressor and thus the intensity and extent of the stress state and the optimum measurement of effect.

Extra-individual factors

In addition to emphasizing the role of the individual, which we have so far done, attention must also be given to social fac-

---

[7] See Cofer and Appley (1964, pp. 449–465) for related discussion for this and subsequent section.

tors—the influence of other individuals or of the social and cultural milieu in producing or reducing stress. The pace setter, the previously habituated, acclimated, or trained companion, or the equally naive sharer of a stressful situation may significantly influence stress reaction. The role of social facilitation, leadership, and that nebulous influence called "social motivation," as related to perception and actual experiencing of physical stressors, further extends the continuum of variables demanding attention. The social anthropologist and social psychologist will remind us, too, of cultural norms in such stressors as pain—as experienced in puberty and other rituals—and of role expectations and the effects of discrepancies between prescribed and attained roles as factors in stress proneness.

It would be an error to conclude that the concern which has been shown for psychological, social, and cultural variables precludes consideration of the impact of physical and physiological factors in stress research. On the contrary, considerable interest has existed in the study of effects of extreme environmental factors on the organism and on performance effectiveness in particular (cf. Trumbull, 1965; Burns, Chambers, & Hendler, 1963; and Weybrew, this volume). One of the particular purposes of the symposium on which this volume is based was to provide an opportunity to examine side-by-side some of the physical, physiological, social, and cultural aspects of stress. It was hoped thereby to open the way to further and more sophisticated studies of stress in which interactions of variables across levels as well as within levels would be involved. The focus of this volume has been at the psychological level by design, but the range of concern has been kept deliberately broad.

As the above discussion suggests, stress is a concept which can have interpretation and relevance at many levels of human organization, from cellular to cultural. The starting point here has been with Selye's concept of systemic stress. It could have been with influences on cell division, cancer development, or nucleic acid production. All of these levels have environments which are compatible with their normal function, and all are susceptible to environmental factors which disrupt normal functioning. Such disrupting influences are usually referred to as stressors, but the effects of incompatibility need not always be assumed to be destructive. Environmental changes can lead to extensions of the range of tolerance so that adaptation (or natural selection) takes place. Thus the absolute levels of stressors should not be expected to be constant over time (or at different time periods) within systems.

Further, environmental change seldom produces uni-dimensional stressors, and the interaction of one stressor with others, sequentially or concomitantly, must be understood (cf. Trumbull, 1965, on cross-adaptation). In some instances effects will be additive, in other instances cancelling. While the study of situations involving single stressors is undoubtedly simpler, extrapolation in anticipation of complex settings is tenuous.

Periodicity and stress

Finally, note should be made of the fact that environmental context not only influences stressor levels but exerts a more subtle influence upon periodicity of function. Recent interest in the influence of temporal factors on psychological stress derives in part, at least, from the pioneering physiological studies of Halberg (cf. 1961, 1962a).

As is well known, but perhaps not appropriately appreciated, there are definite cycles in the various functions of the human system. The more general sleep-waking cycle has enjoyed much recognition in North America since the work of Kleitman (1939, 1963). Unfortunately, not enough attention has been paid to this variable as it relates to studies of vigilance, theories of expectancy, sleep-loss influence on functions, and other attempts at assaying human performance. Indeed, one finds little or no reference in such research reports as to time of day, whether after meals, etc. Maybe one can argue that the impact of these factors might be so small as to merit no further consideration. We submit that we do not know but that unless future research in these areas reports such factors we cannot assess their significance. The time of day one is tested after a period of sleep loss should be correlated with the position it had in his pretest cycle, for example. This is of particular importance in stress research. Recognizing such cycles in breathing rate, basal metabolism (BMR), alpha rhythms, blood pressure, and urine volume, should lead those using such stressors as air mixtures, atmospheric pressure, drugs, and related variables to concern themselves with the coincidence of stressor initiation and the present or anticipated position or level of function of the organ of primary influence.

Attention has here been directed to the probably significant influence of such cycles because we so often find in research that things which seemingly enjoy simple relationships do so only because of our own simple conceptions of them. Growing sophistication in technique then parallels our own growing appreciation of the multiple factors involved. This is the geometric expansion to which Whitehorn referred. The chapters which follow will serve to extend all of our "natural" or "usual" worlds, and we will come to appreciate the scope and complexity that our experimental models will have to encompass for a fuller understanding of psychological stress.

JOHN I. LACEY

2

Somatic response patterning and stress: Some revisions of activation theory [1]

In discussing the implications for the study of stress of some recent developments in psychophysiology, my fundamental purpose will be to present neurophysiological and psychophysiological evidence that "activation" or "arousal theory" needs rather drastic revision.

To develop this theme properly, it will be necessary to consider experiments that do not deal with obviously "stressful" stimuli. Stress, in any case, is as difficult a concept as can be found in the psychophysiological literature. No matter how defined, however, stress shares with other stimulus-situations the ability to evoke a multiplicity of somatic responses. Hopefully, the more knowledge one can gain about somatic functions in a variety of circumstances, the more one will be able to understand stress.

Our main concepts of the role of autonomic responses to stressful stimuli stem historically from Cannon's notions of the "emergency functions" of sympatho-adrenal changes. Most of us expect that an individual in any sort of difficulty, experiencing almost any kind of "emotion," or coping with almost any problem, will exhibit a wide variety of somatic changes like those shown by an organism preparing for "fight or flight." These changes are said to prepare the organism, realistically or unrealistically, for vigorous goal-directed activity requiring the mobilization and

[1] Preparation of this paper, and the reported research originating in the Department of Psychophysiology-Neurophysiology, Fels Research Institute, were supported by grants MH-00623 and FR-00222 from the National Institute of Mental Health, United States Public Health Service.

expenditure of energy and to protect the organism against the hazards of such vigorous activity.

We are all familiar with the gradual transition that took place from this view, which links physiological processes with strong "emotions," to the more inclusive view that electroencephalographic, skeletal motor, and autonomic measures are indices of the "activation" or "arousal level" of the subject, i.e., of the degree to which he is mobilizing his resources for action.

Repetitive demonstrations have been made by neurophysiologists and psychophysiologists of common causes for, and a temporal parallelism between, sympathetic-like changes and those electrocortical events called arousal. Such common causes are easily found. They include electrical stimulation of the ascending reticular activating system, awakening from sleep, and responding to physically simple stimuli characterized by novelty, intensity, or special meaning to the responding subject. These demonstrations have strengthened the acceptance of an identity between sympathetic-like changes and central and behavioral activation or arousal.

The influential writings of Lindsley, Duffy, and Malmo (e.g., Lindsley, 1951; Duffy, 1962; Malmo, 1959) depict a unidimensional continuum of arousal ranging from coma to the most excited and disorganized forms of stressful behavior. They lend support to a large number of experiments which rest on the assumption that the magnitude of autonomic or electro-encephalographic response to a supposed stressor measures the degree of strain, or, in more modern terminology, of activation or arousal. Duffy and Malmo, in particular, have taken this notion one step further. They assert that physiological activation processes are part of the mechanism of drive, that these processes reveal the intensive rather than the directional aspects of behavior, and that they correlate with the measured adequacy of performance.

There is a great deal of evidence in support of each of these generalizations. I would guess that a tabulation of the results of all published experiments would yield more votes in favor of activation theory than against it. But science is not based on polls. There are many experimental results that sharply contradict activation theory. They cannot be dismissed as due to sampling errors, or to poor experimental control, or to unreliability of measurement. I think the experiments show that electroencephalographic, autonomic, motor, and other behavioral systems are imperfectly coupled, complexly interacting systems.

Indeed, I think the evidence shows that electrocortical arousal, autonomic arousal, and behavioral arousal may be considered to be *different forms* of arousal, each complex in itself. I think the evidence also shows that one cannot easily use one form of arousal as a highly valid index of another. That so many investigators do so is attributable to the fact that the three complexes of arousal processes—electrocortical, autonomic, and behavioral—*in general* occur simultaneously. In other words, the assertions of activation and arousal theory seem to me to be true only in an actuarial sense. The limitations of our present knowledge make it impossible to say at present with what frequency and under what conditions these "arousals" do occur together. This difficulty arises primarily, I think, because the representativeness of laboratory experiments is so limited. But even this limited laboratory sampling of psychophysiological relations has yielded many exceptions to the rules of activation theory which somehow have been ignored.

These exceptions do not constitute a set of experimental rarities, with limited application to our daily experimental and clinical attempts to understand and control somatic responses. Instead, they seem to me to lead to a more inclusive view and a broadened interpretation of the role of autonomic responses in the government of behavior.

The key concepts leading to this broadened interpretation are (1) dissociation of somatic and behavioral arousal; (2) dissociation of the physiological functions said to be an index of activation; (3) somatic response patterning, particularly that variety called "stimulus specificity" or "situational stereotypy"; and (4) visceral afferent feedback from the cardiovascular system to the brain, which has *inhibitory* rather than excitatory effects.

Dissociation of somatic and behavioral arousal

Consider a subject in a state of relaxed alertness, sitting or lying in a comfortable position. If he is aroused by any of our commonly used techniques, all the familiar autonomic and electroencephalographic consequences are likely to occur. His heart rate and blood pressure will go up, he will exhibit vasoconstriction in his fingers, his palmar conductance will increase, and his resting 8–12 cps. alpha activity will be reduced to the point of disappearance. All these and many other changes are taken to be quantitative indices of a unidimensional arousal or activation mechanism that underlies and supports the shift of the organism from lower resting levels to higher levels of more active behavior. Easy application of this notion, however, is hindered by the small but growing body of evidence of what Wikler calls "dissociation" of somatic and behavioral arousal.

Such dissociation is rather dramatic when produced pharmacologically or by localized lesions in the central nervous system, because by these methods one can secure a complete contradiction between the electrocortical and behavioral signs of arousal and activation.

Thus, in cats (Bradley, 1958) or dogs (Wikler, 1952), atropine produces high amplitude slow waves similar to those seen in sleep. But the cat is neither drowsy nor behaviorally unresponsive. A normal arousal stimulus produces a normal behavioral response, although cortical desynchronization does not occur. If the stimulant amphetamine is given with atropine, the slow wave pattern characteristic of atropine still appears, although the cat is alert or excited. The atropinized dog, although his cortex is "sleeping" by the orthodox electrophysiological signs, may be so excited that he has to be restrained. This is not a diffuse, non-organized, random discharge: "When released, these atropinized animals jumped off the table and spontaneously returned to the animal quarters . . ." (Wikler, 1952, p. 263).

The combination of an alerted cortex with a behaviorally drowsy animal can also be produced pharmacologically. Physostigmine induces electrical activity characteristic of a thoroughly alerted animal, but the animal is "quiet or even drowsy." If this drug is administered in combination with chlorpromazine, the electrocortical activity again shows arousal or activation, but "the animal remains drowsy and indifferent" (Bradley, 1958). Chlorpromazine, then, did tranquilize behavior to a moderate degree, but it did not tranquilize the cortex.

Bradley was able to reproduce such drug-produced dissociation between somatic arousal and behavioral arousal even in acute *encéphale isolé* preparations. In these preparations "behavioral arousal" consists of opening of the eyes, and movements of eyes, ears, and jaws. Bradley also showed that the dissociation extended to blood pressure responses. Small doses of dl-amphetamine caused a blood pressure rise, without producing electrocortical or behavioral arousal; larger doses resulted in behavioral and electrocortical arousal "without further change in the blood pressure."

Wikler states a conclusion that has enormous significance for those who would use physiological functions as unequivocal indicators of behavioral arousal: "It is evident . . . that the mechanisms which subserve 'sleep' and those which subserve the 'burst-slow wave' EEG patterns are distinct from each other, although they are very often closely interlocked. Furthermore, one cannot state that 'sleep' causes the 'burst-slow wave' patterns or vice-versa. Rather, it appears that they are often concomitant phenomena and that *it is necessary to investigate further the precise conditions under which they can be expected to occur simultaneously*" (p. 264).[2] Wikler goes on to state ". . . the spontaneous electrical activity of the cerebral cortex reflects the activity of neuronal systems which, in part at least, are *independent of those neuronal systems that subserve behavior in general*" (p. 265).[2]

A recent study by Feldman and Waller (1962), employing lesions

[2] Italics not in original.

in cats, clearly showed that wakeful alertness and cortical desynchronization are *not* both dependent on the so-called activating effects of the
ascending reticular system. They were able to separate anatomically the
pathways for behavioral arousal from the pathways for electrocortical
arousal. Cats with nearly complete bilateral lesions of the posterior hypothalamus are somnolent, require tube feeding, show no spontaneous
movements, are unresponsive to sensory stimuli, and cannot be behaviorally aroused. But cortical desynchronization—the usual index of
activation—easily can be produced by peripheral stimulation or by stimulation of the midbrain reticular formation, even in this complete absence of behavioral arousal. Although not as dramatic and complete, the
converse dissociation—a behaviorally aroused animal with a "sleeping"
cortex—was produced by bilateral lesions in the midbrain reticular formation. Animals with these lesions are sluggish in behavior, and the "usual"
parallelism between EEG arousal and behavioral arousal is only approximate, and sometimes altogether absent. Feldman and Waller give
one illustration in which a cat tracked a visual stimulus for a 24-second
interval, during which period the electrocorticogram exhibited the high-
amplitude slow waves characteristic of sleep. Hence, Feldman and Waller
conclude, "although behavioral arousal requires the integrity of the posterior hypothalamic region, induced ECG activation is not critically
dependent on pathways funnelling through this region" (p. 1321).

It is certainly not surprising that dissociation can be demonstrated
at lower levels of the nervous system also, and studies specifically oriented
to the problem are now appearing. Vagotomized, midpontile decerebrate
animals exhibit a triad of hyperactivity: somatic-postural (decerebrate
rigidity), respiratory (apneustic breathing), and cardiovascular (tachycardia
and arterial hypertension). Glasser and Tippett recently (1965) established that the pathways mediating these facilitatory effects are functionally separable by the administration of graded doses of urethane to this
preparation and are capable of independent activity.

In lower animals, then, it seems that we may in truth speak of *different kinds* of arousal—autonomic, electrocortical, and behavioral. They
are functionally and anatomically separable by appropriate experimental
means. Nature's experiments yield confirmatory data in human clinical
subjects. Comatose behavior is not incompatible with a normal EEG, and
apparently normal behavior is not incompatible with background activity
of extremely low frequency. (References cited in Mirsky & Cardon,
1962). In a rather extensive study of the relationship of the EEG to time
estimation, Dureman and Edström (1964) report: "The most veridical
time reproduction performance was found in a group whose EEG records
were flat or dominated by beta activity" (p. 6). This result is entirely in
accordance with activation theory. But, these authors continue, "An
equally high precision was found in a group of EEG records with a sig-

nificant proportion of theta activity. This group consisted almost exclusively of subjects between 15 and 25 years of age. Simple inspection of the EEG records in these cases might have led to an erroneous conclusion of a drowsy state. On the contrary the clinical rating of behavior during the recording period indicated that these youngsters rather were tense and alert" (p. 6).

We do not lack experimental evidence for dissociation in normal human subjects. Mirsky and Cardon (1962) report dissociation between the behavioral and physiological effects of chlorpromazine in human subjects. Both chlorpromazine and sleep deprivation resulted in marked impairment in performance on a continuous test of vigilant attention. But while in the sleep deprivation condition there were marked somatic changes—a slowed EEG, slowed respiration, and digital vasodilation—in the chlorpromazine state the physiological accompaniments of impaired performance were far less marked, although still detectable statistically. Clearly, the degree of impairment of performance was not related to the differential magnitude of physiological changes produced by the two experimental conditions. Mirsky and Cardon, too, speak of "dissociation" and of separate "central neural systems concerned with the regulation of sleep and wakefulness on the one hand, and the regulation of the EEG on the other" (p. 9).

Malmo has produced clear evidence of somatic-behavior dissociation, and although one of the most vigorous proponents of activation theory, is now speaking of the "need to revise the activation concept" (Malmo, 1966). He had subjects tracking manually under conditions of "unified set" and of "divided set." In the "divided set" condition they tracked manually but expected to be required at an unknown time to shift to double tracking (with foot and hand). Performance deteriorated markedly in the "divided set" condition, but this drop in performance was *not* accompanied by physiological changes in a variety of systems (quantified EEG in three frequency bands, action potentials from five muscles, heart rate, respiration, and palmar conductance—surely a satisfactory sampling of somatic systems). Malmo concludes that "set" and "activation" have to be distinguished, and that from the absence of physiological changes accompanying set it may be concluded that "its neural mediation appears not to depend on mechanisms with strong facilitation on the autonomic nervous system." [3] I think this extrapolation from one study of set is un-

---

[3] This quotation was taken from a preprint of Malmo's paper. After seeing a copy of the present paper, Malmo deleted this sentence and, in the just published paper (*J. exper. Psychol.,* 1966, 71, 184–199), concludes that "this study has provided a clear example of dissociation between performance and physiological activation" (p. 189). In personal correspondence, Malmo has clarified some aspects of his own revised theory of activation. In his view, activation is to be measured only by long-term changes in *level* of activity, rather than by briefer dynamic responses. Moreover, he now frankly acknowledges that peripheral activity only incompletely and im-

justified. I will show later (see page 33) that set and expectancy do produce reliable autonomic changes of a somewhat unexpected sort and with somewhat unexpected behavioral correlates. I would conclude, therefore, that Malmo's study simply provides a clear example of somatic-behavioral dissociation.

Partial somatic-behavioral dissociations have also been reported, in which one or more somatic variables fail to correlate with behavioral arousal, while other simultaneously recorded somatic variables behave as one would predict from the usual statements of activation theory. Elliott (1964) compared the somatic responses of young adults and kindergarten children, their relationship to reaction-time performance, and the effects of incentive and nonincentive conditions on somatic responses and on performance. Both children and adults responded to incentives with highly significant decreases in reaction time. But whereas adults showed a parallel and significant activation in all physiological functions measured, the children showed such changes only in heart rate and respiratory rate. Again a wide variety of physiological functions were measured: heart rate, respiratory rate, palmar conductance, muscle potentials, and quantified activity of the EEG in three bands (2–4 cps., 8–12 cps., and 17–28 cps.). The differences between children and adults were not due to differential ranges of physiological activity or to "ceiling effects" due to higher basal levels of children. Young children selected for adult-like low levels of activity behaved no differently than children as a group. Elliott is severely critical of the "hypothetical construct of activation" and of the notion that, as he puts it, "activation operates upon efficiency of performance." He considers physiological and perceptual-motor responses under normal conditions to be "largely independent, not related by any given function, and not so organized that one set has any special influence over the other" (p. 18). This is a sweeping condemnation. To my mind, it represents a welcome corrective to the total acceptance of activation theory that characterizes many current psychophysiological experiments, but it goes too far in de-emphasizing the kinds of interactions between autonomic and central nervous mechanisms that are described in current neurophysiology, some of which I will consider later in this paper.

The evidence seems clear, however, that somatic and behavioral arousal consists of dissociable components, mediated by separate neural mechanisms, but that "commonly" these appear simultaneously. Drugs and lesions produce dramatic dissociations, but such heroic measures are

---

perfectly reflects changes in an hypothetical "arousal system," and he argues that "significantly concordant change in the *direction* of *group* means is the sufficient evidence for change in 'level of activation'" (personal communication). The point is made and accepted that there are many varieties of "activation theory" and that my arguments and disagreements do not extend over the whole spectrum of these theories.

not essential. The evidence just reviewed shows that specific experimental conditions result in specific kinds of dissociations. Later (see p. 35) I will attempt to show that "attentive observation of the external environment" is one such experimental condition that can modify the somatic response to an intellectually stressful problem-solving activity.

It bears repeating, I think, that the widely held opinion that autonomic, electroencephalographic, and skeletal-motor activation occur simultaneously and in equal measure may be traceable partially to the fact that the experimental conditions commonly used by psychophysiologists and neurophysiologists are all too limited. Enormously popular manipulations are used in the vast majority of studies of arousal: aversive physical stimuli, intellectually demanding tasks, convenient perceptual-motor tasks, affects of "fight or flight," and "anxiety-producing" stimuli. We do not as often use nonaversive stimuli, "pleasant affects," tasks without the appeal to the need for academic achievement, or tasks which emphasize set to perform rather than the performance itself. It may be that as we broaden our scope of observation we will be able to begin to meet the need voiced by Wikler to specify the precise conditions under which the phenomena of arousal are concomitant and those under which they are dissociated. Perhaps also we can begin to understand the "why" both of dissociation and association.

Quantitative somatic-somatic dissociations

Activation theory and stress theory require that correlational matrices of those physiological variables said to measure arousal exhibit sizeable communality among measures. Many, if not most, reported matrices are disappointing: correlations among autonomic measures themselves and among autonomic and electroencephalographic variables are low, frequently approaching zero. I have argued elsewhere that the intercorrelations among autonomic measures fall far below the individual reliabilities of measurement. As a result, reliable patterns of reaction are produced, in which an individual may consistently, over time and over diverse stressor-situations, systematically exhibit overreaction (relative to the group of subjects being studied) in one or more variables, only average reactivity in other variables, and underreactivity in still others (Lacey, 1950; Lacey & VanLehn, 1952; Lacey, Bateman, & VanLehn, 1952, 1953; Lacey & Lacey, 1958a, 1962). In these papers and others (Lacey, 1956, 1959), I have dealt at length with the implications of idiosyncratic patterning of somatic response for activation theory. I would point out here again, however, that the degree of activation assigned to a subject or to a stressor condition may depend strikingly on the variable chosen for study. The main facts of idiosyncratic somatic patterning have been widely replicated by others (e.g., Dykman et al., 1959; Engel, 1960; Schnore, 1959; Speisman et al., 1961; Wenger et al., 1961; Roessler et al., 1964).

Although activation theory originally relied heavily on the evidence from intersubject correlations (cf. Duffy, 1962), activation theorists now meet the problem raised by these facts of response patterning by insisting that intersubject correlations are irrelevant to the main sense of their generalization (e.g., Malmo, 1959; Schnore, 1959). They point out that all recorded physiological measures are likely to show displacement toward higher levels when the subject is aroused. With some striking and not uncommon exceptions (Lacey, 1959) this is actuarially a correct statement. The issue, however, is still a quantitative one: how high are the *intra*-individual correlations? How strong is the evidence for a general and generalized arousal? Schnore (1959), who strongly supports the use of physiological measures as quantitative indicators of the arousal-value of different situations, footnotes his main argument concerning concordance among different physiological measures, and the necessity for intra-individual analysis, with a striking statement: "Such correspondence among physiological measures is more pronounced with respect to the direction of change, rather than the amount of change" (p. 126). I think this should be part of the main development of the theory of arousal rather than a footnote! Schnore's statement clearly supports a statement my colleagues and I made earlier on the basis of inter-individual analysis (Lacey, Bateman, & VanLehn, 1953): "The autonomic nervous system does indeed respond to experimentally imposed stress 'as a whole' in the sense that all autonomically innervated structures seem to be activated, usually in the direction of apparent sympathetic predominance. But it does not respond 'as a whole' in the sense that all autonomically innervated structures exhibit equal increments or decrements of function" (p. 8).

The already cited experiment by Elliott (1964) is a pointed example of somatic-somatic dissociation, for in his experiment *intra*-individual rank order correlations were computed, using paired physiological measures in each of fifteen consecutive blocks of time, each block representing a series of counterbalanced experimental conditions. For adults, the average [4] intra-individual correlation between palmar conductance and heart rate was .46; between heart rate and muscle potentials, .45; between conductance and muscle potentials, .35. If one visualizes the scatter-plots for correlations between .35 and .46, it will be agreed, I think, that one cannot predict with any degree of confidence the "acti-

[4] I have some doubt about the validity of these averages, since they were derived by applying Fisher's z-transformation to rank difference correlations. The technique strictly is applicable only to product-moment correlations.

vation level" shown by one physiological measure from the level shown by another.

As I have pointed out before, there is no such thing as *the* correlation among somatic variables. The correlations change as a function of many variables. Age is one such variable, possibly, as Elliott points out, because increasing age is correlated with different perceptions of and adjustments to the experimental situation. For the kindergarten children in his experiment, the average intra-individual correlation between palmar conductance and heart rate was .12, between palmar conductance and muscle potentials, .07, between heart rate and muscle potentials, .08. Certainly there is no support here for arousal theory as it is commonly formulated.

Lazarus and his colleagues (e.g., Lazarus et al., 1963; Mordkoff, 1964; Lazarus, 1965a) have been most enthusiastic proponents of the view that only intra-individual correlations serve as proper tests of activation theory. They have also insisted that the arbitrary measurement conventions often used may account for the low correlations reported. They have been most energetic and productive in developing and testing new intra-individual sampling, combining, and smoothing techniques. They have been able, it must be admitted, to increase the apparent correlation between palmar conductance and heart rate responses to films of a "stressful" and "threatening" kind. But it should be emphasized that even a correlation of .707 only shows shared variance of 50 percent. I'm not sure whether Lazarus and his colleagues can get even this high. In their 1963 paper, the maximum correlation reported was 0.5. Lazarus' more recent conclusion is directly to the point: "Still, the maximum correlation between various indicators of autonomic nervous system reaction is probably only modest even under the most favorable conditions" (Lazarus, 1965a).

It is equally difficult to find sizeable correlations between electroencephalographic and autonomic indices of arousal, despite the trite fact that upon stimulation of a resting organism, one may detect both autonomic and EEG activation. Quantitatively, we again find little, if any, support for the notion of a generalized, communal arousal.

Sternbach (1960) reports a correlational study of 42 young adult males in which Wenger's factor-analytically-derived, weighted score of "sympathetic" or "parasympathetic" activity (thus clearly emphasizing whatever communality may exist among autonomic variables) was correlated with the so-called alpha index. The study is especially important because there can be no question of the reliability of the individual measurements. Wenger and his collaborators have reported many and different tests of reliability of the so-called $\bar{A}$ score, and Sternbach found a reliability of .97 for the determination of his alpha index. The obtained correlation was —.18, not significant. No curvilinear relationship that might account for the low linear correlation could be found. Sternbach concludes that the $\bar{A}$ score and the alpha index are independent and (as an increasing number of people seem to be concluding) that " 'activation' as a concept in emotions cannot refer uniformly to CNS and ANS activity. . . . Clearly, an uncritical use of an 'activation' concept of emotions fails to do justice to the differential activities of the nervous system. . . . a general 'activation' theory of emotions is not yet justified" (Sternbach, 1960, p. 611).

Elliot provides additional data on this point which are of major interest because once more intra-individual correlations are used. For adults the average intra-individual correlation between heart rate and alpha activity was —.16, between beta activity and heart rate, —.11. Comparable correlations between EEG activity and palmar conductance were —.16 and —.08, and between muscle potentials and EEG activity, —.05 and —.07. For kindergarten children the relationships were even poorer, being, in the same order of presentation, .00 and .05; .04 and .02; .00 and .04! There is surely no evidence here, in either child or adult, of a factor of arousal common to the ANS and the CNS measures.

One study by Stennett (1957) is repeatedly cited as a demonstration of intra-individual concordance between electroencephalographic and autonomic activation. Stennett adopted the hypothesis of an inverted-U between autonomic activation, as measured by palmar conductance, and CNS activation, as measured by the amplitude of alpha activity. He analyzed individual curves and then recombined them in a group curve to show that cortical activation was high at high levels of autonomic activation but low at moderate levels of autonomic activation and that alpha activity again disappeared at low levels of autonomic arousal. This is one of the few findings of a substantial relationship between autonomic and electroencephalographic measures of activation. But Surwillo (1965) has recently sharply challenged this study. He finds no relationship between heart rate and alpha amplitude and demonstrates, convincingly, I think, that Stennett's involved data manipulation artifactually produced the appearance of an inverted-U. If Surwillo's arguments prove to be sound, we will be deprived of what has seemed to be a clear-cut demonstration of sizeable concordance between CNS activation, as measured popularly, and ANS activation.

Situational stereotypy

What interpretations can be given to the dual facts that (a) in general, a large number of physiological processes are simultaneously thrown into action, probably by separate but intimately related pathways, by stimuli generally conceded to be arousing, activating, or stressful, but (b) these processes show, at best, only moderate intercorrelations? I propose that activation or arousal processes are not unidimensional but multidimensional and that the activation processes do *not* reflect just the intensive dimension of behavior but also the intended aim or goal of the behavior, or, as I phrased it in an earlier paper, the nature of the transaction between the organism and its environment (Lacey, 1959). The emphasis on multidimensionality of, and the nonenergizing aspects of, the arousal processes is tantamount to saying that different somatic processes have different roles to play in the execution of different kinds of behavior and different interactions with other concurrent responses, and hence appear in different amounts and temporal evolution, depending on the requirements of the intended interaction between the organism and its environment. We have both psychophysiological and neurophysiological warrant to justify this interpretation, at least as an heuristic statement.

There is an increasing number of psychophysiological experiments that demonstrate that different stimulus-situations reliably produce different *patterns* of somatic response. "Anger-directed-outwards," "anger-directed-inwards," "fear," and "anxiety" are said to be differentiable one from the other in terms of the *pattern* of response (Ax, 1953; Schachter, 1957; Funkenstein et al., 1957). Warm and cold stimuli, tapping telegraph keys, looking at pictures, listening to auditory stimuli—these produce different *patterns* of somatic responses (Davis, 1957a; Davis et al., 1955). Noting and detecting external stimuli, with no requirement for motor response, produces a *pattern* of response in which the heart rate decreases, while other autonomic responses—palmar conductance, for example—show the more typical increase (Lacey, 1959; Lacey et al., 1963; Obrist, 1963). Patients with differing "psychosomatic" ailments, a clinically important form of chronically patterned responses, are said to have different persistent attitudes (Graham et al., 1962b). Hypnotic suggestion of different "affective states" results in different physiological response *patterns* (Graham et al., 1960; Graham et al., 1962a). "Attitudes" produce different subjective stimulus-situations, even though the stimuli are objectively the same.

I have called this phenomenon *situational stereotypy,* a term I prefer to another commonly used term, *stimulus specificity,* because the latter term implies that the source of the response pattern lies with the objective nature of the stimulus rather than with the nature of the subject's set and expectation, of his intended response to the stimulus. Needless to say, we cannot yet interpret all these situationally determined patterns of somatic responses by reference to the specific details of the nature of the subject's set or expectation or by an appeal to known differential effects of each of the components of the response pattern. In general, we cannot isolate in pure culture the essential ingredients in our typically complex stimulus situations, which result most often in complex behavioral responses; nor can we specify in great detail the multiple interactions among the somatic responses themselves; nor can we demonstrate convincingly, for each component of the somatic arousal processes, a differential effect on on-going behavior. But there is much evidence that does enable us to make a striking beginning in reinterpreting heart rate and blood pressure responses, two responses which we have found to behave, under specifiable and reproducible experimental conditions, in a manner directly contrary to arousal theory as it is commonly stated. Moreover, current neurophysiology now assigns a unique and rather unexpected role to cardiovascular activity in the *control of the central nervous system,* and psychophysiological investigations, both current and past, assign differential roles to palmar conductance and to cardiovascular responses that are in suggestive agreement with the neurophysiological facts.

Fragments of a neurophysiological theory: Feedback to the central nervous system

The autonomic nervous system is not solely an effector system. From most, if not all, autonomically innervated organs, sensory fibers arise by means of which signals are fed back to the central nervous system. The existence of such visceral afferent feedback loops in the cardiovascular system has been known for decades. A variety of cardiovascular afferents and cardiopulmonary afferents have been described and studied (Neil & Heymans, 1962; Heymans & Neil, 1958), and new ones are still being discovered (Brown, 1965). The reflexive and homeostatic effects on the maintenance of blood pressure and heart rate have been well established. Consider, for example, the so-called pressure-sensitive receptors or baroceptors, with which the aortic arch and carotid sinus are richly endowed. If blood pressure goes up, these receptors, under normal conditions, faithfully increase their rate of discharge and reflexly produce a wide variety of homeostatic adjustments to reduce the blood pressure. They are exquisitely sensitive, and at normal levels of blood pressure and heart rate they faithfully code each recurring systole and diastole of each cardiac cycle. The nerves from the aortic arch and from the carotid sinus join the vagus and glossopharyngeal nerves and terminate in the lower brain stem.

It is now clearly established, however, that *inhibitory* control of *higher* levels of the nervous system is vested in this same visceral afferent pathway. The input from pressoceptors, indeed, is the first known sensory input to the brain which *inhibits* (not *activates*) cortical activity. The history of this important fact stems back at least to the demonstrations in 1929 by Tournade and Malmejac and in 1931 by Koch (see Heymans & Neil, 1958) that stimulation of Hering's nerve (the carotid sinus nerve) or an increase in intrasinusal pressure produced decreased muscle tone in anesthetized animals and to Koch's hotly debated demonstration in 1932 that he could inhibit motor activity, and even produce prolonged sleep, in the dog by sharply increasing pressure in an isolated carotid sinus. But the major proof, and the most detailed studies, have come only recently.

Some twelve years ago, Bonvallet, Dell, and Hiebel (1954) showed, in acute cat studies, that distention of the carotid sinus produced a marked decrease in cortical electrical activity, with reduction of the frequency to as low as three to five per second—an accepted sign of a "sleeping," inactivated, inhibited cortex. Nakao, Ballim, and Gellhorn confirmed this finding in 1956. Several forms of control observations show that this effect is not secondary to the homeostatic reduction of blood pressure produced by stimulating the baroceptors. Bonvallet, Dell, and Hugelin (Bonvallet et al., 1954; Dell et al., 1954) showed a direct neural inhibitory effect on an evoked monosynaptic reflex by increasing intrasinusal pressure, an effect that disappeared when the glossopharyngeal and vagus nerves were cut. Bonvallet and Bloch (1961), and Bonvallet and Allen (1963) have recently published detailed studies of the nature and specific locus of some of these as well as additional effects. They describe an ascending bulbar inhibitory mechanism, separate from the classical ventro-medial inhibitory reticular system, which exerts inhibitory control of cortical, autonomic, and muscular activities. Precisely delimited coagulations of this area do not change the immediate cortical, autonomic, and motor response to an activating stimulus but *prolong* its effects, and spontaneous activity becomes more labile and more frequent. The function of this area, then, is to control the duration of an episode of stimulus-produced activating processes in the brain. Several lines of evidence show that this area is separable from and independent of the more familiar vasodepressor mechanism, which was found to be posterior and medial to the ascending inhibitory area. This bulbar inhibitory area is localized at the head of the nucleus of the tractus solitarius, an area *richly endowed with cardiovascular afferents*. This precise area was designated by Hellner and von Baumgarten in 1961 (see Bonvallet & Allen, 1963) as the "predilection area for cardiovascular neurones," and, as cited in the Bonvallet and Allen article, one can record unitary discharges in this area synchronous with the cardiac rhythm.

These facts obviously suggest that the cardiovascular system has some control of the bulbar inhibitory area, and Bonvallet and Allen in fact found that if the glossopharyngeal and vagus nerves were cut, post-stimulatory cortical activation was prolonged. In other words, elimination of glossopharyngeal and vagal input, the pathways by which blood pressure and heart rate activity are fed back to the central nervous system, resulted in a prolongation of an episode of cortical activation, and indeed also of pupillo-constrictor inhibition (an autonomic response) and of neck muscle activity. Inferentially, increase of cardiovascular afferent traffic along these nerves will result in a prompter termination of an episode of cortical, motor, and other autonomic activation.

Zanchetti and his collaborators have provided rather dramatic additional evidence of the inhibitory effects of the baroceptor pathways (Baccelli et al., 1965; Bartorelli et al., 1960). In acutely decorticated cats, showing spontaneous and stimulus-evoked outbursts of sham rage, low-voltage stimulation of the large pressoceptor fibers of the aortic and sinus nerves resulted in a prompt suppression of both the autonomic and motor manifestations of sham rage.

It is not at all clear whether all of these diverse effects are to be attributed to one mechanism, such as the bulbar inhibitory area of Bonvallet and Allen. Their observations do not account, for example, for the elevation of the threshold of a monosynaptic reflex reported earlier by Bonvallet, Dell, and Hugelin. But it is clear that we must talk about at least two independent sets of effects: homeostatic effects on the cardiovascular system itself and inhibitory effects on the reticular activating system. The inhibitory effects appear in a wide variety of forms: reduction of the frequency of brain waves, elevation of threshold of a monosynaptic reflex, reduction of the duration of stimulus-evoked episodes of cortical, motor, and autonomic activity other than cardiovascular, and suppression of sham rage.

The inhibitory effects apparently can be produced both by changes in blood pressure and by changes in heart rate, although the evidence is much clearer for blood pressure. Indeed, we do not yet have experiments directly showing inhibitory effects of increase in heart rate itself. The psychophysiological evidence that I will present shortly, however, clearly implicates heart rate itself as a partner of blood pressure in the production of inhibitory effects. It is not yet clear neurophysiologically whether these two variables act in concert or can themselves be dissociated insofar as their inhibitory effects are concerned. I will later present some psychophysiological data that suggest that even these two intimately interrelated physiological processes can be dissociated.

Needless to say, extrapolation of these findings from acute neurophysiology to intact humans is a hazardous undertaking, and it requires several intuitive leaps, and the construction of some shaky bridges. But before I plunge into this foolhardy venture, let me quickly introduce and emphasize some important provisos.

Nature is not simple: there is already clear, albeit indirect, evidence that the sequence of events outlined above is not inevitable. We cannot blithely assume that each pressor and accelerative episode exerts in-

hibitory control over excitatory processes. The organism exhibits many
complexly interacting mechanisms, and excitatory processes coexist with
inhibitory processes. Baust and his colleagues (1963), for example, argue
that there are unidentified presso-sensitive structures within the ascending
reticular activating system and that, therefore, blood pressure increase can
directly produce electro-cortical activation! The evidence for this arousing effect is not nearly so extensive as the evidence for the deactivating
effects mediated by the pressoceptors. Nevertheless, it would be the part
of wisdom, in the state of our present knowledge, at least to acknowledge
the possibility of truth in the complicating and complicated assumption
that the same cardiovascular process can simultaneously tend to produce
inhibition and excitation, by means of separate pathways. The ultimate
and final effect would be a resultant, not only of whatever central mechanisms have been thrown into activity by the pressor and accelerative
response but of other simultaneously operative mechanisms.

A second complication is that the carotid sinus, for example, is not a
passive structure, passively responding to bombardment from heart rate
and blood pressure. It has its own mechanical properties which can augment, reduce, or even obliterate the effects of the viscerally produced
stimuli. Note that the presso-sensitive receptors are more properly called
stretch receptors: their adequate stimulus is the rate of deformation of
the walls of the carotid sinus in which they are imbedded (Zotterman,
1953; Peterson, 1962; Ead et al., 1952). The degree to which the carotid
sinus will be stretched is a function not only of the intrasinusal pressure
but of the stiffness of the wall. Peterson and his colleagues (Peterson et
al., 1960; Peterson, 1962) have shown that the stiffness of the wall is
a variable, itself under physiological control. Acetylcholine applied directly to the wall of the carotid sinus produces enlargement of the sinus
(increased strain); norepinephrine produces a smaller carotid sinus,
which stretches less during the systole-diastole of the cardiac cycle. It is
clear, then, that there are structures—perhaps smooth muscle—that can
momentarily change the mechanical properties of the carotid sinus. The
effect of these changes is either to augment or diminish the effectiveness
of incoming pressure waves as stimuli to the baroceptors.

This phenomenon has many parallels in modern neurophysiology,
which is replete with instances of control by higher levels of sensory input. Receptors are not passive energy transducers that only send signals
forward to the central nervous mechanisms. Cortical and subcortical
systems, and peripheral mechanisms, can control at early stages in the
transmission process the very nature and kind of signals that are allowed
to be transmitted and can even determine the variable nature of the
transmission process itself (see Livingston, 1958 and 1959 for reviews of
this area; Galin, 1964). The mechanism for controlling the mechanical
properties of the wall of the carotid sinus, whatever it may turn out to

be, raises the possibility that higher levels of the CNS are able to control the effects of incoming pressor stimuli. Even if this possibility turns out to be false, we will still have to contend with the fact that heart rate and blood pressure changes reveal only the *possibility* of inhibitory action: the truly effective stimulus will be determined by the tone of the wall of the carotid sinus.

Finally we must note an important hole in our knowledge of the operation of this inhibitory mechanism. The neurophysiological investigations so far have examined only the effects from the carotid sinus forward and have treated higher integrating mechanisms as passive recipients of whatever inhibitory influx is allowed to enter. But it is unlikely that this is a one-way street. A possibility that needs to be investigated in detail is that the higher centers, when thrown into activity, call upon the cardiovascular system to provide a sort of homeostatic brake upon their own activity, holding excitability down and terminating the episode of "activation."

We are thus led, with considerable factual support, to a rather radical reinterpretation of the occurrence of blood pressure and heart rate increase due to stressful or activating stimuli. The cardiovascular responses may not be directly part of an activating process but of a restraining inhibitory process that, in common with other homeostatic processes, may be precisely graded to excitatory processes but may undershoot or overshoot the mark, and may be temporally displaced. Moreover, it should be noted that this point of view enables us to interpret the appearance of blood pressure and heart rate *decreases* as part of a response pattern in which other somatic processes show the sympathetic-like changes thought universally to characterize arousal. For, if increases in blood pressure and heart rate signal a physiological attempt to restrain excitatory processes, then it seems likely that their diminution, absence, or conversion to blood pressure and heart rate decrease signify an absence of this restraining process and, therefore, a net increase in excitation: a lowering of threshold, a prolongation of the impact of stimuli, an increase in spontaneous activity, and the like. I will soon present psychophysiological evidence, in intact human subjects, that lends itself precisely to this interpretation.

It should be emphasized that, like many other neurophysiological findings, those just reviewed provide only a point of departure for behavioral scientists, particularly for those interested primarily in intact man. Acute neurophysiology tells us something about the way the nervous system acts under the restrictive experimental conditions of surgical mutilation, anesthesia, and other drugs. Whether the nervous system does in fact act this way in the integrated organism, whether the mechanisms so elegantly exposed to study are actually potent ones in daily behavioral interactions, are questions that can be answered only by specifically designed psychophysiological experiments. For one thing, the neurophysiological findings do not tell us at what behaviors to look. I cannot believe, viewing both the complexity of the neurophysiological findings themselves and the history of attempts at the kind of formulation I am approaching, that a simple blanket formulation can be made that will be applicable always and everywhere.

Our task is to formulate specific statements, so that under specific circumstances a reliable and specifiable set of consequences will follow. Can it be shown that, under some circumstances at least, pressor and accelerative responses restrain or inhibit other accepted signs—behavioral or electroencephalographic—of activation? Can a specific set of arousing circumstances be found in which *de*pressor and *de*celerative responses occur? Do such depressor and decelerative physiological processes accompany *improved* performances? Positive answers can be found to all these questions.

Inhibitory effects of heart rate and blood pressure increase on activation

In 1942, Darrow and his associates demonstrated that two sympathetic-like changes were correlated, with *opposite* signs, with a common index of electro-cortical arousal, namely, alpha block produced by sensory stimulation (Darrow et al., 1942). Darrow called palmar conductance "excitatory" because the greater the conductance increase in response to the sensory inputs, the greater the accompanying alpha block. But he called blood pressure increase "homeostatic," because the greater the pressor response, the less the alpha block. So far as I know, the two important implications of this pioneer study—that different fractions of autonomic arousal may be correlated differently with another form of arousal, and that blood pressure may exert inhibitory control of electro-cortical activation—were never actively pursued, or accorded any importance at all by activation theorists.

In 1959, my colleagues and I found support for these basic implications in an entirely different experiment, in which stimuli to which the subject was instructed not to make a key-releasing response were temporally mixed with other stimuli to which the subject was instructed to respond (Lacey, 1959). The stimuli were automatically administered at low and high values of the spontaneously varying heart rate. We also recorded palmar conductance. The evidence showed that high heart rates accompanied a loss of motor readiness (false responses), whereas for the same trials the occurrence of concomitant or just-preceding conductance increase accompanied an increase of motor readiness.

If you will refer to the original accounts of both Darrow's experiments and ours, you will find the experiments, and the statistical treatment of the data, to be rather complicated. I feel that both experiments are only suggestive and that we badly need more decisive experiments of this kind.

Another promising line of investigation was opened up by Birren, Cardon, and Phillips in 1963. Each cardiac cycle, of course, produces an increase and a subsequent decrease in blood pressure, which can effect aortic arch and carotid sinus baroceptors. Additionally, receptors in atria and ventricles, themselves, are sources of visceral afferent feedback (Neil & Heymans, 1962). One would expect, then, in the light of the theory we have presented, systematic variations in reaction time as a function of the time within the cardiac cycle. Fast reaction times should be found before the heart contracts; reaction times should increase as baroceptors and mechanoceptors start sending impulses to inhibitory "centers," and a cycle of reaction time slowing should start, augment, and subside before the next heart contraction. These were precisely the findings of the study. The fastest auditory reaction times were found during the P-wave, which is the period just before the heart atria contract. With the onset of systole, during the QRS complex, reaction times slowed and then speeded up again through the subsequent time of the cardiac cycle. These results were promptly extended by Callaway and Layne (1964) who, using visual stimuli, found that reaction times were slowest early in the cardiac cycle, fastest in the latter half of the cardiac cycle. The same phenomena were found in two cardiac patients with pacemakers!

Callaway has also been energetically pursuing the nonrandom distribution of other events—spontaneous key presses, EEG phenomena, and evoked potentials—through the cardiac cycle. His results in these areas seem to show cardiac cycle effects, but unfortunately the nature of the time function does not seem to be reproducible from subject to subject (Callaway, 1965).

In my laboratory, Dr. Jean-Marie Coquery and I have been utilizing a closed-loop system, due to Mulholland, in which a flashing light is turned on automatically when the subject's alpha level is high (deactivated); the light stays on until an alpha block is produced and the alpha level subsides to low or activated levels. The light remains off until alpha level becomes high again. The high and low levels of alpha at which the light is turned on and off, respectively, are selected by a variable voltage-comparison device. We thus have an automatically programmed and sustained stimulus-brain feedback loop. According to "activation theory," the heart rate should be high during states of relative cortical activation (low alpha) and low during states of relative deactivation. According to the theory here presented, the reverse should be true. We have run 24 subjects: in 20 out of the 24, the results accord with our hypothesis, and in 13 of these 20 subjects, the results, treated intra-individually, are significant at the .05 level or better. For the group as a whole, the results are significant at the .001 level. The heart rate differences are small but very consistent.

It is perhaps more than coincidence that these studies, all of which yield evidence contrary to activation theory, also are all characterizable by the fact that they deal with the responses to simple environmental inputs as a function of cardiovascular activity. I think it is more than coincidence. Our research in the past five years has shown with increasing clarity and certainty that the cardiovascular system is particularly and peculiarly responsive to the intention of the subject to note and detect external stimuli. We have found repeatedly that *attentive observation of the external environment is productive of cardiac deceleration, cardiac stabilization, and either a blood pressure decrease or a marked diminution of pressure increase.* These results occur simultaneously with other processes, such as vasoconstriction and palmar conductance increase. This is a clear example of situational stereotypy.

Directional fractionation: A striking case of situational stereotypy

The clearest instances of situational stereotypy are like the one just described, in which one or more physiological functions changes decisively in a direction opposite to the expectations inherent in Cannon-like views of the energizing and protective role of sympathetic activity. Because the existence of these response patterns is a fact of considerable significance to current psychophysiological theory, a special label may be useful. I have said that such response patterns demonstrate "directional fractionation" (Lacey, 1959).

If an arousing stimulus produces vasoconstriction, increased palmar conductance, and faster breathing, then we expect to see increased heart rate and elevated blood pressure. We are so familiar with the pressor and accelerative responses that we are surprised to see the opposite effects. We need not be. Activation theorists have ignored the fact that in a variety of experiments in rat, cat, dog, and man—some of them employing aversive unconditioned stimuli—cardiac deceleration is often seen in response to arousing stimuli, although sometimes only as a prominent part of a polyphasic curve. (For a recent sampling, see Lang & Hnatiow, 1962; McDonald et al., 1963; Wenzel, 1961; Wilson, 1964; Jenks & Deane, 1963; Fuhrer, 1964; Geer, 1964; Obrist et al., 1965; Meyers et al., 1963; Davis et al., 1955). Little or no attempt has been made to extract from findings such as these any testable generalization applicable to activation theory. Yet one important generalization was made at the very beginnings of experimental psychophysiology, by Wundt (see Ruckmick, 1936), who found that pleasant stimuli resulted in cardiac deceleration. Pleasant stimuli can be defined as stimuli which the organism wants to approach, to notice, and surely many such stimuli can be considered to be arousing. A long series of early investigations, summarized by Rihl (1926), showed that "attention to visual and acoustic stimuli" produced cardiac deceleration in nine out of ten separate investigations. "Sensory dislike," on the other hand, produced cardiac acceleration in ten out of ten separate investigations. By contrast to attention to the external environment are instances of "mental work," in which the importance of external environmental cues is surely minimized. In eight out of the ten investigations summarized, "mental work" resulted in cardiac acceleration.

In 1929, Darrow published his own research and his own summary of the literature showing differential effects of "sensory" and "ideational" stimuli on the cardiovascular system (Darrow, 1929a, b). He, too, concluded that simple sensory stimuli, calling for "no extensive association of ideas" resulted in cardiac deceleration; on the other hand, either noxious stimulation or a sequence of activity requiring "associative processes" produced cardiac acceleration. With Darrow's 1929 papers this productive line of research stopped. This area of research has never been extended, nor have these early demonstrations been incorporated in our psychophysiological theories. Even in discussions of "stimulus specificity" or, as I prefer to call it, "situational stereotypy," these fruitful ideas have not been brought into the main stream of psychophysiological theory.

In our own work, we started with three separate samples, to increase the representativeness of our results, and we used eight "stressor-situations," administered in different orders to the three samples (Lacey et al., 1963). The "stressors" were roughly arranged along what we thought might be a continuum. Some situations required only attentive observation of the environment, like looking at a flashing light. In other conditions, like mental arithmetic, environmental intake was limited to brief moments of time while a problem was administered orally; the major portion of time was spent in internal processes of cognitive elaboration, retrieval of already stored information, and other problem-solving activity. We completely confirmed the notion—with near identity of results in all samples—that sensory intake *specifically* produced a response pattern that included cardiac deceleration and a restraint of systolic blood pressure increase (we did not measure diastolic pressure) to the vanishing point. In some samples and situations blood pressure decreased. The situations on the other end of the continuum produced the usual massive increases in heart rate and blood pressure. Other variables, such as respiratory rate and palmar conductance, not only showed the more usual activation pattern but did not differentiate the two sets of experimental conditions in any way. We heuristically interpreted these results to mean that depressor-decelerative processes facilitated environmental intake and that pressor-accelerative responses tended to filter out irrelevant stimuli that have distraction-value for the performance of internalized cognitive elaboration. Obrist promptly replicated the findings in every important detail, using a different variety of stimulus-situations and, of course, still another sample of subjects (Obrist, 1963).

In the Fels Department of Psychology, the correlation between attentiveness and cardiac deceleration has been replicated in 6-month-old infants and in first and second grade children (Kagan & Rosman, 1964; Kagan & Lewis, 1965; Lewis et al., 1966). In school children, attention to visual and auditory stimulation produced cardiac deceleration and stabilization, even though respiratory rate increased; "thinking" produced cardiac acceleration, although respiratory rate increases were more modest. The more "analytic" the child was in responding to visual stimuli, the greater was the deceleration. In infancy, a correlation was found between the magnitude of cardiac deceleration and the duration of fixation on visual stimuli.

In these experiments, it is of particular importance to note two things. First of all, only heart rate and blood pressure yielded a clear-cut and dramatic difference between the "environmental detection" situations and what we chose to call, by way of contrast, "environmental rejection." Simultaneously recorded measures, such as palmar conductance, respiratory period, and inspiration-expiration ratios, did not. Secondly, and of the greatest significance for those who wish to infer "activation level" from peripheral physiological processes, is that blood pressure and heart rate responses seem to be something like a sum of at least two opposing forces. In an experimental condition in which we made a deliberate effort to balance the requirements between "environmental detection" and "environmental rejection," the cardiac and pressure responses were essentially zero, although other simultaneously recorded variables, such as palmar conductance and respiration, showed great activation. It seems that the intent to note and detect external stimuli is a powerful factor determining the appearance of a decelerative response, but this influence can be diminished, cancelled, or converted to an accelerative influence when another kind of behavior—for example, internalized problem-solving activity—is mixed with or opposed to external attention. Similarly, external attention can diminish, cancel, or convert cardiac acceleration and blood pressure increase "caused" by suitable behaviors.

Finally, in a series of experiments using reaction time as a measure of sensorimotor integration, of response readiness, Mrs. Lacey and I find a dramatic, highly significant, completely obvious, beat-by-beat deceleration during the preparatory interval—the period of time between the point at which a given trial starts and the onset of the stimulus requiring a key-releasing response. During this foreperiod time, of course, the subject is paying the closest of attention to the external environment; his eyes are fixated on the point of space in which, with almost zero objective uncertainty ("catch trials" were used) and minimum subjective uncertainty, a stimulus is to appear which will release a simple "prepared reflex." Using rigidly controlled fixed foreperiods of four seconds, the phenomenon is completely obvious. Using intermixed foreperiods of three, four, and five seconds, it is not so much an "eye-ball phenomenon," but averaged curves show a highly significant tendency for deceleration. The deceleration continues to a nadir at the point in time at which the stimulus-to-respond comes on and, after the response is made, recovers beat-by-beat. The deceleration is not attributable to simultaneously observed changes in respiratory timing. Indeed, it is as obvious in inspiratory states as in expiratory. By the normal rules of respiratory-cardiac reflexes, of course, inspiration should produce acceleration. The deceleration is equally not attributable to homeostatic adjustment in response to blood pressure increase. There are only small pressure increases.

As would be predicted from the theoretical approach I have been urging, the *deceleration* is accompanied by *speedier* reaction times, and also by sensorimotor readiness as indicated by a lack of susceptibility to both current and preceding foreperiod effects. The decelerator seems to be wide open to his environment, keyed for reception of input and for the release of simple responses to these inputs. Again, as predicted, the modest blood pressure increases that occur show a tendency to be associated with *slower* reaction times.

Note that activation theory would not have predicted these findings on three counts: (1) Sympathetic-like activity was negatively, not positively, correlated with behavioral activation: (2) The cardiovascular system, at least, is sensitive to the nature of the subject's set and expectation and does respond to the "directionality" of behavior: (3) Even such intimately related variables as heart rate and blood pressure show some slight degree of dissociation.

Conclusions

The general conclusions to be drawn can be stated briefly. There is strong neurophysiological and psychophysiological evidence that different fractions of autonomic, electroencephalographic, and motor response are mediated separately, by perhaps "intimately related" but clearly dissociable mechanisms. The dissociation may be biologically useful because the different fractions of response can influence cortical and subcortical functioning in different, and sometimes opposing, ways. While we have not yet really demonstrated that the neurophysiological mechanisms I have discussed account for the observed psychophysiological correlations, the parallels are suggestive. In chronic animals at least, direct tests may be possible of the hypothesis that the visceral afferent negative feedback from heart to brain is in fact operative during attentive observation of the environment, in the ways outlined above, and does in fact, account for the observed relationships. Whether observations such as these have implications for the study of physiological response to "stress" will be left for the reader to decide.

Invited commentary

ALBERT F. AX: Dr. Lacey has brilliantly presented evidence for correcting an oversimplification of the arousal or activation concept, which I think has been handicapping psychophysiological theory for a long time. As he so kindly pointed out, some of us have never accepted the activation concept as a monolithic process which could mobilize all systems of the body to peak activity. Even Cannon knew that for the emergency arousal of fight or flight the visceral parasympathetic activities were inhibited. Arousal is a modulated pattern of adjustment of the body's physiology. Joseph Schachter (1957) and I (1953) were able to demonstrate, for example, that flight and fight—for us, fear and anger—could be differentiated in peripheral response patterns. It seems that when an investigator records or compares more than two or three physiological variables—especially if they stem from such diverse systems as the cardiovascular, skin, striped muscle, and gastrointestinal—he is eventually compelled by the data to recognise the finer differentiations of behavior. Now, even sleep, that ideal base level from which M. A. Wenger (pers. comm.) had hoped to scale all physiological response amplitudes, has been demolished as a unitary concept of minimum arousal.

But must we despair because of the oft-quoted disappointingly low correlations among physiological variables? I think not. Had we found high intercorrelations among the seven variables used in our fear and anger study back in 1949, I would have given up psychophysiology and returned to the Rorschach and TAT! It is exactly because the physiological variables do *not* have high intercorrelations that they are able by their patterning to describe the varieties of arousal, emotion, motivation, anxiety, and stress. These general concepts must be broken down into usable constructs, just as intelligence has been subdivided, and this is what Dr. Lacey is advising us to do.

The innovators of a new concept always try to generalize it as far as possible. Spearman worked diligently to prove the generality of the G factor, but then Guilford showed that intelligence probably consists of some fifty components. An important question, for both theory and research strategy, is whether there is any merit in further effort to describe stress as a general construct. I suppose it was necessary to dramatize the new concept in its introduction to get people interested in and work done on it. Selye thus accomplished a great deal for the stress concept. But now we must take the next step and describe the varieties of stimulus situations which elicit them, the varieties of behavior that may result, and the varieties of people who exhibit such diverse stimulus-response patterns.

There are two facts to be explained. The one that Dr. Lacey emphasized is that different systems of the body do different things during activity. Some systems may show excitation while others may be inhibited. The second fact is that there are variations in activation from moment to moment. Our task is to describe the variations and account for the sources of variance. Convenient ways of grouping these influences are (1) enduring characteristics of the individual, generally referred to as individual response specificity, (2) characteristics of the stimulus, and (3) their interaction, in the sense of the individual's interpretation of the situation and what he intends to do about it. In Dr. Lacey's terms, is he going to take in the environment or is he going to reject it?

Under ideal circumstances, any one of these influences can dominate behavior—any strong unexpected stimulus can produce a startle reaction which is quite uniform, even across species. The orienting response is similarly fairly uniform. On the other hand, an overlearned psychophysiological pattern, such as a psychosomatic disorder, may be very stereotyped, so that a unique arousal pattern is generally given, at least by one individual, to most all stimuli. The great majority of arousal responses to stressors is determined primarily by the "intentions" of the individual. Psychology has a rich vocabulary for what I am here calling "intentions," including set, expectancy, goal, motive, emotion, and stress. This string of concepts—ranging from set to stress—picks up an intensity dimension but little more. The central concept is the *intention* of the organism in a situation as modulated by his interpretation of the opportunities and difficulties, along with his felt competence, to master the situation. Thus, a study of stress is the study of the organismic reactions in the more demanding situations but involves the full range of concepts with which psychology and physiology deal.

Probably the most demanding practical problem facing us is the selection and training of men for high stress tolerance. I would suggest that stress tolerance consists of motivation and discipline, both of which are learned. Ever since the followers of Pavlov demonstrated that just about every organ and physiological process of the body can be conditioned, there is reason to believe that what physiologists have called adaptation is the same as learning. It is possible that basic processes of homeostasis are learned by the usual principles of contingent reinforcement. Without question the secondary social motives—such as striving for money, climbing Mount Everest, or getting to the moon—are all learned.

If a person is to learn anything, then he may be said to have an ability or aptitude for such learning. I propose that the aptitude for physiological learning is distributed among the population as widely as the familiar IQ, although it may be very little correlated with the aptitude for intellectual learning. This physiological learning aptitude can be measured by the parameters of conditioning of the physiological processes, such as GSR and heart rate. Thus, these physiological variables can provide at once a powerful selection for motivation and stress tolerance, as well as serve as monitors during our efforts to train these highly desired characteristics.

In our own laboratory we have tested GSR conditioning in successful and unsuccessful people and find strong support for this notion that autonomic conditioning can be a good index of physiological learning aptitude and thus possibly a useful measure of motivation and stress tolerance. Certainly Dr. Lacey has helped clear the air for stress research by removing one more shibboleth blocking the way for the application of patterning and learning constructs.

Discussion

Dr. Sells: Some considerable mention was made, by both Dr. Lacey and Dr. Ax, of the concepts of set and expectancy. I would like to propose that these be extended to include the posture of the organism at any time as representing some hypothesis concerning the nature of the environment. If we think of behavior as involving feedback systems that enable continual adjustment with the environment, then we should bring in not only the immediate stimulus situation but the total environmental pattern in which the behavior is occurring, including inhibitory processes. Otherwise, the experimenter only focuses on part of the total action. This point is illustrated by the experimental work of Morse in the Pharmacology Department at Harvard (Kelleher & Morse, 1964). He has found that measuring the dosage effects of drugs depends not only on pharmacological and psychophysiological considerations but also on the details of the ongoing behavior. A drug like morphine, for example, may be either an inhibitor or an activator, depending upon the level of behavior taking place at the time.

Dr. Stern: Dr. Lacey has done a beautiful job of demonstrating that nature is complex and not simple, as exemplified in the complexity of cardiovascular central nervous system interactions. I am sure that what is true of the cardiovascular system is equally true of all other physiological response measures. He quite clearly rejects the concept of generalized arousal or activation, preferring an emphasis upon specific responses to stimulation. We tend to restrict ourselves in the concept of arousal or activation to dealing with nonspecific responses to a great variety of stressor stimuli, which we expect to go invariably in a given direction. We then find that there are some physiological systems which respond contrary to that notion. What we are likely to be looking at is systems that have more than one function; that is, they can respond nonspecifically to stressors, but they can also respond specifically to given situations. For example, he points out that cardiac deceleration is commonly not believed to be a measure of activation. But along with cardiac deceleration one can see other measures of activation, such as changes in electrodermal skin resistance. Dr. Lacey would agree, I believe, that one can have both activation and attentive listening at the same time and that if attentive listening is reflected in cardiac deceleration, there is no reason why other physiological response systems, such as alpha desynchronization in the EEG or change in electrodermal resistance, can't demonstrate the activating effect of the stimulus.

The point I would like to make is that cardiac acceleration can be considered a measure of activation and cardiac deceleration can, among other things, be a measure of attentive observation. In our own work, I have become convinced that cardiac deceleration not only occurs under attentive observation but that the orienting response to nonspecific stimuli, at least in the rat, is one of cardiac deceleration. This, however, is different from some of the conditioned cardiac decelerative responses that Dr. Notterman and his colleagues described a number of years ago (1952), where one can get cardiac deceleration in anticipation of a noxious stimulus (which again may have little to do with attentive observation). In other words, cardiac deceleration can mean more than one thing, i.e., can be produced by more than one mechanism. I think the reason that Dr. Lacey has singled out attentive observation as being related to cardiac deceleration is that this is the kind of response measure with which he has been most intimately involved.

Dr. Appley: I'm sure Dr. Lacey would wish not only to distinguish between activation and attentive observation but in the latter case to further differentiate selective responding to the subtle differences in stimulus situations. For example, attentive responses or responses stimulated from the outside would surely differ as between stimuli which are feared or not feared, or unexpected or expected, known or unknown, and so forth.

Dr. Lacey: Yes, very much so. I feel that we must retreat from, or at least supplement, global generalizations about arousal phenomena and seek specific statements concerning specific results under specifiable circumstances. I wish to emphasize that I have not said that cardiac deceleration inevitably implies attentive observation of the environment or, indeed, that the absence of deceleration implies inattention. Indeed, we took pains in our studies of situational stereotypy to show that in a situation requiring prolonged and intense attention to information coming from the external environment *combined* with cognitive elaboration of the information, the heart showed *no* change on the average. Heart rate, then, seems to be a resultant of contradictory tendencies. If externalized attention, without the necessity of cognitive elaboration, predominates in the task, then deceleration seems to occur. If cognitive elaboration predominates, then acceleration results. If both requirements are present in approximately equal amounts, then the heart seems not to change. I might take this opportunity to answer one of Dr. Stern's comments. He states that anticipation of a noxious stimulus has very little to do with attentive observation. I think the opposite is true. If I anticipate a noxious stimulus, I am sure I become anxiously attentive! How the heart will behave will depend, I think, on the specific experimental situation. I suspect cardiac deceleration would yield to acceleration the more noxious the anticipated stimulus.

Dr. Lazarus: We seem to be learning that there is both something general and something specific in the physiological reaction. I think it appropriate to draw a parallel between the assessment of stress reaction at the physiological level of analysis and at the behavioral level. There is specificity also at the behavioral level, but it need not require that we abandon the unifying value of the concept of stress.

For example, a variety of behavioral indicators of stress reaction are employed. One example is gestural or expressive activity. There is no question that when an individual is threatened there is often a gestural or expressive manifestation. The trouble is that the agreement between response indicators of psychological stress, such as expressive acts and reported expressions of distress, instrumental acts or performance changes, is often low. Disagreements among the indicators should not lead us to abandon the unifying concept of threat, of frustration, or of stress, or even to question whether these are all response indicators of stress. They may reveal other things as well. Rather we say that there is something general in all these responses but the commonality is not 100 percent. From an examination of the pattern of response indicators we learn something about the complex intervening psychological mechanisms, which, in turn, may help to explain the divergences.

Dr. Korchin: Dr. Lacey's position can be further extended to include emphasis on the specificities *between* the psychological and physiological realms. He has argued persuasively that the organism does not operate in a monolithic way, with various physiological systems co-varying along a single activation dimension. In the same spirit, I would like to call attention to the dissociations of physiological and psychological variables and the specificities of response between them. In the tradition of activation research—and much of psychophysiology generally—invariant relationships are often assumed between physiological and psychological variables. Such relationships may be no more invariant than those among physiological variables alone. But equating the psychological with the physiological, and using the latter to index the former (e.g., cardiac acceleration or GSR response = anxiety), diverts attention from the empirical study of the conditions under which co-variation does and does not occur. The proper study of stress, it seems to me, must keep psychological and physiological variables conceptually and operationally distinct, as Dr. Lacey has suggested must be done within the physiological realm itself.

But now a question to Dr. Lacey. Today you have emphasized situational stereotypy, but in earlier writings you also called attention to person-specific patterns as another source of specificity in physiological response. What is the current state of your work and thinking about person-specific patterning of physiological response?

Dr. Lacey: A good question! We have the data available to provide at least a preliminary answer but have yet to analyze them. We have subjected a group of approximately 85 young adult males to a variety of stressors on three occasions over a year. The stressors are those we employed in our study of situational stereotypy. We will try to analyze the data to evaluate the amount of variance accounted for by idiosyncratic response-patterns and by situational requirements. My strong preliminary impression is that the situational requirement for externalized attention is going to overwhelm idiosyncratic patterning. If this is true, we are going to have to describe idiosyncratic patterning not over all stressor situations, which is what I thought originally, but over classes of stressor situations.

Dr. Korchin: I wonder, Dr. Lacey, if you would speculate, in terms of neurophysiological theory, as to how you would view a person-specific reaction pattern?

Dr. Lacey: Only on a wildly speculative basis. While presumably all individuals are born with the same basic neural circuitry—to use a rather inelegant and imprecise analogy—individual differences can exist in such things as density of innervation of the carotid sinus and aortic arch, for example, and in metabolism, in concentrations of biochemical substrates, and so on. Moreover, the nervous system is enormously plastic, and learning may certainly account for person-specific response patterning. It is conceivable even that occupations, characterized by often-repeated situational requirements, tend to produce fixed patterns of physiological responses.

Dr. Mandler: Dr. Lacey used the term *situational stereotypy*. A danger with the term, not the concept, is that it implies that the stereotypy is specific to some stimulus situation. I'm sure he would agree that the stereotypy has something to do with what the organism does in the situation.

Dr. Lacey: Yes, in fact I use the term *situational stereotypy*, rather than *stimulus specificity*, which most other people seem to prefer. I think the stereotypy adheres not in the characteristics of the stimulus but in the interaction between the stimulus and the subject.

Dr. Mandler: I am very interested in the postulated continuum of situations which has been discussed here. I have a hunch that what it deals with is how definite a behavioral pattern the organism has laid down prior to the appearance of the stimulus. If the behavioral pattern is well organized, then you should get the attentive "I know what I am going to do, I am going to do it." If the situation is what you might call complex, then the variety of possible behaviors necessary is extremely large, and, as a matter of fact, the organism may not be able to do what he is planning to do. For example, we found some years ago (Mandler & Mandler, 1962) that in a simple associative test cardiac deceleration develops over trials. This suggests that at the beginning the subject didn't know what the situation was about. Later, when the subject knew exactly what was expected and there was a well laid-down behavior sequence which the subject could and did execute, nice clean cardiac deceleration occurred, not only prior to the stimulus but also consequent to it as well.

Dr. Lacey: I agree with what you just said empirically, we find the same thing. I do not agree that it's a continuum of complexity or "knowing what to do," although I think that is an important one to mention.

For the Chairman's summary by Dr. John A. Stern, see end of Chapter 3.

DONALD OKEN

3

The psychophysiology and psychoendocrinology of stress and emotion[1]

The great breadth of my subject precludes the possibility of covering, anywhere near completely, the range of topics which it includes. While this has the disadvantage of forcing selectivity, there is no alternative. The choice of a subject which is so broad is dictated by the inseparability of its several components, a point which I hope to make evident in the course of this discussion.

In his original classic work, Selye (1950) makes clear that the term *stress* refers to the "sum of all *non-*[2] specific systemic reactions of the body" (p. 12). He gives as its major characteristics that this response is adaptive, that it is a syndrome, an integrated constellation of responses, and that it is *general,* emphasizing the point that it "must be distinguished from the specific adaptive reactions"[3] (p. 12). This very generality, fruitful as it has been for understanding common response elements, carries with it the danger of obscuring more specific patterning of response which may be related to classes of stimuli, affect states or defenses, personality characteristics, etc. With the clarification of the

[1] Included in this review are reports of several projects from the Institute for Psychosomatic and Psychiatric Research and Training, Michael Reese Hospital and Medical Center, Chicago, Illinois, which have been generously supported over a number of years by grants from the National Institute of Mental Health and the State of Illinois. Current work is being carried out through the assistance of grant M-5519 from the National Institute of Mental Health and grant 1711 from the State of Illinois Mental Health Fund, acknowledgment of which is gratefully made.

[2] Italics not in original.

[3] Hence it is misleading to use the term *stress* to describe a specific response, such as the effect of insulin upon enzymes involved in glucose metabolism, as Frohman and his colleagues (Tourney, Frohman, et al., 1962) have done.

major features of the generalized stress response, attention has properly turned away to focus on such specificities, and thus away from *stress* itself.

Before proceeding further, it is important to recall another distinction which Selye makes (p. 9). This concerns the proper use of *stress* as a term which denotes response and not a stimulus (the correct term for the latter being *stressor*). This is more than a matter of semantic confusion. There is no *a priori* way to know whether any given stimulus effectively will provoke the stress reaction in a given subject. Even where the stimulus is a physical one, intrinsic factors, such as the state of immunity and genetic variations, will help to determine the reaction. But the distinction of a response definition has special relevance to psychological stress, where individual meaning will determine whether a situation will indeed prove stressful for a given person. The point is a crucial one, deserving great emphasis, since it is all too easy to slip into the vernacular use of the term to characterize a stimulus situation. To do so can lead to serious errors in research. Even the most "obviously" stressful situation may produce no response in a particular person. This is not to imply that the response must be disintegrative or harmful. Defensive adaptations quite properly may be viewed as stress. But only when observable response has taken place can we speak properly of stress.

Because we are concerned with a generalized response with widespread manifestations, attention is directed to the great integrating systems of the body, the endocrines and nervous system. In approaching the study of these systems, it is useful to focus on measures which are most central, for these have the broadest effects; while peripheral responses also are more subject to idiosyncratic intrapersonal variations and minor environmental shifts. This is not to deny the feedback effects of peripheral responses (some of which John Lacey has so beautifully described in Chapter 2). Stress, as all psychosomatic processes, can be understood only within a transactional, field-theoretical framework.

Hydroxycorticosteroids

The secretion of 17-hydroxycorticosteroids (17-OHCS) [4] by

[4] For practical purposes, in man this can be considered to be hydrocortisone. Small amounts of several additional "glucocorticoids" are produced, but these have very similar physiological properties. The adrenal cortex also produces aldosterone, which will be considered in a later section of this paper, and small amounts of other "mineralocorticoids." In addition, some estrogens and endrogens are synthesized, but these are not relevant to the present discussion.

Methods for measuring blood 17-OHCS (based on Porter-Silber chromogens) are generally accepted to be satisfactory. Comparable methods applied to urine probably measure only about 25 percent of the original 17-OHCS. In addition to problems arising from gluconuride and sulfate conjugation (which may be solvable), the metabolism the adrenal cortex is so central a part of the stress response that sometimes the two have been considered synonymous. The question has even been raised whether stress can occur in the absence of adrenals. It can, of course. The pattern of response is altered and the tolerance for stressful stimuli markedly reduced. An adrenalectomized organism will survive, provided that stressors are not too great in number, intensity, frequency, or acuteness. This differential mortality emphasizes the adaptive role of the adrenocortical response to physical stress. Increased levels of 17-OHCS induce a variety of metabolic changes (many concerned with the supply of energy) useful to an organism struggling to cope with environmental forces which may cause physical damage or in dealing with what damage ensues. Physiological mobilization in anticipation of such situations, triggered psychologically, is of obvious value. Whether this physiological mobilization is adaptive when *only* psychological responses are needed and no action is called for, is another matter. Literal fight or flight are not often necessary for man. The stereotyped emergence of the response when there appears to be no "use" for steroids is maladaptive and may be viewed as an evolutionary anachronism (Hamburg, 1961).

That psychological stimuli trigger an adrenocortical response is well established. Many of the early studies have been reviewed previously by Mason (1959a, b). Stimuli which have been found to be effective include competitive sports (Hill et al., 1956; Frost et al., 1951); paratrooper training (Basowitz et al., 1955); admission to a research ward (Fishman et al., 1962a), to a mental hospital (Board et al., 1956), or a surgical ward and the anticipation of surgery (Price et al., 1957); college examinations (Bliss et al., 1956); emotion-arousing interviews (Hetzel et al., 1955; Persky et al., 1958); perceptual distortion (Korchin et al., 1958); and initial exposure to the psychosomatic laboratory (Sabshin et al., 1957). In addition, similar changes have been produced in monkeys as a result of changes in housing or shifts in surrounding environmental activity as well as by conditioning techniques associated with avoidance, punishment (e.g., electric shock), and "anxiety" (Mason 1958, 1959a, b). This list is by no means exhaustive. Stress stimuli are a ubiquitous feature of real life.

The question, however, is what in these complex situations is re-

---

of hydrocortisone and related steroids yields some compounds which do not give the Porter-Silber reaction. Most of these will be included in assays of 17-ketosteroid and 17-ketogenic steroid fractions which most research has not included. The issue is complicated further by the likelihood that there are stress-induced shifts in metabolic pathways leading to more or less production of various steroid compounds. Nevertheless, there are good grounds for considering the studies cited in this paper as valid insofar as they indicate a 17-OHCS stress response, even when they depend on urinary assays or (as in early research) on indirect measures of adrenocortical activity. Final clarification of these issues which may have important bearing on specificities of response is an object of current research. Earlier relevant work can be found by consulting the volume edited by Wolstenholme and Cameron (1955).

lated to the adrenal response. Perhaps most can be viewed in traditional terms of threat or conflict. From this conceptual framework, interest centers on anxiety (Grinker et al., 1956; Grinker, 1959). And, indeed, anxiety is related to the steroid response (e.g., Bliss et al., 1956; Persky et al., 1958). But the *specificity* of this relationship is questionable. In our own studies, 17-OHCS levels were related to other affective responses as well as to anxiety and, in general, seemed somewhat more closely related to overall emotional response. Similarly, Price et al. (1957) felt that the best correlate of steroid levels in patients anticipating surgery was a global measure of distress and emotional involvement. Sachar et al. (1963), studying acute schizophrenics, noted that corticoid elevations were related to periods of overall affective arousal, including both anxiety and depression, rather than to any one emotional state. At least three studies (Board et al., 1956, 1957; Bunney et al., 1963) have demonstrated elevated 17-OHCS levels in patients with depressive illnesses, with a variety of indicators of the intensity of emotional distress being the best correlates of such elevations. The conclusion seems to be that almost any situation of affective arousal leads to a rise in 17-OHCS.

Should this situation lead you to feel mixed emotions, let me emphasize that this is exactly what was true of the subjects. Moreover, controlled laboratory studies are no more effective in producing pure affect states (Oken, 1960). Any given stressful stimulus has a great likelihood of producing a variety of affective patterns within a subject group and mixtures of affect states within individuals. Not only can one not assume that a correctly chosen stimulus will produce a pure affect state but the evidence points to the contrary. This applies as well to studies in which the focus has been on autonomic or other responses; and it may well be the crucial factor which makes it difficult for us to uncover specific response patterns. It should be noted, moreover, that the existence of this situation was documented through the application of operational rating scales for quantifying affects (Persky, Grinker, et al., 1950, 1952; Hamburg et al., 1958; Oken, 1960). As Grinker (1961) has emphasized, the development of such scales for several types of behavioral phenomena has been one of the most important methodological advances of recent years. The use of these more precise measures may make it possible eventually to tease out finer specificities. Even if many affects are associated with the common features of a general stress response, the question remains as to what additional differences exist between affect states.

In an attempt at clarification, there have been imaginative efforts to find more affect-specific stimuli. One such method relies on the use of motion pictures. The usual approach is to utilize a film with *prima facia* anxiety-inducing properties, such as enucleation of the eye (Oken et al., 1962) or crude genital "surgery" (Lazarus et al., 1962). However, again, the evidence is that such stimuli produce a mixture of affects (Oken et al.,

1962) and of defenses. Professional Hollywood films would seem to have the same disadvantage, though they have the value of great effectiveness in involving the observer. They can be used even with children (Stern-bach, 1962). Their very complexity has been utilized ingeniously in studies by the late Franz Alexander (1950), who selected films in which the overall story line corresponds to the "specific dynamic constellations" he hypothesized to occur with each "psychosomatic disease." Measures of radioactive blood protein bound iodine (measuring thyroxin output) rose in thyrotoxic patients and fell in controls after viewing the film *Wages of Fear,* selected to induce anxiety specifically on the basis of the constellation proposed for thyrotoxicosis (F. Alexander et al., 1961).

A more promising technique may be hypnosis, by which means otherwise nonexistent pure affect states do seem to be produced with some regularity (e.g., Keho & Ironside, 1963). Orne (1959), however, has raised serious questions about the nature of affects produced during hypnosis and has presented data (Damaser et al., 1963) indicating that subjects who simulate the hypnotic state may have equal physiological changes. Moreover, the data of Levitt et al. (1964) indicate a marked inconsistency in adrenocortical response despite the successful stimulation of anxiety.[5]

The matter is not so simple even when one considers anxiety alone, for it may not be a unitary phenomenon. In our study of paratroop trainees, differences in response could be linked to two types of anxiety: that related to physical harm and that associated with shame and possible failure (Basowitz et al., 1955). A subsequent study (Persky et al., 1958) revealed a third relevant dimension. Those psychiatric patients who developed "disintegrative anxiety" about impending ego disruption had higher 17-OHCS levels than others subjected to the same stressful interviews whose anxiety levels were equal but did not have this quality. In normal subjects, the production of disintegrative feelings by the use of a perceptual distortion technique proved more stressful than a failure stimulus (Korchin & Herz, 1960).

There must be further doubt about the role of anxiety of any type as a necessary feature of psychological stress. In several of the stimulus conditions which have been used, the presence of anxiety is questionable. Perhaps, one might implicate anxiety as a factor in the response to competitive sports by invoking fear of failure and, possibly, of harm. Feelings of pleasurable "excitement" may be of significance. But, certainly, the stress response exceeds the level of anxiety which can be observed. The same problem arises with respect to the adrenocortical response to "novelty," one of the most consistently effective of stressors. A wide variety of environmental changes have been shown to be effective stress stimuli in many species (Mason 1959a, b; Fishman et al., 1962a). Since these include initial contact with the psychosomatic laboratory (Sabshin

[5] A further problem arising with the use of hypnosis will be indicated below.

et al., 1957) or even simple venipuncture (J. O. Davis et al., 1962a), adequate research design requires the inclusion of controls for this effect. To explain novelty stress, again one could implicate anxiety either in terms of fear of the unknown, with its potential dangers, or in terms of the need for some optimum level of patterned sensory input [6] and for cognitive structuring. But, again, the steroid response is disproportionate to the manifest anxiety (Sabshin et al., 1957).

This dilemma might be resolved by invoking "unconscious anxiety" as a hypothetical construct linked to increased 17-OHCS. This is permissible only if that construct is made operationally definable in terms of observed behaviors. Included among these would be instrumental coping activity (which deals with the threat or removes it), manifestations of psychological defense (which block the emergence of anxiety), and overt symptoms (which "bind" the anxiety). [An example from animal research is the finding that 17-OHCS levels in monkeys performing an avoidance task were related to lever pressing rate—an instrumental response—as well as to the frequency of receiving shocks (Sidman et al., 1962)]. Beginning attempts at such studies in man have been made which suggest that it is not the amount of defense (or, therefore, of unconscious anxiety) but the *effectiveness* of defense which is the significant factor. In a study of chronic psychiatric patients who had an extraordinarily well-developed capacity to avoid conflict, 17-OHCS and other responses to a provocative interview were more sharply limited in time than those of more acutely ill subjects or normals; and this was related to their more effective, albeit maladaptive, capacity to bring avoidance defenses into play (Oken et al., 1960). In a subsequent study where we rated the intensity of defenses (Oken, 1962), we were unable to elicit any significant relationship to steroid levels. In a more recent study of the parents of leukemic children at the NIMH (Wolff et al., 1964a, b), where the parent group generally was found to have elevated steroid levels, the rated effectiveness of defenses was a significant inverse predictor of an individual's steroid output. Of special interest was the finding that this was true even when defensive maneuvers involved heightened affect levels (e.g., in parents who utilized diffuse hysterical hyperemotionality to avoid a more meaningful affective involvement with real concerns about their children).

Whereas most research has focused on adrenocortical activation, more recently some exciting studies have been conducted on situations in which steroid levels *decrease*. One such is that of the hypnotic trance state (Persky, Gross et al., 1959; Sachar et al., 1964), although the decreases which occur are inconsistent both within and between subjects. What further determinants are involved awaits clarification.[7] This finding makes it necessary to reevaluate previous studies which utilized hypnosis

---

[6] This touches on the area of *sensory deprivation* and related topics, which I have chosen to ignore in view of Dr. Cohen's presentation in the next chapter.

[7] In Persky's data, there is a suggestion that a sex difference may be involved.

as the vehicle for stress stimulation. [Indeed, a variety of physiological changes may sometimes occur during the hypnotic trance alone (Levitt & Brady, 1963)].

Of perhaps greater interest are the findings reported by Handlon (1962; Handlon et al., 1962) on the response to viewing Disney nature films. Significant falls in plasma 17-OHCS were noted in comparison with a control period. When emotionally arousing films (i.e., those producing anxiety, primarily) were shown, there was a rise. The appropriateness of Handlon's reference to the Disney films as "bland" is open to some question. His own data include evidence of the development of pleasurable affect states during their viewing. And I have heard numerous informal reports of feelings of "excitement" occurring, particularly while watching scenes of the competitive features of animal life.

These data at once bring to mind Lacey's reports of drops in cardiovascular measures occurring with pleasurable stimuli requiring externalized cognitive attention.[8] As a prototype of this phenomenon, Lacey mentions the findings of R. C. Davis (1957a) in male subjects looking at pictures of nude females. The view (sic!) that such experiences produce unmixed pleasure, or are "a clear-cut example of an individual wanting to 'take in the environment'" (Lacey 1959, p. 199) seems oversimplified to a clinician. Some subjects will experience significant anxiety, shame, or guilt in this situation—and some may even have the defensive impulse to look away! Preliminary data of our own (Kling et al., unpublished data) suggest that sexually arousing "party" films produce steroid rises in some male subjects and decreases in others.

Handlon (1962) indicates that drops in steroid levels may occur also during the "easements"[9] of normal life. Such data help to undermine an erroneous tendency to think of stress as a discontinuous, all-or-none phenomenon. "There is a continuous series of transitions between the definitely physiologic adaptive processes to the strains of everyday life and to the most severe alarm reactions which cause death . . ." (Selye, 1950, p. 27). Moreover, there is some evidence that an individual's steroid levels tend to remain within a range characteristic for him (Fishman et al., 1962a), a range which may be related to personality characteristics, such as that revealed by the Taylor MAS scale (Fiorica & Muehl, 1962).

Central nervous mechanisms

Thus far I have discussed the adrenocortical system without reference to central nervous system function. There is considerable in-

[8] For further clarification of this oversimplified statement, see Lacey's chapter in this volume and his previous publications (1958, 1959), as well as my further discussion below.
[9] The term is his.

formation about the CNS pathways through which the impact of psychological stimuli are transmitted. Production of 17-OHCS is, of course, under control of the anterior pituitary gland through its varying release of ACTH (adrenocorticotrophin). The relation between the hypothalamus and ACTH release is well established. Hypothalamic cells produce a corticotrophin-releasing factor (CRF) [10] which passes directly to the pituitary through a vascular linkage via the portal system. The hypothalamus has multiple connections with limbic structures (Papez, 1937; MacClean, 1958; Nauta, 1960) which subserve a variety of functions connected with emotion and "instinctual" behavior, including "oral" and sexual functions. Stimulation of one of these limbic structures, the amygdala, was found by Mason (1958) to produce 17-OHCS release in monkeys; while stimulation of a closely related area, the hippocampus, produced a delayed drop or reversed the effects of previous amygdala stimulation. This has been confirmed in man (Mandell et al., 1963). The hippocampus thus may serve as an integrating mechanism with the important function of shutting off the ACTH response when subsequent information reveals a threat to have been a false alarm or to be no longer present.

More recent studies performed by Kling (1963) provide confirmation and additional data of interest. Large amygdala lesions blocked the effects of conditioning situations associated with electrical shock which produced a consistent rise in 17-OHCS in normal monkeys, but the same lesions did not block the steroid response to a physical stressor. However, lever pressing for food reward which was associated with *drops* in steroid levels [11] was unaffected by these lesions. This drop is reminiscent of that occurring during pleasant movies (see above) and of Lacey's findings of decreased cardiovascular measures associated with pleasurable emotional states.

A neurohumoral basis for these steroid decreases also may exist. By a series of remarkable experiments, Egdahl (1962, 1964) obtained data from which he concludes the existence of a corticotrophin *inhibitory* factor produced also by the hypothalamus (probably in its more posterior portions with connections to the mesencephalic tegmentum and the fields of Forel). He suggests that the cerebral cortex exerts a tonic inhibitory influence on ACTH through this mechanism, via its connections to the reticular activating system.

Of great interest also are the findings (in animals) summarized by Pribram (1960, pp. 13–14) that electrical activity occurs in the amygdala

[10] I might add that the posterior pituitary hormone Vasopressin [the amino acid structure of which has been elucidated and identified, for man, as arginine Vasopressin (Sawyer et al., 1960)], once postulated to be CRF, is no longer accepted as such, although it is chemically similar and does have some like properties (Nichols, 1961). Nor is epinephrine any longer accepted as the trigger for ACTH release (Ganong & Forsham, 1960).

[11] Confirming an earlier unsystematic observation of Mason (1959b).

with novel events or those associated with reward or punishment; and that in a learning or conditioning situation, electrical activity can be recorded from the hippocampus, which activity subsequently disappears during successful action, only to recur when errors are made.

Aldosterone

The 17-hydroxycorticosteroids are not the only adrenocortical hormones important in stress. For some time it had been known that the cortex synthesized other hormones whose primary effect was upon water and electrolyte metabolism. But it was not until 1953–54 that Aldosterone was isolated and identified as the primary such "mineralo-corticoid" hormone in man (Conn, 1956). Aldosterone production is increased by ACTH and therefore can be influenced by the same mechanisms already detailed for 17-OHCS (Fortier, 1962). But the usual, major control mechanism is a different one. Renin produced by the juxta-glomerular apparatus in the kidney activates Angiotensin II from its inactive precursor (produced by the liver); and it is this circulating agent which stimulates Aldosterone production and release (J. O. Davis, et al., 1962b, Schmidt, 1962). The usual stimulus to the juxtaglomerular apparatus is probably a shift in blood volume acting through renal hemodynamic changes.[12] Details of these processes are quite intricate and remain a problem for current research.[13]

The complexities of these interrelationships in addition to those occurring within the autonomic nervous system (Gellhorn & Loofbourrow, 1963) underscore the problems of understanding what has taken place when changes in a peripheral measure, such as blood pressure, are recorded. The sphygmomanometer reading represents the end product of multiple interrelated neural and endocrine processes which may have additive, opposing, or potentiating effects in different parts of the system. Blood pressure and other peripheral indices represent a "final common pathway" of response.

Three recent reviews (August et al., 1958; Hoagland, 1961; El-madjian, 1962a) document the relationship of increased Aldosterone levels and psychological stress. Effective stimuli included medical school examinations, military combat, and the presentation of scientific papers.[14]

[12] Probably the juxtaglomerular apparatus is responsive to changes in electrolyte levels also (Wright, 1962b). While there may be additional mechanisms, the hypothesized pineal hormone *adrenoglomerulotrophin* appears to be another of the nonexistent functions of the "seat of the soul."

[13] For example, the issue is complicated by the fact that Angiotensin has direct vascular effects of its own and that both Renin and Angiotensin appear to affect sympathetic receptors so as to enhance their response to endogenous norepinephrine (McCubbin & Page, 1963).

[14] Any similarity among these is purely coincidental!

While the increases were ascribed to anxiety (Venning et al., 1957; Elmadjian, 1962a), no evidence was provided to support this specific relationship. In addition, Elmadjian (1962b) describes elevated urinary
output of Aldosterone in patients with acute schizophrenia and non-
psychotic anxiety states which was "related to the subject's emotional
state, rather than to any diagnostic classification" (p. 415); whereas
chronic schizophrenics frequently had low levels. In several of these
studies, Aldosterone rises are noted to take place independently from
increases in 17-OHCS (or catechol amines). This argues against the
response being due to ACTH release. And, more important, it reveals
the limitations inherent in a unitary view of stress. All the various
hormones apparently can be released more-or-less independently. Current
research utilizes simultaneous measures of multiple hormones[15] at varying
intervals following stimulation, in an attempt to uncover differential
patterns and to discover the psychological concomitants of these.

There is evidence that significant changes in renal blood flow patterns can occur with psychological stress (Baines et al., 1962; Wolf et al.,
1955). This may be due to a direct neurogenic influence as well as to
increased output of catechol amines. It seems likely that such changes are
associated with shifts in Aldosterone levels. Changes in urinary output
are frequent, well-known concomitants of emotional states. Both oliguria
and diuresis can be produced as conditioned responses (Dykman et al.,
1962; Hofer & Hinkle, 1964).

Epinephrine and norepinephrine

Our adrenal saga proceeds now interiorly to the medulla
and to the catecholamines, epinephrine (E) and norepinephrine (norE).
In considering norE, however, it must be made clear that we really are
talking not about the adrenal medulla but rather the autonomic nervous
system, and more specifically, its sympathetic branch. Norepinephrine is
the chemical transmitter of the postganglionic sympathetic nerves (von
Euler, 1951). Very little comes from the adrenal in man, as revealed by
the slight effect of total adrenalectomy (von Euler, 1955). From a practical standpoint, research usually includes simultaneous measures of both
these closely related compounds. The stimulus for adrenomedullary
discharge travels via preganglionic sympathetic pathways from the hypothalamic nuclei which are in close anatomical relation to the autonomic "centers" (Folkow & von Euler, 1954). Sympathetic activation
ordinarily accompanies adrenomedullary discharge.

[15] Because of space limitations it is impossible to cover in this review the relation
of several major hormones to stress. This omission does not seem too serious, however,
for, except for the thyroid (e.g., Board et al., 1956), to date there are few relevant
published studies of merit.

It is interesting to reflect that at one time Cannon and Rosenbleuth (1937) postulated two chemical mediators ("sympathin E" and "I"). Less well known and still controversial is Ahlquist's (1948) hypothesis of two types of sympathetic receptor sites.[16] Based on studies of relative responsiveness to a series of sympathomimetic amines, he postulates an alpha receptor, associated with most excitatory functions and one important inhibitory function, intestinal relaxation; and a beta receptor associated with most inhibitory functions and one excitatory function, myocardial stimulation.

Cannon (1929), of course, carried out the classical studies demonstrating an acute adrenomedullary activation during both physiological and psychological stress. His conclusions necessarily were based on indirect end-organ measures. Recent research utilizes direct bioassay or chemical measure of the catecholamines (Elmadjian, 1962b, c). Before considering these data, I wish to emphasize certain important methodological limitations. There seems to be general agreement that techniques for measuring catecholamines in blood are not yet adequate. But even if they were, these molecules are extremely evanescent (Lund, 1951), with a half-life of less than a minute. Hence, in dealing with an acute reaction, blood samples must be taken without delay or they are worthless. Moreover, significantly effective local concentrations of norE apparently can occur without producing a measurable change in overall blood levels. These must be important considerations in evaluating experimental design.

Most research, therefore, has been based on urinary output. Such measures of E and norE excretions seem adequate to indicate the direction of change or major state differences, though they do represent only a small fraction of the total catecholamine production [17] (von Euler, Luft, et al., 1951, 1953; Elmadjian, 1963). Moreover, excretion measures at best reflect only the *in toto* balance for the system over time. With a single source (as for E) this has validity. But with a diffuse, complex system like the sympathetic (for norE), this balance has minimal value. Overall changes can be due to response in any part or parts of the system, and sufficient changes in one part can obscure even opposite changes elsewhere.

Despite these caveats, there is dependable evidence of increased E production in psychologically stressful conditions. Elevations have been demonstrated during competitive sports, operation of a pursuit meter,

[16] This neglected hypothesis could turn out to be an important one for psychophysiologists to pursue.

[17] There are at least three important metabolites which must be measured also for quantification of total catecholamine output: metanephrine, normetanephrine, and vanillylmandelic acid (VMA). Changes in E and norE excretion levels alone, however, seem to parallel the total amount of these substances originally secreted. Further details are available in the several papers of Elmadjian.

and in psychiatric patients appearing before a staff conference (Elmadjian et al., 1958; Elmadjian, 1963); in other athletes and in pilots and their military passengers (von Euler, 1956a, b); during pressured work and during motion pictures described as "aggression-" or "anxiety-provoking" (Levi, 1961, 1965). Moreover, an "amusing" film had the same effect, while with a "bland natural-scenery film" a *fall* occurred [18] (Levi, 1965).

The norE picture is much less clear, however. Elmadjian et al., (1958) report high levels in "aggressive-active" disturbed psychiatric patients compared with those who were "passive and self-effacing." But the groups differed in their activity levels. NorE increases with muscular activity alone (von Euler & Hellner, 1952; von Euler, 1956b). The same issue arises in interpreting elevations occurring during aggressive athletics (Elmadjian et al., 1958). Like Elmadjian, Silverman et al. (1961) tend to make specific linkages of E to anxiety and norE to anger, though their data refer primarily to personality characteristics rather than transient states. Their findings also are contaminated by differences in muscular tension and activity, although when these were controlled there was said to be evidence of increased norE excretion in "some" subjects.

Recent interest has focused on the level of free (unesterified) fatty acids (FFA), in part because of their possible significance to the pathogenesis of atherosclerosis and coronary disease.[19] Both E and norE cause FFA to increase (Bogdonoff & Estes, 1961). Rises in FFA levels were noted to occur during hypnotically-induced states of anger, fear, and depression (Fishman et al., 1962b), but only in subjects who achieved a deep hypnotic trance. All of these had FFA changes in at least one affect state but inconsistently. Marked emotional responses occurred at times with no FFA shifts. FFA rises occurring during a group task were reported to bear a relationship to several measures of group interaction [20] (Bogdonoff et al., 1964). Whether such factors mediate their influence through changes in intrapersonal variables remains to be seen. There is a report of rises in FFA resulting from the viewing of a sexually arousing film (Gustafson et al., 1963), but, unfortunately, no detail is given about subjective responses. FFA levels can vary also with expectancy of response as influenced by experimental instructions (Penick & Fisher, 1965). These data extend the findings of S. Schachter (Schachter & Singer, 1962) in that they indicate that physiological indices can be altered by expectation just as can subjective affective states.

[18] A finding like that reported for 17-OHCS, as noted above.

[19] It is perhaps germane that at a recent Psychosomatic Society meeting, when one investigator was asked why he chose this variable, he indicated that it was because of the ease and convenience of its measurements. This candid response is not without significance for the light it throws on the "current state of the art."

[20] Increasing attention has been directed recently to the psychophysiology of group-dynamic processes, for example studies on GSR (Kaplan, 1963).

Autonomic Responses

I would like to turn now to consider some studies of autonomic stress responses—more accurately of peripheral measures of autonomically innervated response systems. This is an immense area by itself in which I will be necessarily highly selective, restricting discussion to questions which I have raised previously or to issues of general import.[21]

Several studies have been directed to the search for affect-specific links to epinephrine and norepinephrine. Ax (1953), Funkenstein et al. (1957), and J. Schachter (1957) all report differential patterning of autonomic responses for anger and anxiety. These, however, were subtle and generally required complex statistical techniques to tease them out from other response determinants. All three investigators likened the anxiety response to that produced by E injection. The anger pattern was less consistent, being reported as norE-like (Funkenstein), as like mixed E and norE (Ax), and as being E-like at extreme intensities but norE-like at moderate levels (Schachter). Apart from this discrepancy,[22] there are serious conceptual questions about any attempt to dichotomize strictly norE and E response patterns. I have indicated that there is no unitary norE release mechanism analogous to that for E. The description of a response pattern as being "norE-like," because it is similar to the effects of intravenously administered norE, is based on a technique which simply has no counterpart in physiology. Further, there is accumulating evidence which points to different kinds of patterning *within* the sympathetic nervous system. These are related to stimulus characteristics (R. C. Davis, 1957a; Lacey, 1959; Lacey et al., 1963; Engel, 1960), as well as the tendency for individuals to respond in a stable idiosyncratic fashion: Lacey's "response specificity and stereotopy" (Lacey & Lacey, 1958b; Wenger et al., 1961; Oken et al., 1962).[23]

The basis for these findings, which require the measurement of fine differences, rests on steady progress in technology. Physiological measures have become more specific and sensitive (as well as more complicated!), increasing our accuracy and making additional systems accessible. I will mention a few illustrations. There has been a revival of interest in techniques for measuring skin resistance and nonspecific GSR [24] and, more

---

[21] Some of my omissions are corrected by the consideration of additional topics which fall into this area in several other chapters in this volume, particularly those by Lacey, Cohen, and Weybrew.

[22] Questions arise also from the use, particularly by Funkenstein, of measures derived from balistocardiography, a technique no longer considered acceptable for this type of experimental work.

[23] These will not be detailed further here since they have already been discussed in Chapter 2.

[24] Several pertinent articles on this topic can be found in the July, 1964, issue of *Psychophysiology*. This journal and its predecessor, the *Psychophysiology Newsletter*,

recently, in the use of palmar sweat measures (Ferreire & Winter, 1963). Gastric activity can be measured by the UCLA magnetometer, the electrogastrogram (Coddington et al., 1964), and, possibly, by the use of external abdominal electrodes (R. C. Davis & Berry, 1963). Measures of urinary pepsinogen have also been used, though there is a serious question about the validity of this method. Our own recent work has concentrated on muscle tension, based on accurate surface electromyography, as developed by J. F. Davis (1959). Using this measure, we found that the neuromuscular system exhibits individual response specificity (Goldstein et al., 1964), just as the autonomic. We were able also to demonstrate that personality variables play a role in determining muscle tension both at rest and during stress (Shipman et al., 1964; Goldstein, 1964). The elucidation of personality trait correlates to patterns of physiological response appears to be a fruitful area for exploration. Another technique has been described recently for measuring muscle activity through recording surface microvibrations (Williams, 1964).

Progress has been facilitated also by improved data handling methods. Investigators have become increasingly aware of the methodological implications inherent in the choice of a score used to represent response (e.g., post-stimulus levels, pre-post differences, and percentage change). The spontaneous periodicity of fluctuation of levels appears also to represent a significant variable (Lacey & Lacey, 1958b; Doust, 1962, Alexander et al., 1963). Even the decision as to the unit of measurement for recording observations affects results (Lipton et al., 1961a). The need to develop scores free from the influence of prestimulus levels (the "Law of Initial Values"), as emphasized by Lacey, has led to techniques for data adjustment (Lacey, 1956; Oken & Heath, 1963; Heath & Oken, 1965). Since not all variables show the initial values effect (Hord et al., 1964), correction should not be applied indiscriminately. Its basis must rest on empirical considerations. This is true also of decisions as to the choice between mean and peak response or as to the time parameters to be used. The very terms *stimulus* and *response* are vast oversimplifications. The former may include multiple stimuli with differing effects and the latter proceeds in a sequence over time. Practical considerations lead us to make arbitrary decisions as to taking measures at specific times. To characterize responses fully requires continuous measures with analysis of the entire response sequence. The problem is especially pressing for responses which are biphasic or still more complex. Correct measures of overall group response when individuals vary in the time dynamics of their reactions may require special averaging techniques (Lipton et al., 1961b).

---

probably represent the best source of information on technical and related methodological advance in this area.

"Environmental acceptance versus rejection"

Some of the most important research on autonomic psycho-physiology has been done by Dr. Lacey and his colleagues (cf. Chapter 2). We have pursued many similar interests in our own laboratories, often following up leads first suggested by him. In a study still in progress, we have had the opportunity to study and compare the responses to one of the stimuli used by Lacey, white noise, and that to an anxiety stimulus. The former would be classified by him as largely in the category associated with "environmental acceptance," with minor noxious properties, the latter clearly as one stimulating "environmental rejection." [25]

Thus far we have data on 33 subjects. Preliminary visits to the laboratory were included to permit acclimatization. Following the attachment of electrodes, etc., there was a period of rest, the last minute of which was used for "basal" measures. White noise was then delivered through earphones for one minute, as the subjects had been told beforehand. After a five-minute recovery period, an unexpected situation of simulated danger was suddenly introduced. The technique involved was an elaboration of that developed by Ax (1953). In brief, the subject received mild electric shocks while apparatus in the room began to arc visibly, emit loud static, and release small amounts of smoke which could be smelled and sometimes faintly seen. The supervising experimenter who rushed in indicated that something had gone wrong, resulting in dangerous high voltage. After the "short circuit" was "fixed," recovery measures were taken. Subsequently, but prior to the subject's being informed of the counterfeit, an interview was held to determine his psychological reaction. Ratings of affect and other data confirm our general success in convincing subjects of the "danger" and in eliciting anxiety.

Our physiological measures included electromyograms from seven locations, heart rate, blood pressure, and skin conductance. Data summarizing [26] the mean physiological responses to the two different stresses are given in Table 3-1. All physiological variables responded to the anxiety condition with a rise, confirming the reports of subjective experience. With the noise, the muscles responded in a similar fashion, as did systolic pressure, heart rate, and skin conductance. However, the diastolic blood pressure dropped significantly, the direction of response thus being opposite to that during the anxiety stress.

Comparisons of the degree of response during the two stress conditions are given in Table 3-2. These data reveal a pattern of significantly

25 The reader is referred to Dr. Lacey's paper for details as to the usage of these terms and of his findings and conclusions which will not be repeated here except as they are appropriate to the specific issues which I wish to discuss.

26 Full details of this study will be published elsewhere at a later date.

Table 3-1. Probability (p) levels of differences between mean stress values and preceding rest periods.*

	Noise Stress	Psychological Stress
Trapezius	≅ .02	< .001
Sterno-cleido-mastoid	< .001	< .001
Frontalis	< .05	< .001
Biceps	< .05	< .001
Forearm	< .001	< .001
Quadriceps	< .02	< .001
Gastrocnemius	< .01	< .001
Heart rate	< .001	< .001
Systolic BP	< .001	< .001
Diastolic BP	< .02 (drop)	< .001 (increase)
Skin conductance	< .001	< .001

* The rest period value is the mean of the minute just preceding the stimulus.

lesser response during the noise condition, using as the basis for comparison levels, peak responses and several indices of change.

What are we to make of these results? On one hand, they are reasonably consistent with what Lacey would predict for a stimulus with mixed properties, requiring sensory attentiveness but being mildly noxious. Diastolic pressure fell while the other cardiovascular variables rose.

Table 3-2. Probability (p) levels of differences between responses to comparable sound and psychological stress occasions for the group as a whole (Student's test or "t equivalent") (N = 31 to 33, except GSR = 29).*

	Means	Peaks	Peaks #2	Mean Change	Peak Change	Peak #2 Change
Trapezius	< .001	< .001	< .001	< .001	< .001	< .001
Sterno-cleido-mastoid	< .001	< .001	< .001	< .001	< .001	< .001
Frontalis	< .10	< .10	< .001	NS	NS	< .05
Biceps	< .001	< .001	< .001	< .001	< .001	< .001
Extensor	< .001	< .001	< .001	< .001	< .001	< .001
Quadriceps	< .01	< .001	< .001	< .001	< .001	< .001
Gastrocnemius	< .001	< .001	< .001	< .001	< .001	< .001
Heart rate	< .001	< .001	< .001	< .001	< .001	< .001
Systolic BP	< .01	< .01	< .001	< .01	< .01	< .001
Diastolic BP	< .001	< .001	< .001	< .001	< .001	< .001
GSR	< .001	< .001	< .001	< .05	< .01	< .01

* Peaks are the highest thirty-second value during the noise or during the corresponding first minute of the psychological stress. Peaks #2 uses the highest thirty-second value occurring at any time during the (five-minute) psychological stress. Change scores are calculated by subtracting from the mean or peak the mean value for the minute of the just preceding rest period.

Yet another way to view these data may be in terms of epinephrine release. There is a mistaken notion that E raises blood pressure. Actually, diastolic pressure falls when E is administered intravenously, unless the dose is quite large. This is due to its vasodilator properties. (In contrast, norE produces only vasoconstriction). Epinephrine will cause systolic blood pressure and heart rate increases due to its (positive inotropic) cardiac effects. Perhaps, therefore, it is tenable to view the noise response as being related to E release with minimal sympathetic activation, while that due to the anxiety stress represented a greater, diffuse sympatho-adrenal discharge. Put another way, the issue may be one of *degree of stress* rather than different patterns with two different classes of stimuli.

Earlier I discussed situations causing drops in hormone levels and suggested some value in viewing stress as a continuous function. Everyday active normal function may lie towards the middle of such a continuum rather than towards the low end. Nature films and like stimuli might be conceived of as a kind of distraction which reduces overall sensory input below idling levels. Perhaps Lacey's data can be similarly understood. One serious problem with this explanation is the rise, which Lacey reports, in at least one other variable, GSR, from the same stimuli causing heart rate and blood pressure decreases. Since Lacey's past publications include only a general statement but no specific data on blood pressure, it is not clear if the drop in this variable he mentions involves diastolic or systolic levels or both, and therefore if it is comparable to our results.

Certainly the question arises whether responses occurring with relatively simple sensory inputs should be viewed at all in terms of the stress concept. Lacey has judiciously avoided the term. Most of the stimuli he has used strike a clinician as being pretty tame. And they are quite transient compared with events in real life. A minute or two of mental arithmetic [27] hardly seems of great moment (sic!).

A concern with this issue has led me to reanalyze some data from a previous experiment (Oken et al., 1962). One interest in that study was a comparison of psychological stress with one that was physical: heat. Because we wished to produce a strong anxiety response, multiple stimuli were used on the psychological stress occasion. These included introduction to the laboratory without warning, administration of a supposed "new drug" with suggested formidable properties, a purposefully inept experimenter, and finally, the viewing of a movie showing surgical enucleation of the eye. Although we had treated the data from this succession of stimuli as a single stress occasion, I have recently broken this down to compare the mean levels of six physiological variables during the showing of the film—which constituted the last in the stressor series—

[27] I do not mean to imply that this is not an effective stimulus which produces a distinct physiological response. My comment refers only to its psychological impact.

with the preceding sections of the stress period. These data, given in Table 3-3, indicate that during the showing of the film there was a significant drop in heart rate. Systolic and diastolic blood pressure dropped also, although not significantly, as did respiration rate and finger temperature. Most important, skin conductance dropped too, and this was significant in extent. In this situation, then, it seems reasonable to consider these effects of viewing the film—of attentiveness to the external environment—as fitting within the framework of a general reduction in overall stress response. The results are fully consistent with those from our current research described just above.

Table 3-3. Mean response to film and to preceding psychological stress (N = 18, except Finger temperature N = 15).

Measure	Preceding Film	During Film	Significance of Difference
Heart rate	70.2	68.0	$p < .02$
Systolic BP	126.1	125.0	NS
Diastolic BP	75.9	74.1	NS
Respiration	18.2	17.4	$.05 < p < .10$
Skin conductance	1123	1073	$p < .01$
Finger temperature	29.69	29.45	NS

Our original report documented the significant similarity of intra-individual response patterns over the two stress days. We regarded this as a strong confirmation of the principle of autonomic response specificity in view of the marked stimulus differences and the convincing intensity of the anxiety stress, conditions which earlier research had not tested. But I want to emphasize the fact that this result came from analyses in which we used change in diastolic blood pressure *regardless* of sign. That is, we reflected the drops in diastolic pressure which are a typical feature of the physiology of environmental heat. This suggests that individuals who respond with greater rises in diastolic pressure to stimuli which cause such rises are the same as those who have greater falls with stimuli which produce falls: a most interesting hypothesis which deserves further test.

Comments

In this review, I have attempted to cover a wide variety of data from several important areas within psychophysiology and psychoendocrinology. Necessarily I have been selective, concentrating on those topics which seemed of greater importance and selecting from the myriad of available studies those which I judged to be most illustrative of the significant issues. In doing so I have been guided by a wish to pull together the major trends which have emerged over many years of work by excellent investigators from several fields. One is the interdependence of related areas. Just as endocrinology cannot be separated from physiology more broadly, stress, affect, defenses, and like phenomena are all interwoven in a complex transactional pattern. A given study may focus on one or another but can be understood only in the context of all. A second is the emphasis placed on clarifying underlying mechanisms. Our concern is not just with what happens but with how it does. Finally, time has led not merely to expanded knowledge in the same track. With progress there has been growth, or more properly evolution, and a significant shift in approach.

The stress syndrome has been of tremendous value as a concept around which to organize a variety of data. But so far as psychophysiological research is concerned, the usefulness of this concept when limited to its *original* terms has diminished. A crucial aspect of stress is its generality. It is concerned with changes which arise in response to a variety of stimuli. The nature of many of these nonspecific processes and their underlying mechanisms have been worked out. We may not know everything about them but we know a great deal.

In the process of this development, and because of it, it has become increasingly apparent that a number of subtle specificities are included within the general data. Research emphasis has shifted, therefore, to the elucidation of factors responsible for these, and away from a concern with *stress* itself. Among the significant sources of variation are different types of stimuli and their meanings to the person; different affect states, defenses, and coping devices which develop to deal with the stimulus and with its effects; individually patterned subsystem hierarchies of physiological responsiveness; personality characteristics; group-dynamic phenomena; and doubtless others.

Many specificities operate simultaneously in any given situation. The difficulties of separating these are compounded by still other sources of variance. Hence psychosomatic research progress has required the development of improved methodology, including research design, data analysis, and techniques of physiological and psychological measurement. This has been an exacting, laborious process. Our knowledge of specific patterns remains very meager. There are no glamorous major insights, no "breakthroughs" to report. Our necessary preoccupation with methodology has placed increasing demands on the sophistication of the experimenter. Only by the most careful attention to sound scientific principles on *both* the psychological and the physiological sides can real progress be made. Psychological measures need to be as precise as those from the biochemistry laboratory. Fortunately, high caliber research with these characteristics is beginning to appear in increasing amounts, despite the difficulties. Our field has entered a new phase of maturity which gives promise of achieving much new understanding.

Invited commentary

EVERETT W. BOVARD, JR.: This has been a most provocative and stimulating paper. Each of us, I am sure, has his own reaction to it. My own would be that an understanding of the neural mechanisms mediating the response to stress, particularly emotional stress, may shed a great deal of light on the phenomena Dr. Oken has brought to our attention—as, for example, the inhibition of hydrocortisone output by positive reinforcement.

Stimulation and lesion studies of the hypothalamus, summarized elsewhere (Bovard, 1961), have suggested that the hypothalamus is organized into two reciprocally inhibitory zones. These two zones, the anterior and lateral zone on the one hand, and the posterior and medial zone on the other, appear to have opposite functions with respect to both the autonomic and the pituitary-adrenal responses to stress. Experimental work to date has suggested that the anterior and lateral zone inhibits the response to stress, including both sympathetic autonomic response and the output of adrenocorticotrophin (ACTH) from the anterior pituitary. The same work indicates that the posterior and medial zone *facilitates* the response to stress. Both zones, as can be seen from Figure *3-1,* converge on the median eminence, the final common pathway for neural influence on the anterior pituitary. Also, both zones, from evidence so far available, are reciprocally inhibitory: activity of one zone dampens activity of the other.

This reciprocal inhibition would now enable us to account for the inhibition of hydrocortisone output by positively reinforcing stimuli, brought to our attention by Dr. Oken. If it can be assumed that such positively reinforcing stimuli are mediated by the positive brain system (Bovard, 1962), which is represented in the anterior and lateral hypothalamus, then it would follow by virtue of the reciprocal inhibition of the anterior and posterior zones that the activity of the posterior zone, and hence the output of ACTH from the anterior pituitary and the output of hydrocortisone from the adrenal cortex, would be inhibited.

The exact pathways mediating positively reinforcing stimuli are not known, but they involve the amygdala at the tip of the temporal lobe and likely its short ventral amygdala hypothalamic (VAH) pathway to the anterior zone of the hypothalamus (Fig. *3-1*).

But if the hypothalamus is organized into reciprocally inhibitory zones

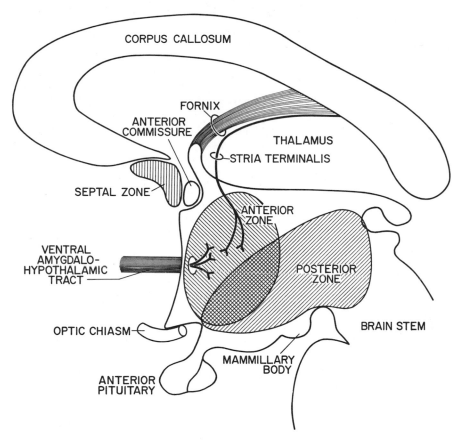

FIGURE 3-1.   The (right) human hypothalamus and pituitary, shown in median sagittal section. Functional division of the hypothalamus into two reciprocally inhibitory zones, anterior and posterior, is illustrated here. Activity in the anterior zone inhibits the pituitary-adrenal cortical and sympathetico-adrenal medullary responses to stress, while activity of the posterior zone facilitates these responses. Also shown is input to the hypothalamus from the temporal lobe, including the stria terminalis and the ventral amygdalo-hypothalamic tract from the amygdala, and the fornix from the hippocampus. In general, this input modulates the balance of activity between anterior and posterior zones.

modulating the response to stress, in particular the response to emotional stress, what governs the relative dominance of these two zones?

The most tempting suggestion here is that the amygdala governs the balance between the anterior and posterior zones by its two pathways to the hypothalamus, the VAH mentioned above, and another tract coming the long way around the thalamus from the temporal lobe below, the stria terminalis

(ST; see Fig. *3-1*). Evidence to date suggests that the VAH mediates positively reinforcing stimuli, while the ST mediates negatively reinforcing or noxious stimuli.

The objection may be raised that neither pathway terminates in the posterior zone, which mediates the response to stress. But such termination is really not necessary, given the reciprocal inhibition noted above: to depress posterior zone activity one need only stimulate the anterior zone; to increase posterior zone activity one need only inhibit the anterior zone. Presumably this is the mechanism for amygdaloid modulation of the hypothalamic response to stress, including the sympathetic-adrenal medullary response and the pituitary-adrenal cortical response.

These mechanisms would therefore account for the finding, previously predicted (Bovard, 1961), that positively reinforcing stimuli inhibit the response to stress.

One more point occurs to me in this general connection. Many of us have been working hopefully for years on use of skin temperature and other indices, direct and indirect, of autonomic activity to get at internal mood and feeling states of the human subject. Unfortunately for these labors, recent work by Dr. Carl Sem-Jacobsen (1963) of Norway has shown in electrical stimulation of the human brain that there is little or no correlation between mood responses of the patient, produced by electrical stimulation of the positive brain system, and cardiovascular and vegetative changes, produced by stimulation at other sites. These two systems are entirely separate, and therefore getting at mood or feeling changes by the use of peripheral autonomic measurement is indeed a hopeless task.

Discussion

Dr. Cohen: Hasn't there been some other work—for example by Malmo (1961)—in which stimulation of the so-called pleasure spots or the reward centers was associated with parasympathetic discharge, while the negative centers seemed to be associated with sympathetic discharge? If this is so, it's rather interesting in terms of some of the other factors which have been presented, in that it might account for the cardio-deceleration which has been reported while passively observing pictures of pretty girls.

Dr. Bovard: This is very true. I should have emphasized more specifically that our anterior zone mediates parasympathetic function and our posterior zone mediates sympathetic. I didn't emphasize that enough.

Dr. Cohen: Then aren't there more of the pleasure spots in the anterior zone?

Dr. Bovard: No, this is not specifically true of the rat hypothalamus. I would say, however, that available evidence suggests the positive brain system is represented in the anterior and lateral hypothalamic zone and that this positive system extends from the fronto-orbital region back to the midbrain.

Dr. Arnold: Dr. Oken raised the question as to why novelty should produce a stress response similar to that in anxiety, when the subjective report does not indicate that any anxiety was felt. Could an entirely novel situation not produce the fear of not being able to cope with it, and would that not account for the similarity with the physiological response to anxiety?

Dr. Oken: I think the problem is that although uncertainty is present, there is no corresponding *affective* response—at least not of sufficient intensity. Perhaps the cognitive state does explain the steroid response, but it is not anxiety.

Dr. Arnold: The subjective report depends so often on the questions asked. The subject might not admit that he feels "anxiety" because that sounds as if he were neurotic. But he might mention, if you give him a chance, that he felt at a loss, didn't know what to do, etc.

Dr. Oken: I think our interviews are far more subtle and unstructured than I was able to indicate here. Only towards the end of them do we get into specific, concrete questioning. But I think the point still remains that if you do get this report—and I don't doubt that there is frequently a sense of uncertainty experienced—there is a difference between this uncertainty and an affective dread, or fright, or fear. And, at least so far as we can determine, there is a disproportion between the affective response and the steroid response. So you have to bring something else in besides anxiety to account for the discrepancy.

Dr. Nowlis: A recent doctoral study by Stuart Valins, a student of Stanley Schachter, raises some interesting points about the interaction between cognitive appraisal and bodily signs of activation. Each subject was put into an apparatus which let him hear what was said to be the sound of his own heart beat. Actually the beats were provided by the experimenter. Subjects were shown pictures of "playmates" from *Playboy.* For two of these pictures the heartbeat stimulus was accelerated markedly. At the end of the session, when asked to select his favorite pictures, the subject tended to select those which had been associated with the accelerated heartbeats. This effect lasted for some months. I should like to know whether conditioning of the heart rate to these two pictures could result from pairing them with the sound of the accelerated rate. But even more relevant to the present issue is the following question. If they had been shown horrible pictures which resulted in negative cognitive appraisals, would the two pictures accompanied by accelerated heart rate then have become the two most *disliked* pictures?

Dr. Cohen: I can answer that. The experimenter, Dr. Stuart Valins, is a post-doctoral student in our laboratory. He is doing some of the things you suggested, e.g., showing horrible pictures. However, there is another thing that will be done that is important in evaluating one of the intervening cognitive variables. One group will be informed about Dr. Lacey's findings—that is, when you see a pretty girl your heartbeat often goes slower and when you see something noxious it often goes faster. None of the people in the previous work knew about this finding. We can assume they had the usual stereotyped attitude, namely that when you see something exciting your heart goes faster.

Dr. Back: This study (Valins, in preparation) is most extreme in showing predominance of cognition. Subjects who were led to believe that their heart rate changed at all (either accelerated or decelerated) preferred the picture where this was supposed to have occurred.

Dr. Mandler: May I suggest that none of these data have very much to do with the topic at hand. If you tell a subject what to do he'll do it. I would suggest that when a subject is fed back an accelerated heartbeat, he may say "Oh, that means I have a specific response to this picture, I must remember this picture." Whether the attention directing stimulus is an accelerated heartbeat, a decelerated heartbeat, a gun going off, or the roof falling in may not make any difference. Until more controls have been introduced, these data don't necessarily concern the psychophysiology of stress or affect. They may only have something to do with how subjects interpret a particular situation.

Dr. Korchin: I'd like to return to the issue raised with respect to novelty. One of the core phenomena in the study of stress and affect is the organism's response to the unknown. Some have postulated that this is the prototype which, in more elaborated forms, appears in anger, anxiety, and other negative affects. For example, Liddell (1950) described anxiety in animals as an extension of the Pavlovian "What-is-it?" reflex which occurs in response to an unexpected or novel stimulus. I am myself impressed by the same literature Dr. Oken called attention to, which shows that bringing an organism, whether human or primate, into an environment which has potential, but undefined, danger leads to adreno-cortical activation. An important finding is that the danger need not have conscious representation; the person need not say "I am afraid." The dissociation of felt affect from physiological response is an important area for study.

   The proper question is not "What is the true measure of affect?" but such questions as "What is affect?" "How can it be measured?" "When, and how, does affect change under stress?" "Does affective change suppose physiological change?" and the like. What I mean to suggest is that these are different realms of functioning, and they need to be conceptualized and measured separately. Then, the research issue is to discover the conditions for the presence or absence of relationship. For a long time, as Dr. Lacey pointed out in the case of physiological variables, we have assumed that there must be correlation. We need to investigate the conditions under which correlation might not exist. The case of novelty makes a point because here is a situation in which there might or might not be affective response but in which there may well be physiological response.

Dr. Stern: Let me make one point, based on research on the heart rate in the rat where we really can't get into the cognitive structure. What we can do is to stimulate an animal for any number of trials with a given stimulus. The what-is-it or orienting response, as Pavlov and more recently people like Sokolov have called it, is we believe, one of cardiac deceleration. If we look at the cardiac response of the rat in response to any kind of novel stimulation—be it electric shock or tone stimulation—over a number of trials, what we find is that contrary to what the literature tells you during initial trials of presenting animals with shock, the averaged curve for heart rate response is something like that shown in Figure 3-2. Maximum cardiac acceleration in the rat does not occur

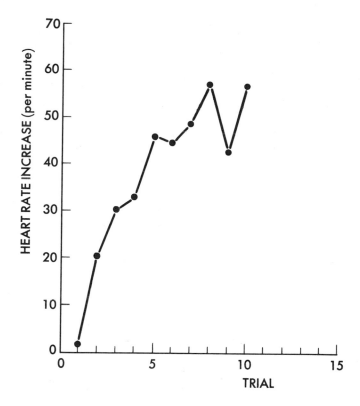

FIGURE 3-2.   Heart rate response to shock stimulation as related to number of shock trials. Modified by permission from Stern & Word (1962).

until you have given him approximately ten trials of shock stimulation. With other stimuli the curve goes up more steeply, so you can discriminate between an orienting or what-is-it response, which I think is cardiac deceleration, and a defensive response, which is cardiac acceleration. I would maintain that the stress response that you measured is cardiac deceleration. This is a *nonspecific* response which occurs to *any* kind of stressor situation, whereas cardiac acceleration is a *specific* response to either shock or some types of tone stimulation. I would then define a stress response as, in this type of situation, the orienting response which is characteristic of response to many different types of stimulation.

Dr. Sells: I would like to comment on the semantics of novelty and perhaps stimulus structure in relation to the cognitive structure of the situation. It is possible for a novel response to induce pleasant, as well as unpleasant, affects, depending upon the nature of the preceding events and the general situation. When the stimulus is structured in relation to learned responses, the response would usually be more specific and there would be less variability within individuals than between individuals. When the stimulus is unstructured, then the subject may attempt to structure the situation, and, here again, personality, past experience, and many other factors as well as the surrounding situation are very important. A sudden loud noise in a room, for example, might be interpreted quite differently from the same noise on an airplane.

Dr. Oken: Well, as I think you know, this is the reason that I made that comment about Davis' work and then quoted Dr. Lacey—to point up this issue, namely, that you have to find out *what* the subjective response is or whether there indeed *is* any subjective response. You cannot assume subjective response from the nature of the stimulus.

Dr. Appley: I wonder if the point that Dr. Stern just made, namely, that of a nonspecific stress response being deceleration and a specific response being acceleration, can't be challenged. What may account for the shift from deceleration to acceleration is not that an appropriate or specific response has begun but simply that something like a strategy or course of action has been determined. This state would be quite general regardless of what the particular strategy turned out to be. A shift from deceleration to acceleration might be a reasonable expectation at such a point. It would still, though, be a nonspecific response that is being marked by the shift, namely, that some course of action has been decided by the internal computer.

Dr. Stern: Well, I would suspect along with John Lacey that if you take a stimulus with continually changing intensity value that we would see continued decelerative responses. And if, for example, instead of giving a series of shocks one gave a shock, a tone, an olfactory stimulus, and so on to an animal, it would continue to show cardiac deceleration to the series of stimuli. We don't have the evidence but that is our suspicion at the present time.

Dr. Bovard: I find myself a little bit disturbed at the direction of the conversation here. When we talk about the nonspecific response to stress in the medical literature, and as Dr. Oken referred to it, we are referring to the release of adrenocorticotrophic hormone (ACTH) from the anterior pituitary into the bloodstream and the consequent release of adrenal cortical hormones like hydrocortisone into the bloodstream. This response, as Selye discovered, is a nonspecific response to a wide range of noxious stimuli, both physical and psychological. The twin arms of the response to stress include both the neuro-endocrine and autonomic nervous systems. To stretch the meaning of the term *nonspecific response to stress* any further would, I think, do violence to its generally accepted meaning in the medical literature. We should be careful about using terms that encompass too much territory.

Dr. Lazarus: Symington and his colleagues (1955) have studied the adrenals of patients who were dying and who were unconscious during the death process. They apparently find no adrenal cortical changes on autopsy as compared with patients who were dying and who were also responsive and aware of their terminal condition. I wonder if there is any evidence that the adrenal cortical changes are produced without psychological mediation. I don't know anyone who takes seriously the possibility that adrenal activity depends exclusively on psychological mediation. Yet, in all the research involving physical assault of some sort on the organism, the recognition of this assault by the animal is never specifically eliminated, except in the case of Symington's work, as a mediating process. I am wondering if it can be clearly established that adrenal stress response changes are produced without psychological mediation.

Dr. Lacey: Clearly it can be. For example, direct brain stimulation in an anes-thetized cat, dog, or monkey will produce an adrenocortical response.

Dr. Lazarus: I don't think this is the same thing.

Dr. Oken: There is a methodological problem here in trying to tease out the components of the stimulus. The question is: if you anesthetize an animal and stimulate it peripherally, does *any* message get through? If you block the pain sensation you may block also the "meaning" of pain but you may also block the nonpsychological meaning, i.e., the nerve pathways themselves. You run into the risk that nothing gets through: that it may be incorrect to consider that there is a "stimulus" at all.

Dr. Arnold: Irradiation, which is not felt as particularly unpleasant, still pro-duces the GAS (General Adaptation Syndrome).

Dr. Cohen: Stress is not necessarily defined as being synonymous with ACTH release and adrenal cortical activity. Certainly, according to the views of the late Frank Engel (1957) and Dwight Ingle (1954), a major function of adrenocortical activity is a permissive action, and adaptive change is a function of the end organ. What adrenocortical hormones do is to assist, in a sense, the end organ in its activity when needed. I think that the people who ascribe to this approach would, if they were going to define state of stress (which I think they would avoid), make it much more synonymous with CNS activation. If one wanted to be more specific, reference might be made to the facilitating effects of the anterior reticular system. One of these effects could be the release of ACTH but it might not be. The release would depend upon peripheral and metabolic factors. The circulatory levels of hormones (naturally the activity of the adrenal medulla) would have to be considered here if one wanted to consider the relation of acute emergency responses to a state of stress.

Dr. Oken: Even Selye, although he has been preoccupied with the adrenal cortex, would say that you can take out the adrenals and still get a response. But while this is *the* most characteristic part of the response, it is not a *sine qua non;* and indeed the adrenal medullary and a general sympathetic response may precede that of the adrenal cortex.

Dr. Ruff: A question not yet addressed is whether there is any response to a stress situation which cannot be produced by the threat of that situation. For example, it has been found that acceleration on the centrifuge increases catecholamine excretion. But we demonstrated that if you take subjects who are ready for a centrifuge run and then collect urine without spinning them, you get almost the same total catecholamine output as if they had been accelerated.

Dr. Stern: I think there is good experimental evidence that the anticipation of dreaded events that the person has gone through will produce changes in physiological responses as great as being exposed to the event itself.

Dr. Trumbull: A most interesting corollary comes from the work of Orne and others on hypnosis, as Dr. Oken has indicated. By redefining that which is truly an assault on the organism through hypnosis, one can eliminate the usual stress response. That is, if you tell him that a real danger is *not* one, that there is *no* threat when there is one, that he isn't going to be burned, for example, or shocked, you can change the response of the system even when damage is in fact induced.

Dr. Ruff: To do that, you have to have a situation like acceleration where subjects know they are going to be spun at high *g* levels. In the average experiment, as Orne has pointed out, subjects rarely think you're going to hurt them.

Dr. Mandler: There is very little doubt that in an adult human organism, the coding of the input is what determines whether a particular response will occur or not occur. But we are dealing primarily with adult organisms where input coding is the norm. I think there is very little recoding, for example, in the newborn. We would have to go quite a way out to say that when the neonate is dropped and you get a nice fullblown stress reaction, he is recoding this act of being dropped as, "Oh yes, this is a stressful event just like I was dropped yesterday when I was only one day old." Thus, I think there is evidence that some stress reactions will occur without recoding, but I think there are likely few cases of input to the adult organism where the input isn't classified, conceptualized, coded, before it has a particular effect. We have been misled by some stimuli, such as extreme shock, that do not permit much choice of recoding. There is a certain stimulus intensity that channels coding into one direction, namely, "This is unpleasant." It is extremely difficult for certain stimuli to be recoded, such as "Oh yes, this is very nice and pleasant," when in fact it is a high level shock. We have been misled by these extremely insistent stimuli to think that there are cases in which no coding occurs, but I think even the intense ones simply insist only on certain kinds of codes. They do not by themselves "produce" the reponse. I am saying, in short, that recoding is the general principle and nonrecoding is the occasional exception.

Dr. Weybrew: I would like to ask Dr. Oken two questions. First, is there any substantial evidence that differences in endocrine response patterns in humans are systematically related to individual differences in the quality of adjustment to the day-to-day stresses of life? And, secondly, how relevant is the stress history of the animal or human for predicting his potentiality to withstand stress? Obviously the second question has to do with the problem of the accumulation of the effects of repeated exposure to stress as related to stress adaptability.

Dr. Oken: The only study I know that may have some relevance to the first question is the NIMH study of parents of leukemic children, in which the kind of response, at least in terms of affectivity—and that's a pretty non-specific measure already—did seem to correlate with the steroid level. Although I presented it as if there was a simple hydrocortisone response, that was a bit of an oversimplification. Even within the 17-OHCS series there are some related hormones that are produced. And often metabolic pathways are changed for the breakdown of the hydrocortisone, for example. So there may be much more specificity that we don't yet know about because the standard approach has been to study only hydrocortisone levels.

As to adaptation, I don't have much data except for the novelty effect. There is a clear effect from anything you do the first time which on repetition will adapt out. But I suppose, again, the answer would depend upon the subjective response, i.e., if you continued to get a psychological response. If, in Dr. Mandler's terms, the stimulus is *not* recoded to indicate: "Well I've been through this before and it's not so bad," then I would think you would probably get the same physiological response.

Dr. Sells: To return to the matter of anticipation, I think it is necessary to make a distinction between anticipation which is not accompanied by specific information and which leads to dread, and anticipation based on knowledge of what to expect. Janis' work (1958, 1965) has certainly shown the importance of anticipatory communication in reducing fear by alerting the individual to the events that will happen. This has been true in situations such as disasters, mothers of children with fatal diseases in hospitals, and cancer patients approaching terminal conditions. Actually, when we speak of anticipation, the important thing is to try to make the statement more specific by dealing with the information that the subject has about the events that are approaching.

Dr. Lanzetta: We have just completed a series of studies where shock is non-avoidable though an uncertain outcome. Subjects are put in the position of either being able to obtain information about the outcome or not—they have a choice. In another case, reward was the uncertain outcome, a chip being delivered which was worth a certain amount of money. We had very strong intra-individual correlations in information preferences whether the outcome was shock, reward, or shock or reward. There were strong intra-individual correlations but very, very strong individual differences in preference for information.

I am not sure the role of information is necessarily uniform. Some people avoid it, others show a decided preference for the information state.

Dr. Sells: Dr. Lanzetta's report confirms my feeling about the use of electric shock as the laboratory symbol of stress. There are many people who develop a phobic reaction to electric shock, regardless of the level, and I think that this may account more than anything else for the differences and for some of the very extreme reactions that you may see.

Dr. Stern: I am sure that the way you instruct the subject has marked effects on how he responds to shock. For example, when we tell people they are going to get a shock, we get an altogether different response than when we tell them that they are going to experience a tingling sensation. You get marked differences in physiological responses as well as their subjective reports of the feeling of the same objective stimulus. We are doing some of the coding for them—we tell them what to expect.

Dr. Wilkins: Janis' use of the phrase "use of information" should be further clarified. If I remember his case of the patient who was in analysis and had the operation, the purpose of the use of information was not to allay the anxiety but to mobilize it.

Dr. Sells: In my opinion, the Janis paradigm, which is very important, is that when the individual is presented with a novel, potentially dangerous, situation for which he has not developed a coping mechanism, he may react with extreme fear and irrational behavior, which we call stress. Janis has used terms like "the work of worry." The preparatory communication which induces worry gives the individual an opportunity to consider alternatives and to cope vicariously before the actual situation arises. The existence of coping mechanisms, which include passive acceptance when there is nothing else to do, tends to give the individual an opportunity to react with some preparation as distinguished from being confronted with a situation for which he has no ability to react in advance.

Dr. Mechanic: This brings us back to the matter of attention which Dr. Lacey discussed. In most experimental situations where the stimulus or expected stimulus isn't defined, we are dealing with more than the attentiveness variable. In the initial trials the subject also experiences some uncertainty as to what the stimulus will be and how capably he will deal with it. I suspect that if you followed the same subjects for some time and varied the test difficulty so that the subjects' coping skills were adequate in some situations but not in others, you would obtain very different physiological responses. The initial undefined situation may be an inappropriate trial for studying physiological correlates of attentiveness, since it is not clear to what extent the reactions are due to attentiveness and to what extent they are due to uncertainty and the subject's feelings about his coping adequacy.

Dr. Lazarus: In our own work we have used the Subincision film twice in the same session. When this is done we find that there is no change in the autonomic response pattern. But when the same film is shown at intervals of one week apart, almost all of the initial autonomic reaction to the film has disappeared. If different films are shown separated by intervals of say a week, there is no loss in the impact. Although the data I am alluding to were not systematically collected to answer the question, I think they support what has been implied here—that is, when the subject has a chance to do something, to work out the experience, then there is "adaptation." Something of psychological importance has taken place in the time interval between presentations, something we don't yet understand. If the material presented is either strange (a new film), or the individual hasn't had a chance to work over it psychologically, the adaptation is negligible.

Dr. Mechanic: If you use films that are very similar, where you would expect some kind of generalization of whatever coping techniques are applicable, you should probably expect a much smaller film impact than if you use films that share few components.

Dr. Lazarus: That seems sensible, but we don't actually know.

Dr. Appley: On the general question of adaptation, I think it would be useful to distinguish between two categories more explicitly. One is a kind of physical stimulus immunity that may develop over successive exposures, exemplified by a sensory threshold rise. The second is a form of adaptation or pseudo-adaptation, derived from a strategy of coping with a known noxious event, even if it can't be avoided. When one devises a strategy of coping, the uncertainty of a potentially noxious situation—if not the pain—is reduced, and the physiological indices should probably reflect this. Any index of adaptation in the first case should show a gradual change, whereas an abrupt shift might be expected in the second instance.

Dr. Lazarus: I would seriously question whether or not adaptation in this context can be described merely as physiological adaptation without psychological mediation of some sort.

Dr. Bovard: I should just like to mention an experiment here that shows conclusively previous experience of a highly traumatic stress (tumbling in the Noble-Collip drum) increases survival rate for the mouse. The animal can't cope with the drum, it is a very traumatic experience, but in some way the mere experience of the trauma over time has been protective for the animal, just as experience at the front line is protective in combat.

Dr. Levine: An interesting example of recoding might be the "working-through process" in psychoanalysis, while the kind of adaptation which occurs through repeated trials might be more akin to behavioral therapy.

Dr. Pepitone: I would like to separate two issues that seem to have been coalesced in the preceding discussion. One theoretical matter concerns the extent of cognitive control over the response to stressful stimuli. It seems to me by now we know enough to say that such control can be complete or maximum. We can observe anxiety type reactions to pleasurable stimuli and pleasurable reactions to painful stimuli, depending upon training and natural experience. The other issue in stress theory concerns the role of uncertainty. It may be useful in this connection to distinguish risk and uncertainty. In a risky situation the individual estimates a probability of experiencing a loss of some valued object which is psychologically a part of him. In an uncertain situation, the individual cannot estimate a probability at all or the probability estimates that he can make exist over a greater or lesser range. In a series of experimental studies carried out some years ago (1957), we found that the vigor of avoidance responses which subjects could make in the threatening circumstances in which we placed them was much greater under uncertainty than under risk. But a lot of parametric work has yet to be done comparing different magnitudes of risk with different magnitudes of uncertainty as to their stressor power.

Dr. Stern: Dr. Oken suggested that there may be characteristic ranges of steroid levels for individuals and that these might be related to personality characteristics. Could he elaborate on this?

Dr. Oken: It would be speculation. There is a little bit of data that I can speculate from, i.e., our one study about the hyper-defended chronic patients who had a highly focalized response, so that the response was present but was pretty hard to get to. There is another bit of data from a study done by our group earlier on heart rate, which is, in a sense, the other side of this coin. Normal people had much more focal responses and much more capacity to respond to immediate stress, while patients who were very anxiety-prone had chronically high levels across a series of stress stimuli and much less focal response. So I suppose the speculation would be in terms of the effectiveness to filter out threat. There may be effectiveness or hypo-effectiveness and maladaptive over-effectiveness which totally shuts out threat. If you can shut it out, if you can effectively defend yourself by whatever device, there should be less response. I think this is interesting and maybe touches on some of Dr. Lazarus' comments about whether a stimulus "works." If you can do this, not perceive the threat, probably there is a general dampening effect on, I would guess, transmission between cortical levels.

Dr. Biderman: I hesitate to ask this because it may be a long question. I am interested in the relationship of most of the experimentation that has been discussed to the way some of these questions are usually put from a lay perspective. First of all, most of the experimentation deals with very short time orders relative to the kinds of things that come to mind when we talk about something as a "stressful experience." The experiments deal with immediate reactions to immediate stressors—time orders of seconds, minutes, perhaps occasionally hours. There have been just a few mentions here of things which subjects have to endure for so much as a week. Observationally, we see quite great differences between responses to long continued assaults and hazards as opposed to short-duration ones. For example, there are many situations of stress in which the behaviors of people are spoken of as characteristically flat, "cool," and other such terms, as contrasted with the startle kinds of responses to an immediate assault. So this temporal order is one kind of consideration insufficiently considered thus far in the discussion here of physiological observations.

The other consideration is the order of intensity of magnitude of the stressor. Here, too, there is a good deal of confusion arising from the purely observational kinds of data we have of behaviors which we couple with inferences. Sometimes, there seem to be reactions of greater "intensity" to things that seem to be relatively minor in terms of their significance for the person. I recall in a hospital I was with during the war in Europe, it was a frequent remark that patients reacted with more overt intensity about not getting in to see the movie on a night the theater hut was overcrowded than on being carted to surgery or on being moved to what was known to be a terminal ward. While I want to stress our need to worry about whether the mechanisms of response are the same for stressors of small and great intensity, we also have to be guarded in the imputations we make regarding intensities as we move from one system to another. The relationships between the physical, physiological, and subjective intensities are in each instance problematic.

One unrelated comment: It was particularly interesting to me in Dr. Bovard's discussion to learn of his theory regarding the mutually inhibitory, equilibrium-maintaining facilitory and inhibitory regions—the opposition of the anterior and posterior—in that it fits the introspectively-based data gathered in some work going on in our shop under Klausner. He is studying people who go out to seek stress. What they are usually after, he finds, is an exhilarating feeling of mastery. Plausibly, what goes on is that these people boost the source of negative feeling states in order to derive a feeling of exhilaration when that is removed.

Dr. Stern: You're saying it feels so good when you stop.

Dr. Biderman: Yes, when you stop, that's right, because if we equate the mechanisms inhibiting stress responses with those that provide pleasurable feelings, as Dr. Bovard seemed to me to suggest, then extreme stress experiences allow these to build up to extremely high levels. Thus, when the stress is suddenly terminated, one might expect this surge of unusually intense pleasurable feeling—as analogous to the effect of releasing the opposing thumb in finger-snapping. In his study of sky divers, Klausner analyzes their experience in terms of mutually opposing psychological dispositions. We have a difficulty in relating his observations to the finger-snapping analogy I use in that while a large number of his subjects report the maximum elation after the stress is removed (on completing their jump), others locate it at the point they identify as that of greatest hazard, and yet others in the anticipatory period. At any rate, I wish to indicate the importance to our interests of the stress-seeking as well as stress-avoiding and stress-reducing behavior.

Chairman's summary [28]

JOHN A. STERN: One of the common failings of scientists, especially psychologists, is our tendency to overgeneralize from limited data. Overgeneraliz-

[28] This is a summary of chapters 2 and 3.

ing or "theorizing" serves a useful function in that it allows for experimentation to test for the validity of such generalizations. Unfortunately, all too often we forget that most of our theories are unproven and act as if they were established facts. Dr. Lacey does a good job of demonstrating that new, as well as old, facts often are contradictory to such theories, in this case activation theory. In the face of such evidence one can act in three ways. If the data do not fit the theory, (a) get rid of the data; (b) get rid of the theory; or (c) modify the theory to accept the data. Of course there is yet a fourth possibility, that the data have no relevance to the theory. Which of these possibilities applies we will, in Quinn McNemar's inimical words, "leave to the discriminating reader" to determine. How "activation theorists" choose to respond to the data presented will, of course, be of considerable interest to all of us.

Both Drs. Lacey and Oken point out, and demonstrate convincingly, that a unitary view of either activation or stress is no longer tenable.

Dr. Lacey alludes to the lack of relationship, in any but a crude way, across a variety of physiological measures when an organism is "stressed" or stimulated with a more restrictive range of stimuli. Dr. Oken states, "All the various hormones apparently can be released more-or-less independently." Both authors, however, point out that situationally-determined patterns of somatic responses do occur and that these have to be specified not in terms of the stimulus parameters but in terms of their "impact" or "meaning" to the organism. This makes the experimenter's task somewhat more difficult, but, as Lacey has indicated, "Nature is not simple . . ." (p. 28), and experimentation in the vast area of psychophysiology and psychoendocrinology will seriously have to heed this consideration in the design of experiments.

Dr. Lacey, for example, points to the lack of relationship found between measures of arousal in different physiological systems to dissociation between behavioral and somatic arousal. As both he and Dr. Oken indicate, one can have both specific as well as nonspecific responses to "stressors" or "arousing stimuli." Since nature is complex, could the lack of relationship found be a function of the confusion between specific and nonspecific responses? For example, alpha desynchronization in the occipitally-derived EEG is considered to be one measure of arousal, yet alpha desynchronization can occur as a specific response to light stimulation long after other measures of "arousal" have abated. Thus, the lack of relationship between different measures of arousal may, in part, be a function of some organ systems, responding to more than the arousing nature of the stimulus, while others are responding primarily to the latter attribute.

I found both of these papers excellent, in terms of reviewing relevant literature and, what is more important, in bringing us face to face with challenging questions.

SANFORD I. COHEN

4

Central nervous system functioning in altered sensory environments

Since the historic work of Hebb, Heron, Bexton, and Scott (cf. Bexton, Heron, & Scott, 1954; Hebb, 1955a; Heron, Bexton, & Hebb, 1953; Heron, 1957, 1961; Scott et al., 1959) and Lilly (1956a) some ten years ago, there has been an increasing number of laboratory studies and clinical reports related to sensory deprivation and perceptual isolation. Such conditions were seen, from the beginning, as an experimental means of inducing psychological stress leading to a number of psychopathologic-like phenomena.

The first major symposium (1961) concerned with this research brought together applied, clinical, and basic behavioral and biological scientists who reported the effects of perceptual isolation on cognitive, perceptual, and sensorimotor functioning. Other reports were concerned with the effects of altered sensory environments on biological development and the consequences of altered sensory conditions on the functioning of pilots, radar operators, drivers, and mental patients. A number of theoretical constructs have been developed, from perceptual, psychoanalytic, and neurophysiological points of view, in attempts to organize the array of confusing findings and to develop meaningful directions in which research could be pursued.

As studies accumulated, it soon became apparent to many of the initial investigators, however, that a variety of experimental conditions and life situations, which actually differed in many respects, were being subsumed under the rubric of sensory deprivation or perceptual isolation. What was somewhat misleading was that some of the rather profound psychological experiences reported by individuals exposed to life experiences in which they were isolated (cf. Burney, 1952; Byrd, 1938; Gibson, 1953; Hunter, 1952; Ritter, 1954; Slocum, 1900) and by subjects who were isolated in altered sensory environments for long periods (cf. Bexton, Heron, Scott, 1954; Heron, Bexton, & Hebb, 1953; Vernon & Hoffman, 1956) were reported to be similar phenomena. Reports from both settings contained descriptions of illusions and hallucinations, disorganizations of goal-directed thinking, impaired time perception, distortion of body image, increased preoccupation with body sensations and inner thought processes. However, it was apparent that the particular definitions of both the environmental conditions and the reported phenomena varied considerably amongst reviewers and investigators. Often omitted were precise descriptions of the duration of the subjects' experience, the manner in which the sensory input was modified, the degree of restriction of mobility, the attitude of the subjects, the instructions given to subjects, etc. More important, perhaps, was the lack of uniformity in criteria used for evaluating the impact of the experience upon the subjects.

The problems which emerged in this particular research area were not unique to the group of investigators interested in so-called sensory deprivation research but were and are fairly typical of any area of research derived from life situations which supposedly have some traumatic impact on individuals and are considered to be psychologically stressful. *Stress* is one of those peculiar terms which is understood by everyone when used in a very general context but understood by few when an operational definition is desired which is sufficiently specific to enable the precise testing of certain relationships. Communication between investigators often becomes quite chaotic in regard to individual predictor variables, experimental conditions, strategies, technique, etc., when the term *stress* is introduced into an experimental setting. The ambiguity of the term is in part a function of the fact that it is applied by some to situations, conditions, or stimuli evoking the responses of subjects, and by others to the response dimensions, whether subjective, psychological, endocrine, or CNS. Sometimes *stress* is used to denote a situation in which some condition noxious to an organism is imposed upon it, sometimes to indicate a state or a syndrome.

Zuckerman (1964) analyzed the possible sources of stress in perceptual isolation experiments and the relation of personality factors to the subject's reactions. He concluded that the stress effects of perceptual isolation vary markedly from subject to subject and that different investigators use different measures to indicate the presence of stress.

The present chapter will focus on central nervous system (CNS) processes intervening between the stimulus field presented to subjects and a number of interacting behavioral, perceptual, and physiological responses. One major interest is the specific and nonspecific consequences of central and peripheral nervous system activation, resulting from exposure to particular types of experimental conditions (or life situations).

EXPERIMENTAL APPROACHES AND VARIABLES INFLUENCING RESPONSE PATTERNS

Kubzansky (1961) and Zubek (1964), among others, have reviewed a number of the effects on human behavior and human performance that a reduction in variability in visual, auditory, and tactual sensory stimulation can have. Attempts to achieve such reduction in environmental stimulation have been referred to by a number of terms —psychological and/or sensory isolation and deprivation, or perceptual isolation or deprivation.

The experimental approaches which have been used to investigate sensory deprivation, perceptual and social isolation have been categorized as (1) efforts directed at reducing the absolute input of sensory stimuli, as typified in the water immersion studies initiated by Lilly (1956), Shurley (1960); (2) the work of Bexton, Heron, and Scott (1954), concerned with reduced *patterning* of sensory input while retaining input levels near normal; and (3) studies consisting mainly of homogenous environments—of the absence of change in the external sensory field.

Ruff (1961) identified eight categories of variables which may influence the results of deprivation experiments. Among these categories are the subject's expectations, motivations, attitudes, and the type of instruction received. These variables are particularly significant for self-reported subjective experiences. Numerous variables of a procedural and experimental nature are also possibly significant, for example, those relating to quantity and intensity of the stimulus pattern of sensory input, the sense modality involved, the duration of experiment, the degree of social interaction between subject and experimenter, aloneness, the extent of physical restraint, diet, the type of tests used and when they are administered.

Ziskind (1962) has attempted to explain some of the phenomena noted in sensory deprivation type experiments, particularly the imagery or hallucinatory experiences. He suggests that hallucinations are nothing more than fragments of normal imagery unrecognized because of reduced conscious awareness and not "real" hallucinations. However, Ziskind does not consider the possibility that the phenomena which have been identified clinically as hallucinations may actually be explained by the mechanism which he utilizes to explain the imagery of the subjects. The fact that imagery varies with instruction, with various physical conditions, or with the internal state does not in itself prove that these are not "real" hallucinations but may indicate that what we have been identifying as hallucinations are "imagery" phenomena produced by the interaction of both internal psychological and physiological and external situational factors. The imagery phenomena may become pathological, i.e., an hallucination, when it is invested with certain meaning by the patient: when it is used as a basis for action by the patient (as if it were reality) or when it becomes indistinguishable from reality. Hence, the element of certainty about the source of imagery (internal or external) may define its pathologic nature.

PHYSIOLOGICAL RESPONSES IN SENSORY DEPRIVATION AND ISOLATION STUDIES

In Kubzansky's 1961 review, he found very few studies which had employed physiological measures. Some had utilized EEG in the hope of clarifying the nature of cortical activity and/or the sleep/wakefulness cycle in isolation and deprivation experiments. Since that time, however, a number of investigations have included measures of central and autonomic nervous system activity, and a few have investigated endocrine levels during the experimental conditions. Initially, these studies utilized physiological measures primarily as multiple indices of "arousal" or "stress." Later studies attempted to correlate physiological changes with the psychological reactions observed. More recent studies have been concerned with the influence of individual and situational variables on specific physiological response systems. There has also been more interest in the interaction or correlation between physiological variables. Such inter-measure correlations (negative or positive) can reflect a causal relationship, such as a change in heart rate occurring as a compensatory response to peripheral vascular constriction. They may also suggest that two systems are activated or inhibited because of changes in a third system affecting or controlling both (e.g., an increase in adrenaline and peripheral autonomic activity resulting from sympathetico-adrenal excitation following posterior hypothalamic discharge).

However there has been a shift in emphasis in psychophysiological research away from the use of physiological measures merely as a means of obtaining more objectivity in measuring psychological variables, and I think there is a return to the idea that one should measure psychological variables with psychological techniques and physiological variables with physiological techniques. The two levels may reflect similar processes but there isn't necessarily a causal relationship between them. There has been an effort to treat physiological and psychological variables as independent dimensions reflecting integrative CNS activity. As a result, more careful consideration is being given to individual differences in the resting state and in stimulated response patterns in the various systems; and more attention is being paid to the effects of varying levels of CNS activity on the various systems and the influence of the initial level of activity on later response patterns.

Integrative neurological findings

Petrie, Collins, and Solomon (1960) reported an inverse relationship between pain tolerance and endurance in a perceptual deprivation environment. This as well as other experiments (see below) suggested that neurosensory characteristics were related to the ability to tolerate environments in which there was a decrease in stimulation of visual and auditory sense modalities, or that integrative neurological and somatosensory characteristics—or other perceptual, neurophysiological or personality dimensions—were partial determinants of the subject's reaction.

However, Zubek et al. (1961) did not confirm the findings reported by Petrie when he tested the predictive value of pain tolerance to sensory deprivation tolerance. In one experiment, Zubek was interested in the effect of prolonged visual deprivation on cutaneous sensitivity. He felt it was plausible to assume that subjects who show difficulties with some integrative CNS functions on the skin surface may be adversely affected by situations in which discrimination by distance receptors is made more difficult. Subjects were kept in the dark for one week in an otherwise normal and varied sensory environment. Tactual acuity (tested by two-point discrimination) decreased during the deprivation but returned to the same discriminatory level following the deprivation. Pain and heat sensitivity both showed the same effects. Zubek et al. (1963, 1961) felt that the cutaneous super-sensitivity suggested that one of the effects of the functional deafferentation produced by visual deprivation may be to sensitize certain areas of the nervous systems. Some support for this hypothesis was offered by the report that in some congenitally-blind children, the non-specific cortical responses evoked by tactile and auditory stimuli were unusually large. Zubek also points out that Krech and his colleagues (Krech, Rosenzweig, & Bennett, 1963) have demonstrated that rats subjected to peripheral blinding at the time of weaning subsequently show an increase in the weight and cholinesterase activity of the somesthetic cortex. Furthermore, Krech observed similar somato-sensory changes in rats reared in darkness. Zubek concluded that visual deprivation alone could produce cortical changes of a type which might lead to cutaneous supersensitivity, although it remains an unanswered question whether the same changes occur in the brain of man.

EEG findings

Heron (1961) found a progressive slowing of EEG activity in the parieto-occipital region of six subjects isolated for four days. Some of the changes persisted three and one-half hours after emergence from the experiment. However, when a two-day, rather than a four-day, period of isolation was used, the slowing persisted for only an hour. Records obtained when a subject was hallucinating showed greatly reduced amplitude, similar to that which might be obtained from a subject in an altered state.[1] These investigators had the impression that subjects slept more during the early part of their stay in isolation and less later in the period of confinement.

W. Cohen and Cadwallader (1958) hypothesized that under conditions of uniform visual stimulation, termination of the visual experience would be accompanied by a return of alpha activity. Despite considerable individual differences, he found strong alpha activity in the EEG following the onset of the white-out phenomenon.

Recently, Zubek, Welch, and Saunders (1963) exposed three subjects to fourteen days of perceptual deprivation. Not only was there a progressive decrease in mean occipital lobe frequency but the decrease appeared to be twice as great during the second week. The EEG slowing has not been as pronounced during shorter isolation studies [e.g., Leiderman (1962) found no change in alpha activity after two hours of isolation].

In later work, Zubek (1964) observed that seven days' exposure to perceptual deprivation (reduced *patterning* but not level of sensory input) produced a significantly greater decrease in mean occipital lobe frequencies than did the same period of sensory deprivation (reduction of sensory input to as low a *level* as possible). The differential effect may be related to the greater behavioral impairments which seem to occur after prolonged perceptual deprivation.

The records for experimental subjects were characterized by an excess of theta waves, particularly in tracings from the temporal lobe. Involvement of the temporal lobes was supported by some observations of Baldwin, Lewis, and Frost (1957). When chimpanzees were subjected to bilateral removal of their temporal lobes followed by thirteen days of sensory deprivation, they exhibited none of the perceptual, motor, and emotional disturbances which control animals showed after the same length of isolation. Furthermore, the lobectomized animals also were immune to the effects of lysergic acid which in control animals produced striking behavioral effects. Some of the human deprivation phenomena may also have a temporal lobe origin. The impairment of memory for nonsense words, indicated earlier by Zubek et al. (1962), may be one of these cases. This suggestion is supported by the fact that patients with

---

[1] However, this could have been due to the subject talking.

temporal lobe lesions, particularly in the hippocampal region, exhibit severe and long-lasting impairments of recent memory. Some of the perceptual changes, too, may have a temporal lobe origin. It has also been reported that ictal patterns of temporal lobe epilepsy are sometimes characterized by illusions of color, shape, size, and depth.

Zuckerman (1964) has suggested a relationship between the slow brain wave activity and the motivational loss about which subjects complain following a long-term isolation. Zubek has reported certain dramatic and prolonged behavioral changes of a motivational rather than a perceptual nature. After fourteen days of isolation, two of Zubek's subjects reported (in their diaries) severe motivational losses. Sample reports were: an "inability to get started doing anything," a "loathing to do any work requiring even the slightest degree of physical or mental exertion," and a "don't-give-a-darn attitude toward everything." In one of the two subjects these symptoms lasted for eight days; in the other, for six days. The third subject reported similar motivational losses but felt that he had completely recovered by the third day. Zubek noted that the post-isolation EEG record for this subject was characterized by a greater initial degree of recovery than the records for the others.

Zubek and Wilgosh (1963) found a significant decrease in occipital lobe frequencies in subjects enduring a week of immobilization without perceptual isolation. Subjects required to perform physical exercise during one week of isolation with unpatterned light and white noise manifested an increase in EEG frequencies and showed fewer impairments on fifteen behavioral measures than did subjects who were not required to exercise during the same period. Apparently restriction of movement was partly responsible for the decrease in EEG activity, but visual and auditory restriction increased the effect to a significant degree.

Zubek speculated that the ascending reticular activating system may mediate facilitation and may be disturbed by decreases in level and variability of sensory input. He further felt that exercise may introduce variability in kinesthetic and proprioceptive stimuli which offsets the unvaried visual and auditory sensation. However, one would also have to consider the vascular effects of exercise and an increase in cerebral vascular flow with exercise.

The slowed brain wave pattern typical of long-term isolation is not necessarily indicative of *stress* in the usual sense since this is more often characterized by fast waves associated with alerting or activation.

Autonomic and skeletal motor responses

R. C. Davis (1959) reported the results of an experiment involving approximately 45 minutes of diminished visual and auditory stimuli. During the experimental conditions, the subjects showed significantly higher levels of muscle activity than did control subjects. These results might appear contrary to the concept that brief periods of reduction in sensory input lead to relaxation and eventual sleep. However, Davis' experimental procedure suggested that instructions to stay awake may in fact have constituted a relatively difficult task for the subjects under the sensory deprivation conditions. Relevant to this possibility are the observations by Malmo (1959) that the physiological level of activity is dependent upon task demands, as well as upon sensory input.

Davis' experimental subjects not only showed significantly higher muscle tension but tended to exhibit a pattern of greater muscular and circulatory activity and inhibition of respiration characteristic of "anticipation of a stimulus."

Stern (n.d.) conducted an experiment (within the framework of Davis' short-term sensory deprivation study) to test the hypothesis that the level of somatic activity (autonomic and skeletal muscle) will increase for subjects with a vigilance task but will decrease for subjects with no specific task. The hypothesis required comparisons of level of somatic activity between two groups over a period of eighty minutes. Physiological recordings were obtained at five-minute intervals, the first two being pretreatment and the last two post-treatment.

One group, the "vigil" subjects, were told that they had to keep track of the direction of movement of a small light by pressing buttons for the sixty minutes of the treatment phase of the experiment. The "rest" subjects were instructed simply to relax and ignore the small light.

Breathing *rate* did not differentiate between the two groups used in this study but the breathing *amplitude* did. Amplitude of the rest group fell rapidly to about 80 percent of the initial level while the vigil group fluctuated around 100 percent. Heart rate of the vigil group remained at approximately the 100 percent level, but the rest group gradually fell to 85 percent of their pre-treatment level. Base skin conductance level of the vigil group was higher than the rest group during the entire treatment phase, but there was a gradual decrease in conductance for both groups. Analysis of variance revealed that the difference between groups was significant. As was the case with heart rate, the rest group showed a much greater decrease, resulting in a significant groups $\times$ trials interaction. The vigil group had consistently more spontaneous GSRs than the rest group. This difference appeared almost immediately and remained relatively stable during the course of the treatment session.

In the post-treatment phase, the relative amount of activity of the two groups reversed; whereas the vigil group was showing a higher level of activation until the latter part of the treatment phase, the rest group usually responded at a higher level during the post-treatment period.

According to the hypothesis, the rest group should have shown a decrease in activity over time, which it did. The vigil group should have shown an increase in activity over their pre-treatment resting level. However, they also showed a decrease in activity in the post-treatment period. This decrease in activity of both groups is reflected in the significant trials effect, which was found for heart rate and skin conductance.

The results supported Malmo's (1959) hypothesis that level of somatic activity increases with a specific task, as compared with instructions to relax for one hour. It appears that a low sensory input situation, when used for a relatively brief period of time, can be conducive to relaxation and even sleep if no task demands are made on the subjects. However, it should be noted that a task may be a function of the set of the subject, i.e., the expectations he has or he feels the experimenter has, even if not explicitly stated. The vigil group in Stern's experiment showed very similar response patterns to field-dependent subjects tested at Duke in an experiment in which they were isolated for two hours without any task or instructions and compared to field dependent subjects who were informed about the details of the experiment to reduce their uncertainty (Cohen, Silverman, & Shmavonian, 1962a, b). It is conceivable that subjects who depend on external cues to orient themselves may more actively scan their environment and be more attentive to their surroundings (like the vigil group of Stern) than informed field-dependent subjects.

Jackson and Kelly (1962) and Jackson and Pollard (1962), claimed that the effect of perceptual isolation can be explained by social psychological or nondeprivation variables, such as set and suggestion, and that physiological explanations are superfluous. They felt that subjects reported peculiar effects because their expectations were aroused by what they had heard about similar situations. If this hypothesis is correct, according to Zuckerman (1964), then physiological indices of stress reactions should be more pronounced at the onset of an isolation period than after the subjects have had the chance to adapt; and the physiological indices should not be particularly sensitive to changes in physical conditions unless social variables were also altered.

In order to test this, Zuckerman conducted an experiment with 36 female undergraduates based on the hypothesis that total perceptual isolation (darkness and silence) is more stressful than partial isolation (darkness with sound or silence with light). The *stress* effect in this experiment was assessed with verbal and physiological (GSR) measures. A secondary hypothesis was concerned with the effect of time on an increase in the stress effect in the total isolation group. Uncertainty was reduced by informing the subjects of the general conditions of the experiment.

The total and partial isolation groups both showed some decline in skin conductance in the first fifteen–twenty minutes with little differentiation between the groups. After the first hour and one-half the basal conductance in the total isolation group rose sharply. It remained level in the two partial isolation groups (which did show a sharp rise in conductance in the last five–fifteen minutes). The analysis of variance revealed no group differences on pre-isolation conductance. A significant between-periods F-ratio indicated that the duration of the experiment had significant effects on all groups taken together. Differences between groups were different at different periods of the experiment. During the first one and one-half hours, none of the effects was significant; during the second one and one-half hours both the periods and the groups-by-periods interaction were significant at better than the .01 level.

All groups showed an increase during the first hour and one-half in the number of nonspecific GSRs, but during the second hour and one-half the GSR fluctuations rose sharply in the total isolation group and remained above those in the other groups. The pre-isolation number of GSRs did not differentiate these groups.

Zuckerman examined the relationship of the GSR measures to the interview and test indices of stress. The rise in basal skin conductance correlated significantly with the number of nonspecific GSRs, interview anxiety rating, the interview stress ratings, and the AACL score (Affect Adjective Check List). This finding is similar to the results of Duke studies where a relationship was observed between a post-experimental interview rating of discomfort, the change in GSR fluctuations, and post-experimental adrenaline levels.

On the basis of this, Zuckerman suggested that restricting input to two sense modalities is more stressful than restriction of one sense modality. The effects appeared after one and one-half hours of isolation and were indicated in this experiment by the increase in basal skin conductance and a greater number of nonspecific GSRs, interpreted as indices of autonomic and possible CNS activation.

Zuckerman's hypothesis, that stress is a function of time and isolation rather than an initial response to a strange and suggestive situation, was in part supported. He did indicate, however, that it is conceivable that a point can be reached where a subject may finally adapt to the situation and show lowered responsivity.

The verbal indices of stress employed by Zuckerman failed to differentiate total and partial isolation, although his pre- and post-isolation test measures—such as the AACL and the SCCL (Somatic Complaint Check List)—did show rises for all groups. This suggested to Zuckerman that verbal stress reactions are a function of the social isolation and confinement rather than the amount of perceptual isolation.

The results indicated that three hours of perceptual isolation are stressful apart from the factors of confinement, social isolation, and set. The latter factors are probably important in inducing verbalized stress response.

Jackson and Pollard's conclusions in which the importance of set and expectation are highlighted appear to be based on frequency of verbal response.

Zubek (1964) commented that measures of skin resistance are often taken as a gross index of arousal of the CNS and, in general, show a type of change related to the nature of the behavioral reactions exhibited during isolation. Leiderman (1962) conducted a study to evaluate the effects on behavior, skin potential, and heart rate of varying stimulus conditions. He studied six subjects in four counterbalanced sessions, each of two-hour duration, involving (1) vision and sound; (2) vision, sound absent (white noise); (3) vision absent (homogenous light field), sound present, and, (4) vision and sound absent. Galvanic skin potential was obtained at fifteen-minute intervals during two-hour sessions and showed no systematic relationship to sessions or to sensory conditions. Heart rate was highest in Session I for five of the six subjects but showed no systematic relationships to conditions of isolation.

In a second experiment by Leiderman (1962), sixteen subjects were isolated under conditions of visual restriction with a homogenous field and visual stimulation with travel slides. The conditions, counterbalanced in two sessions separated by one- to two-week intervals, had no effect on skin potential. A significant interaction between conditions and sex of the subject was found for heart beat, with the rates being highest for males in the visual stimulation condition and higher for females in the visual restriction condition. The two experiments revealed no clear effect of the degree of perceptual isolation on the GSR and heart rate.

In another experiment, Shapiro, Leiderman, and Morningstar (1963) tested 84 women who performed a simple task under conditions of social isolation and social interaction in a three-person group. Success and failure in the task were made equivalent in both conditions and the order of the experience was balanced. Mean level and variability of behavioral initiation, galvanic skin potential, and heart rate were compared.

The results were that:

1. Number and variability of initiations were greater for individuals working alone than in groups.

2. Level of galvanic skin potential was higher and heart rate tended to be lower under conditions of group interaction. The variability of these measures, as measured by the mean square successive difference, did not differ between the conditions.

3. Levels of initiation and galvanic skin potential were consistent for individuals relative to one another when the group situation preceded the "alone" situation.

4. Individual differences in heart rate level and galvanic skin potential variability were consistent, regardless of temporal order of the isolation and interaction experience.

The authors indicate that the social condition can set behavioral and physiological norms which carry over into a subsequent experience. Some measures are sensitive to the social conditions and the order in which they occur, while others appear to reflect relatively stable characteristics of the individual. The findings were felt to have implications for future research on the socialization of behavioral and physiological processes.

Some water immersion studies have shown a significant alteration in the normal physiology. The cardiovascular system seems to be influenced by immersion, with deleterious cardiovascular effects manifesting themselves after the subject has come out of the water. As would be expected with reflex mechanisms, Graveline (1963) and Clark and Graveline (1957) have reported marked postural hypotension on the tilt table after immersion, evidenced by a sharp rise in pulse rate, a marked decrease in systolic blood pressure, and an abnormal EKG. Beckman and his colleagues' (1961) 23-hour immersion subject developed atrial tachycardia beginning at the twenty-second hour and on removal became syncopal upon sitting upright. Beckman also reported that the negative pressure breathing situation of immersion to neck level resulted in a change in pattern and an increase in respiratory rate. These findings suggest that physiological changes may occur in certain types of isolation experiments which may result in psychological changes in addition to the usual finding that psychological factors lead to physiological changes in these types of experiments.

Biochemical studies

Urinary 11-oxycorticoids were studied in nine of Bexton's (1954) subjects, with no consistent increase in excretion noted, leading to the conclusion that the adrenal cortex was not activated by perceptual isolation. However, the subjects were resting much more than subjects exposed to the exigencies of everyday life, and different normative values would be needed (e.g., a group resting but not isolated) for proper comparison.

Mendelson et al. (1961) determined catecholamine level, using urine collected from ten males in isolation. Both adrenaline and noradrenaline rose from the pre-experimental to the experimental period and fell from the experimental to the post-experimental period. The rise in adrenaline and noradrenaline and the post-experimental fall for noradrenaline was significant. The magnitude of the fall in noradrenaline excretion was negatively correlated with verbalizations, somatic references, and errors.

Zubek (1964) pointed out that the activity of the adrenal medulla and cortex has been studied to determine whether the deprivation situation may be classed with other stressors. No clear answer, however, has been given, and what little evidence exists indicates that the output of both adrenaline and noradrenaline increases during perceptual deprivation but the activity of the cortex—indicated by changes in steroid levels—does not appear to be affected.

Persky, Zuckerman, et al. (1965) recently reported a study in which a number of blood and urine samples of hormonal measures were collected, following experimental sessions in which subjects were isolated and confined but perceptually stimulated, and following a session in which they were isolated and perceptually deprived. Thyroid-stimulating hormone, 17-ketosteroids (index of testicular activity) and 17-ketogenic steroids (index of adrenal cortex) levels were higher after isolation than after the stimulation condition. The authors tentatively suggest that pituitary adrenal activity during isolation may be a response to reduced input and arousal. Physiological indices showed a fall in number of GSRs and in respiratory and cardiac rate and an increase in skin conductance. They point out that this pattern is similar to the one Lacey and Lacey (1958a) and Lacey et al. (1963) identified as occurring with the anticipation of a stimulus. Physiological responses were not impressively different in the stimulated and nonstimulated groups. However, the authors suggest that the stimulated group would have been expected to show more activity, and the lack of difference may suggest more physiological activity in the nonstimulated group than was anticipated.

Psychophysiological studies at Duke University

A number of investigations had been concerned with assessing the influence of individual or subject variables on the responses to altered sensory and social conditions (e.g., Holt & Goldberger, 1959). Although there was a lack of convergence, many studies indicated that differences between subjects might be sufficiently important to obscure the measurement of a variety of responses.

A series of studies was begun at Duke concerned with assessing the influence of individual differences in perceptual mode characteristics on the physiological as well as the psychological responses to isolated conditions of two hours duration (Cohen et al., 1961, 1962a, b). These studies utilized the work of Witkin et al. (1954, 1962), who classified subjects as field-oriented (or field-dependent) when their perception of the vertical position of a luminous rod was strongly influenced by a surrounding luminous frame. Body-oriented or field-independent subjects, in contrast, were less influenced by the visual cues provided by the frame and moved the rod closer to the true gravitational vertical.

The perceptual mode characteristics were related by Witkin to a number of personality characteristics, with field-dependent persons showing more passivity in dealing with the environment, more submissiveness to authority, lower self-esteem, and a less distinct body image.

Subjects who were field-oriented [2] showed after two hours, more anxiety, more suspiciousness, more disorganization of thought, more visual and auditory imagery, more discomfort with body sensations, more inner feelings and fantasies, and more movement than field-independent subjects. EEG and skin resistance findings (cf. Burch & Greiner, 1960; Cohen, Silverman, & Shmavonian, 1962a, b; Edelburg & Burch, 1962; Silverman, Cohen, & Shmavonian, 1959; Silverman, et al., 1961) suggested a higher level of CNS alerting in field-dependent subjects during the two-hour isolation experiment, although both groups started at about the same level. The field-oriented subjects revealed less ability to discriminate somato-sensory cues (e.g., tests of two-point discrimination and letter identification), this difference being most pronounced after the two-hour experiment.

The differences in psychological responses in body- and field-oriented subjects were similar to findings reported by (1) Leiderman (1962), who found the type and amount of imagery in subjects in sensory-deprivation experiments to be determined to a large extent by individual rather than environmental variables; (2) Shurely (1960), who found introspective subjects were most comfortable in water immersion experiments; and (3) Goldberger and Holt (1958), who described the adaptive reactor to perceptual isolation conditions as a person who was not overly rigid or controlled, who did not habitually complain of body symptoms, and who had a high ego-strength score. Maladaptive reactors had high MMPI hypochondriasis scores and were described as outer-directed. The characteristics of the maladaptive reactors seemed to be related to field-dependence.

Work by Culver et al. (1964) has indicated that field-dependent subjects perform more poorly than body-oriented on three tests of spatial-perceptual ability, including tactile localization, embedded figures, and laterality discrimination (see Table 4-1). These findings, together with the somato-sensory and autonomic response findings in the previous experiment, suggested that differences in integrative CNS functions might possibly be related to or correlates of perceptual mode differences. In one experiment a composite of scores on the three perceptual tests was used

---

[2] Subjects were classified as field-independent and field-dependent on the basis of their scores on the Rod and Frame Test. The determinations were made using the standard short form Rod and Frame procedure described by Witkin et al. (1954, 1962) with the subject upright. Subjects who had mean deviations of 7 degrees or more were placed in the field-dependent group and subjects with mean scores of 2 degrees or less were placed in the field-independent group. These values were not known to the person conducting any of the experiments until the data were analyzed.

Table 4-1. Perceptual test performance of body and field subjects.

Measure	Body Subjects (N=12)	Field Subjects (N=12)	p Value
Gottschaldt Latency (average per design, in seconds)	20.24	44.56	< .025
Laterality Discrimination Latency (average per drawing, in seconds)	1.41	2.01	< .005
Laterality Discrimination Errors (number of errors made on 28 drawings)	.92	3.17	< .005
Tactile Localization (average amounts of error per stimulus, in mm.)	13.31	17.84	< .05

SOURCE: Culver, Cohen, Silverman, & Shmavonian, 1964, 6, p. 125. By permission of Plenum Press.

to isolate good and poor extreme groups. The physiological data during a two-hour isolation experiment showed an enhancement of the differential responsivity noted when field orientation was used to categorize the subjects. The results were consistent with the hypothesis that body and field subjects differ with respect to a basic spatial-perceptual dimension and that this dimension may be better measured by a group of correlated tests than by any single test. The situation may be analogous to the measurement of an ability like verbal intelligence, where the most reliable estimate may be made combining several subtest scores.

Some indirect support for the concept that perceptual mode differences may reflect (in some persons) CNS differences was found in Teuber's work (1959, 1961), in which he reported that brain damaged, in contrast to non-brain damaged, subjects had difficulties in accurately performing a number of tests of integrative neurological and complex perceptual functions. Many of these tests were similar to those used in identifying the less accurate performance of field-oriented subjects (e.g., two-point discrimination, tactile localization, embedded figures).

Exploratory work was undertaken by Reckless et al. (1962) and Cohen et al. (1962) to determine if small doses of drugs affecting the CNS would alter the previously noted response differences in body- and field-oriented subjects. It was tentatively hypothesized that drug agents which altered the central excitatory level might affect the two types of subjects differently by altering the perception of and reaction to the environmental conditions or by modifying some CNS factor related to perceptual mode.

Fifteen each of "extreme" body- and field-oriented subjects were tested in an experiment identical to that described previously, except that just before the experimenter left the chamber a pill containing either a sedative, stimulant, or placebo was placed in the subject's mouth and he was asked to drink some water and swallow it.

The response patterns (EEG and GSR) of both perceptual mode groups given a placebo were similar to those observed in the previous experiment, with the greatest increase in EEG beta wave activity from the first to the last five periods occurring in the field-dependent placebo group, although the initial level of this group did not differ from that of the other two field-dependent groups. Responses to the sedative and the stimulant were different in the differently oriented groups. The field-dependent subjects given either a stimulant *or* a sedative showed a decrease in CNS activation (decrease in beta and increase in alpha EEG activity and an increase in skin resistance) and a more relaxed psychological state as the experiment progressed, while the body-oriented subjects showed alerting to the stimulant and mixed responses to the sedative. Table *4-2*

Table 4-2. Body-field drug experiment I. Mean EEG change from first to last five-minute period.*

	BODY				FIELD			
	Group Mean			Group Arousal Trend	Group Mean			Group Arousal Trend
	Beta	Alpha	Theta		Beta	Alpha	Theta	
Placebo	+614	−466	+126	↑	+1478	−770	−102	↑
Sedative	+426	−256	+108	↑	−1530	−374	+240	↓
Stimulant	+2850	−644	−10	↑	−760	+150	+50	↓

* N = 30 (5/subgroup)
↓ = Trend toward relaxation
↑ = Trend toward arousal

shows the mean change in alpha, beta, and theta wave count from first to last five-minute recording period in the differently oriented groups for the three conditions.[3]

[3] Analyses of variance for the effects of the three drug conditions, the two perceptual mode conditions, and for time (seven periods) were carried out for each EEG

From one point of view it appeared that the two groups showed differential responsivity to a stimulant (and a suggestive differential trend with a sedative). From another point of view, the data suggested that altering either the internal physiological or psychological state of the two subject groups altered their response patterns to a low sensory input environment. The findings were reminiscent of those from a number of studies which have reported variability in drug responsivity related to psychological differences in the subjects. Klerman, Dimascio, et al. (1959) suggested that personality patterns (determined by MMPI and psychiatric interviews) modified the action of drugs. Lasagna et al. (1954) noted that placebo reactors were more anxious and more dependent on outside stimulation than on their own mental processes (similar to field-dependent subjects). Other studies have emphasized the influences of the subject's expectations or the conditions of the experiment in determining the response to drugs.

Additional studies were then carried out to verify the finding of differential ANS and CNS responsivity in field-dependent and -independent subjects to whom a placebo, sedative, or stimulant was administered. The results of the replication revealed that field-independent subjects given amphetamine showed an increase in beta wave and a decrease in alpha wave count on the EEG. In contrast, the field-dependent subjects again showed a decrease in the beta wave count and an increase in alpha count with the stimulant (as shown in Table *4-3*). A 3×3 analysis of variance for the change in beta wave count from first to last five-minute period was almost significant for perceptual mode ($F{=}2.04$) but was significant for drug condition ($F = 2.83$, $p < .05$). The interaction was significant ($F = 2.97$, $p < .05$).

The differences noted in the responses to the stimulant drugs may be related to differences in the subject's personality makeup and the ef-

---

band separately, in addition to a complex analysis in which all three bands were considered.

The analysis revealed that the interaction of time and perceptual mode was a significant influence on a number of beta waves ($F = 2.58$, $p < .05$), and on alpha wave activity ($F = 2.10$, $p < .05$). The interaction of perceptual mode, time, and drug condition was also significant ($F = 2.0$, $p < .05$).

Perhaps of more importance, however, is the complex analysis of variance on the effects of the drugs, the body/field perceptual mode, and time on all three EEG bands (the total pattern of EEG activity, as reflected by an increase in beta and decrease in alpha and theta waves, or a decrease in beta and an increase in alpha and theta waves). This analysis revealed that the only significant source of variance for this complex EEG measure was the interaction of perceptual mode, the drug variable, and time ($F = 5.449$, $p < 0.01$). This finding suggests that none of the major independent variables separately had a significant influence but that all three together did have a significant effect.

Analysis of variance of basal skin resistance during the seven five-minute recording periods for the two perceptual mode groups in the three drug conditions showed a significant interaction effect of time $\times$ perceptual mode ($F = 3.20$, $p < .01$).

Table 4-3. Body-field drug experiment II. Mean EEG change from first to last five-minute period.*

	BODY				FIELD			
	Group Mean			Group Arousal Trend	Group Mean			Group Arousal Trend
	Beta	Alpha	Theta		Beta	Alpha	Theta	
Placebo	−1222	−458	+276	↓	+98	−116	+10	↑?
Sedative	−488	−582	+90	↓	−109	−88	+42	↓
Stimulant	+258	−70	+40	↑	−140	+92	−48	↓

*N = 30 (5/subgroup)
↓ = Trend toward relaxation
↑? = Questionable arousal pattern
↑ = Trend toward arousal

fects of the mood quality affecting the subject's psychological reaction to the condition of this particular experiment. Perhaps the increased sympathetic tone increases the proprioceptive awareness in the field-dependent subject. It has been noted earlier that the field-dependent subjects tended to be less able to utilize body sensations for spatial or temporal orientation and are more uncomfortable with body sensations. With the increased clarity of internal sensations, there might be an increase in orienting information within the CNS and a secondary adjustment with relaxation to the environment. Whatever the explanation, the data do suggest that altering the internal state of the two subject groups reversed the patterns of responses previously noted in situations characterized by a low sensory input, uncertainty, and brief social isolation.

The role played by uncertainty in producing differential responsivity to a low sensory input situation was examined by Culver et al. (1964). The subject's response to cognitive structuring was experimentally manipulated by informing one group of field-independent and field-dependent subjects what the design of a two-hour experiment would be and not informing another group. The psychological data from this experiment suggested that uninformed field-dependent subjects were more aroused and uncomfortable than uninformed field-independent subjects or than field-dependent subjects who had received information about the experiment. However, some informed field-independent subjects were surprisingly suspicious and uncomfortable.

The number of nonspecific GSR fluctuations of the body and field groups (i.e., summed across experimental and control conditions) almost overlapped (Fig. 4-1), whereas the number of nonspecific GSR fluctuations for the overall experimental and control conditions (i.e., summed across body and field groups) showed that subjects in the unstructured experi-

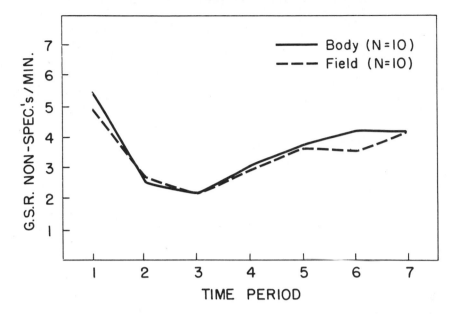

FIGURE   4-1.   Mean number of nonspecific fluctuations in skin resistance in field-independent (body) and dependent (field) subjects. Reproduced by permission from Culver, Cohen, Silverman, & Shmavonian
(1964, Fig. 1, p. 122).

mental condition had consistently more nonspecific reactions than did
subjects in the more structured control condition (Fig. 4-2). This difference, however, only approached significance (p — 0.1).

Within each perceptual mode group, the subjects experiencing the
experimental condition showed the greater number of nonspecific reactions, though this effect may have been stronger in the Body group. The
similarities and differences in GSR responsivity in the Duke experiments
and those of Zuckerman and Stern are summarized in Table 4-4.

The heart rate measure employed in this experiment was the average
number of heart beats per minute shown by a subject during each five-
minute period of recording. There were no heart rate differences attributable to either overall Body-Field groups or overall Experimental-Con-
trol conditions. There did appear, however, to be a type of interaction
effect between these two variables, in that the Field-dependent experimental (unstructured) subjects showed a higher heart rate than did the
field-controls (Fig. 4-3), while within the Body group it was the control
subjects who had a higher heart rate (Fig. 4-4). This interaction effect,
however, only approached significance.

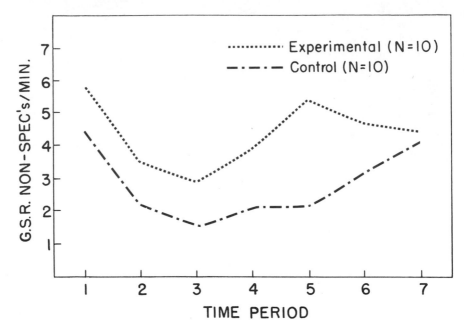

FIGURE 4-2.   Mean number of nonspecific fluctuations in skin re-sistance in experimental and control groups. Reproduced by permission from Culver, Cohen, Silverman, & Shmavonian (1964, Fig. 2, p. 122).

The degree of cognitive structuring appeared to have some effect on subjects' physiological responses to perceptual isolation, although this effect only approached statistical significance. The tendency in both per-

Table 4-4. Frequency of nonspecific GSR in different groups in short-term low sensory input experiments.

Investigator	Finding
Stern (n.d.)	Vigil group > resting group
Zuckerman (1964)	Light and sound deprived > light only or sound only
Cohen, Silverman, et al. (1962a, 1962b)	Field-dependent > field-independent
Reckless, Cohen, et al. (1962, 1964)	Placebo condition field-dependent > field-independent Placebo-field-dependent > stimulant field-dependent Stimulant field-independent > field-dependent Stimulant field-dependent > sedative field-dependent
Culver, Cohen, et al. (1964)	Field-dependent unstructured > field-dependent structured Field-independent unstructured > field-independent structured

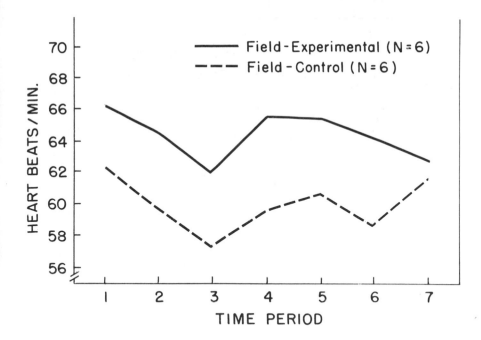

FIGURE 4-3.   Mean number of heart beats in field-experimental and field-control groups. Reproduced by permission from Culver, Cohen, Silverman, & Shmavonian (1964, Fig. 5, p. 124).

ceptual mode groups for a greater number of nonspecific GSRs to occur during the unstructured experimental condition is consistent with the hypothesis that the subjects were in a relatively more alert state than subjects who had received pre-isolation information about the nature of the experiment. However, the suggestion of a differential effect of the experimental and control conditions on the heart rate of the Body and Field groups was unexpected. One explanation would be to suppose that the two conditions were differentially arousing to the two groups in this particular autonomic system. This explanation would be difficult to integrate with the GSR findings. An alternative explanation is suggested by Lacey et al.'s (1958a, 1963) work on situational stereotopy.

   The field-independent subject who is in a situation of reduced visual and auditory stimulation and a lack of orienting information may be more alert when he is informed pre-experimentally (reflected by higher number of GSRs). However, he may be sufficiently comfortable to sit and passively observe the experimental process. (Lacey noted a brachycardia in response to a stimulus which the subject was asked to observe passively although a skin resistance response often occurred with the

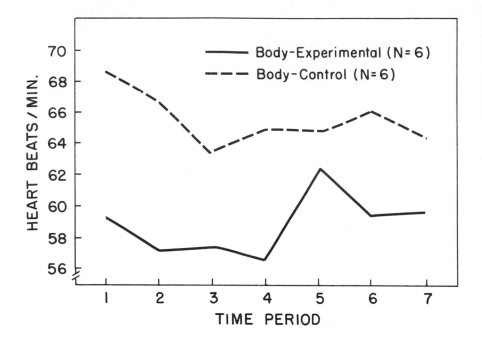

FIGURE 4-4.   Mean number of heart beats in the body-experimental and body-control groups. Reproduced by permission from Culver, Cohen, Silverman, & Shmavonian (1964, Fig. 6, p. 124).

presentation of the stimulus.) When the field-independent subjects were informed about the experiment, some of them may have become more preoccupied with or attentive to internal events, thoughts, fantasies (i.e., generally more internally oriented). This may be analogous to Lacey's findings that subjects asked to carry out active internal problem-solving operations often demonstrated a cardiac acceleration. Lacey hypothesized that a cardio-acceleratory response might diminish the reception of disturbing external stimuli through the effect of increased carotid sinus pressure on electro-cortical activity. The field-dependent subject in an unstructured setting responds more like Stern's subjects who were asked to actively attend to a visual cue. The field-dependent person experienced more subjective discomfort and seemed to have been more actively attentive to environmental stimuli.

Noxious stimuli, vigilance, or problem solving may account for the higher heart rate and GSR in field-dependent subjects in an unstructured setting. However, the main factor accounting for the experimental and control heart rate difference may be the difference in the rates during the first five minutes. The Body control (informed group) had a higher initial rate than the Body experimental group and showed a slight gradual decrease, while the experimental group showed a slight increase. The same finding was noted in the two Field groups, except that the experimental group had a higher initial rate. It may be that the instructions given just before the subject was isolated had a different initial impact on the two perceptual-mode groups which determined the rate differences during the remainder of the experiment. The small groups and low significance levels make the reasoning very speculative and require that more subjects be tested. The influences of environmental-situational and individual variables on heart rate in this and in the Shapiro and Leiderman and Stern experiments are summarized in Table 4-5.

Table 4-5. Mean heart rate in different groups tested in short-term isolation experiments.

Investigator	Finding
Shapiro, Leiderman, and Morningstar (1963)	Individuals in isolation doing task > group interacting during task First experimental session > second experimental session
Stern (n.d.)	Individual in isolation maintaining vigil > individual in isolation resting
Culver, Cohen, et al. (1964)	Field-independent informed > field-dependent informed Field-dependent uninformed > field-independent uninformed Field-independent informed > field-independent uninformed Field-dependent uninformed > field-dependent informed

In another study the responses of subjects given LSD during a two-hour low sensory input experiment were compared to responses of subjects given a placebo (Cohen, Silverman, & Shmavonian, 1962a, b). Very slight differences were noted during the period when minimal stimuli were perceived in the chamber, but rather noticeable perceptual and psychological differences were noted after the two hours of isolation when the subjects were exposed to environmental sensory cues. This suggested that LSD was affecting individual input processes, as suggested by Elkes and others (1957, 1958). However, the LSD and placebo groups did show a few differences during isolation. For example, the LSD group had slightly higher level of GSR and EEG activity and reported more imagery. The imagery appeared to be an elaboration of minimal auditory and visual cues occurring during the experiment. Hence, a psychochemical drug believed to affect visual functions produced reaction patterns similar to that of field-dependent subjects. A recent study by Edwards and Cohen (1965) reported findings similar to some aspects of this experiment in that they also found that two hours of sensory deprivation attenuated the effects of LSD. Subjects tested in sensory deprivation-type conditions who received a placebo showed less physiologic activity than subjects who received LSD. However, the latter groups showed less activation than subjects given LSD and kept in normal sensory conditions.

Witkin's (1962, 1954) findings indicated that the field-dependent subjects were influenced by distracting external signals, such as the position of the frame in judging verticality of a rotating rod within the frame, whereas field-independent subjects were less influenced. He further noted differences in cognitive and personality characteristics in the two groups, with the field-independent subjects showing more aggressive personality characteristics, more active coping, and greater comfort with internal values and drives. These characteristics were reflected in perceptual tasks by the subjects' ability to analyze more actively "figure from the ground." Recently, Witkin has suggested that field-independence is related to the level of psychological differentiation attained and is a function of developmental factors. However, the work at Duke has suggested that the psychological and perceptual differences may also have a foundation in the nervous system.

In the studies conducted by Culver et al. (1964), the two perceptual mode groups showed differences in integrative perceptual tasks, which emphasized the previously noted difficulty in accurately localizing stimuli received on the surface of the skin experienced by field-dependent subjects. Further support to possible CNS differences in some subjects with perceptual mode differences was noted by McGough, Silverman, et al. (1965) in a study in which insulin-induced hypoglycemia was produced in extreme field-dependent and -independent subjects. Following insulin injection, field-independent subjects showed a larger rise in free fatty acids than the field-dependent subjects. Other studies have suggested that free fatty acid is mobilized by sympathetico-adrenal activity. Further, differences in sympathetico-adrenal activity in response to insulin-induced hypoglycemia may in part reflect differences in hypothalamic reactivity. Hence, the lessened response to insulin noted in the field-dependent subjects lent some support to the notion of CNS differences in the two groups.

Studies with aged subjects (Cohen & Shmavonian, in press; Cohen et al., 1961; Bergsman, 1959), revealed that they had less of an increase in urinary adrenaline levels in response to insulin than did young subjects, in spite of similar pre-injection levels. In these studies, there was other evidence suggesting that changes in hypothalamic functioning or sympathetico-adrenal activity were associated with aging. However, the involvement of peripheral tissue, metabolic, and a number of other endocrine factors, cannot be ruled out. This area of research has some relevance to this discussion in that a population of aged subjects tested with the Rod and Frame had a skewed distribution with a predominance of field-dependency. Further, Axelrod & Cohen (1961), and Eisdorfer (1960), report sensory impairments in the aged similar to that shown by field-dependent young subjects (e.g., tactile localization, two-point discrimination).

These findings are reminiscent of Teuber's finding (1959) in brain damaged subjects who showed characteristics on a number of spatial, perceptual, and integrative neurologic tests suggestive of a greater dependence on external signals and a poorer integration of sensory cues. Apter's work (1958) with conditioned reflexes in aging is of interest in that he suggested that aging was associated with poorer differentiation of inhibitory and excitatory stimuli and an increased latency of conditional reflexes. The important implication of the experiments with the aged and brain damaged is not that they demonstrate that extreme field-dependent subjects have deficiencies in CNS function. It is rather that when persons with a mode of orientation similar to that occurring when there is alteration in brain function are exposed to tests and test conditions which highlight the perceptual trait, they give response patterns similar to those of persons with changes in CNS functions.

Differences in personality, spatial-perceptual, and somato-sensory test results, in the response to low sensory input environments, drug agents, and in response to insulin-induced hypoglycemia, suggest CNS reactivity differences associated with perceptual mode. The CNS reaction pattern could possibly be a determinant of the type of response given by subjects under different environmental conditions. The possible neurophysiologic basis of some of the body-field differences was further suggested in the experiment in which subjects given LSD and isolated for two hours had response patterns more similar to the field subjects than persons given placebo capsules (Cohen, Silverman, & Shmavonian, 1962b).

In an attempt further to delineate dimensions of CNS reactivity related to patterns of external sensory stimuli, body- and field-oriented subjects were tested in a conditional reflex experiment. This exploratory study (Hein, Cohen, & Shmavonian, 1965) was designed to highlight so-called inhibitory and excitatory conditional reflex characteristics, as outlined by Pavlov. In part, the investigation was derived from Pavlov's description of inhibitory and excitatory types of nervous systems, since there were a number of similarities in the "personality" and behavioral traits described by Pavlov and the characteristics correlated with different perceptual modes. Although Pavlov's original descriptions of excitatory and inhibitory were referable to motor behavior, more recent research, especially from the Soviet Union, has employed electrophysiological response characteristics of higher CNS activity to classify subjects (cf. Anokhin, 1961; Sokolov, 1960).

Eleven body-oriented and eleven field-oriented undergraduates were tested in an experiment in which colored lights were the CS and shock the US (Hein, Cohen, & Shmavonian, 1965). EEG, GSR, EKG, plethysmographic and respiratory measures were obtained. A 3×5 inch ground glass plate was used to present five colored lights which would remain on for fifteen seconds with a green light being paired with shock during a last five seconds. After twenty adaptation trials, the green light was reinforced for ten presentations, following which there were twenty extinction trials. The mean value of conductance in micromhos of the initial specific GSR response to each light presentation for all subjects showed a leveling off of responsiveness with no differential response to the colors during the adaptation trials, a typical acquisition curve during the shock reinforced trials and differential responsiveness to the green light during extinction. However, when the data were analyzed for field-dependent and field-independent groups, two differences appeared: (1) a faster dropoff in responsivity of the field-dependent subjects during the adaptation period, along with less responsivity during the shock trials; and (2) a larger differential response given to the reinforced green light by the field-independent group during the extinction period. Figure 4-5 shows the nonspecific GSR activity in the fifteen-second pre-stimulus period for the field-dependent and -independent groups through the adaptation, shock trials, and extinction periods. Table 4-6 gives the analysis of the data from the adaptation period.

The field-independent subjects demonstrated more activity—which could be taken to indicate that they responded more appropriately, in that in an unknown situation (during adaptation) they have evidence of

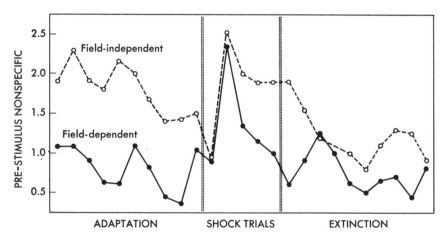

FIGURE 4-5.   Graphs of the number of nonspecific GSR responses during the fifteen seconds prior to each light presentation throughout the experiment. For purposes of simplicity in making the illustration, every other trial is plotted. Reproduced by permission from Hein, Cohen, & Shmavonian (1965, Fig. 3, p. 75).

Table 4-6. Analysis of variance of the nonspecific GSR responses of field-dependent and field-independent groups over time in the adaptation period (see text).

Source	df	MS	F	P
Groups (a)	1	64.00	6.02	< .025
Error$_b$	18	10.63		
Trials (b)	19	1.76	2.23	
AB	19	0.65	<1	
Error$_w$	326	0.79		

SOURCE: Hein, Cohen, & Shmavonian, 1965, 7, 76.
By permission of Plenum Press.

activation, which gradually levels off.[4] As soon as the shock trials begin, they become aroused again and remain aroused as long as the shock is continuing; whereas, the field-dependent group inappropriately starts adapting out to the shock. In the extinction period, the field-independent subjects show arousal initially and then show a decrease, as if they are certain no more environmental stress is forthcoming, whereas the field-dependent people level at a much earlier period.

Table 4-7 shows the analysis of variance of the difference in responsivity between adaptation and extinction to all lights. The data (see Fig. 4-6) demonstrate that the green light elicited larger GSR responses than did other colors for all subjects. There was, however, a differential color responsivity between the two perceptual mode groups. The differential response to color was not significant ($F = 2.24$, $p > 0.1$) in the

Table 4-7. Analysis of variance of the difference in specific responsivity between the extinction and adaptation periods for each of the colored lights for field-dependent and field-independent groups (see text).

Source	df	MS	F	P
Groups (a)	1	0.64	<1	
Error$_b$	20	8.35		
Colors (b)	4	23.24	14.43	< .001
AB	4	7.15	4.44	< .01
Error$_w$	80	1.61		

SOURCE: Hein, Cohen, & Shmavonian, 1965, 7, 76.
By permission of Plenum Press.

[4] These results are similar to those of Stern et al. (1961), who found that differentiation of GSR responsivity was more distinct in subjects who had a higher initial level of GSR activations as reflected by the number of nonspecific fluctuations.

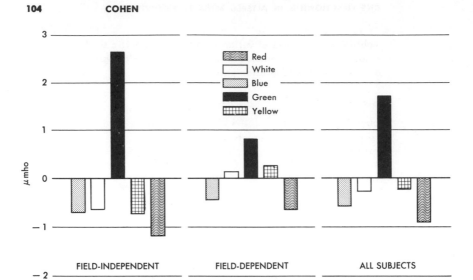

FIGURE 4-6.   Graphs of the value in micromhos of the mean initial specific responses in adaptation subtracted from the mean initial specific responses in extinction for each of the five colors. This was calculated for each subject and averaged together for field-dependent and field-independent subjects. Reproduced by permission from Hein, Cohen, & Shmavonian (1965, Fig. 4, p. 75).

field-dependent subjects, whereas the field-independent subjects exhibited a highly significant differential response to the green light ($F = 16.63$, $p < 0.0001$). The field-independent, when compared with field-dependent subjects, had a greater increase to the green light but did not differ in change in response to other lights.

Courter, Waltanmaker, and Ax (1965) have recently reported that subjects categorized as field-independent on the basis of the closure flexibility test, showed better GSR discrimination between conditioned tones and unreinforced tones than field-dependent persons. They suggest that one explanation of the finding is that a field-dependent person has a less well-differentiated autonomic nervous system.

THEORETICAL EXPLANATIONS OF SENSORY DEPRIVATION PHENOMENA

Zuckerman and Cohen (1964a, b), very neatly summarized the more recent attempts to explain the phenomena in sensory deprivation into four approaches: (1) neurophysiological, (2) cognitive theory, (3) social psychological theory, and (4) psychoanalytic. In addition to commenting on these four categories, a few remarks are included describing some notions of Soviet investigators of the neurodynamic basis for responses in altered sensory environments, following which some of the results of the Duke experiments are discussed.

Neurophysiological.   These explanations point to specific sensory effects and to nonspecific CNS effects. Several investigators have cited Granit's work (1955) in which he shows that spontaneous discharge of the retinal ganglion cells takes place in the dark-adapted eye as well as in the light-adapted eye. Hence, random noise factors may furnish the sensory basis for visual sensations despite the reduction or limitation of external stimulation. Doane et al. (1959) relate visual isolation phenomena to visual sensations noted in cataract cases and to phantom phenomena in amputees. They suggest that sensory deprivation may result in a functional denervation of sensory neurons, leading to a sensitization or lowering of thresholds of neurons further up in the nervous system. This concept is partially supported by the finding that visual sensations typically progress from simple to complex.

Evarts (1962) theorized that the neurophysiological processes which produce hallucinations are similar to those which occur in dreams during sleep. Scheibel & Scheibel (1962) stressed the role of the brain-stem reticular core, in that "the gradual development of visual sensation phenomena may represent simply a normal expression of physiologic function of brain cells whose modulation by specific sensory and nonspecific reticular input drops below a critical level with consequent changes in cell biasing and concomitant increased sensitivity to what is usually background activity" (p. 29). The former theory would suggest that visual sensations occur in stages of light sleep or transitional stages while the latter theory suggests that visual sensations would occur in alert, wakeful stages during perceptual isolation. Leiderman's work (1962) supports Evarts' concept, since his subjects showed imagery as they were *becoming* drowsy or when they were awakening.

West (1962) attempted to integrate the findings of a number of studies in his perceptual release theory, which contains constructs involving sensory input and CNS variables to explain the imagery so frequently reported in sensory deprivation studies. He holds that during wakefulness information input through sensory pathways serves to maintain the organization of scanning and screening activities and, if this is working well, may exclude internal and external information which is undesirable or of low priority. However, if the sensory input is decreased, then its organizing effect is diminished and there is a decrease in reticular activating system stimulation by sensory impulses. This may lead to a decrease of the inhibitory effects usually exerted on perceptual traces, which can thus be released and re-experienced. The two prerequisites for perceptual traces to emerge into consciousness are (1) a sufficient level of arousal for awareness, and (2) the necessity for perceptual trace circuits to fire. In sensory deprivation, then, if external stimulation decreases and CNS arousal is maintained, visual imagery or hallucinatory phenomena may occur. Bridger (1964) feels that the neurophysiological correlates of sensory deprivation share common features with drowsiness and light sleep. He considers sleep to be associated with neocortical inhibition and limbic activation. Further, it has been speculated that this state is associated with interference in reality testing between symbol and object (internal and external referents).

Cognitive theory.   This type of theory, as presented by Bruner (1961), Freedman, Grunebaum, and Greenblatt (1961), and Freedman et al. (1962), suggests that visual imagery may be due to the organism's attempt to maintain ordered relationships in its perceptual environment. Visual sensations may be the result of the organism's attempt to fit the random noise sensations from the retina or inner-ear to previously acquired cognitive schemes.

Work of Mackworth (1956), Freedman, Grunebaum, and Greenblatt (1961), and Freedman et al. (1962) suggests that the effects of altered sensory environments on perceptual functions may be best characterized as a general decrease in the ability to perceive reality—which may be associated with a weakened or a diminished stable "internal norm" against which to evaluate perceptual experiences. The "internal norm" may involve some functional quality of the manner in which external signals or stimuli are received and integrated in the CNS. In part, this may be based on past experiences and the subjective psychological meaning of the stimulus. However, it may also be a function of the neurophysiological characteristics of an individual.

Witkin's finding (Witkin et al., 1962, 1954) that children are initially field-dependent and become more field-independent as they mature, suggests that field-dependency may be associated with a more primitive, less mature, less integrated, or less organized perceptual apparatus or CNS, especially as it concerns integration of external and internal signals and the formation of a stable internal norm.

The concept that differences in CNS functioning exist in field-independent and -dependent subjects as a function of innate or early developmental influences could be enlarged to include the possibility that CNS differences may exist which lead to varying degrees of awareness of cues from the inside and the outside of the body. This differential awareness of cues may influence the *perceptual* mode which later develops. Hence, CNS differences may require a different degree of dependence on cues from the environment. This may then lead to differing behavior response patterns to external events, differences in how other persons are perceived, and differences in interpersonal interactions (e.g., with mother). Personality traits which develop because of these characteristics might later reinforce the individual's perceptual style.

Bruner (1961) has suggested that perception may be seen as an instrumental behavior permitting the organism to manage the necessary transaction with the environment. Successful management of these transactions may depend on acquiring an adequate internal model of the external world, and early deprivation may interfere with the learning of the stable model. The hypothesis is raised whether field-dependent subjects have a less adequate model than field-independent subjects.

Social-psychological theory.   This class of theory was developed by authors, such as Orne and Scheibe (1964), Jackson and Kelly (1962), Jackson and Pollard (1962), and Pollard et al. (1963), who questioned some of the theoretical interpretations of visual sensations because some experimenters have failed to obtain them. They suggest that other variables may be quite influential, such as the subject's knowledge of expected reactions, his motivations to experience and report, and the use of continuous reporting instructions which have a self-suggestive effect. These authors also wonder about the role of specific instructions for certain types of responses which may be more sensitive than others and certain types of visual sensations which may be more responsive to suggestion than others. However, Zuckerman and Cohen (1964a) feel that set alone cannot explain visual or auditory sensations in many of the reported studies.

Psychoanalytic theory.   Authors such as Azima and Cramer (1956), Goldberger and Holt (1958), Goldfried (1960), and Kubie (1961) indicate that isolation leads to a kind of regression which decreases the efficiency of secondary process thinking characterized by logical, problem-solving, goal-directed thinking and increases primary process thinking. Visual imagery may be one aspect of primary process thinking. (Imagery would be explained in a Pavlovian framework as the emergence of primary signals following a decrease in the inhibitory effect of secondary—verbal symbolic—signals.) However, individuals who are severely threatened by primary process may develop anxiety. Goldberger and Holt (1958) correlated a pre-isolation Rorschach measure of controlled primary process with imagery during isolation (0.5). Rapaport (1958) emphasized the abrogation of ego functions as a major determinant of the emergence of primary process.

Zuckerman and Cohen (1964) have concluded that most of the theoretical positions discussed above are not incompatible with each other but could easily incorporate one another. Cognitive and perceptual, psychoanalytic and neurophysiological constructs can be developed into a model which might have some usefulness for testing the influence of altered sensory conditions on complex neural functions.

        Neurodynamic theory.   The effects of isolation and sensory deprivation stressor conditions on CNS functions are explained by Soviet researchers on a neurodynamic basis (Anokhin 1961; Gorbov & Myasnikov, 1963), emphasizing the excitatory state of the cortex. Agents which decrease excitability will release cortical dominance over subcortical centers, providing that these agents do not block the subcortical centers transmitting the exteroceptive reflexes. Insulin hypoglycemia, compensated acidosis, hypoxia, and fatigue are examples of agents which may decrease cortical dominance, while an increase in external sensory stimulation or environmental activity will increase cortical excitability and dominance.

    When cortical dominance is strong, visceral responses, such as cardiovascular, respiratory, and skin potential reaction, are quickly extinguished following a few exteroceptive stimulations. However, when the activity of the cortex is depressed, the visceral reflexes aroused by exteroceptive stimulation are said to persist and to be extinguished slowly after many trials. Hence, physiological changes in altered sensory environments would be a function of the effects of a lowered sensory input on the state of cortical dominance, and subsequently the effect of changed cortical dominance on subcortical centers associated with visceral responsivity. The conceptual model of the CNS which is suggested assumes that integrative processes consist of interactions among various inhibitory and excitatory inputs coming from a variety of areas in the nervous system, peripheral afferents and/or from changes in internal chemical environment.

PERCEPTUAL MODE, CNS REACTIVITY, AND THE RESPONSE TO ALTERED ENVIRONMENTS

    The experiments conducted at Duke suggested that persons with differing perceptual and personality characteristics responded differently to an isolated low sensory input environment. Differences were noted in measures related to central and autonomic nervous system activity, in measures of integrative neurological functions, and in measures of psychological adaptation. The response differences were, in part, a function of how the individual interpreted and reacted to the conditions to which he was exposed.

    The most promising personality variable, according to Zuckerman,

Levine, and Biase (1964), in terms of replicated findings relating to a broad spectrum of various stress responses, is that of field-independence-dependence. This trait has been correlated with endurance, verbalized stress, physiologic aspects of stress, and gross movement. In addition, a number of correlates of perceptual mode have emerged from studies conducted at Duke (see Table 4-8), and a number of other personality

Table 4-8. Response correlates of perceptual mode.

CHARACTERISTIC	PERFORMANCE	
	Field-Independent	Field-Dependent
1. Two-point discrimination	Good	Poor
2. Laterality discrimination	Good	Poor
3. Gottschaldt performance	Good	Poor
4. GSR and EEG activity pre-(LSI)*	High	High
GSR and EEG activity post-(LSI)	Low	High
5. Urinary catechol amines (LSI, CA)†	Frequently high pre-experimentally	Variable
6. Plasma free fatty acids	Consistent	Variable
7. Venous spasm	Seldom	Frequent
8. Behavior (CA, LSI)	High adaptive	Often inappropriate
9. Subjective discomfort (LSI)	Low	High
10. Psychological mechanisms (LSI)	Adaptive	Often denial projection
11. CNS response to		
stimulant (LSI)	Alert	Relax
placebo (LSI)	Relax	Alert
sedative (LSI)	Variable	Relax
12. Cognitive structuring of LSI	Variable	Relax
13. Perception of parents test ‡	MFF	MMM
14. Conditional reflex typology	Excitatory and/or balanced	Inhibitory and/or unbalanced
15. LSD vs. placebo responsivity	Like placebo	Like LSD

* LSI = Low Sensory Input experiment
† CA = Conditioned Avoidance experiment
‡ MFF and MMM refer to which parent is perceived as major source of affection, major source of punishment, and role model respectively.

and perceptual dimensions seem related to perceptual mode characteristics (see Table 4-9). The variables which are presented in Tables 4-8 and 4-9 range over a variety of dimensions, and it may be of some value to attempt to integrate some of these findings in an effort to understand the determinants of an individual's response to altered environmental conditions.

When the data of the field-dependent and -independent subjects in

Table 4-9. Inferred or demonstrated correlates of perceptual mode.

CHARACTERISTIC	PERFORMANCE	
	Field-Independent	Field-Dependent
1. Reisman categories	Inner-directed	Outer-directed
2. Eysenck categories	Introvert	Extrovert
3. Autonomic specificity (Lacey)	Cardiac labile	Cardiac stabile
4. Tolerance of pain (Petrie)	Reducer	Nonreducer
5. Perceptual style (Foa, Holzman, Gardner)	Leveler	Sharpener
6. Perceptual defense style	Sensitizer	Repressor
7. Personologic correlates (Holt)	MMPI, low hypochondriasis and high ego strength	High hypochondriasis and low ego strength
8. Personality correlates (Witkin)	Conform to internal values, not passive or submissive	Conform to external values, passive and submissive
9. Body boundary (Fisher)	Distinct	Diffuse
10. Tactile discrimination, embedded figures in aged and young (Axelrod, Eisdorfer)	Like young	Like aged
11. Conditional reflexes in aging (Apter)	Like young subjects	Like aged subjects
12. Integrative neurologic tests (Teuber)	Like normal controls	Like brain damaged

the conditional reflex experiment were analyzed separately, they differentiated along two dimensions: the first being the greater and more prolonged GSR responsivity to specific external stimuli on the part of the field-independent subjects (which may also be related to an overall heightening of the level of CNS activation which they showed at the beginning of the experiment). The second dimension was a more pronounced differentiation of reinforced from nonreinforced CS in the field-independent group. Whether this represents specific skin response sensitization or the formation of the conditional reflex is an issue which is not a major question at this point.

There would appear to be a parallel between psychological differentiations, as described by Witkin, for the field-independent person and the dimension of greater GSR conditional reflex discrimination in response to reinforced and nonreinforced cues. The relation of peripheral GSR measures to CNS functions is still speculative, but previous work has indicated that nonspecific fluctuations of skin resistance may be related to mesencephalic reticular activating system activity which appears to be associated with such phenomena as attention, perception, and motivation. Lindsley (1961) has pointed out that the reticular activating system serves the homeostatic function of adjusting input and output relationship. Recently, it has been suggested that the reticular formation is concerned with sensory integration—more specifically that it might be involved in a gating-mechanism to sharpen discrimination. It has also been hypothesized that if the reticular formation selectively facilitates recurrent inhibition in sensory nuclei, then its effects on sensory discrimination may be separable from a general arousal function.

The field-independent subjects tended to show a more direct sensory input nonspecific GSR-output relationship. The field-dependent showed a more sustained level of nonspecific GSR during low sensory input and less sustained levels with periodic input during the conditioning experiment, while in the low sensory input experiment, the field-independent began with a high level of nonspecific GSR which fell off much more rapidly than that of the field-dependent.

The field-independent and -dependent subjects both responded to the CS during the trials, but only the field-independent group showed differential responsivity to reinforced versus nonreinforced CS during the extinction period. These responses to the reinforced CS were greater in magnitude in extinction than in adaptation and equal to that during the trials, although the responses to nonreinforced CS were less in extinction than in the adaptation period. Hence, the field-independent subjects showed a highly selective and appropriate response pattern which persisted, in contrast to the field-dependent subjects, who responded to the reinforced CS only when it was reinforced.

One possible explanation is that generalized activation of a more adaptive nature occurs in field-independent subjects, while field-dependent subjects are activated in an environment with a reduction of cues, perhaps as a function of the increased scanning and searching for orienting signals. As Hein, Cohen, and Shmavonian (1965) put it, it is almost as if the homeostatic input-output adjusting mechanism is "frozen." Further, the field-dependent appear to be more stimulus-bound, as reflected by their responding to the CS during the trials but not during extinction. The field-independent continue to respond differentially to the reinforced CS during extinction, almost as if they have acquired a more stable and internal model similar to that described by Bruner (1961) and similar to Sokolov's neuronal model (1960).

It is hoped that the studies now in progress and planned will establish with greater certainty the relationship noted between such dimensions as perceptual mode, CR typology, personality patterns, autonomic specificity, and somato-sensory discrimination. The interaction of individual autonomic response, personality and perceptual differences, and situational factors in influencing physiological and behavioral responses has been shown by a number of investigators. Studies by Lacey et al. (1958a, 1963) and by Callaway & Bruxbaum (n. d.) have been specifically related to the interaction of cardiovascular, perceptual, and behavioral functions.

It has been noted that extreme field-independent subjects show greater variability in cardiac rate than do field-dependent subjects. This correlates with Lacey's findings that subjects who are cardiac labile (persons who show more beat-to-beat variations in cardiac rate) show psychological characteristics similar to those of the field-independent perceptual group. Lacey's research led him to conclude that patterns of heart rate and skin conductance responses are dependent on the tasks or stimuli used. Cardiac deceleration was associated with "external orientation," in which a subject attends to environmental stimuli, whereas cardiac acceleration was associated with "internal orientation," under such circumstances as when subjects are employed in problem solving or are exposed to noxious stimuli (i.e., conditions leading to the rejection of external stimuli). Some of the Duke studies suggested that differences in central and autonomic nervous system reactivity might be associated with perceptual mode, and the question is raised whether CNS reaction patterns are possible determinants of the type of response given by the subjects to different environmental conditions.

Current work at Duke is concerned mainly with verifying and extending the kinds of studies that have suggested that variations in environmental sensory input, different programs of environmental contingencies, specific drug agents, and different attitudinal sets can produce predictable differential response patterns in subjects with differences in perceptual, personality, or autonomic characteristics. However, the long-range aims are concerned with the development of techniques to predict the effects of life situational stress as well as to develop methods to modify these effects by pharmacological agents, cognitive restructuring, or environmental manipulation.

One result of reviewing the studies which have been referred to in this chapter is to identify the fallaciousness of thinking of sensory deprivation as a unified experimental condition and the unreasonableness of attempting to find a single explanatory construct which would ultimately integrate the differing findings in the various experiments. On the other hand, a variety of different types of studies—such as perceptual isolation, administration of psychochemicals, reports from psychoanalysis, reports from blind and deaf patients and patients with toxic clinical disorders, reports from prisoners, pilots and radar operators—have suggested that some similarities exist in the experiences which are reported. It is suggested that a clearer definition of the response phenomena and a clearer delineation of the environmental and individual variables responsible for these phenomena might lead to the understanding of relationships which would lend themselves to the development of improved models of CNS functioning.

Invited commentary

JAMES W. PRESCOTT: In Dr. Cohen's impressive review of data and theoretical positions, he has emphasized three major areas: (1) individual differences, (2) the role of early and prior experiences in perceptual mode and later behavior, and (3) a multidisciplinary orientation, utilizing and integrating information from neurophysiology, biochemistry, a perceptual-cognitive approach, and a socio-developmental view.

I get the impression from this review that early investigators have tended to treat *stress* and measures of *arousal* as equivalent. Such use of *arousal* measures to index stress has marked limitations, on both theoretical and experimental grounds. Apart from the many problems attending the use of peripheral physiological response measures for inferring states of CNS activity (e.g., individual differences as exemplified by the principles of response specificity and stereotypy), there is the inherent limitation of arousal theory in accounting for the many complex behaviors encountered in altered sensory environments.

This problem of inferring states of CNS activity—which is usually equated with *arousal* or *activation* in behavioral studies—can also be appreciated from the studies reported on insulin-induced hypoglycemia and the resultant mobilization of free fatty acids (FFA) via sympathetico-adrenal activity. Since many factors, e.g. muscular exercise, carbohydrate metabolism, and various emotional states can precipitate sympathetico-adrenal activity, the meaning or interpretation of the inferred states of CNS activity may vary considerably. Dr. Cohen has rightly pointed out the possible involvement of peripheral tissue, metabolic, and a number of other endocrine factors in sympathetico-adrenal activity.

Considering that similar end-results (e.g. mobilization of FFA) can be produced by different mechanisms, the often stated conclusion that "CNS differences exist" may prove to be too general to be of value. The broad range of CNS phenomena (hypothalamic and temporal lobe functioning, brain damage, aging, drug reactivity) that Dr. Cohen has related to sensory deprivation and perceptual mode (field-dependency constructs) would seem to support this point of view. In some cases, inferring CNS activity that is of primary concern from a behavioral point of view may be questionable.

Thus, the activity of CNS mechanisms associated with metabolic processes may be unrelated to the activity of those same CNS mechanisms when associated with specific "alerting" processes, such as reticular activation. The point of emphasis is that the activity of specific isolated structures should not be the primary object of interest *per se* but rather the activity of those structures within the context of specific functional systems.

I find myself in disagreement with Dr. Cohen's conclusions, namely, that it is fallacious to think of sensory deprivation as a unified experimental condition and unreasonable to seek a single explanatory construct to integrate the differing experimental findings. On the contrary, I feel that an examination of early experiences which modify and determine, through developmental processes, those neurophysiological structures that mediate perception, learning, motivation, and affect, may provide such an explanatory construct.

I would propose that sensory deprivation—or restricted experiences—in the early critical and formative years of development results in a permanent neurophysiological deficit that manifests itself by chronic "stimulation-seeking" behavior (i.e., undue dependence upon environmental stimulation) for the maintenance of controlled and integrated behavior by the deprived organism. I would call such a condition a "neurophysiological addiction" for sensory stimulation.

Riesen (1961) has shown that normal environmental stimulation after severe early sensory deprivation can result in (a) hyperexcitability; (b) increased susceptibility to convulsive disorder; and (c) localized motor dysfunction. In addition, he reported a case of severe response inhibition which resulted in death. Thus, *hyper-* and *hypo-*excitability can result from restricted early experiences, depending upon its severity and the nature of subsequent stimulation.

The studies of Butler (1953, 1957); Butler and Alexander (1955); Melzack and Thompson (1956); and Melzack and Scott (1957) document the hyperexcitability effects and would seem to support the "addiction" for sensory stimulation hypothesis. In these studies, early experiences in exploratory behavior were highly restricted, with subsequent adult animal behavior characterized by states of hyper-attention to the environment. Recent findings of Arnott (1965) give even more striking support for the stimulation addiction hypothesis. In Arnott's study, cats were born in darkness and remained in a totally deprived visual environment for one year. The animals were then placed in a two-story Skinner box where they could either press a bar for light stimulation on the first floor or go to the second floor of the box for food. Animals were found to bar press continuously from eight to twenty hours per day or to hold the bar down permanently until fatigue intervened. The light reward was preferred to food when the animals were deprived of food for 24 hours, this preference being sustained for the six-month testing period. Similar effects have been reported for maternally-deprived monkeys where somesthetic stimulation from terry-cloth "mothers" was preferred to food (Harlow, 1958).

The distinctions by Witkin et al. (1954), of field-dependent versus field-independent individuals; by Eysenck (1957), of extraverts versus introverts; by Petrie (1960), of nonreducers versus reducers; and by Riesman (1950), of the outer versus inner-directed—are all consistent with the proposed neuro-developmental model that relates early experiences to later perceptual and behavior modes. Hunt (1961), it should be noted, has also assigned a central role to early experience in the development of intellectual and cognitive abilities. Thus, subjects characterized as field-dependents, extroverts, nonreducers, and outer-directed in these theoretical systems should evidence stimulus addictive behavior.

Under conditions of reduced sensory input for such groups it may be hypothesized that compensatory mechanisms of internal stimulation are evoked to maintain a given level of stimulation or CNS excitation. This would account for the greater CNS activation of field-dependent subjects under reduced sensory input, as just reported. The dependency upon environmental stimulation for the maintenance of controlled and integrated behavior by such subjects is manifested by their decrements in spatial-perceptual abilities, impaired discrimination of somato-sensory cues, and general thought disorganization under reduced sensory input, as reported.

The proposed hypothesis might further account for the paradoxical drug effects reported by Dr. Cohen, where field-dependent subjects show a decrease in CNS activation (decreased beta and increased GSR) under stimulant medication. I would suggest that the pharmacological stimulant provides internal stimulation and thus substitutes for environmental stimulation in satisfying the neurophysiological addiction for stimulation. Stimulus-seeking behavior is therefore reduced and the field-dependent subjects manifest a more relaxed psychological and behavioral state.

Since internal and external sources of "stimulation" are multidimensional in nature, a multivariate model, which can account for the many and diverse effects of altered sensory environments upon behavior, seems required. For example, the mechanisms of pharmacological stimulation may differ from the compensatory mechanisms of internal stimulation which were postulated to mediate increased CNS activity under conditions of reduced sensory input. Additionally, the modes of internal stimulation may relate differentially to task performance variables, such that "arousal" level would be affected under one set of conditions and "discriminatory capacity" would be affected in another. The specific and diffuse projection systems of the CNS, in addition to the different mechanisms mediating d-amphetamine and antidepressant "stimulation," for example, support the requirement that "hypothetical constructs" be multidimensional in nature.

The drug effects reported with field-dependent subjects are not unrelated to similar paradoxical drug effects found with some hyperkinetic children. It is known that stimulants have a quieting and sedative effect upon some hyperkinetic children while barbituates produce increased excitation rather than sedation (Fisher, 1959; Eisenberg, 1963). Clearly, the behavior of hyperkinetic children would be classified as "stimulus-seeking" behavior, and, although studies have yet to demonstrate that hyperkinetic children are more field-dependent than normal controls, such a prediction would seem reasonable. We would further expect that restricted early experiences are a major etiological factor in hyperkinetic children, although again, data to confirm this relationship are lacking.

In order to assess the "neurophysiological addiction to sensory stimulation" hypothesis, it is suggested that the *temporal* properties of neural functioning will yield more useful information than the more usual measurement of response *intensity*.

There has been a recent increase of interest in biological rhythms, particularly circadian (approximately 24-hour) rhythms, but there is as yet limited information on the relations of these biological rhythms to human behavior.

Halberg (1962b) has described the roles of external and internal timing and synchronization of circadian rhythms in normal and physiopathologic conditions. He states:

The internal timing of a circadian system describes the time relations among certain of its circadian rhythms themselves; it may be expressed as a difference in time units, e.g., in hours, inter alia, between peaks, troughs or slopes of 2 rhythms. Study of internal timing, by definition, calls for the concomitant evaluation of two or more physiologic functions: the multivariate approach.

External timing is largely adaptive and entirely flexible as to clock hour—so long as the synchronizer's cycle length is acceptable to the system. Internal timing, subservient to functional integration as well, shows considerable although not unlimited plasticity. Circadian charts, descriptive of external and internal timing, reveal the organism's adapted time structure along a 24-hour scale.

. . . More often than not, circadian systems are indeed synchronized with some environmental change such as a light-dark cycle or social routine. The synchronizing environmental change has been referred to as "cue," time-giver, "clue" or entraining agent, as well as "synchronizer" (pp. 56–57).

Halberg (1962b) postulates that circadian desynchronization (internal or external) reflects a physiopathological state. He demonstrates *external* desynchronization of a circadian rhythm (rectal temperature) from the lighting cycle by experimentally blinding the animals. Rectal temperature in such animals was found to be consistently shorter than 24 hours, and this shortening of the circadian temperature rhythm was considered to be an additional criterion of the physiopathological state. It was emphasized that *internal* desynchronization can also occur, i.e. "the appearance of different circadian periods in two or more previously synchronized functions of the same physiologic system" (p. 59)— e.g. heart rate and body temperature changes which are normally "in phase" (i.e., maximal and minimal points coincide).

Halberg (1962b) summarizes: "The reference function in studies of desynchronization can be chosen from within a circadian system as well as from without. Accordingly, circadian desynchronization is internal or external and the former as well as the latter may be associated with disease" (p. 69).

Hauty (1962) demonstrated that a subject who failed to adapt his biological rhythms (heart and respiratory rate) to a new eight-hour day (i.e., four hours rest, four hours work), showed progressive deterioration of performance through a 168-hour confinement. More significantly, this was accompanied by desynchronization of heart and respiratory rate. Conversely, the subject who maintained synchronization of heart and respiratory rate and who also synchronized his biological rhythms with the new eight-hour day maintained performance proficiency throughout a 168-hour confinement (condition of continuous bright light).

Hauty's study demonstrated the effects of altered sensory environments upon biological rhythms and their intimate relation to human performance capabilities. It is suggested that the ability to adapt circadian biological rhythms to new cycles is primarily a function of biological conditionability and that organisms are equally dependent upon the *cyclic* nature of environmental stimulation as well as the *levels* of environmental stimulation for normal integrated behavior.

Thus, we could expect that field-dependent subjects, being less conditionable than field-independent subjects, would be characterized by greater disruption of their circadian rhythms when the cyclic environmental cues are either altered or eliminated.

It is possible that the *stress process* may be reflected in the disruption of the neural-temporal organization of physiological processes (desynchronization of biological rhythms), and consequently, circadian desynchrony under conditions of sensory isolation may be worth exploring as a measure of stress-proneness.

The delayed conditioning paradigm employed at Duke offers another useful technique for the monitoring of stress-proneness, since it permits the assessment of the *temporal* processes of CNS activity associated with the formation of CRs. I do not believe, however, that they fully exploited their conditioning technique. In delayed conditioning studies, the CRs of interest are to be found at the point in time of reinforcement from CS onset, e.g., given a fifteen-second delay of reinforcement, CRs will appear approximately fifteen seconds after CS onset, not immediately after stimulus onset (Prescott, 1965). Pavlov (1927) has described and documented the phenomena of delayed CRs associated with the internal inhibition of delay. Consequently, it is questionable whether responses occurring at points in time other than that defined by when reinforcement is applied can be considered CRs which are equivalent to those defined at the point in time of reinforcement. Clearly, the multidimensionality of CRs is an unsolved problem.

The delayed conditioning paradigm, however, is a powerful technique to assess neural timing mechanisms. For example, measures of the mean and variance of CRs developed at the point in time of reinforcement would reflect the precision of neural timing in the mediation of these CRs.

These measures could then be related to the precision of circadian synchronization and to the prediction of an organism's ability to be conditioned to new noncircadian periodicities.

The results of the conditioning studies previously cited are extremely intriguing from yet another point of view, for they permit an interpretation within adaptation-level theory (Helson, 1959, 1964). A major postulate of this system (cf. Bevan, 1963), the principle of "pooling," is relevant to the conditioning process. Briefly, "pooling" processes or mechanisms (integration of sensory experiences) establish an internal norm or adaptation level (AL) with which all ongoing stimulation is compared and evaluated. Thus, the value of a given stimulus is dependent not only upon its own physical magnitude but upon the internal norms of the organism being stimulated.

From the above described principle, Bevan and Adamson (1961) have generated a reinforcement model that defines the effectiveness of a reinforcer as a function of (a) the difference between the primary (reinforcing) stimuli and the established internal norm or background (AL) level; and (b) tension level of the organism, which is related to performance according to the Yerkes-Dodson law.

The lack of conditioned discrimination by field-dependent subjects can be accounted for in terms of the Bevan-Adamson reinforcement model in the following manner. Briefly, field-dependent subjects' (FDs) "background level" or established norm is postulated to more nearly approximate the level of focal or environmental stimulation than that of field-independent subjects (FIDs). Consequently, effective reinforcement is reduced for FDs and poor conditioning results. The maintenance of minimal differences between background level of activity and primary stimulation by FDs would also account for their lesser responsivity to shock and their greater habituation. The decreased "tension-state" of FDSs, as measured by their small number of nonspecific GSRs, is also consistent with the obtained poor conditioning of FDSs, as would be predicted by the model.

The ability to relate *AL* theory to lack of conditionability in FDs provides a link to extend *AL* concepts to altered sensory environments, stimulus-seeking behavior (continual process of establishing and equating internal norms with level of environmental stimulation), and neurophysiological deficits associated with restricted early experiences.

Further, the necessity to postulate differences in pooling mechanisms between FDs and FIDs suggests that the development of perceptual mass and its subsequent role in the interpretation of sensory stimuli may prove to be a fruitful area of research in accounting for the effects of altered sensory environments upon behavior.

Discussion

Dr. Ruff: Dr. Cohen's fine review has focused primarily on studies which have been stressful. But I know Dr. Cohen would agree that many studies of sensory deprivation are not stress studies. For example, in our work (see Chapter 11), a majority of subjects have enjoyed the experience and have not shown psychophysiological changes indicating stress. Furthermore, some procedures labeled as sensory deprivation probably shouldn't be considered as sensory deprivation studies at all. In one experiment Dr. Cohen referred to, subjects were put in a dark chamber for sixty minutes. Under one condition they paid attention to a light; under the other, they didn't. It was found that in the non-vigilance condition, the heart rate was lower. But if you go through the report, you could remove every reference to sensory deprivation. It was neither an independent nor dependent variable. What the experiment did was to compare a task with rest on several psychophysiological variables. The lack of light and sound could simply have been summarized in the description of method as one of the experimental conditions.

Dr. Cohen: I certainly agree. The study in question was included because it was listed as a sensory deprivation study, having been executed under a grant supporting sensory deprivation research.

Dr. Sells: In Dr. Prescott's critique he makes reference to neurophysiological deprivation. I wonder why he wouldn't settle for experience deprivation and what evidence he has that it is truly a neurophysiological deficit and not merely a deficit in experience.

Dr. Prescott: There are several studies that document the effects of light deprivation upon the morphological, electrophysiological, and biochemical properties of neural tissue.

Wiesel and Hubel (1963) found that unilateral visual deprivation in the cat produced marked histological changes in the lateral geniculate body and that these changes were identified in the specific layers of the geniculate which received afferent connections from the deprived eye. Electrophysiological activity of single cells was also altered, as determined by micro-electrode techniques. Additionally, kittens which were deprived of patterned visual experience for a few months manifested serious visual field disorganization with gross anatomical changes in the visual elements.

Chow, Riesen, and Newell (1957) demonstrated that degeneration of ganglion cells occurs in infant chimpanzees reared in darkness. Schimke (1959) raised rabbits in the dark and demonstrated changes in enzymatic activity of retinal ganglion cells. Brattgard (1952) also raised rabbits in the dark and found changes in the nucleo-protein fraction and size of retinal ganglion cells. He concluded that adequate sensory stimulation during the early postnatal period was essential for the normal development of nerve cells, their metabolism, and chemical composition.

Gyllenstein, Malmfors, and Norrlin (1965) demonstrated in growing mice, which were reared in darkness from birth, a highly significant decrease in the relative volume of internuclear material in a number of visual centers. The decrease was greatest in the geniculate bodies and in the granular and supra-granular layers of the cortex as compared to the infragranular layer. Highly significant decreases in the thickness of the visual cortex and in the diameter of its cell nuclei were also reported. Since the effects of visual deprivation were reported to be greater in the lateral geniculate bodies than in the superior colliculi and the cortex, it was hypothesized that nonvisual functions in the visual cortex increase during and after deprivation. The existence of more non-visual afferent connections to the cortex and superior colliculi support this interpretation.

Although these studies have been confined to the visual system, it seems highly likely that similar effects could be demonstrated in other sense modalities. I've been particularly intrigued by the possibility of finding irreversible neurophysiological and neurochemical changes in brain structures that mediate affect and emotion (limbic system) for animals that have been socially and maternally deprived. Unfortunately, Harlow has not conducted histological studies of his experimental animals, so far as I am aware. Positive findings in this area would go a long way in establishing a scientific basis for penal reform, for example, in the treatment of certain behavioral disorders. Quay (1965), for example, has provided a psychophysiological rationale for psychopathic behavior, namely, pathological stimulation-seeking behavior related to abnormal adaptation to sensory stimulation.

Experience deprivation is a good term; however, its effects must be ultimately referable to neural processes and particularly when such deprivation occurs during critical periods, i.e., when neural growth and development is most rapid. If we can interpret experience in its broadest sense, then we can include the internal environment, i.e., the biochemistry of the individual.

We are all too familiar, for example, with the irreversible effects of hypothyroidism in infants, resulting in cretinism. Hypothyroidism in adults, on the other hand, results in symptoms of myxedema, which are reversible with proper treatment. Another example of the hypersensitivity of the developing organism to "experiences" is the teratogenic effects of thalidomide which occur when the drug is administered during the first trimester of pregnancy. This temporal specificity is in many ways quite remarkable and highlights the issue under discussion.

In short, certain experiences may prove disastrous early in life and benign later in life. The problem of relating individual differences in experience to neuro-structural and neuro-chemical development and to subsequent behavioral patterns is an enormous but essential task for the behavioral sciences.

Dr. Sells: Dr. Cohen has tried to generalize experimental findings to life situations and to life stresses, as, for example, to shipwrecks. In the life situation, the components of social isolation, confinement, sensory deprivation, danger, and threat, are usually combined rather than isolated. When you go into the laboratory and control these other components out and try to get down to just the variables with which you are concerned, do you not feel that the results you obtain may be of an order which is small in comparison to the differences you would get when these other components are thrown back in the situation to which you are attempting to generalize?

Dr. Cohen: I can tell you how we would like to deal with that problem ideally, though not necessarily how we have dealt with it. I quite agree that the experimental paradigms we have used are contrived experimental situations. At best, they represent components of life situations and they may not even be realistic components. I briefly alluded to three kinds of experiments: changed sensory conditions, conditional reflex type experiments, and drug studies, and the next stage of research which involves a combination of these conditions. For example, the two perceptual mode groups might be conditioned prior to being placed in an altered sensory environment. The subjects might be given the trials prior to two hours of deprivation, isolation, uncertainty, and then the extinction period given after, or the subjects might be placed in a low sensory input situation for two hours and then given the trials. Later designs would include the administration of drugs before and after training. This still doesn't answer the point, of course, because the situation is still artificial and contrived.

Let me back up for a moment to indicate that one of the reasons we began two-hour low sensory input experiments (which have now been conducted with 250 subjects) was to have a distribution of responses on a number of measures in our laboratory for a period of time similar in length to that of most of our acute experiments. One of the problems we chronically have to deal with is with what should we compare the bio-electric, endocrine, and psychological responses in our subjects. We didn't have a population of normal responses, or an actuarial table of physiological data for our laboratory conditions. Further, we really didn't know what the characteristic patterns of the GSR and the heart rate were over a two-hour period under the experimental conditions that we used.

Hence, one of our first goals was to test a large number of subjects, who represented a broad distribution of various perceptual and personality characteristics, during conditions where external sensory input was kept at a minimum. We have also been interested in collecting the same type of "actuarial" data in conditioning studies, where the environmental input was programmed. Naturally we couldn't define the subject's response, only the environmental input. Some might call these studies base lines, but it isn't really base line information. It is merely establishing the range and distribution of physiological responses over a two-hour time period.

We are now initiating a program to collect systematically the same type of data from individuals in a hospital setting for a similar time period, using the same kinds of environmental conditions. Later we plan to study response patterns for similar time periods during other natural life conditions. I realize that doesn't answer the question but hopefully it makes clear what our goals are.

Dr. Sells: It is clear that if we are to pursue the study of stress we must go beyond the laboratory analogues of stress. Although Dr. Cohen is correct in pointing out that we need normative data, it is equally clear that we need more and better studies of life situations and life stresses.

Dr. Cohen: My associates and I were and still are interested in this. Where we bumped into the stone wall was our inability to be certain of what short-time samples of physiological measures meant, since we lacked data on intra-individual variability, inter-situation variability, and inter-individual variability.

Dr. Lazarus: I would like to raise some question about the meaning of field-dependence and field-independence. As used by Dr. Prescott, field-dependence sounds like a loaded, value-oriented word, with the implication of a physiological defect in such individuals. When we consider the evolutionary aspects, the implication is even stronger. The studies that have been described hardly deal with the extremes of the distribution of field-dependence and body-dependence. Therefore, we are getting into dangerous water in talking about these tendencies in terms of capacities. It seems to me that any performance may be maladaptive in one task or setting and adaptive in another. Thus, referring to field-dependence as a defect of capacity is, I think, highly misleading.

Chairman's summary

JOSEPH M. NOTTERMAN: It has not only been instructive but rather reassuring for me, as a nonpsychophysiological psychologist, to have followed this discussion. I have learned that the problems presented by *stress* are only special cases of the general problems that concern experimental psychologists by and large.

It seems to me that the term *stress* is used to describe two broad sets of behavioral operations. One of these is an examination of the consequences of aversive stimulation, both of an unconditioned and conditioned sort. These stress phenomena clearly fall into the domain of negative reinforcement and may well lend themselves to examination by means of the familiar Pavlovian conditioning, escape, and avoidance paradigms. The second broad set of behavioral operations is one with which I, at least, am less familiar. It deals with the consequences of aversive *non*stimulation, in terms of either reduction or constancy of stimuli. Perhaps it is not too great an exaggeration to say that were it not for the assiduous investigation of the peculiar phenomena of aversive non-stimulation, research in conditioning, learning, and perception would still be proceeding on the basis of overly-simplified homeostatic models of behavior.

This brings me to my second major impression: scientists doing work in the field of stress all rely upon one or another adaptive, or feedback, or self-regulating, or servo-mechanistic view of the behaving biological organism. Dr. Cohen called attention to this early in his paper. Dr. Prescott's emphasis upon biological rhythms is, of course, an even more sharply focused attempt to use the self-regulating system as a means toward understanding stress, for biological synchrony could not be maintained without appropriate deviation-detecting and deviation-correcting processes.

I cannot let this opportunity pass, however, without remarking that what seems to be true of the field of experimental psychology in general is also true of the field of stress research in particular. Although everyone knows that the biological organism does not respond in simple yes-no open loop fashion to presentations of on-off stimuli, we tend to design our research in this convenient binary digital manner. Dr. Trumbull and I made some observations along these lines several years ago (1959), and, barring certain notable exceptions—as illustrated by Dr. Lacey's brilliant contribution to this volume—the situation today seems largely the same. What makes this more than a matter of individual research prejudice is a plain fact: if our behavior does indeed rest upon physiological and behavioral feedback loops, then we can further assume that these systems are probably complicated by nonlinearities. This, in turn, means that even though step-function inputs may lead to step-function outputs—the way a rat can be trained to press a bar when a light comes on, and not press when the light is off—there is little likelihood that such demonstration has any predictive value for the organism's analogue responses to changing, or time-variant, stimuli. This is especially the case if we complete the loop in terms of providing an experimental situation in which the organism's physiological or behavioral output feeds back to the input, and thereby joins in determining the ensuing moment's stimulus value.

Is stimulus poverty stressful because of the low absolute level of stimulation, or is it stressful because of the absence of changing stimuli, or is it stressful because of the open loop character of the stimulus environment? Dr. Cohen's discussion of the field-independent versus the field-dependent subjects certainly reveals concern for this question, and extends it to the relative roles played by exteroceptive, kinesthetic, and CNS feedback loops. It should be apparent that we cannot solve adaptive, closed loop problems with nonadaptive, open loop techniques.

5

Stress and emotion

Before we go into the relation between stress and emotion, let us recall our understanding of the term *stress*. Selye, to whom we owe the concept of stress in biology, first applied the term to extreme disturbances: traumatic shock, shock from burns or loss of blood. Later, when the "General Adaptation Syndrome" (GAS) was recognized in more and more instances, stress came to be thought of as the result of almost any environmental interference. Unfortunately, as Beach (1950) said, "if the word is going to refer to everything from homeostatic mechanisms . . . to cerebral activity . . . , we are apt to arrive at a very inclusive but equally indefinite concept" (p. 119).

Originally, Selye defined stress as the "biologic equivalent of physical stress"; as the result of "the interaction between a force and the resistance opposed to it." But in the functioning of an organism there is always an interaction between a force and the resistance to it. Breathing, opening or closing the eyes, speaking, even standing and lying down, involve an interaction between force and resistance. So do organismic processes like blood flow and digestion. If every instance of normal functioning involves stress, the concept has lost all meaning.

Surely, if the biological equivalent of the physicist's definition of stress really is the force and resistance involved in normal functioning, we would have to find a different term for the stress that disturbs normal functioning and brings about a "stress syndrome." This is even more true for psychological functioning. Normal physiological functioning requires the integrated activity of various organ systems but also a normal rhythm of waking and sleeping. The minimal waking activity of the individual man or animal is to find food and eat it. That means looking for food, and wanting it, which implies emotion and goal-directed action even in the animal. In man, it also implies planning, thinking,

and deliberate choice of action: a man may get food by growing vege-
tables and keeping pigs, but also by directing a symphony or giving a
lecture.

We could go further and say that the emotions included in this
chain of normal functioning are all positive emotions: we want something, we enjoy finding it, we take pleasure in having it. Or to put it in
another way: so long as we feel positive emotions, psychological functioning is smooth, carried on with optimal dispatch. When planning
meets no obstacle, there is no sense of pressure, no necessity for extra
effort, no stress. Normal physiological functioning means that every
organ and organ system is healthy and can utilize the materials supplied
from outside for the maintenance and repair of the organism. On the
biochemical level, normal functioning means a dynamic balance between
various hormones and enzymes.

But normal functioning may be disturbed. If plan after plan mis-
carries and the goal seems more and more difficult to obtain, we are
aware of stress and frustration. We may react with increased effort and
usually with emotion. On the physiological level, such disturbance is
experienced as discomfort, malaise. It can come about either as an interference with normal functioning (e.g., eating something that disagrees)
or as an increased demand on the organism's resources (being prevented
from sleeping, exposed to intense heat or cold). An interference with
normal functioning can also come about through lack of a necessary
hormone or enzyme, or their too abundant supply.

We could say, then, that stress should be called any condition of
disturbed normal functioning. Consequently, the organismic reaction in
stress is the *extra*-ordinary, intensified activity that is required to counter-
act the disturbance and restore normal functioning. Such extraordinary
activity often includes goal-directed action—pain arouses an urge to escape, anger, an urge to fight. Thus, emotion is aroused together with the
organic changes that are implied when we speak of the "stress syndrome,"
whenever we experience psychological stress. Such a definition of stress as
a disturbance of normal functioning, an extra load to be handled, is in
agreement with common usage and also with Selye's original use of the
term. During shock, the organism is all but overwhelmed and will rally
only if vital reactions produce resistance.

When the organismic balance is disturbed by an invasion of bacteria,
by severe cold or heat, there is a subjective experience of discomfort and
unpleasantness. When a man's psychological functioning is severely disturbed by suffering a loss, be it of his love, his job, or his fortune, or
when he cannot achieve what he wants, he also experiences a disturbance.
This psychological stress, however, is accompanied by *emotions* (the most
obvious of which are grief, fear, anger) while physiological stress of any
kind is merely accompanied by *feelings,* varying from discomfort to pain,
depending on the organismic state. Consequently, some emotions are

invariably connected with stress, but that does not mean that psychological stress can be equated with emotion. There are many emotions that have nothing to do with stress (love, joy, delight). Nor can physiological stress be equated with feelings; pleasantness, for instance, does not stem from stress.

The emotions that do accompany psychological stress are what I have called *contending* emotions: primarily anger and fear and their combinations. Because of its reassuringly scientific ring, the notion of psychological stress has in recent years tended to supplant the term *emotion*. But however objective its sound, psychological stress is necessarily subjective. What one man may take in stride, another finds exhausting. What is at most a slight delay for A may be a severe frustration for B. It could even be said that psychological stress occurs only when a man is aware of disturbance and feels some contending emotion.

In one sense, every action implies either positive or negative emotions. Only when we want something will we bother to move toward it. Only when we dislike something do we bother to avoid it. If we are completely indifferent to anything, we simply leave it aside and move toward something else. But the minimal emotion needed for action is part and parcel of our daily living. Without it, there would be no attention, no interest, no action. Usually we pay no particular attention to these fleeting likes and dislikes and are convinced that we go about our business in a strictly objective, unemotional way.

The evaluation that leads to an emotion is intuitive, almost automatic; we are not aware of it as an appraisal but merely as a liking or dislike, a favorable or unfavorable inclination toward something. Only by later reflection can we come to see that some kind of evaluation is involved in every encounter with the environment. Whatever it is we see or experience, we have to see it in relation to ourselves: what does this mean to me here and now?

This evaluation, experienced as liking or disliking, arouses an action tendency felt as a simple inclination or an intense urge to a particular action. This is the emotion. Accordingly, an emotion can be defined as a felt tendency away from something appraised as harmful, unsuitable, or burdensome or toward something appraised as pleasurable, beneficial, useful (Arnold, 1960). These emotional action tendencies accompany our reflective evaluation of the situation and will lead to action unless the actions to which emotion urges are reflectively appraised as unsuitable and the whole situation is re-evaluated. Usually, we become aware of these action tendencies as emotions only when they are intense. Only when something is appraised as a definite obstacle to be overcome, a real danger to be avoided, will the resulting emotion be intense enough to be noticed. If all we experience is a slight wanting or a slight dislike we often do not even realize that it is emotional in nature.

What is eventually done about the situation depends entirely on the subjective evaluation, though not always on the emotion. One man may decide to eliminate an obstacle by force, another may prefer to avoid it, a third to circumvent it. Whether a particular difficulty is felt as psychological stress, appraised as a threat, and results in contending emotion, depends entirely on the individual's intuitive estimate of the situation. And this depends on his state of mind as much as on the objective situation. He may avoid a slight threat yet decide to fight a serious danger. The same threat may arouse fighting anger in one man and abject fear in the next. A third man may simply decide to face the obstacle and go about his business despite frustration; his emotion may pull him one way but his efforts to cope with the situation may force him to an action he dislikes though he realizes it has to be done.

We cannot really speak of psychological stress without considering this subjective evaluation, for what is stress for one man may be a welcome challenge to another. A situation may be considered under several aspects, and the appraisal will change according to the aspect considered. We may consider the possible danger involved in it; and the more our attention is captured by it, the greater the danger will seem until finally we feel it cannot be overcome and must be avoided at all costs: the emotion produced by such an appraisal will be fear. Or we consider ways and means of coping with the difficulties involved and finally feel confident that we can overcome them: the emotion will be confidence, courage, even audacity. Or, when the danger is not a mere possibility but is imminent (for instance in a hand-to-hand fight) we may either concentrate on overcoming it, and the emotion will be anger; or we may concentrate on the impossibility of overcoming what is already upon us (e.g., when taken prisoner), and the result is dejection. While these emotions do not determine the action that will be taken, because reflective judgment may correct the intuitive judgment, they do determine the physiological effects and will influence the decisiveness with which action is undertaken. A man who has appraised some difficulty as serious but is confident of overcoming it will meet the situation with courage which increases his chance of succeeding. The man who feels the situation is hopeless will barely make an effort and, when that is not immediately successful, feel justified in giving up. In the first case, stress will be overcome with a minimum of disturbance. In the second, the disturbance will be profound and the outcome uncertain even when his resources are considerable. Thus, the *conditions* of the intuitive appraisal or rather the *aspects* of the situation being appraised determine the emotion, though not necessarily the action. Though emotions influence the action and its outcome, they do not immediately lead to action. Over and above the intuitive appraisal, human beings also appraise each situation reflectively, on the basis of their convictions and knowledge as well as on the basis of an immediate attraction or repulsion. For this reason, emotions are not "coping" responses. Some emotions help us to cope with the situation (e.g., anger, confidence), others hinder coping action (e.g., fear, embarrassment, grief). But contending emotions do indicate that the situation has been appraised as stressful. Indeed, such emotions seem to be as reliable as signs of psychological stress as the "alarm reaction" is of physiological stress.

For the scientific investigation of psychological stress, there is a genuine advantage in starting our analysis from contending or stress emotions rather than from stress itself. Stress is accessible to analysis only after it has been perceived and assessed, and this assessment is indicated by the emotion. In starting from the emotion, we save ourselves the difficulty of finding a criterion of stress and have the advantage of knowing that a man exposed to stress really experiences it.

There are many ways in which psychological stress can be investigated. My own interest has been to discover, first, what are the physiological effects of stress emotions like anger and fear, and second, what is the neural pathway that mediates these as well as other emotions. I propose to show that at least in these problems a phenomenological analysis of the way stress emotions come about is of inestimable advantage.

Physiological effects of anger and fear

According to Cannon (1915), all emotions have the same physiological state. But phenomenologically this is hard to accept. Psychological experience surely is not something so isolated from the physiological state that we can have two distinct psychological experiences (anger or fear) while the physiological state remains the same. It is part of the experience of anger that we feel full of energy and wrath, are flushed and excited; and it is part of the experience of fear that we tremble, that our knees threaten to give way, and it becomes difficult to think and speak. In recent years, these different experiences have actually been found to have a different physiological basis. Ax (1953), for example, has found that anger and anxiety (or fear) are accompanied by very different patterns of physiological changes. And Wolff (1950a) has reported that the mucous membranes of nose and stomach redden and swell during anger and may become congested to the point of hemorrhage. In fear, on the other hand, the mucous membranes of nose and stomach are pale and shrunken. Apparently, fear (like cold) has primarily adrenergic effects; and so does exhausting exercise and adrenaline injection. In contrast, anger (like heat, injections of mecholyl or insulin) seems to have primarily cholinergic effects. Thus, physiological observations confirm our experience that fear and anger are not only different but even opposed in their physiological effects.

Psychological experience also makes it seem unlikely that every type of "stressor" produces essentially the same three stages of organismic reaction as described in Selye's "General Adaptation Syndrome." Selye attributed the differences sometimes found in the initial phase to specific effects of stressor and various "conditioning" factors. However, the general effects of stress seem to show certain similarities among a group of stressors. Since the primary effect of *adrenergic* stressors differs from that of *cholinergic* stressors, the final or exhaustion phase should differ also. This is actually the case in heat and cold. During exposure to cold or forced exercise, a marked shrinking of thymus gland, lymph nodes, and spleen is found in the first phase of the GAS. During the second or resistance stage, their size returns to approximately normal, but in the third or exhaustion stage, thymus and spleen shrink even more than they did during the first stage. In contrast, during exposure to severe heat, the spleen becomes enlarged, returns to normal on recovery, but shows a further enlargement if the animal finally succumbs to heat (Selye, 1950). Thus, the effect of cold or heat is compensated for during the second phase, but becomes again apparent during the third or exhaustion phase. Since the first and last phases of the "Adaptation syndrome" show sharp differences between adrenergic and cholinergic stressors, there cannot be one always identical GAS to physiological stress; rather, there must be a reaction that is adapted to two different types of stressors.

Thus the subjective experience of anger when compared to the subjective experience of fear seems to have given us a clue to the differences that exist in the physiological state accompanying these emotions and also to the type of organismic reaction necessary to restore normal equilibrium.[1]

Nervous pathways mediating stress emotions

And now let us turn to the second question, namely, how psychological stress and stress emotions are mediated. Whatever the central mediation of physiological stress, whether the signals leading to the GAS are primarily of nervous origin or whether they are mediated by the circulatory system, there is no doubt that the psychological evaluation of a stress situation must be mediated by the CNS. Here again, there is a genuine advantage in starting with a phenomenological analysis of experience. No matter how popular a strictly objective approach may be, we are now dealing with the no-man's land between stimulus and response, the black box to which the behaviorist has lost the key. What goes on psychologically before action is undertaken must be mediated by the nervous system; but to identify the structures that mediate such

[1] For a more extensive discussion of this problem see Arnold, 1960, ch. 7.

processes, we must first work out the exact sequence of psychological activities from perception to action.

When we refuse to make this preliminary phenomenological analysis and depend exclusively on neurological research to provide clues, we are bound to go astray. One example of an hypothesis based on neurological findings without psychological analysis is, for instance, the activation hypothesis, discussed in Chapter 2. This was at least partially supported by the finding that destruction of the reticular formation in the brain stem and the thalamic reticular nuclei produced animals that were awake only for the brief periods of sensory stimulation (Magoun, 1954). Since these first experiments were reported, further research has established that some cells in these areas are active in every sense experience; that is, visual stimulation may activate the same cells that are activated also by auditory or somesthetic stimulation. Moreover, it has been found that sensory stimulation produces electrical potentials in the reticular formation 7–14 milliseconds later than in the sensory pathways at the same level of the brain stem (Collins & O'Leary, 1954). Since the collaterals from the sensory pathways to the reticular system are extremely short, the relays to the reticular formation must have travelled not over these collaterals but over a rather roundabout circuit. This suggests that the function of the reticular system is far more complicated than a simple "activation" of the brain.

I would like to take you now very briefly through a phenomenological analysis of emotion to demonstrate the rationale we are following in a series of experiments which we hope will give us more information about the pathways active in the psychological experiences from perception to emotion and action.

When we encounter a frustrating situation, we perceive it over various sense modalities, but we must appraise it in relation to ourselves before we can deal with it. This evaluation is unwitting, intuitive, experienced merely as a liking or disliking, or even as a positive or negative attitude, though it can also be reflective. It is based not only on the immediate sense experience but also on *what we remember* of similar situations and their effects on us; only in this way is it possible to decide that this thing or person is to be approached or avoided, and just what is the best way to meet it. Even to attend to something, to explore it, to recall relevant data, we must find it worthwhile in some way. Whatever is experienced must be assessed in its relation to us before we can think, remember, act. Consequently, we arrive at this sequence: sense experience, appraisal (that this is good to know or explore), recall of relevant earlier experiences, affective recall; next the appraisal that this thing or situation (now identified) is dangerous, annoying, burdensome—which produces a tendency to flee, strike out in anger, withdraw in shock; these stress emotions urge to action, but renewed recall of past actions and the expectation of possible consequences will lead to an appraisal of action possibilities and eventually to the choice of behavior that seems appropriate.

On the basis of this analysis and an exhaustive review of relevant research data, I have suggested (Arnold, 1960, 2) that appraisal is mediated by the limbic system (subcallosal, cingulate, retrosplenial, and

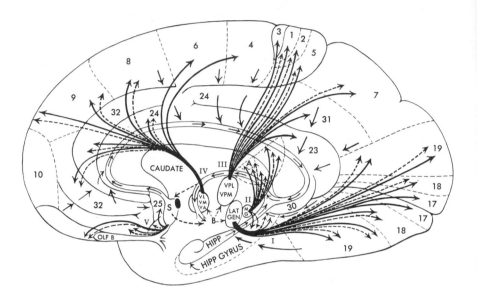

————reception and registration. – – –recall. (Arrows indicate the direction of conduction. Short arrows indicate the connections for appraisal and recall.) **I** visual system. **II** auditory system. **III** somesthetic system (including taste). **IV** motor system. **V** olfactory system. Arabic numerals represent Brodmann areas. **A** cortical auditory area. **B** brain stem. **HIPP** hippocampus. **LAT GEN** lateral geniculate nucleus. **MG** medial geniculate nucleus. **OLF B** olfactory bulb. **S** septal area. **VA** anterior ventral nucleus. **VM** ventromedial thalamic nucleus. **VL** ventrolateral thalamic nucleus. **VL** ventrolateral nucleus. **VPL** ventroposterolateral nucleus. **VPM** ventroposteromedial nucleus.

FIGURE 5-1.   Circuits mediating sense experience and recall. Sensory impulses travel via thalamic sensory nuclei to cortical sensory and association areas, mediating sensory experience. Associated impulses are relayed to limbic areas (25, 32, 24, 31, 23, 30, and hippocampal gyrus), mediating appraisal. This appraisal of something seen, heard, felt, etc. initiates the spontaneous recall of similar things which is mediated via hippocampus, thalamic sensory nuclei, and the various cortical association and limbic areas. Motor impulses travel via ventral thalamic nuclei to frontal motor and association areas (see Figure 5-3) and are similarly registered and recalled. Reproduced by permission from Magda B. Arnold (1960, Vol. 2, Fig. 1, p. 69).

hippocampal gyri and insula) which receives relays from the neighboring sensory and motor association areas. This system allows for an appraisal of sense impressions registered in neighboring association areas. The recall of these impressions seems to be mediated by a circuit which connects the various portions of the limbic system via the hippocampal system (indusium griseum, hippocampus, and fornix) with the midbrain, from where relays go via the sensory thalamic nuclei back to the cortical association areas (Fig. 5-1). Affective memory (i.e., the reliving of the original liking or dislike, of a favorable or unfavorable attitude) seems to be mediated by a circuit which also includes the hippocampal

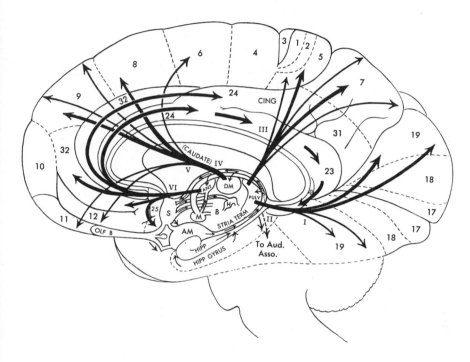

I visual imagination. II auditory imagination. III somesthetic imagination (including taste). IV motor imagination. V olfactory imagination. VI affective memory. AM amygdala. ANT anterior thalamic nucleus. B brain stem. CING cingulate gyrus. DM dorsomedial thalamic nucleus. H habenula. HIPP hippocampus. M mammillary body. OLF olfactory bulb. PULV pulvinar. S septal area. STRIA TERM stria terminalis.

FIGURE 5-2. The imagination circuit and the revival of affect. Identification of object by recalling similar things (via memory circuit) and their effects on us (via affective memory circuit VI) results in *imagining* what might happen and what can be done about it (imagination circuits I-V). Reproduced by permission from Magda B. Arnold (1960, Vol. 2, Fig. 2, p. 72).

system but relays impulses to the anterior thalamic nuclei and the cingulate gyrus. Imagination (making plans, hypotheses, etc.) would be mediated by a circuit from limbic system to amygdala and thalamus to cortical association areas (Fig. 5-2). The emotion itself, as a felt action tendency, seems to be experienced when relays from the limbic system connect via the brain stem reticular formation, hypothalamus and ventral thalamus with the premotor cortex (Fig. 5-3).[2]

This theory implies that appraisal, recall, and imagination are not unitary functions but are modality-specific, just like sense experience. Though sense impressions are registered and preserved in cortical association areas, recall of these memories requires a circuit which can switch into these areas whenever something is appraised as "worth investigating." This can perhaps explain why in one sense nothing is ever forgotten (as proved by hypnotic recall) and in another sense forgetting is so common. Once registered in the association areas, memories are potentially available. But their retrieval is difficult because it depends on a switching process that can be facilitated by training but is easily disorganized by disuse, shock, or concussion.

Since the late 1920's, when Lashley popularized the "mass action of the brain" concept, such an approach to brain function has been suspect. Yet Lashley's notion was but an inference from the results of extirpation experiments—and these permit an alternative explanation. In a maze which can be learned on the basis of motor, tactual, visual, and perhaps even auditory cues, the destruction of cortex serving any one modality will only mildly interfere with learning. But the more cortex is destroyed, the greater the deficit—not because the brain acts as a whole but because more and more memory modalities are lost that could be used to solve a maze problem.

Memory deficits after hippocampal system lesions

Since it is appraisal that initiates emotion, any stimulation or destruction of parts of the limbic appraisal system might be expected to give us relevant information. However, this appraisal is always based on memory, except in the neonate, and the neonate animal is difficult to test. For this reason, we decided to investigate first the proposed memory circuit. If our hypothesis is correct and this memory circuit does collect impulses from different memory modalities, it is necessary to use learning problems that are modality-specific so that the only cues available will be cues in the modality to be tested.

[2] The subcortical portions of the limbic appraisal system include the areas of maximum "reward" mapped by Olds (1956) in his studies of self-stimulation of the brain in animals.

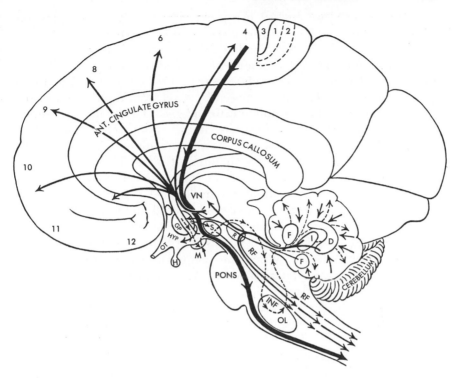

– – –relay from hippocampus to cerebellum. ———relay from cerebellum to extrapyramidal and hypothalamic effectors. ■■■■relay from cerebellum to frontal lobe. ■■■pyramidal tract. **D** dentate nucleus. **F** fastigial nucleus. **GP** globus pallidus. **H** hypophysis. **HYP** hypothalamus. **IN** interposited nucleus. **INF OL** inferior olive. **M** mammillary body. **OT** optic tract. **R** red nucleus. **RF** brain stem reticular formation. **S** subtantia nigra. **VN** ventral thalamic nuclei.

FIGURE 5-3.   The circuit mediating emotion and action. When something is appraised as good (via relays to the limbic cortex), a tendency to action is aroused which is mediated by relays from limbic cortex via the hippocampus-fornix to brain stem and cerebellum. From the cerebellar roof nuclei (dentate, fastigial, interposited) the organized action pattern is relayed: (a) via ventral thalamic nuclei to the frontal lobe, connecting with corticobulbar and corticospinal tracts and mediating the felt tendency to action as well as the intended movement; (b) via globus pallidus to extrapyramidal pathways, exciting the autonomic nervous system and organizing background motions; (c) via globus pallidus to hypothalamic neurosecretory nuclei, initiating the secretion of appropriate hormones. Reproduced by permission from Magda B. Arnold (1960, Vol. 2, Fig. 3, p. 83).

Consequently, we devised five problems, each designed to test one particular modality. For *olfactory* discrimination, we used three different kinds of apparatus, of which the last one is the simplest. It consists of a small cage with a glassed-in front which accommodates a tray one inch wide and thirty inches long, holding small cups of water at distances of about three inches. The tray is moved by hand from right to left so that one cup at a time appears underneath the glass. Each cup also contains an odorant. Vanilla odor indicates that the cup contains water, while lemon odor indicates that the cup contains a quinine solution. For the *motor* problem, we used a single alteration T-maze. The rat must recall in which direction it has run before and find water in the opposite direction. The *tactual* discrimination uses an elevated Y-maze with exchangeable flooring: the corrugated rubber floor leads to water, the smooth rubber floor does not. (The rats are run in a darkened room to exclude visual cues.) For the *visual* discrimination, a Skinner box with accessory electronic panels is used. When the houselight flashes, the rat has to press the bar to obtain water. When the houselight is steady, a bar press brings a slight shock to the hind legs. For the *auditory* discrimination, the bar has to be pressed when there is a clicking sound. During the silent intervals, a bar press brings a slight shock to the hind legs.[3]

Experiment 1.   According to my theory, memory based on olfactory cues should be impaired when the hippocampal rudiment (indusium griseum) is transected bilaterally so as to exclude relays from the olfactory association area, i.e., *at the genu* of the corpus callosum. Histological examination of lesions in this area showed that five animals with complete bilateral rudiment lesions failed to learn the olfactory discrimination and four animals which had learned it before operation failed to retain or relearn it.

Experiment 2.   Moreover, after bilateral hippocampal rudiment transection *just caudal to the motor cortex,* the animals should not remember what they had done before, i.e. should fail in the alternation problem. Two rats with such lesions failed to learn the single alternation T-maze, and two failed to retain or relearn it. Animals with incomplete transections showed a learning or retention deficit but were able to learn or relearn.

Experiment 3.   Also, the animals should not be able to learn or retain a tactual discrimination after the hippocampal rudiment is transected bilaterally at the *splenium of the corpus callosum.* How-

[3] The greater part of this investigation was supported by Grant 1791 from the Mental Health Authority of the State of Illinois.

ever, four rats with such lesions showed no deficit. This may be either because recall on the basis of tactual cues is not mediated by the hippocampal rudiment, thus disproving this part of the theory. Or it may be because this is a simultaneous discrimination instead of the successive discriminations used in all other problems of this series. In the tactual maze, both the corrugated and the smooth rubber floor are available for choice at the point where the two pathways fork. Several investigators (Hunt & Diamond, 1959; Thompson & Malin, 1961) have reported that brain lesions which produce a deficit in successive discrimination leave simultaneous discrimination unimpaired. It is likely that affective memory (i.e., the reliving of the experience that the rough floor is good to walk on) is sufficient for simultaneous discrimination; and affective memory only requires a connection via the cingulum to the fornix, anterior thalamic nuclei, and cingulate gyrus, structures that were left intact by the lesion.

Experiment 4. According to theory, a bilateral transection of the *hippocampus* should interfere with visual or auditory discrimination, or with both combined, depending on the locus of the lesion. Two animals with incomplete transections of both hippocampi (approximately 3 millimeters from the midline) were unable to retain or relearn the auditory discrimination but did eventually relearn the visual discrimination. Since these animals did not respond to startle tests while all other animals in this experiment did, it may be assumed that they were deafened by the earplugs used in the stereotaxic instrument. However, there seems to have been a considerable central deficit as well, as attested by the visual discrimination deficit which was more pronounced than in any other animal in this group. Also, in the course of our experiments it was discovered that the speaker (which was fastened to the wall of the Skinner box) produced not only a clicking sound but also noticeable vibrations. Several animals with fornix lesions (Experiment 5) were able to learn or relearn the discrimination when the speaker was inside the box but failed to do so when a larger speaker was suspended from the ceiling outside the box; this seems to indicate that the animals employed auditory and vibratory cues whenever the speaker was fastened inside. The two animals which were deafened by the earplugs, however, failed to learn the discrimination on the basis of the vibratory cues alone.

Among the animals with complete hippocampal lesions, two showed an auditory retention deficit and one showed a learning deficit in auditory-vibratory discrimination; all these animals responded to startle tests. Visual learning or retention deficits were found in three animals with incomplete hippocampal lesions and in three animals with complete lesions. This seems to show that the influx from the visual association areas reaches not only the dorsal hippocampi but also the severed lateral parts.

Experiment 5.   Finally, according to this theory, complete bilateral transection of the *fornix* should make recall impossible in all memory modalities. In practice, however, such a lesion is almost impossible to achieve because some fornix fibers perforate the corpus callosum in their course to the septal area and hypothalamus. Our fornix lesions were placed about 2 millimeters behind the genu. A slim knife (or, in some lesions, a unipolar electrode) was introduced obliquely, about 1 mm. from the midline, right and left, so as to cross immediately beneath the corpus callosum. According to the histological report, two animals had bilateral lesions of both the pre- and post-commissural fornix, and seventeen had partial or complete transections of the precommissural fornix only, sometimes combined with lesions of the hippocampal rudiment.

The whole group showed significant learning and retention deficits in all discriminations (visual, auditory-vibratory, auditory, olfactory, motor); only tactual discrimination was unimpaired, which was again the only simultaneous discrimination in the series. In auditory discrimination, three out of three lesioned animals did not achieve criterion on postoperative learning; eight out of nine animals did not achieve it in postoperative retention. All animals responded in a startle test. One animal with a bilateral lesion in the medial part of the hippocampal commissure had a visual discrimination deficit but no olfactory impairment. Table *5-1* shows the number of animals with learning or retention deficits in various modalities after hippocampal system lesions. In the two earlier experiments, the animals were tested only on the critical modality, but in the later experiments we attempted to test them on two or more modalities. The sites of lesions in all five experiments are shown in Figure *5-4*.

These findings seem to support the notion that recall is mediated by a circuit that includes the hippocampal rudiment, hippocampus, and fornix. In every case, the lesion was minimal, (about 1 mm. in anteroposterior extent in electrode lesions, a clean knife cut in the hippocampal transections). Thus, the deficit is not likely to be caused by the loss of nerve tissue but rather by the interruption of a circuit necessary for recall. Control lesions in neighboring structures did not produce any deficit.

Results from other laboratories do not contradict this interpretation, although they are complicated by the fact that lesions in hippocampal structures are usually extensive and often include limbic and neocortical areas as well. The effect of hippocampal rudiment lesions has not been reported before, though there are many reports of deficits after hippocampus and fornix lesions. Hippocampal lesions have resulted in im-

Table 5-1. Number of animals showing an *inability* to learn or relearn or a learning/retention *deficit* in various modalities.

LESION	OLFACT.		MOTOR		TACTUAL		VISUAL		AUDI-TORY		AUD.-VIBR.	
	in.	def.	in.	def.	in.	def.	in.	def.	in.	def.	in.	def.
Experiment 1 (N 9)												
Hippocampal rudiment (genu)	9	0	−*	−	−	−	−	−	−	−	−	−
Experiment 2 (N 13)												
Hippocampal rudiment caudal to motor area (N 4)	−	−	4	0	−	−	−	−	−	−	−	−
Partial do. (N 9)	−	−	0	5	−	−	−	−	−	−	−	−
Experiment 3 (N 9)												
Hippocampal rudiment (splenium) (N 8)	−	−	−	−	0	0	0	0	−	−	−	−
do. + medial part of hippocampal commissure (N 1)	−	−	−	−	0	0	0	1	−	−	−	−
Experiment 4 (N 9)												
Hippocampi (N 5)	0	0	0	3	−	−	0	3	0	2	−	1
Incomplete do. (N 5)	0	0	−	−	−	−	0	3	(2) †	0	(2)	0
Experiment 5 (N 20)												
Pre- and postcommissural fornix (N 2)	0	1	0	2	0	0	0	2	2	0	2	0
Precommissural fornix (N 17)	0	3a	0	4b	0	0	0	3c	8d	0	6e	7e
Medial hippocampal commissure (N 1)	0	0	−	−	−	−	1	0	−	−	−	−

* − not tested in this discrimination
† (2) Animals did not respond to startle test.
a = out of 13 tested
b = out of 9 tested
c = out of 3 tested
d = out of 9 tested
e = out of 15 tested

paired maze performance, bright/dark and stripe discrimination (Niki, 1962; Kimble, 1963), which agrees with the deficit in successive visual discrimination observed by us. Milner and Penfield (1955) reported on patients who showed a loss of "recent memory" after ablation of both hippocampi and hippocampal gyri. These patients could no longer report recent experiences when asked about them, though they could recount earlier experiences spontaneously. Hence, Milner (1959) concluded that

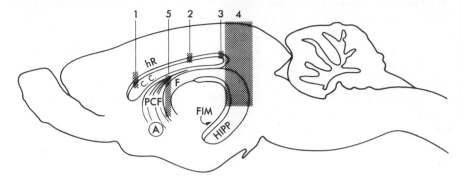

hR   hippocampal rudiment
CC   corpus callosum
PFC   precommissural fornix
F   postcommissural fornix
HIPP hippocampus
FIM   fimbria of hippocampus
A   anterior commissure

1. bilateral lesion of hippocampal rudiment at genu of corpus callosum (*Experiment 1*)
2. bilateral lesion of hippocampal rudiment caudal to motor area (*Experiment 2*)
3. bilateral lesion of hippocampal rudiment at splenium of corpus callosum (*Experiment 3*)
4. bilateral lesion transecting hippocampus (*Experiment 4*)
5. bilateral lesion transecting fornix (*Experiment 5*)

FIGURE 5-4.   Schematic diagram of rat brain showing lesion sites.

the hippocampus plays a role in the consolidation of memory traces. But other investigators found that animals with hippocampal damage are unimpaired in simultaneous visual discrimination and retain such a habit; thus they are not defective in "recent memory" (Kimble, 1963). The patients' inability to recall what they did when asked about it can be explained as an inability to remember on the basis of auditory cues; recall on the basis of motor (speech) cues was apparently unimpaired. This would be the same deficit in recall on the basis of auditory cues found in our animals with hippocampal transections. Kimble's animals were not defective in simultaneous visual discrimination because the affective memory circuit was intact, just as our animals showed no deficit in simultaneous tactual discrimination.

Affective memory

It is obvious that the appraisal of stress situations depends not only on intact sensory and motor memory but also on intact affective memory. We not only remember what we have seen, heard, touched, done. We also remember the effect of past experiences, pleasant or unpleasant, and we do it by *reliving* our positive or negative attitude rather than by having a memory image of something pleasant or unpleasant. How profoundly we are touched by emotion, how intensely we experience stress may depend on the strength of this affective memory. If affective memory is mediated by the proposed circuit from cingulum to fornix, mammillary bodies, anterior thalamic nuclei, and cingulate gyrus, a lesion along this circuit should interfere with fear but also with positive emotion and motivation and, as a result, with learning as well.

In a later series of experiments we have sectioned the cingulum bilaterally (1) at the genu of the corpus callosum, (2) just caudal to the motor area, (3) at the splenium of the corpus callosum. If affective recall is mediated by the projection to the cingulum, any one of these lesions should result in a learning deficit.

The lesioned animals have thus far been tested only on the olfactory discrimination, but it is abundantly clear that their behavior is different from that of intact animals or animals with hippocampal system lesions. Animals with cingulum transection require "shaping" in the olfactory apparatus in which intact animals usually acquire the discrimination in the second session. They do not immediately run to the front end of the apparatus to sniff; and when they do, they may drink without hesitation when the cup has a vanilla odor (correct), but they hesitate for some time when there is a lemon odor (incorrect), yet take a sip of the quinine solution eventually. In short, they behave as if they did not remember that they had obtained water at the front of the box or that some of the liquid was unpleasant. Accordingly, the group of animals with intended cingulum lesions take 175 trials to learn to criterion (range 110 to 420) as against 50 trials (range 30 to 90) for operated controls.

From other laboratories come reports of various types of deficit after cingulum lesions. In a well-known study, Ward (1948) reports that monkeys with lesions of the anterior cingulate gyrus show a loss of "social conscience," that they take food out of other monkeys' hands, walk or sit on them, entirely unprepared for their retaliation. To explain this behavior as "tameness," as Ward does, gives us no clue as to what function was really impaired. On Arnold's hypothesis, this lesion would destroy the monkeys' affective memory and so impair their ability to assess the consequences of their actions. As a result, they do what they want without regard to the harm that can come to them. Pribram and Fulton's (1954) "experimental critique" does not disprove the reported deficits. It merely demonstrates that a simultaneous *visual discrimination* habit is retained after ablation of the anterior cingulate gyrus. While the animals may be able to approach what they see and have learned to like, they may not be able to refrain from doing something they want to do because they cannot remember the consequences.

These and similar lesion studies are often difficult to evaluate, because, in addition to the cingulum, a considerable portion of the cingulate gyrus is usually destroyed as well. However, Thomas and Slotnick (1963) produced incomplete cingulum lesions in rats and reported that an active avoidance response to a light signalling an electric shock was seriously impaired by the lesions while maze performance was unaffected. Schneider, Crosby, and Kahn (1963) have recently reported that bilateral transection of the cingulum (about 1 cm. caudal to the genu of the corpus callosum) in cancer patients brings relief from the anxiety connected with their pain without the personality changes resulting from prefrontal lobotomy, which brings similar relief. Since lobotomy also interrupts the projection from the anterior thalamic nuclei to the cingulum, it seems reasonable to suppose that the interruption of this circuit has made it impossible to relive past pain and so suffer fear in addition to pain.

Apparently, an intact affective memory circuit is necessary to experience fear or other contending emotions that depend on reliving past harm. Without affective memory, environmental or organic stress is no longer so burdensome. On the other hand, without an intense experience of stress, little effort will be made to overcome or avoid it.

I hope I have said enough to show that a phenomenological analysis of the sequence from perception to emotion and action can help to identify the structures mediating these experiences and to devise experiments that will prove or disprove our hypotheses. Thus far, it has only been possible to make a beginning in investigating the circuits that seem to serve recall in various memory modalities as well as affective memory. As our investigations progress, we hope to provide more data on the role of memory in the experience of stress.

Invited commentary

SHELDON J. KORCHIN: I have deep sympathy with the effort to bridge, theoretically and empirically, the realm of the phenomenal analysis of personal experience to that of research on brain mechanisms, and I share Dr. Arnold's faith in the importance of the effort. Lashley argued long ago that it was important to coalesce neurology and psychology but cautioned that we must be as ready to move from the psychological to the neurological as in the reverse direction. To many psychologists the workings of the brain are viewed as most primary, and they try to reason from the neurological to the psychological. Research is done on the brain to discover the correlated changes in behavior. But Lashley reminds us that we know a great deal about psychological functions, perhaps more than about brain processes, and it might be equally or more reasonable to try to infer the properties of the nervous system necessary to support such functions. Dr. Arnold, I believe, is in this tradition.

I am hesitant to comment on her specific research contributions which are well out of my competence, nor can I evaluate the particular evidence she gives in defense of her thesis of modality-specific learning. However, starting from her conceptualization of stress, I find it hard to understand the logic which leads her to a concern with modality-specific cognitive acts and finally the particular brain processes she studies. Perhaps she can help me retrace these steps.

But let us consider Dr. Arnold's concept of stress because it touches some of the main concerns of this volume. The sequence she proposes is: sense experience, an act of appraisal, then affective recall, another appraisal act, then stress emotions, and finally action. The first act of appraisal is actually an arousal of attention, and she points to the specific role of midbrain mechanisms at this stage. It is a rapid, intuitive, simple act which judges that the stimulus is relevant or not relevant, but does not otherwise evaluate it. Further evaluation depends on a second act of appraisal which follows affective recall. Relevant earlier experience is recalled and gives context to a more extended cognitive analysis which judges the event to be benign or dangerous, annoying or burdensome. It is a novel notion of Dr. Arnold's to note the occurrence of two cognitive acts in the two stages of appraisal. Her emphasis on the brain mechanisms associated with the first of these is not meant to imply that these midbrain structures are equally important in the second cognitive stage. Obviously, evaluation of potential threat, by relating it to past events, must involve the cortex extensively.

However, I am puzzled by the emphasis given to modality-specific mechanisms. She states: "This theory implies that appraisal, recall, and imagination are not unitary functions, but are modality-specific just like sense experience" (p. 132). She reports a considerable body of experimental research showing that rats dealing with modality-specific learning problems in her laboratory, which are then given lesions in appropriate areas, show hypothesized decrements in performance in the tasks involving these areas. I confess to being confused as to the implication of such findings to the understanding of stress in humans. The insistent fact in human cognition, including the appraisal acts involved in evaluating psychological threat, is that it operates at the symbolic level, implies cross-modality equivalences, and the action of higher integrative functions. Certainly, a particular threat, whether sensed through vision or audition, would have the same meaning for the subject.

In general, however, the emphasis on cognitive appraisal in Dr. Arnold's paper parallels similar concepts in many stress theories. It is a truism that a threat does not threaten unless it is evaluated as threatening by a subject. In a more general formulation, no stimulus has meaning for the organism without some act of appraisal. But there are serious questions as to how such appraisal goes on, whether and how represented consciously, what mechanisms are involved, and like issues, which are the research problems of our field.

For years, psychology has known, although periodically we need to be reminded, that a stimulus as such has no psychological value. Intended to illustrate his concept of behavior occurring in a behavioral rather than physical environment, Koffka's appealing anecdote makes a point for students of stress. In a blinding blizzard, a man came galloping across the frozen expanse of Lake Constance to the back door of a Swiss inn. When informed of what he had just done by the startled innkeeper, he promptly dropped dead. As an undefined frozen expanse, Lake Constance, however dangerous objectively, was not a stressful experience until it was recognized as such psychologically.

It is clear that intervening between the stressful stimulus and stress response are a variety of operations, including cognitive appraisal (as well as defense and other personality mechanisms beyond our present concern). Understanding how these function is our research task. I would caution, however, against limiting the scope of our inquiry. The phrase "cognitive appraisal" should not imply only conscious evaluation and judgment. Evaluation may be so instantaneous that the subject has no experience of having evaluated, nor does the observer have any evidence of an appraisal act, except by inference from later consequences. So, too, the emotional reactions which Dr. Arnold describes may be visible for only a fleeting moment or perhaps not at all, because of the swift action of defense mechanisms. Clarifying the sequence of events connecting stressful stimulus to response is perhaps our central task, however subtle the links might be.

Perhaps Dr. Arnold could clarify the relation she sees between the conception of stress she has described and the modality-specific cognitive acts and the neurological mechanisms she discusses.

Discussion

Dr. Arnold: Let me reply first to the question of modality-specificity. Sense experience is modality-specific, but all the modalities together give us one cognitive experience, as long as the organism is intact. We *see* a man moving his lips and we *hear* speech, but we *know* it is this man who is speaking. Modality-specificity becomes important, however, in some brain injuries. In some cases, danger or stress can be appraised via one modality but not another, or stress can be experienced but can no longer be evaluated for appropriate action.

Now as to broader connections, I have tried to show that contending emotions are reactions to psychological stress, indeed, are the signs of it. I have also suggested that a phenomenological analysis of these reactions to stress may help to identify the physiological changes that go with stress emotions (cf. p. 127 ff). Such an analysis may also help to identify the structures in the brain that mediate both the appraisal of stress and the contending emotions that flow from it (cf. p. 128 ff).

The sequence of psychological activities from perception to appraisal, emotion, and action turned out to be quite complicated upon analysis: memory and imagination are included in every appraisal, for without memory we cannot appraise a situation accurately, and without imagination we cannot plan how to cope with it. Neurologically speaking, there must be connections between the sensory and the motor cortex before a stimulus can evoke a response. Psychologically speaking, sensory and affective memory, imagination, appraisal, and emotion seem to bridge the gap between sense experience and action. This would suggest that there must be circuits serving recall, imagination, and emotion (see Figs. 5-1 through 5-3). Eventually, we are hoping to test all these circuits experimentally. Up to now we have made a mere beginning by investigating the circuit serving various memory modalities and affective memory. We hope to investigate the circuit serving emotion and action at a later date.

Dr. Pepitone: While the phenomenological stages Dr. Arnold proposes resonate very closely with what I think my own phenomenology is, when I try to look at the stage sequences more conceptually it is not clear what specific processes are involved. I can think of a number of different processes. One, an assessment of the relevance of the event for my existing state—motivational, emotional, or role or physical position. Two, an estimate of the degree of danger residing in the event or posed by the external stimulus. Three, an assessment of the resources at my disposal. Four, a judgment or decision as to whether I have generally to fight or to flee. Fifth, the structuring of the tactics of my defense or escape. In other words, there are several distinct cognitive acts involved, and their specific functions have to be mapped in detail.

Dr. Arnold: These assessments are made one after another, always on the basis of what we remember has happened and what has been its effect on us in the past. Even when something entirely new is encountered, memory is active—if only to serve the appraisal that this is different from everything familiar and liked, and so may be harmful. Here is an example. When my daughter was seven or eight months old, she began standing up in the playpen, so I thought she needed shoes with stiff soles. Thinking to surprise her, I put the new shoes beside her while she was asleep in her crib. When she woke up, she gave one look at the pair of black patent leather shoes and drew back, screaming with terror. Now the shoes did not harm her in any way. But she was afraid because up to this time she had only had soft white shoes and this was something completely unknown and so might be harmful. Spitz and Wolf (1946), you remember, reported that the fear of strangers, which is a similar kind of fear, appears first around age eight months ("eight months anxiety"). This fear presupposes the ability to distinguish between what is familiar (and remembered affectively as good in some way), and something new (for which no affective memory is available); what is unfamiliar, and so is not liked at first glance, may be dangerous and so arouse fear. Actually, there are only a few things that can be appraised at first encounter *without* affective memory: a painful blow, pleasant warmth, being dropped, etc.

Dr. Mandler: The anecdote you just told us immediately presents difficulties for your position. It is, of course, quite consistent with Hebb's notion of fear, and the experience of your daughter is very similar to the experience of Hebb's chimpanzee when presented with the severed head of a chimpanzee

(Hebb, 1946a). But you said appraisal is in terms of like or dislike. Here is a brand new experience and obviously the child's response is one of negative affect, not in terms of some past experience but rather in terms of *no* past experience. The discrepant is disliked because it has *not* been experienced before. You have insisted that the appraisal produces approach or withdrawal, and yet here is withdrawal without past experience.

Dr. Arnold: On the contrary, there is withdrawal because of past experience. In Dr. Hebb's laboratory, the severed head of a chimpanzee and the laboratory assistant without his white coat had suddenly taken on a strange aspect, so that affective memory no longer served the chimpanzee. Living chimpanzees and white-coated assistants are familiar and liked; accordingly, as soon as they appear all is well. When they suddenly become strange, something has gone wrong, which may mean danger—so the chimpanzee is afraid. This fear of the unfamiliar and strange may also explain the chimpanzee's fear of snakes. A snake slides along the ground instead of running. Its shape is different from that of every other animal. Is it surprising that something so strange may also hold unexpected dangers for the chimpanzee?

Dr. Prescott: Would Dr. Arnold explain in the same way the findings of Tin-bergen (1948) with respect to fear responses in ducklings? A cardboard sil-houette was moved across a cage in such a way as to cast a shadow resembling a hawk when moved in one direction and resembling a long-necked goose when moved in the other. The ducklings responded with fear in the former case but not in the latter.

Dr. Arnold: Although both seem to be new experiences, I think this can also be explained as fear of the unfamiliar. When the shape is going in one direction it has a long neck and short body, like ducks and geese, and so is familiar, re-assuring. The same shape going in the other direction has a short neck and a long body and tail, and so is unfamiliar, potentially dangerous. If a duckling brought up in isolation shows this fear also, we would have to assume an innate appraisal. Such an innate appraisal would be that shapes with long necks are good, i.e., likeable, shapes with short necks bad, i.e., disliked. We also have to assume an innate appraisal when an infant eagerly swallows anything warm and sweet but refuses to swallow anything sour or bitter. But there are only a few innate appraisals on the basis of somatosensory experience, as I have mentioned before; gradually, the human and animal young learn to appraise on the basis of memory what they see or hear, so that they can avoid what may hurt them when it comes close.

Dr. Trumbull: One of the problems here lies in relating this to the develop-ment of perceptual mass or experience with the sensory world. We do not place equal emphasis on each of our own available sensory systems and, between people, there are also differences in dependence upon them. Thus, in situations of sensory deprivation, that which is denied, i.e., vision or hearing, will have different values or stress potential, related to dependence upon it, developed over time.

Dr. Arnold: I do not believe that affective memory will result in a whole memory modality being favored or disregarded. After all, the avenues over which we experience various situations are not experienced separately. All we experience is some *thing:* we see it, hear it, smell it, perhaps touch it when it comes close enough. What is appraised is this thing or situation, not the sensory modality. But as far as a particular thing or situation is concerned, we certainly do build up favorable or unfavorable attitudes, even when we have forgotten the exact circumstances which led to each separate like or dislike. Sometimes this attitude, built up through affective memory, can be neutralized by a corrective experience; in the case of fear, however, this is not easy because we immediately withdraw as soon as we remember that something has brought pain in the past, i.e., when we are afraid of it. During psychotherapy, these fears have to be gradually overcome through the support of the therapist who helps the patient to court such corrective experiences.

Dr. Sells: Perhaps we can tie a lot of this together if we look on the events that occur in terms of anticipations, and then the situations that appear are either confirmatory or dissonant to the expectations. When they are reasonably confirmatory, the reception is pleasant; when they are dissonant, it is unpleasant. Where you use the term *evaluation* or *assessment,* it seems to me that what you have is not always an experienced cognitive act but merely an implicit comparison of the event that occurs with the event that is expected. The appraisal makes it sound as though there is a cognitive act being performed.

On the same model, I would also raise the question whether it is necessary to invoke phenomenology at all. I am more impressed with the cybernetic model, and much of this appraisal of information or classification of information as it occurs can be explained without conscious experience. When we bring phenomenology in we are evoking a process about which we have no understanding and yet we can think of the—to use your term—*appraisal* as part of the total perceptual experience without necessarily making it a phenomenological event.

Dr. Arnold: In the first place, I wonder whether a comparison of the present event with a past one is not as much of a cognitive act as is an appraisal. In the second place, we really know more about what we ourselves do (e.g. that we remember, plan, like, or dislike something) than most of us know about the computer model. If we try to reinterpret what we do by looking to see what a computer does, we may go wrong. After all, a given problem can be tackled in a variety of ways, and the way the computer goes about it is only one of many possible ways.

As for dissonance between event and expectation being unpleasant and consonance pleasant, there are dissonances that are quite pleasant. If a student is afraid he has failed in an important examination and he finds he has come out near the top, the dissonance between expectation and actuality is grave, yet it surely brings pleasure, not disappointment.

Dr. Korchin: On the matter of consciousness, I think we must, as psychologists, be concerned with the realm of experience, but this should not be equated with consciousness. We have to have theory which accounts for events which are not represented in consciousness. If there is, for example, a dangerous threat and I react with panic, the sequence of events can be stated in terms of sense experience, evaluation, stress, emotion, and response. But suppose I break out in panic when there is no appropriate stimulus and consequently no apparent act of appraisal? The panic is just as real, as students of pathological anxiety in psychiatric patients know. In the *déjà vu*, there may be stimulus, but it is unknown to the subject, and yet strong emotion may result, of the sort Dr. Arnold calls "stress emotion." The mechanisms in such situations, I believe, cannot be described in terms of a defined external event, a clear cognitive appraisal, and subsequent emotional or other response. Dr. Arnold suggests the sequence of sensation, cognition, affection, and behavioral response. Often enough, the emotion seems to precede any act of appraisal.

Dr. Arnold: The appraisal that leads to emotion is *unwitting, immediate, experienced only as liking or dislike.* It is not a "clear, cognitive appraisal." It may be triggered by a stimulus situation, but also by something remembered or thought about. Sometimes a casual encounter may bring back a liking or dislike originally aroused by a similar situation even though we cannot recall the earlier experience. In such a case, the emotion follows the re-lived appraisal (affective memory) though the actual situation cannot account for it (*déjà vu* experience).

Dr. Korchin: The important thing, nevertheless, is that we may feel fear, then evaluate what it is that we are afraid of, rather than the reverse. It is possible, too, as James and Lange once suggested, that the sequence may be cycled through physiological response, which is then sensed and responded to. I am trying to suggest that we should not reduce the complexity of stress behavior by assuming any one sequence of events.

Dr. Arnold: There is no doubt that a reflective appraisal will follow upon the felt emotion unless the emotion is sudden and overwhelming. But some rudimentary unwitting appraisal is necessary before an emotion can be felt at all. Unless we like or dislike something, it would leave us completely indifferent. We then reappraise the situation reflectively and may even evaluate our emotion and the physiological changes that go with it. There is a continuity of perception, emotion, and action but no linear sequence. Ordinarily, we engage in a continuous cycle of cognition, appraisal, planning for action, in which intuitive appraisals produce emotion and reflective appraisals finally lead to action.

Dr. Ruff: I agree that in addition to what we appraise as dangerous, whatever the organism cannot make meaningful in terms of some past experience is threatening. This can occur either with or without awareness. When listening to a psychoanalytic patient, for example, it often seems that most of what is threatening occurs outside awareness. What the observer sees, therefore, is never the appraisal but a defense which occurs automatically. From this he has to infer what is underneath.

Another observation analogous to Dr. Arnold's example of her seven-month-old daughter comes from our isolation experiments. We found that many subjects showed evidence of anxiety when first confronted with a completely novel and unstructured situation. We had the impression that anxiety decreased as the subject made the experience meaningful in the terms of the past. The military subject, for example, begins to structure the experiment as a mission: "I guess they want me to do so and so, I'm going to explore the chamber, I'm going to see what's here, I'm going to plan my time." This was like saying "It's a shoe like my white shoe, only it's black." With this structuring there is a decrease in the affective state.

Dr. Nowlis: I would like to defend Dr. Arnold against the criticism that she is attempting to explain how brain processes are involved in awareness and consciousness. It seems to me that she, like Lashley and his student Hebb, uses the various general classes of conscious experience as sources of hypotheses about what might be going on in the brain. I am reminded of how Roy John used four such concepts (affect, motivation, memory, and conation) in developing a physiological model for discrimination learning, a model he calls the general representational system (John, 1962). He assumes that each system lies in brain structures which do not belong to any specific sensory system and that each system loops widely through the different structures which underlie affect, motivation, etc. When a system is activated, all four components become involved, providing representation of the affect, motivation, memory, and conation typically present during the original development (through learning) of the system.

Dr. Lazarus: I think Dr. Arnold's concept of appraisal is an important one. It has also been implicit in a great deal of writing about stress. However, I think the need to detail the specific functions of the cognitive appraisal act and identify the factors which contribute to it, as Dr. Pepitone earlier suggested, is essential if we are able to make the concept empirically useful.

Some of these factors lie within the individual in the form of beliefs, expectations, and the motivational system. Some of them lie in the stimulus situation whose harmful significance is interpreted by the individual. We must separate also the processes concerned with threat, from those concerning the consequences of threat, that is, what the individual does about it; for example, whether he expresses anger and attacks, whether he is angry but inhibits the attack, whether he is frightened and withdraws, and whether he is frightened and doesn't withdraw. Many kinds of appraisals must be involved. Different factors within the person and in the stimulus configuration should lead to different appraisals and different ways of coping with threat. I can't speak for the comparable physiological theory, but at the behavioral level, a theory which is useful must lead us to the empirical conditions that determine the different reaction patterns we observe.

Dr. Cohen: I personally like a neurobiological explanation for some of the appraisal sequencing which was described. I am afraid someone like Stanley Schachter (1965) has raised some serious questions in terms of appraisal of things like bodily states or the cognitive labelling of bodily states. He recently described some as yet unpublished work on the eating habits and hunger experiences of obese and non-obese persons. The type of general theoretical framework with which he is working is that obese persons are probably unable to differentiate the state of hunger from other states of activation. Briefly what he did (and this will not do justice to his work) was to administer adrenalin and a placebo to an obese group and a non-obese group. They were told that the study was some sort of a taste test. The criterion measure he used was the number of crackers eaten by the subject. He found that non-obese subjects ate fewer crackers under adrenalin than without it. This might be expected since adrenalin is often associated with activation—more specifically with fear responses. The usual idea is that there is a suppression of gastrointestinal activity with fear. The obese group, on the other hand, ate more crackers with adrenalin. This is very consistent with his hypothesis that they would be unable to distinguish states of activation (i.e., to label the specific state of hunger). This is important for several reasons. First, how one identifies or labels bodily states and secondly, what specific bodily states exist. The reason I raise the question of the relation of specific body states to emotion is the matter of the association of noradrenalin and anger. Noradrenalin increase is a function of sympathetic discharge and is not primarily a function of secretion from the adrenal medulla. There are no metabolic effects, so far as we know, from noradrenalin, and the only subjective experience one might anticipate is from the peripheral vasoconstriction that is associated with it.

Dr. Arnold: In addition to the secretion of noradrenaline there seem to be cholinergic effects of anger which would be neutralized by adrenaline but not by noradrenaline. As for Schachter's results with obese patients, it would be rather difficult to explain what could have gone wrong psychologically and physiologically that prevented them from labeling their activation state correctly. Phenomenologically, obese patients have learned to depend on the pleasure that comes from eating and resort to it whenever they feel uneasy, dejected, or bored. An adrenaline injection produces a feeling of restlessness or malaise which calls for the same remedy as any other difficulty they are facing: food. Did the obese patients actually say they were hungry or did they simply use the so-called "taste test" to indulge in their favorite pleasure? Any addiction, whether to eating, drinking, or smoking, means not only a physical habit but also an inclination to think of food or drink or a smoke whenever the opportunity offers; and the opportunity to eat was surely given by the test.

Dr. Mandler: If I may return to an earlier comment of Dr. Arnold's (see p. 145), I want to take exception to her slur on the cybernetic or computer model, her accusation that it is misleading. Sure, it is misleading, every model is misleading. So is the phenomenological model, which has been extremely misleading in the area of thought processes, concept formation, etc. We run time and time again into subjects reporting certain strategies in problem solving, but their report and what in fact they did do are completely uncorrelated. In other words, they make up stories. The human always makes up hypotheses as to what he has just done. Those hypotheses may not be at all consistent with what actually happened. To listen to our subjects or to listen to our own phenomenological experience and to believe that they are "true," that the stories can substitute for a theory, can be terribly misleading. I want to warn against this model, even as Dr. Arnold apparently feels unhappy about the computer model. Models are models! They either work or they don't work! I feel very strongly that the phenomenological model frequently doesn't work. Obviously Dr. Arnold feels that the computer model doesn't work. Let's find out which ones work and not build on some preconceptions that just because we experience something it's a psychological theory.

Dr. Lacey: One of the main problems with phenomenology is that nobody is working on it, and so we are restricted to the insidious empathic labelling habits of the person having the phenomenological experience. We don't work on phenomenology. We are not developing a language for it, we are not developing functional relations.

Dr. Mandler: Just because we have the phenomenological experience of liking something doesn't mean that the appraisal is *a priori* "I like" or "I don't like." Everything that Dr. Arnold says on appraisal can be replaced by saying that the subject first avoids and then says "I avoided that and therefore I don't like it" or "I approached it and therefore I like it." In other words, the "liking" appraisal may be subsequent to a coding transformation that says "X occurs, avoid X; Y occurs, approach Y." You can take the "liking" out and simply say that it is something the subject puts at the end of the sequence; liking is unnecessary, the appraisal can be called a tendency to approach or to avoid.

Dr. Arnold: Surely, it is a fact of experience that we do like some things and dislike others, and that by and large we try to obtain the one and avoid the other. Appraisal and emotion may be unnecessary for the computer, but human beings cannot help experiencing them.

Since a scientist may employ any type of analysis that seems useful to him, why not a phenomenological analysis? It has the advantage of using terms familiar from our own experience and can also offer clues to the way the brain works. The computer model may have its own virtues, but we have no guarantee that the brain works the way a computer works, and considerable evidence that it does not. For instance, the computer input is restricted to one modality. Drawing on the computer model, it would never occur to us to look for different memory modalities—yet they seem to exist, as our own results and the findings of other investigators show. In computer language, we may talk of *coding* and *recoding*, but these terms give us no hint which structures might do the recoding. If we speak instead of an appraisal of the situation that is experienced as a like or dislike, we may be moved to consider whether the limbic cortex and its connections (Olds' "reward system") might not be the structures that mediate this experience. I had no intention of presenting a phenomenological "model." All I wanted to show was that the analysis of experience is both possible and fruitful.

Chairman's summary

ERNEST A. HAGGARD: Among other things, Dr. Arnold has here demonstrated her broad range of interests and has touched upon the variety of factors that should be taken into consideration in order fully to understand stress and related phenomena. This includes her point that the individual's experience is an important datum, and may be a key to help us understand concurrent neurological and physiological events. It is all too easy to oversimplify a complex problem; frequently this is the scholar's defense mechanism for avoiding the type of stress that is sometimes called cognitive dissonance.

Dr. Korchin's discussion summarizes very cogently many of my questions, or reservations, about Dr. Arnold's paper. To his comments I might add that I am intrigued at the apparent neatness of the one-to-one correspondence between the locus of neurological lesions in rats and deficits in modality-specific learning and retention. But additional research now underway will support or modify these findings. Also, I would wonder whether one can assume that such a neat correspondence will hold in man, given the greater complexity of the latter's neural structures and mental processes. I also suspect that, in the limited time available, Dr. Arnold tried to paint too broad a canvas, and in the process had to omit many crucial details which might have helped us bridge the gap between, say, a phenomenological analysis of emotions and the functioning of particular neurological structures. Nevertheless, her theorizing and findings might serve to reawaken interest in establishing psychophysiological relationships, particularly as they are involved in stress situations. Before such relationships can be established, however, I should think it would be necessary first to develop a comprehensive taxonomy of mental experiences and acts, including emotional states, which could then be related to neurological structures and functions. On the other hand, I don't see how anyone can argue with the proposition that an individual's appraisal of and response to a stressful situation is an important component of the stress reaction and, furthermore, that an individual undergoing such experiences also is likely to know something of what is going on inside himself. Surely, some of the research on individuals' reactions to stress would have been enriched if such factors had been considered.

RICHARD S. LAZARUS

6

Cognitive and personality factors underlying threat and coping

It has been traditional, especially in casual analysis, to view the emotions as causes of cognitive and behavioral reactions, especially when these reactions appear to the observer as "irrational" or maladaptive. When the emotions involved are negatively-toned ones like fear, anger, or depression, we then speak of psychological stress. Stress reactions are said to organize our thinking and our actions, making an individual do things that he would not otherwise do.

I would like to propose that this conceptualization, which blames emotion or stress for irrational thought or maladaptive behavior, is misleading in that it covers up some conceptual confusions and directs our attention to the wrong problems. My purpose here is to support an alternative way of thinking about psychological stress and emotions which reflects increasing concern with cognitive processes (see Lazarus, 1966).

Some confusions in the traditional conceptions of stress and emotion

There are three sources of confusion in the traditional conception that emotion organizes behavior. One of these concerns the hedonistic implication that it is the pain of negatively-toned emotions that motivates coping behavior. It is commonly stated, for example, that the individual is reacting against anxiety when he engages in some defensive process. Although Freud introduced the alternative conception that anxiety produces defense by serving as a signal of danger, it is still implied in much literature that it is the pain of anxiety against which the individual is defending.

The notion of the cue value of anxiety tends to turn our attention toward the cognitive processes underlying the anxiety and defense reaction, and as such it is a step forward in our thinking. Anxiety is said to provide information to the individual about his fate should defensive activity not be called into play. It is not the anxiety, *per se,* that activates the defense but the signal of danger. There remains an unstated difficulty about this formulation, however, a confusion which I wish to note here. To what agency does the anxiety serve as a signal? The Freudian answer would appear to be, "to the ego." But why does the ego, whose function it is to cognize the danger in the first place, have to be informed about what it has already done, that is, appraise danger. Why can't any stimulus be interpreted as a sign of danger if it has previously been followed by harm in the experience of the individual? Why should anxiety be necessary? It appears odd that the agency or structure which engages in a function must be informed that this function has indeed been engaged in.

The third confusion arises because, in psychological stress analysis and in conflict theory, anxiety alone is made the intervening variable. Yet, in practice, clinicians speak of reaction formation as a defense against anger and of manic euphoria as a defense against depression. In the latter instances, there appear to be many emotional intervening variables rather than just one. Thus, the emphasis on anxiety alone is far too simple in stress analysis. Stress theory speaks of anxiety as the culprit, while in practice, any emotional state is presumed to have behavior-organizing properties.

The overriding importance of cognitive processes in psychological stress and emotion

By making emotion the cause rather than the effect, I believe that we turn our attention away from the critical problem in psychological stress analysis—namely, identifying the processes and conditions that produce different stress reactions. We must explain not only the presence of a defense mechanism but also why one mechanism occurs and not another. I want to support the notion that the whole equation should be turned around, that emotional reactions should be regarded as effects rather than causes, and that these effects, in turn, depend heavily on cognitive processes. It is the cognitive processes leading to emotion that organize behavior, not the emotions themselves. Our theoretical and research problem then becomes, "What are these cognitive processes, and what are the conditions that determine them?" Such a view is compatible, of course, with the treatment of anxiety as at least one hypothetical construct, since it then becomes necessary to identify the antecedent and consequent conditions that result in anxiety and the coping processes that arise from it. However, traditional associative-learning conflict theory tends to be oversimple in the number of intervening constructs, in its identification of such variables, in the classes of coping processes dealt with, and in the patterns of reactions that are studied in consequence.

For some years now, there has been an increasing tendency for psychologists interested in psychological stress and emotion to emphasize the cognitions producing these reactions. For example, Magda Arnold (1960 and again in this volume) has emphasized the process of appraisal in the production of emotion. A recent and influential study by Schachter and Singer (1962) not only attacks the unidimensional concept of arousal in defining emotion but also points up the crucial role played by cognitive activity in the production of emotion. In his recent review on emotion, Peters (1963) again and again underscores the "tendency to ignore the cognitive . . . elements . . . in emotion." I, too, regard appraisal as the intervening process in psychological stress analysis, as the precursor of stress reaction. Research from my laboratory has shown that a stressful film will produce less stress reaction if the appraisal of the harmful significance of the events portrayed is altered.

In the full analysis of psychological stress, it is necessary to separate processes involved in threat production from those concerned with coping. The mere fact that the individual anticipates harm and is therefore threatened or anxious does not, by itself, permit us to predict the nature of the reaction. Knowing that he is threatened does not allow us to specify, for example, why anger occurs instead of fear, or why anxiety, depression, or guilt are experienced rather than some other affect. It does not enable us to understand the variable behavioral and physiological pattern of reaction within the same individual across occasions, and between individuals, and the apparent contradictions that appear between levels of measurement. For example, when the individual shows physiological signs of threat but gives verbal reports denying that anything is wrong, the intervening psychological processes are evidently different than when his reported affect agrees with the physiological measures.

The importance of discrepancies between stress indicators—an empirical example

Before proceeding with the remainder of my thesis, I want to digress by describing some data that provide a concrete, empirical example of one commonly observed discrepancy between the response indicators of psychological stress. This example illustrates how the nature of the inferences we make about the intervening psychological process varies with the type of patterning of these indicators. Elsewhere (Lazarus, 1965b), I have tried more systematically to make the general point that, without exception, all indicators of psychological stress are subject to individual response and stimulus specificity. Different intervening mechanisms are often reflected by each indicator and by the pattern of these indicators. The example comes from a recent attempt by my colleagues and me to study Japanese stress reactions. The material I will present here is part of a larger study which is to be published elsewhere (Lazarus, Tomita, Opton, & Kodama, 1966).

In our original planning, we wanted to answer a number of cross-cultural questions, for example, whether Japanese reactions to a silent film entitled "Subincision" would be similar to those of Americans. Earlier studies (Lazarus, Speisman, Mordkoff, & Davison, 1962) had shown that this film, which depicts a puberty ceremony in an Australian stone age culture involving partial dissection of the penises of adolescent boys by means of a stone knife, was highly disturbing to watch. In addition, further research had demonstrated that the magnitude of the reaction could be reduced by the introduction of experimentally-created sound tracks based on the ego-defensive concepts of denial and intellectualization (Speisman, Lazarus, Mordkoff, & Davison, 1964b). Moreover, self-reported affective disturbance to the film, as well as autonomic indicators of threat, such as heart rate and skin conductance, could be "short-circuited" by playing the denial and intellectualization passages to the individual before he viewed the Subincision film (Lazarus & Alfert, 1964). In effect, the defense-oriented passages served prophylactically to reduce the stress reaction normally produced by watching the film, presumably by altering the subjects' appraisal of the disturbing events that were depicted. We wanted to see whether these passages had the same effect on people living in a different culture. As it turned out, none of the original questions posed in this research could be properly answered because of an unexpected difference between Japanese and Americans in the way in which the experience of being an experimental subject was handled.

In brief, two populations were sampled, a college group of eighty young men from Waseda University in Tokyo and an older sample of sixty men between the ages of 36 and 58, roughly matched socioeconomically and educationally. On entering the laboratory individually, GSR electrodes were attached to the subject. After a baseline period, a control movie was shown on the subject of rice-farming in Japan. Subsequently, one of four orientation conditions was administered to the subjects. There were twenty subjects in each of these conditions. Following this set of conditions, another base line reading was obtained, and then the Subincision film was shown. During both film presentations, skin conductance was measured continuously, and a series of self-reported estimates of degree of distress was obtained at numerous intervals during both films. This latter was done by inserting five-second blank leaders into the film and requesting the subject to rate on a seven-point scale his degree of distress during the preceding film segment whenever a blank leader appeared on the screen. In this way, a near-continuous picture of self-reported distress could be obtained as well as a continuous record of skin conductance. There were other procedures in the experiment that I shall not mention here because they are not germane to the findings I want to present.

The graphs in Figure 6-1 represent the self-reported distress of the subjects in the Japanese groups as they watched the control and stressful movie. Because we are not interested here in the effects of the experimental treatments, these conditions are combined into one curve. For comparison purposes, a curve of reported affective disturbance obtained

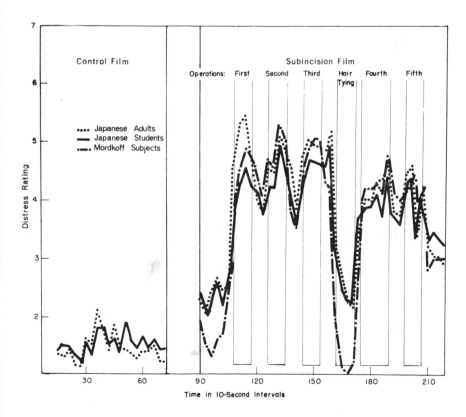

FIGURE 6-1.   Self-reported distress ratings of Japanese and American groups (see text).

by Mordkoff (1964), using a similar procedure with American subjects, is presented also. One notes that ratings of distress are rather low during the control film but show a consistent pattern of disturbances during the Subincision film. Rises to the highest levels of distress are reported during the operation scenes of the film, with sharp drops occurring during the benign scenes in-between operations and during a long ceremonial period just past the middle of the film. This pattern of reported distress shown by the Japanese subjects is identical to that observed by Mordkoff among American students.

The picture changes dramatically when we examine the variable of skin conductance, as is seen in Figure 6-2. Here are shown the Japanese population's curve of skin conductance during the rice-farming and Subincision films and, for comparative purposes, data from Mordkoff showing control and Subincision film levels among American students. We have used this film many times in the United States, and the pattern

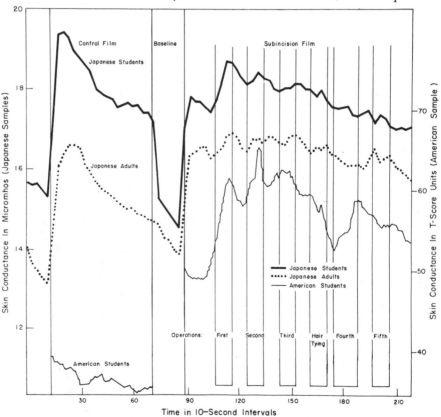

FIGURE 6-2.   Skin conductance of Japanese and American groups (see text). From *Psychological Stress and the Coping Process* by Richard S. Lazarus. Copyright 1966. McGraw-Hill Book Company. Used by permission.

is always roughly the same: low levels of autonomic reactivity during the control film, high levels during the Subincision film. Moreover, these levels nicely reflect the contents of the film, going up sharply during operation sequences, down during the non-operation scenes. Actually, Mordkoff's curves are not the clearest or best with which to make this point, but they were selected because they were most readily available for this comparison. Both the Japanese students and older subjects show essentially the same picture.

There is little change in skin conductance between the control film level and that for the Subincision film in the Japanese subjects. Moreover, the correspondence between reactivity level and the content of the scenes is very poor, fluctuations in level appearing almost random. There is clearly something different occurring as between the Japanese and American samples. What are some of the possible explanations?

One possibility is that racial differences in sweat gland activity or skin characteristics might exist between orientals and caucasians. Johnson and Corah (1963) and Bernstein (1965) have demonstrated, for example, the existence of racial differences (for Negroes and whites) in basal skin resistance. However, this is not likely to be the explanation for our data. Close examination of the Japanese skin conductance curves shows that their baseline levels are low and comparable to those observed in our other studies of Americans. Moreover, during the second baseline period, the Japanese subjects show a sharp drop in skin conductance, rising again only when the experiment resumes.

The best hypothesis seems to be a psychological one, namely, that the Japanese are unusually sensitive to the total experimental situation and react with marked and continued apprehension during all phases of that situation. The apprehension temporarily wanes during the baseline periods because the experiment appears to the subject to be temporarily suspended in accordance with the instructions.

As our Japanese colleagues have pointed out, the Japanese are unaccustomed to the impersonal probing and observation characteristic of a laboratory situation. Moreover, most analyses of their national character suggest that Japanese tend to be threatened by being observed, especially from outside the group with whom they are identified, being more easily threatened with ridicule or criticism in a situation in which they must measure up to some standard (for example, see Benedict, 1946). Thus, they are reacting, not to the specific contents of the experiment or to the distinctions between what the experimenter regards as benign or threatening, but rather to the total evaluative situation. This general apprehension overshadows any specific variation there might be in the impact of the different film contents.

Close analogies to this can be found in certain experiments within the American literature on psychological stress. For example, using heart rate as their index of stress reaction, Glickstein et al. (1957) have shown that subjects with high levels of independently assessed anxiety showed uniformly high levels of heart rate during both benign and stressful procedures of an experiment, while those low in anxiety exhibited low heart rates for the benign portions but reacted sharply to the stressful aspects as defined by the experimenters. Similar findings with serum hydrocortisone as the stress measure are reported by Persky et al. (1959), and by other groups of researchers as well. Recently, for example, a finding similar to this has also been reported by White (1965), who divided subjects on the basis of a questionnaire measure of anxiety. In discussing their findings, Glickstein et al. have written:

> The more disturbed subject, we might suppose, starts each experimental day with a distinctly greater amount of anticipatory anxiety. Taken from familiar surroundings and people with whom he has worked out some mode of adjustment, he is acutely aware of the potential threats in a strange laboratory, with its imposing wires and machinery and the business-like, but somewhat cold, experimenters. . . . *To be in an experiment in the first place is the stress. . . . With somewhat less anxiety, a patient becomes less sensitive to the more implicit threats of the situation in general and, simultaneously, is more capable of distinguishing and reacting to the more explicitly disturbing events.* (1957, p. 106) [1]

But we still must explain why the self-report picture displayed by the Japanese subjects conforms so closely to that of the American subjects in exquisitely reflecting the disturbing and nondisturbing sequences of the Subincision film and distinguishing so nicely between the benign control and stressful movie. Here, too, there are alternative interpretations. One is that the Japanese were simply dutifully expressing verbally what appeared to them as appropriate reactions without, indeed, experiencing comparable states of disturbance. In effect, they might be giving the experimenter what they thought he expected, as communicated by the "demand characteristics" of the situation.

A more probable guess is that the report did, indeed, reflect genuinely experienced ups and downs of distress, but that these were comparatively small in magnitude against the larger impact of the apprehension over being in the experimental situation itself. When asked to attend to the distress experienced in relation to the specific movie scenes, or to the differential impact of the control and stressful movie, they could indeed make clear discriminations. But with respect to the autonomic reaction, the larger and more continuous apprehension created by being a subject overshadowed the more minor variations resulting from specific stimuli.

This latter explanation has both methodological and theoretical

---

[1] Italics not in original.

implications. Methodologically, it implies the possibility that individual sources of stress reaction are not additive with respect to such
autonomic indicators of arousal as skin conductance. Any simple, unidimensional indicator (as exclusive of multidimensional response patterns) reflects the largest source of disturbance, regardless of what it is.
Alternatively, but not exclusive of the above, when the level of disturbance is high for any reason, a single measure (such as skin conductance) is less sensitive to small sources of variation than it is when the
level of disturbance is low.

With respect to the intervening psychological mechanisms, we see
here an instance of failure of agreement between different indicators
of psychological stress processes. Either the disagreement is the result
of different ways in which the Japanese cope with situations, or it derives from different sources of threat in the two populations. If the
latter, we would say the Japanese subjects are more threatened by being
in an experiment than the Americans. If the former, we might say that
the Japanese are more sensitive than the Americans to what is expected
in social situations and therefore comply more readily with the demand
characteristics of the situation. They thus report distress accordingly. In
either case, the pattern of response indicators provides the basis for different inferences about the underlying psychological processes. It is
clear that we must learn more about the psychological rules which explain agreements and disagreements between behavioral and physiological indicators of stress reaction.

In the remainder of this chapter, I shall focus on one phase of this
problem, namely that dealing with the importance of individual differences in coping processes that arise in response to threat and which
influence the observable reaction pattern. I want to underscore two main
themes: (1) that *stress reactions are reflections or consequences of coping
processes* intended to reduce threat, and (2) that *these coping processes
(and the observable reactions themselves) depend, in part, on cognitive
activity* very similar in kind to the process of threat appraisal.

Stress reactions are reflections of coping processes

With respect to the first point, when the individual is
threatened, activities are aroused to ward off the anticipated harm. Unless something is done to protect the psychological system, a damaging
state of affairs will occur (by the definition of threat). The individual
may attempt to avoid the danger, overcome it by attack on the harmful
agent, or engage in autoplastic defense activity, reappraising the danger
even in defiance of reality. It follows that the observable reactions to
threat will depend on the nature of the coping process that is activated.

For example, anger accompanied by behavioral attack on the threatening agent will appear to be quite different in response characteristics
than anger in which the behavioral expression of aggression is inhibited, and even more different from the reaction of fear associated
with behavioral flight to avoid the impending harm. The motor-be-
havioral correlates of different forms of coping will obviously differ, as
will the affects experienced and the physiological stress reaction observed. While there may be physiological features in common (for example, as postulated in the concept of arousal and in Selye's adaptation
syndrome), the patterns of reaction will also diverge in important details
as a function of different types of coping processes.

This point is more obvious when it involves patterns of behavior and
affect rather than physiological response patterns, but its significance is
the same. There is evidence that even the pattern of autonomic nervous
system activity, as revealed by end-organ reactions, such as heart-
rate, skin conductance, and respiration, is determined by the nature of
the coping process. The recent research of Lacey, Kagan, Lacey, and
Moss (1963) suggests, for example, that when the individual is oriented
to take in environmental input, there will be cardiac deceleration; con-
trariwise, an orientation to reject the environment would be associated
with heart-rate acceleration.[2] In an earlier study by Weiner, Singer, and
Reiser (1962), processes of coping in a threatening situation were shown
to insulate hypertensive patients from the relationship with the experimenter in such a way as to prevent the heightened blood pressure that
might have been expected on the basis of their characteristic symptom
pattern.

What do these findings mean? I think they say that the type of coping process (or as Lacey et al. put it, the orientation with respect to the
stimulus) influences the physiological pattern of reaction. If we take this
seriously, it means that to understand and predict the physiological
pattern of stress reaction we must know the nature of coping; conversely,
the coping processes can be inferred from the pattern of reaction.

It is necessary now to raise the question of how different coping
mechanisms are capable of producing different kinds of response patterns, including discrepancies between behavioral and physiological indicators. The fullest statement of the principle is that all categories of
the observed threat reaction reflect the nature of the process of coping
with threat.

I think the same position has been taken by Arnold (1960) in her
analysis of emotions.[3] Arnold suggests that the quality of an emotion
(fear as opposed to anger) is explained by the motoric impulse that is
generated by the stimulus whose value to the individual is appraised as

2 See also Lacey's discussion in Chapter 2.
3 See also Arnold's discussion in Chapter 5.

positive or negative. In fact, says Arnold, this impulse with its psychological and physiological correlates *is* the emotion. She writes:

> As soon as we appraise something as worth having in an immediate and intuitive way we feel an attraction toward it. As soon as we intuitively judge that something is threatening, we feel repelled from it, we feel urged to avoid it. The intuitive appraisal of the situation initiates an *action tendency that is felt as emotion,* expressed in various bodily changes, and that eventually may lead to overt action. (1960, *1*, p. 177)

The action tendency, which in Arnold's view is the emotional reaction, should be interpreted functionally in psychological stress analysis as the process of coping with threat when the emotions involved are activated by the anticipation of harm. Since the action tendency is considered to be motivated by threat, its goal is the reduction or elimination of the anticipated harm. In effect, the action tendency resulting from the appraisal of threat is an effort on the part of the individual to cope with the harmful condition.

If an individual attempts to cope with a defense such as denial, then his self-report concerning affective distress will reflect this denial. But unless the denial is successful in eliminating the threat, the physiological stress reaction will remain, producing a pattern of discrepancy between the observed reaction at each level. As Lazarus and Alfert (1964) have shown, subjects prone to denial defenses do indeed report less anxiety but show larger autonomic disturbance than nondeniers who exhibit less autonomic evidence of stress reaction and report considerable anxiety. Such discrepancies between self-report and physiological indicators of stress reaction are usually accounted for by coping processes that intervene between threat and the observed stress reaction. It is perhaps a little more unusual to maintain, as is done by Lacey and his associates (1963), that even the physiological response pattern reflects the orientation toward, or as I would say, the form of coping with, the demands or threats of the situation.

Coping processes are, in turn, dependent on the cognitive process of appraisal

Now I come to my second major theme—that the coping process itself depends, in part, on cognitive activity that is loosely called appraisal. When Arnold states that "The intuitive appraisal of the situation initiates an action tendency that is felt as emotion . . . ," she manages ingeniously to link cognitive activity with the characteristics of the emotional reaction. Arnold, too, treats emotion as an effect of cognitive processes. But she does not tell us how the appraisal leads to the particular action tendency, and so we are unable to take the next step of specifying the conditions under which one or another action tendency or emotion will occur. Remember that in psychological stress analysis, Arnold's action tendency is regarded as a process of coping with threat. We need ultimately to describe the kinds of appraisal that lead to each action tendency or coping impulse and the conditions that determine each kind of appraisal.

What is the significance of making this assertion that cognitive processes underlie not only threat but the form of coping with threat selected by the individual? Partly it adds the crucial dimension to our analysis of interaction between stimulus factors and the personality or dispositional factors characteristic of the individual. Up to now we have tended to emphasize either of these alone in predicting the reaction. For example, if we speak of stimulus specificity in physiological analysis, we mean that some portion of the variance of the reaction is normatively predicated on variations in the stimulus. If we speak of response or individual specificity, then we are saying that characteristics of the individual determine the reaction in a wide range of stimulus conditions. We have our stimulus and response specificities at the behavioral level too. For example, most social psychological research involves systematic variation in the social structure and the measurement of the main effects of this variation. Most personality research, in contrast, involves systematic variation in the traits or dispositions in which individuals vary and the measurement of the main effects of these traits on the observed behavior.

But we are somehow reasonably sure that it is the combination or interaction of stimulus and dispositional properties that determines much of the reaction. And when we say that an individual appraises a situation in choosing a form of coping process, we are opening the way to seeing the effects as caused by a transaction with a particular environment by an individual with a particular psychological structure. We are implying in this way that if we knew the factors in the stimulus configuration and those within the psychological structure that jointly influence this appraisal, we could then predict the coping process and the observed reaction. In my mind, appraisal signifies such a transaction, and, as such, offers an advance over purely stimulus and trait centered analysis of psychological stress. How is this so?

The concept of appraisal makes us ask about the information concerning the environment that is relevant to the decision about how the individual will cope with threat. In effect, we are asking what the individual needs to know or believe about the situation for him to react in one way or another.

You will notice that I have repeatedly said that cognitive processes *in part* determine coping activities. I mean by this qualification to recognize that not all personality characteristics influence coping by the mediating cognitive process of appraisal, but that many do. For example, social constraints may not have much force in inhibiting the expression of a coping impulse if the individual lacks what is often called the capacity to control impulse expression. We even speak of this kind of individual as not "looking before he leaps," as being impulsive and often regretting actions after they have been made rather than evaluating their consequences beforehand and inhibiting the course of action which may be damaging. Thus, the capacity to control impulse expression, as studied by Block and Block (1952), is an example of a personality trait that influences coping directly, without the mediation of an appraisal process.

Interactions between situational and personality determinants of appraisal and coping

I said earlier that the concept of appraisal makes us ask what information is relevant to the decision about coping, information which comprises the external and internal conditions of appraisal. What are some of the factors in the stimulus configuration that research has indicated are important? Degree of threat is one. Greater sacrifices of other goals will be made, for example, if the goal that is endangered is important than if it is not. Another is the location of the agent of harm. For example, attack cannot be mounted, or flight mobilized, if a harmful agent is not identified, that is, if there is nothing to attack or flee. The viability of alternative actions is a third. As Berkowitz (1962) has said in paraphrasing Janis (1958), ". . . the extent to which this emotion (fear) is stronger than anger may be a function of the individual's perceived power to control or hurt his frustrator relative to the frustrator's power to control or harm him" (1962, p. 45). An interesting example of this principle is the observation that in situations of extreme helplessness, such as the concentration camp, people show surprisingly little anger against the agents of their distress but are very quick to show anger against their fellow prisoners, or outsiders, who are less able to retaliate. A fourth factor is the social or situational constraints that catapult the individual into further harm were he to cope with threat in a particular way.

As I have said, the role of these situational variables in coping depends on factors within the psychological structure, some of which are important in influencing appraisal. One example would be the motivational structure of the individual which determines whether any given result of coping will be appraised as harmful and to what degree. Another comprises the general beliefs of the individual about the environment and his resources for coping with it. Highly generalized attitudes, such as trust or distrust, as described by Erikson (1950), should be very important in determining what reliance the individual will place on environmental resources for mastering dangers.

Qualities of the psychological or personality structure will determine how this information is to be utilized or modified. For example, if the individual believes that attack on the threatening agent cannot possibly overcome the threat, then attack as the coping impulse is not likely to be activated. Or if attack might overcome the threat, but the individual believes it is wrong or will be severely punished, then even if it arises as the coping impulse or action tendency, it is likely to be inhibited.

The role of appraisal in coping is nicely illustrated in some of the research reviewed by Berkowitz (1962), which shows that aggression is not an automatic or inevitable accompaniment of frustrating or threatening conditions. Its evocation depends on a number of antecedent conditions, for example, the arbitrariness of the frustrator, his power to retaliate against aggression, and the presence of internalized values against aggression. In effect, the individual evaluates complex social cues, and the coping process is dependent on this evaluation.

In my view, it is not as useful to say that anger is caused by the stimulus situation, and that anger, the intervening variable, modified by personality factors, then causes the behavior, as it is to say that the objective stimulus situation is appraised on the basis of its characteristics as well as traits of personality, this cognitive activity of appraisal being the intervening process. If both external and internal controls permit it, the outcome will be the emotion, anger, and the behavior of aggression. If internal controls permit anger, but the appraisal of the objective situation is that aggression would be dangerous, and assuming the individual has the capacity to control impulses, then the outcome will be anger but no direct aggression. If internal personality prohibitions against aggression are especially strong, then the appraisal may lead to other emotions and behaviors, for example, fear or depression but not anger or aggression. In this view, depression should be regarded as based on the appraisal of a frustrating or threatening condition in which externally directed anger and retaliation are not viable alternatives.

The same reasoning must apply to coping processes other than aggression, for example, flight, the choice of defense, and efforts to prepare against the harm—as when graduate students study for threatening examinations and plan strategies for coping with the anticipated danger of failing, as observed by Mechanic (1962). The personal and social consequences of any action tendency are appraised by the individual and thus shape the coping strategy which is selected out of many alternative possibilities. Let me give you a further example of this principle from the sociological literature.

Attempting to distinguish between the conditions producing panic or riot, Smelser (1963) has pointed out that these outbursts depend on widely shared beliefs about how the harmful social condition is being caused and how it can be modified or eliminated, and that the hostile action will be condoned, or at least not retaliated against. In the riot, there is the identification of dangerous or evil persons who are held responsible for the damaging situation, and there is the belief that the problem can be overcome by hostile action. In the case of panic a very different appraisal is involved. Discussing the kinds of escape possibilities, for example, that permit panic, Smelser quotes Quarantelli (1954–55) as follows:

The important aspect is the belief or feeling of *possible* entrapment. This is reiterated again and again in the remarks of panic participants. It is not that affected individuals believe or feel they are definitely trapped. In such instances panic does not follow . . . The flight of panic arises only when being trapped is sensed or thought of as a possibility rather than an actuality . . . (Quarantelli, 1954–55, p. 273)

[Smelser adds:] In addition, people who panic sense that this "limited number of escape routes" is "closing" (not closed) so that escape must be made quickly (1963, p. 136)

[And further:] . . . reactions such as terror or infantile regression can occur in such settings (when escape routes are conceived to be completely blocked), but not panic. Marshall (1947) notes that in amphibious attacks during World War II immobility in the face of enemy fire was a common response: . . . the sea was at (the troops') back; there was no place to run even had they been capable of movement. They sat there dumbly in the line of fire, their minds blanked out, their fingers too nerveless to hold a weapon. (1963, p. 136)

Analysis of mine and submarine disasters also supports the idea that only when there is the possibility of escape which may be closed will there be panic. In other words, one particular kind of appraisal encourages panic rather than some other form of coping reaction.

The well-known experiments of Mintz (1951) on "bottlenecks" or "traffic jams" as groups of subjects must withdraw corks on the ends of strings from a narrow-necked bottle also suggest the importance of appraisal of alternatives, even though Mintz emphasizes the reward structure of the situation. Recent studies by Kelley et al. (1965), extending Mintz's work, support the role of appraisal of what others in the group will do in panic situations in determining the coping strategy selected by the individuals in those settings. If we take one traditional view of emotion and coping, we would have to say that Mintz's subjects in the panic-engendering conditions became frightened, and as a consequence, could not properly assess the futility of precipitous "escape." They attempted "escape," although it was maladaptive, because emotions superseded rational thought and action. The view that I think is more fruitful is that the dangers or gains are apprehended by the individual, and this leads to the decision to act in accordance with this appraisal. Fear, or some other emotion, is the *consequence* of this appraisal and the action tendency or coping impulse it activates. If Mintz is correct in his observation that the reward structure is important, then this structure must have been appraised by his subjects on the basis of the stimulus configuration and on the basis of shared motivational characteristics and beliefs about how others will react in such a situation. No effort was made by Mintz to study individual differences in reaction that might have highlighted some of the personality determinants of varieties of appraisal and coping.

Although I have argued that the cognitive process of appraisal underlies the coping process and the observed stress reaction pattern, empirical research must be directed at the interactive role of observable antecedent conditions in the stimulus configuration and personality traits in determining that reaction. Wolff, Friedman, Hofer, and Mason (1964a) have shown that parents of children dying of leukemia who exhibited strong denial defenses showed significantly less evidence of adrenal cortical secretions than those without such defenses. The parental reactions were treated as a defense because information about the child's outlook had been forcibly brought home to the individual by the physicians and others around him. However, in many situations, failure to interpret dangers realistically can occur simply because the cues of danger are not made available to the individual, as when a physician withholds threatening information. Whether it is withheld or not is often determined by the physician's reading of the patient's reaction to minimal information of disaster. The physician senses (or believes) that the patient will react badly to threatening cues. He responds to these inferred defensive needs on the part of the patient with behaviors that are, from his point of view, protective. In this kind of interchange between the stimulus situation, as represented by the physician's behavior and the personality of the patient, we see a clinical example of the complexity of the problem and the importance of emphasizing the cognitive transactions between a person with a particular personality and the variable kinds of cues of danger the stimulus configuration contains. What the individual will do in the way of coping with the threat is also influenced by a variety of social constraints based on anticipated environmental reactions. For example, in the same study of parents of children with cancer, if the parents did not appear to suffer visibly, they often were exposed to severe criticism from relatives and friends who might regard them as heartless or indifferent to the plight of their child—social pressures which not only added to their already heavy burden but also served to shape their coping reactions as well. The evidence is strong that the observed reaction pattern depends on intervening cognitive processes involving complex interplays between particular personalities and stimulus patterns.

With respect to laboratory studies of personality traits and coping, a fascinating experiment by Conn and Crowne (1964) supports the principle that motivation for approval as a trait results in the inhibition of aggressive behavior as a method of coping when the individual is threatened, by virtue of his appraisal of the consequences of assertive acts that could lead to social disapproval. They observed the amount of euphoria following a strong provocation to anger. First, a measure of need for approval was obtained from male undergraduate students, based on a standardized questionnaire scale in which the subject attributes to himself or denies culturally-disapproved statements. In the experimental situation, the subject is joined with an accomplice of the experimenter and introduced to a situation in which he could win considerable money (up to $5.00) along with the accomplice who is his partner. The experimenter is unexpectedly called out of the room, whereupon the accomplice proposes that the two of them enter into collusion in order to maximize their winnings. However, when the experimenter returns and the game begins, the accomplice exasperatingly violates his agreement leading to minimal payments for the subject.

At the conclusion of the game, the subject and accomplice are escorted into another room to wait until the apparatus is ready for the next part of the experiment. In a fashion comparable to that of the Schachter and Singer study (1962), a euphoria-stimulating condition is then created by the accomplice, who makes bad jokes, laughs uproariously, plays makeshift games in which he attempts to involve the subject and generally acts exuberantly and enthusiastically. If the subject mentions the violation of the agreement by the accomplice, the latter laughs and replies, "Well, that's the way it goes."

The authors find that approval-oriented subjects exhibited significantly more euphoria in the experimental condition than did subjects assumed to be low in need for approval, a difference that did not occur in the control condition, in which there was no previous experience of treachery. The behavior of the subjects is described by the authors as follows:

. . . After being treated in a dastardly manner by the experimental accomplice, approval-striving Ss endorsed by word and action the simulated jubilation of the accomplice and interacted with him as a friend and admirer. In dramatic contrast is the reaction of the low need for approval Ss. Following the same instigation to anger, they became sullen and resentful in facial expression and communication and refused to endorse the accomplice's "ode of joy." Instead, they directed derogatory comments at him and spurned his invitations to play. (Conn & Crowne, 1964, p. 177)

For the relationship found by Conn and Crowne to take place, the individual must have taken into account the meaning of the social situation—the potential dangers to his social status were he to act assertively.

The subject low in need for approval selects a coping strategy (in this case conformity to social pressure and lack of assertiveness) on the basis of having evaluated what is called for in the situation to preserve needed social relationships. If the subject had really believed the partner would like him better if he acted assertively, a totally different outcome would have to be predicted. The approval-seeking subjects would have acted even more assertively than those low in need for approval.

Appraisal and irrationality

I must return briefly to my initial assertion that we should regard threat and coping with threat as the consequences of cognitive processes. At first glance, it would seem that this focus on appraisal places an undue emphasis on cognitive processes in the psychodynamics of stress. It is as if the individual is continually making rational judgments about coping processes, for example, judgments of what course of action is viable or imposes the possibility of further threats. Have we placed ourselves in the position of no longer being able to comprehend irrationality?

It might appear that cognitive appraisal, to which so much importance is attached, is a conscious, rational, balanced consideration of the evidence, leading to a conclusion justified by the facts that a given situation is actually threatening or benign and shaped by the requirement that a given solution will be successful in eliminating or reducing the threat. But the term *cognitive* does not imply awareness, good reality testing, or adaptiveness. It only implies that thought processes are involved, not the kind or quality of the thought. What is meant is that beliefs, expectations, perceptions, and their motivations underlie how a threat stimulus is reacted to. Furthermore, the cognitions involved need not be reportable.

The point is that the stress reaction is the effect of these cognitive appraisal processes and the conditions that determine them. The irrationality or maladaptiveness does not come primarily from the intervention of emotions in thought processes, but rather from the fact that threat places the psychological system in jeopardy and that the alternatives for coping with threat are tied to motives, beliefs, and expectations concerning the situation, which differ from person to person.

It is true that one finds abundant clinical examples of individuals who have acted "irrationally" under accompanying intense emotional disturbance. A lay tradition has grown up which makes emotional disturbance the cause rather than effect of maladaptive behavior. Since negatively-toned emotion is an inevitable accompaniment or correlate of threat and coping, it only *seems* as though the emotion is "causing" the trouble. The culprit is really the recognition of threat or danger, and the cognitions that underlie the effort to cope with it. The correlation between threat and emotion makes it easy to confuse cause and effect, especially since the emotional state is the most obtrusive feature of the entire psychological event. The hypothetical construct has mistakenly become the literally conceived cause.

Concluding remarks

What we must do in psychological stress analysis is to identify the cognitions that underlie threat, and the specific appraisals that lead to each form of coping, with its observable behavioral and physiological response pattern. Particular appraisals underlie attack which is expressed behaviorally; somewhat different appraisals underlie the impulse to attack which is inhibited. Still different appraisals underlie flight patterns. The same might be said for each form of defense as well. Time does not permit me to do more than make the general point here. These appraisals are, in turn, shaped by the stimulus configuration and personality as they interact.

Two fundamental assumptions must be made if what I have said is to make sense, and these assumptions have made up the two interrelated themes of this chapter. First, the observed pattern of reaction depends on intervening psychological activities, such as the coping process. Secondly, underlying each type of coping is a particular kind of appraisal in which the consequences of cues are interpreted. This appraisal leads to the selection of a coping process that is appropriate to it, though not necessarily to what is required for good adaptiveness or reality testing. I believe that research on the conditions that determine the coping process and the observed patterns of stress reaction would proceed faster and more fruitfully if we sought to conceptualize the appraisals involved in each type of coping, if we ceased to fear phenomenological terms and concepts and used them to the fullest extent to locate the empirical conditions accounting for varieties of stress reaction.

Invited commentary

MORTIMER H. APPLEY: First, I would say that I am in full agreement with the emphasis that Dr. Lazarus has given to the contextual, transactional nature of stress in his most interesting paper and the importance which he and Dr. Arnold have placed on appraisal processes. In a paper prepared for the 1960 Bonn Congress (Appley, 1962), I talked about the necessity for conceiving of "a perceptual screen of meaning" between stressor and reaction in order to understand the variations in response that obviously occur to similar stimuli. I am glad to substitute the term *appraisal* for perceptual screen, since the concept of appraisal has now been cleared of the implication that it is conscious and since it may in fact be used to describe a continuous or sequential rather than instantaneous process. To Magda Arnold's use of the phrase "a continuous unconscious appraisal," I would add "and *re*appraisal," perhaps making it more compatible with a kind of computer model.

To pursue Dr. Lazarus' invitation to conceptualize the appraisal process(es) more carefully, I would suggest that there is the possibility of at least three kinds of simultaneous evaluation or appraisal processes going on. First, *an appraisal of task requirements* and one's competence in relation to them. This is obviously a complex and multi-stage evaluative process. Secondly, *an appraisal of one's own role* in relation to task requirements—the shifting role or roles, in fact, that one plays. For instance, a student in a class may appraise himself in relation to the subject matter being discussed, in relation to the other students present, in relation to the instructor, in relation to the time in the term and to the closeness of an examination or a paper assignment, and so on. As regards coping behavior, he would appraise the impact of speaking up in terms of all these dimensions. Similarly, if he answered a question and his answer proved to be wrong, what would the various effects be: on his standing in the class, with his peers, etc. All of these simultaneous appraisals—some taking momentary precedence over others—go on as part of a constant evaluation of the environment.

And thirdly, some form of *appraisal of environmental constraints.* This would be reality testing (whether done realistically or not). The three appraisal processes can obviously not be independent and must feed into a continuing process of evaluation and reevaluation. A further dimension of this evaluative process—and I can only imagine a computer model for this—would be the assessment of action in respect to all of one's existent goals—positive and negative, short-range and long. Some goals and some aversions would be more pressing than others. Thus, I would add to the example of the classroom situation the hardness of the seat one is sitting on, the closeness to or recency of lunch, and so on—situational factors which may gain ascendancy in determining a particular momentary outcome. All of these dimensions—and more—would have to be taken into account if we once begin to analyze the appraisal process.

Dr. Lazarus would agree, I am sure, with this estimate of the scope of the problem, although his paper did not go this far.

If we now turn to coping behaviors, I believe that a similar analysis would be useful—coping in relation to the task or tasks—the dimension of *competence,* perhaps; coping in relation to one's own role or roles—the dimension of *relevance,* perhaps; and coping in relation to a kind of deeper level, on-going ego development—the dimension of *significance,* perhaps, which would account for base line levels at different physical, social, or psychological stages. These are with respect to the effects of threat upon task, role, and ego—and I'm using these terms very loosely—but we must also look at coping in relation not only to the threatening stimulus but to the likelihood of the threat eventuating into the danger. That is to say, there are both the annoyance—the threatening stimulus— which is interacted with and appraised in its own right and some kind of further appraisal of the probabilites of the real danger occurring. Here such dimensions as the intensity or nature of the danger—whether it is a task-inter-rupting threat or a status-threat or a life-threat—would need to be appraised.

Once we deal with coping in relation to the threatening stimulus and then in relation to the danger, I think we have to add also an evaluation of the *consequences* of coping behavior into the appraisal formula. An individual faced with a problem may begin to cope at one level or at several levels simul-taneously. Assuming the problem is not resolved completely and instantaneously, there must be an appraisal of the effectiveness of the behavior he engages in, and in the event of its failure or partial failure, we may find that a second order threat has developed and enters into successive appraisals. In short, once an individual starts to react to a situation he must then appraise what his reaction (resulting from a previous appraisal) is producing.

I would go further to suggest the notion that stress is a complex *residual* of the processes resulting from appraisals of threat, of danger, and of the effectiveness of coping. There is a tendency to deal with stress, as Dr. Notter-man noted earlier, as if it were a binary—on or off—process, and surely this is an unacceptable model. If we look at stress—or this whole range of things we are calling stress—in terms of a continuum involving successive thresholds, we may be better able to understand what is going on.

There is, we would all agree, a continuum rather than a dichotomy between the normal and the abnormal. I suggest the phenomena of anxiety and stress could be placed on this continuum. Starting at the "normal" end, I believe that there is a step-ordered series of thresholds from the initiation of new exploratory coping behavior in any case where innate or habitual coping responses are found to be inadequate.[4] This we call an *instigation threshold*, and it is defined as a point of change from innate or habitual to new coping behavior, or conversely, defined by the exhaustion (or the anticipated ex-haustion) of the repertoire of readily available effective coping responses. (We've obviously written into this formulation the assumption of a habit pattern, implying that the threshold would be reached by different individuals at different times, depending upon the extensity of their response repertoire and their history of reinforcements.) Training would obviously have an effect on the point at which this instigation-to-new-learning threshold was reached.

Thus, we go from nonlearning or some habit level to a change required by circumstances of the environment. A second or *frustration threshold* is posited in the event that goal behavior is interfered with or that such inter-ference is anticipated. I see a useful distinction between these two related thresholds. Perhaps the following illustrations will make clear what is in-tended. In the first place, a person may be in a room and apply to his usual routine for egress. Finding this door locked, he looks around for another door,

[4] The concept of stress thresholds is treated more fully elsewhere (Cofer & Appley, 1964, pp. 451 ff).

perhaps chooses the nearest one, and exits by it. Here we would see an instigation to action, created by the closed door in combination with the desire and/or need to exit. If the second door is closed, there is a likelihood of further searching behavior. However, at this point—or at the third door, or at the fourth, depending on how many exits the room contains and/or how badly the person wants or needs out—the process would possibly reach a higher order of invigoration or activation, which is the "frustration threshold." We are saying that these processes are step-ordered. This latter threshold is linked with threat perception and would undoubtedly be associated with intensification and perhaps a repetition of responses. So-called "anxiety-related responses" would be expected to intrude at this point. We have suggested that this is the point at which a shift will occur from, what we call "task-oriented" to "ego-oriented" behavior. Now if (and when) the engagement in both task- and ego-oriented behaviors proves ineffective in producing change in the situation, a third or *stress threshold* will then be reached. We speak of this as a period identified with the perception of danger and such terms as *desperation* or *panic* might become relevant here.

In sum, I am suggesting a graded increase from mild distress or mild discomfort—which leads to or instigates change in behavior—to a state of frustration and a beginning of worry about the self and self-threat, possibly accompanied by psychosomatic changes, to a more active disturbance which we are calling stress. To complete the picture it would be fair to speak of an *exhaustion threshold* or point of helplessness or hopelessness in which ego-defensive behaviors and the enervating physiological changes give way to energy-conserving inactivity, or to disordered behavior.

How do we relate this to Selye's (1950) notions? One of our problems in trying to translate Selye's ideas into psychology has been our failure to recognize that what he describes as a coping or compensatory period would be made up, in a behavior model, of a whole series of complex coping responses and include as well the feedback into the system of the effects of these responses. Selye has properly focused on the area where the largest physiological changes occur and then deals with a compensatory period. I think that it behooves us, as psychologists, to focus on the processes—both physiological and psychological —that make up the rather complex set of interactions involved in compensatory coping. In attacking this problem I would hope that the threshold notions I have briefly indicated might have some value.

One comment about Dr. Lazarus' intriguing experimental findings with his Japanese subjects. I think he might wish to examine two possible additional explanations. First, that there was merely a displacement of time between the GSR index and the verbal response. For example, had he taken GSR measures earlier, he might have found a heightened response followed by a response level drop when the verbal response was given. Thus, the two responses may be correlated if a correction for time displacement is made. Secondly, it is not unreasonable, in light of the appraisal analysis I have suggested, to conceive of the two reactions as representing two dimensions of coping. The verbal response, as Dr. Lazarus has perhaps implied, represents a form of coping with the experimenter requirement, the GSR response with the film. What is implied is perhaps the failure of the American subjects to be sufficiently selective in their responses to the stimulus elements of the total situation Dr. Lazarus' studies provide!

Discussion

Dr. Opler: I may not have seen the particular film that Dr. Lazarus has been using, but those I have seen showed the Arunta Subincision operation to be quite horrendous and horrible to watch. At least, it seemed so if one made inferences about the amount of pain from an operation without anesthetic and done with stone knives. Despite that, every once in a while you saw the Arunta boys appearing to be very proud. I question then whether the subincision rite was a castration threat episode at all. It seemed to me it was just the opposite, something that could be viewed in terms of growing into adulthood. As a matter of fact, these Australian aborigines tell the boys just that.

As regards the Japanese, I spent a number of years among Japanese, in the California relocation centers in World War II and later both teaching and conducting research among the Japanese in Hawaii; and I would agree that Dr. Lazarus' statement, that the Japanese students were not more anxious overall than Americans, is a good cautionary statement. But I wouldn't know quite what that statement means by itself, except as a cultural stereotype. It is true that the arousal of attention or concern in regard to anything in the realm of the classroom—a teacher, a test, a film shown in school, etc.—would produce arousal in the Japanese because they are very concerned about schools, education, and such tests. Not only the evaluations being required of them but the test situation itself should bring forth in them the kind of high level of arousal at the beginning of the study that was reported. I think therefore that this is an effect of the test and educational value system, rather than just merely an effect of the kind of film shown. In Hawaii, my Japanese university students had the same high level of arousal in the general setting of education. Colleagues at the university always labelled the Japanese students as hard-working. In the relocation centers, without other ethnic groups to compare them with, one noted that the term *sensei* for teacher, professor, or doctor was a quick way to arouse attention and even respect almost automatically. Consequently, in one center, I went by such a term to promote one kind of *rapport*.

Now as regards self-reporting, a further effect should be expected. Japanese are very concerned with matching their cultural ideality—which is to please the other person—and would make an effort to give a report which is consistent with what they thought was either the polite and expected answer or the one desired. I remember Ruth Benedict's story, for example, that if two Japanese meet in the rain, or the rain starts, and one is carrying an umbrella, he will not open it because it is a blot on the escutcheon of the other to imply that he was dumb enough not to bring his umbrella along. This polite compliance to the principle is better than opening it and sharing it. This is a kind of feudalistic interpersonal concern about the feelings of others, about reciprocities, duties, and obligations, etc. In the relocation centers, terms like *duty, obligation,* and *taking account of others' feelings* were constantly being used.

Dr. Korchin: Dr. Lazarus' findings with his Japanese subjects point up a distinction made in a series of our studies in Chicago, which he mentions, between response to situation-stress (the threat which inheres in the situation in general, without the experimenter's specific intent) and stimulus-stress (the specifically intended stressful event). In these experiments, subjects were tested on four consecutive days. The first of these days was a control day on which the various dependent measures were taken, without there being an explicit experimental stress. On the following three days, the main event was a stressful interview or other psychological stressor, with the same measures being made before and after. When subjects were anxious patients, it was found that plasma hydro-cortisone levels and rated anxiety were significantly higher on the pre-experi-mental day than in response to the intended stress (Sabshin et al., 1957). In a later study, using another stressor but essentially the same design, this finding was replicated for another group of anxious patients, but normal subjects run through the same procedure showed relatively more stimulus-stress than situa-tion-stress response (Persky et al., 1959). These studies show that subjects in the laboratory may be more sensitive to the novel, potentially threatening aspects of the situation-in-general than to the stressor-in-particular, particularly so the more generally anxious they are. Basowitz and I (Korchin & Basowitz, 1956) distinguished between these two sources of anxiety earlier in contrasting older and younger subjects.

A particularly ingenious analysis of heart-rate data was done by Mitchell Glickstein in the study mentioned by Dr. Lazarus (Glickstein et al., 1957). Glickstein took the continuous heart-rate record of each of the subjects (anxious, hospitalized patients) on each of three experimental days and obtained the means for fifteen subperiods, defined by various *pre*tests, *post*tests, the times between tests, and the stressor itself (a stressful interview). These subperiods are indicated along the abcissa of Figure 6–3. The values for each subject were averaged over the three days, thus obtaining an array of fifteen values for each subject. Subjects were correlated in pairs and an inverse factor analysis done. Two significant centroid factors emerged, and two sub-groups of subjects best exemplifying each of these factors were isolated for further study. The mean heart rates for the two groups (labeled A and B), and for the total group of subjects, are given in Figure 6–3 for each of the fifteen subperiods of the aver-aged experimental days. The two patterns are clear: *Group A* starts the day at a high level, which descends continuously, with little specific response to the particular experimental events; *Group B* is at a generally lower level, shows no time-related trend but distinct response to the stressful interview and to having blood drawn. (Recall that these two groups were empirically derived by factor analysis.) But when the groups were compared, in terms of all other available information, the A group was decidedly more anxious in general and disturbed in the situation. For these more disturbed subjects, the specific events of the experiment were relatively insignificant, compared to the more encompassing danger of being in the experiment itself. Their curve, we suggested, shows greater sensitivity to "situation-stress" and overall adaptation. By contrast, the relatively less anxious patients were "better" subjects—they responded to the events we intended to be stressful!

I believe that the differences Dr. Lazarus found between his Japanese and American subjects can be understood in terms of the distinction between these two sources of stress. For whatever cultural and personality reasons, the Japa-nese when entering an experimental situation seem to be like our more anxious

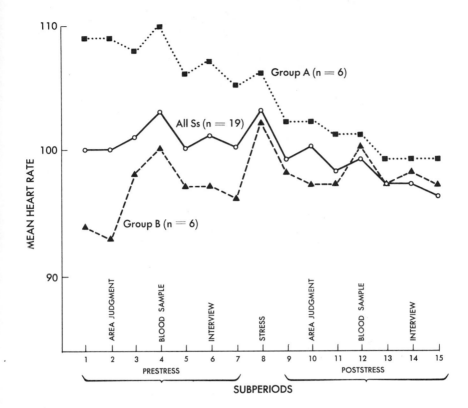

FIGURE 6-3.   Comparison of mean heart rates for factorially derived subgroups with mean for all subjects. Reproduced by permission from Glickstein et al. (1957, Fig. 1, p. 104).

patients; just coming to be studied, the paraphenalia of autonomic measurement, imputing greater importance to the outcome, or whatever made the entire situation more threatening for them. The fact that Dr. Lazarus' GSR curves descend from their prestressor movie position, and then plateau during the Subincision film, suggests that the film is not without effect, but that it is operating against the background of adaptation to the more pervasive situation stress. The plateau, rather than further decline, may indicate the effect of the film. This assumption could be tested experimentally. If you had another group of Japanese subjects who were shown the Subincision film *first,* then measured in the control condition, I would predict that the GSR level would be initially even higher and then fall off more rapidly and continuously than you found in the present study. Reversing the order of *stressor* and *control* conditions might help distinguish the contribution of the two sources of stress.

Dr. Oken: I just want to add to Dr. Korchin's presentation some additional data from our (then mutual) laboratory, because a subsequent study (Oken et al., 1960) showed an even further accentuation of the same thing. In chronic patients whose defense is to shut out everything, the response was even more focal, if you looked at it in a microscopic way, being very sharply peaked and very flat and lower other than during the actual stress.

In the Glickstein study described by Dr. Korchin, the *post*stimulus levels of the two subgroups were the same. This I think is a more valid baseline than the *pre*stimulus levels which were different, with the high anxious group being higher. This last is, I believe, attributable to the greater anticipatory anxiety in this group which tended to respond more nonspecifically.

In the study I mentioned (Oken et al., 1960), which includes steroid and affect rating data in addition to heart rate, the chronic nonresponsive group had lower baselines both before and after on all three variables.

Dr. Lazarus: There is a further check on my inferences that I would like to have. It is to determine whether the Japanese can become sufficiently adapted to this kind of situation so they show a B pattern rather than the A pattern. I am really interested in other possible differences between the Japanese and the Americans, deriving from the social sources of threat. For example, when a Japanese is confronted with a situation in which he is disapproved or criticized by a mentor, a superior, or someone in authority, will he be more threatened than an American? There are reasons to assume this interpersonal situation involves different significances for members of the two cultures. To test such an idea, one needs to have the Japanese relaxed until the explicitly threatening event occurred. If we could not relax the Japanese sufficiently with reference to the experiment as a whole, we cannot expect them to be selectively responsive to specific threat contents.

The cross cultural issues of greatest interest would then be refractory to study by experimental approaches. I am also sure that there are many experiments in which the stress reaction to the total experimental situation cannot be separated from that due to specific things the experimenter does.

Let me comment briefly on the question about the baselines. They are low. At the end of the control film procedures there is a second five-minute baseline period when nothing happens; the subject simply sits there quietly for five minutes. The experiment is temporarily suspended. From the subject's point of view it is not part of the experimental situation at all. In consequence, we obtain a very sharp drop in skin conductance level, which then sharply rises again as soon as the film is turned on.

Dr. Bovard: Depth electrode stimulation of the human brain has shown that you can obtain mood changes without any relation whatsoever to autonomic or vegetative changes. I would agree with the hypothesis that the Japanese are feeling these stressful episodes just the same as we would, but that their autonomic level is already very high and can't go any higher.

Dr. Stern: Dr. Lazarus apparently was initially surprised by the dissociation he obtained between the self-report and the autonomic response of his Japanese subjects. This doesn't bother me at all, because we often see such dissociation between tonic and phasic electrodermal responses. It may simply be that your

Japanese population does not show the phasic response. We demonstrated a few years ago in children in St. Louis and adult naval recruits in San Diego that there are marked differences in resting levels of skin resistance as a function of race (tonic response).

I would like to mention some findings that we are in the process of analyzing, dealing with spontaneous fluctuations in electrodermal activity as related to resting levels of skin resistance—which can range from a low level of spontaneous fluctuations to a high level—and I'll use skin resistance here rather than conductance. Skin resistance can vary again from a low level to a high level, and the pattern that we invariably see in a white population, whether they are children or adults (and we now have data on some 150 seven-year-old white children), fits the distribution depicted in Figure 6-4. Let me put it another way, associated with a high level of spontaneous fluctuations you will invariably find a low level of skin resistance (the converse is not necessarily true for other reasons which we won't go into here). If you do the same type of scatter plot for a Negro population (and we have, I think, roughly eighty children that we did this with), the plot is a random plot (see Fig. 6-5). So I think that another possibility that you might have to take into consideration is not only cognitive set and coping behavior but racial differences in electrodermal responsiveness.

Dr. Lazarus: The issue is really joined here, and it is too bad we can't resolve it. It is whether or not the variation in response characteristics has *psychological* significance or not. I am asserting that it does have psychological meaning. There are, of course, other alternatives, but for me they are not as persuasive.

Dr. Biderman: Two things concerned me about Dr. Lazarus' presentation. One, I thought he was a little cavalier in his interpretation of the significance of the base measurements, given the importance in his other interpretations of the peaking kind of hypothesis, and then second, in his relating his observations to the theory with respect to the cortisone and heart rate experiments described by Dr. Korchin. In these studies it seemed clear that there were different patterns for the general situational reactions in contrast to the specific treatment reactions. This has some relevance to my own feelings about the matter of baseline, namely, that if the situational reaction is as important as it figures in Dr. Lazarus' interpretation, then the more global kind of situational reaction should color the baseline reaction as well.

Dr. Ruff: I'd like to pursue for a moment a point which was raised both by Dr. Lazarus in referring to his earlier work and by Dr. Opler in his discussion. Dr. Lazarus selected a potentially disturbing stressor and then measured physiological and psychological variables which suggest that a disturbance indeed occurred. But he quite properly did not assume that this disturbance was related to castration anxiety. Other investigators have often tried to produce a particular kind of disturbance without any way of demonstrating that they achieved it. When the Subincision film is shown, I have no doubt that it will arouse castration fears in some subjects. However, other subjects may identify with the person who is doing the cutting. These sadistic impulses might lead to guilt and produce distress which would be reflected by our psychological and perhaps by our physiological indices. Still other subjects might identify with the boy who is cut and have a masochistic response which would arouse fear of passivity. It's easy to assume that one of these reactions has occurred, when it may actually have been something quite different.

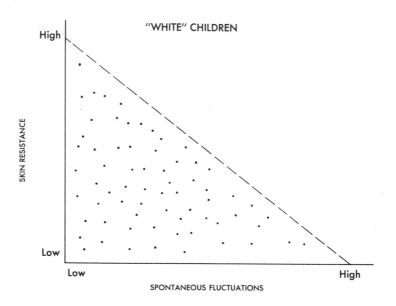

FIGURE   6-4.   Scatterplot of the relationship between skin resistance and spontaneous electrodermal responses for white subjects.

Dr. Lazarus: I don't know why the Subincision film produces the reaction it does. Speisman et al. (1964a) obtained some evidence that the effects were quite complex. As an example, one of the women who became very distressed watching this film described a previous relevant experience that had happened eight years earlier. She was accused by her husband of being interested in other men's genitals and of continually looking at them. He turned out to be paranoid, and they were divorced. But the wife was convinced that he was right, and she said she felt terribly guilty about it. The whole thing had been apparently encapsulated for eight years, when suddenly, upon being brought into our laboratory, she found herself in conflict over wanting to look and her guilt and shame about it. Half the time she had her eyes closed during the film. In other cases we have had homosexual fantasies reported while subjects watched this film. I think, therefore, it is a difficult problem to isolate and evaluate the sources of threat produced by the film. The whole matter should be thought of in transactional terms, that is, what it is about the individual that makes him regard this situation in the way he does.

Undoubtedly stimulus factors produce shared reactions. But this is a highly complex problem, and it is necessary to begin to isolate the content that threatens people. This can't be done easily with a film like this. There is also the fascinating business of the threat being vicarious which we haven't talked about here.

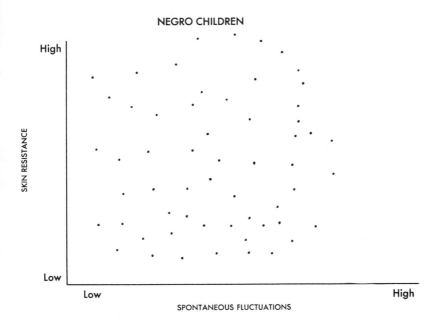

FIGURE 6-5. Scatterplot of the relationship between skin resistance and spontaneous electrodermal responses for a series of Negro children.

In reply to Dr. Biderman, I would not want to be cavalier, only provocative. The correct interpretation of our findings is by no means settled, otherwise I wouldn't be trying to do additional experiments to try to pin it down. There are still all sorts of possibilities. The suggestion has been made, for example, that we are dealing with a ceiling in the physiological reaction. This is possible, but I don't regard it as the best answer, although an interesting problem is highlighted by such a suggestion about which we have little evidence.

In general, the dilemma in the measurement of stress reaction could be stated as follows: every stress response can also be produced by other internal conditions. The disjunction among indicators is exactly what we should be studying carefully. Some writers, such as Krause (1961) and Martin (1961), stress the idea that one can only make the inference of anxiety when the response indicators at different levels of analysis agree.

But then we are narrowly limited to those situations where response agreement occurs, whereas we should really be studying just those instances where our response measures don't agree. This disagreement is not random or unlawful. Divergence between responses has been used for a long time to make inferences about intervening psychological processes. This is especially obvious in the diagnostic function of the clinician. While this outlook makes the problem of measurement complicated, this very complication is the fascinating side of the psychodynamics of stress and, as in the case of the specificities at the physiological level, is probably the most fruitful direction in which to push our research.

Chairman's summary

RICHARD TRUMBULL: In his paper, Dr. Lazarus illustrates one of the most fruitful returns from good experimentation—new questions. It is encouraging to find a study that focuses and relates many formerly discrete research problems. This is not a physiological psychologist or a social psychologist studying his own type of problem, but someone who is trying to make sense out of the welter of information derived from an experiment. He asks himself the possible implications of appraisal processes, the roles of anxiety, of coping and cognitive processes, and the reasons for inconsistencies between behavioral and physiological indicators. Maybe it required a cross-cultural exposure to bring emphasis upon how the cultural pattern influences responses, responses keyed to the apparent desires of the experimenter and responses which establish base lines about which stressor-induced responses must vary significantly. Certainly, we know that these same methodological problems exist in research here, but we needed this reminder.

We do not find the final definition here of *appraisal* any more than we did in the previous chapter by Dr. Arnold. This area will continue to be one interpreted in different ways by different investigators. But, we do find a good elaboration of its relationship to subsequent coping behavior and the feedback which makes this a continuing and dynamic process. It is vital to any concept attempting to relate behavior or response of the moment to "personality or predispositional factors characteristic of the individual." Beyond these factors are the social or situational constraints of the moment and pre-established. Dr. Lazarus' familiarity with these broader ramifications provides additional significance to the appraisal concept developed by Dr. Arnold, while making the requirements for understanding all relevant variables a challenge to researchers in this area of stress. It comes as no surprise then that Drs. Appley, Korchin, Oken, and Stern find reflections of the same problems and results in their own work, and admonitions for caution in interpreting results on the basis of assumed or experimenter-determined stressors are appropriate. This is especially true when one is faced with the fact, as stated by Dr. Lazarus, that "every stress response can also be produced by other internal conditions." This disjunction and the complexity of factors related to the response potential of man require much greater attention.

Dr. Lazarus has broadened our scope of concern. There is still another aspect which has concerned me as we do stress research without adequate knowledge of the subject *before* we have him at our disposal. We also must draw upon experience in another field of psychology—industrial—before we leave our "experiment." I have in mind a process called the exit interview. I can't help but ask myself, when we have these stress situations and we know that we have done something to these subjects, whether we don't often use them like we do white rats. Do we bring them in and run them through these experiments and simply say, "Thank you for helping me?" In the meantime, we may have given some of them an extreme experience of failure, a real challenge to self-concepts, and a number of other concepts we talk about. For example, when we place volunteer students in sensory deprivation experiments, it certainly is known to their dormitory or fraternity mates that they are participating in somebody's stress study—because this is the sort of thing they do tell people—and then they may be back within two hours when the study is supposed to last for four days. Does anyone really give them exit interviews? Do we ever do anything to help get these men back in line with the community to which we are returning them? Do we let them appreciate just what happened to them, that their reactions may not be so terribly unusual? Don't we have a debt, as experimenters, to the people we use as subjects? I am still concerned, for example, with the possible effects of the films Dr. Lazarus used with his Japanese subjects. Can one picture all these Japanese children running around with castration complexes? What did he do with these youngsters who had been exposed to the traumatic sound track? Did he go back and try to explain to them what this whole thing was about and that that particular track was a fake? Did he then play for them the accurate track and reorient them before he walked away? As an experimenter, I must raise this kind of question. We are playing a lot of games with people, and no one has ever asked us, so far as I know.

7

Self, social environment, and stress

Stress has been defined and used by the social and biological sciences in a number of different ways. Sometimes the notion refers to a disturbance in the organism which the organism tries to eliminate or reduce. In this sense, stress is little different from unpleasant states, like anxiety or from aversive motivations, like pain and dissonance. Stress has also been considered as a set of physiological or behavioral responses, which are symptoms of a disturbing inner state or instrumentally designed to quash the disturbance. Such stress-coping responses or indicators are observed in several areas of the organism's functioning, including the emotional, the action, and the cognitive. Finally, stress has been regarded as an event or condition of the physical or social environment which leads to avoidant, escapist, aggressive, or problem-solving measures specifically designed to remove or weaken the offending condition. Such a notion—of *stressors*—is similar, in function at least, to danger, threat, pressure, conflict, frustration, and extreme situation. Research on stress, if it can be simply characterized, consists of specifying the relationships between the *input* stressor variables and *output* stress symptom or behavioral response variables, often with attention given to the mediating stress-state variables.

Let it be said at once that there is no one correct definition of stress; nor can the research paradigms based on these conceptualizations be evaluated as right or wrong. Evaluation of designs and theoretical formulations can only be in terms of usefulness in producing research, in interpreting research data, and ultimately, in building knowledge.

The approach of social psychology to stress does not mesh exactly with most of the research in this field. Primarily, this is because of social psychology's commitment to a relatively large unit of analysis. Thus, from a social psychological point of view, stressor variables are typically seen as imbedded in certain kinds of global social situations. Specific stress-reducing responses and physiological symptoms of stress are often regarded as a part of the molar behaviors produced by such social situations as competition, frustration, and the like. This chapter will attempt to reflect this social psychology perspective in focusing upon stressful social and problem-solving situations, the behavioral consequences of which are often accompanied by the more conventional physiological and psychological indicators of stress. We shall not deal with particular stress symptoms and the particular stressors which produce them. Our aim is rather to analyze certain well-known stressful social situations and *self-dynamics*. It is to be hoped that such an analysis can contribute to a knowledge of the background or context in which autonomic and other peripheral stress symptoms and behaviors frequently appear.

Stress in achievement situations

In general, an achievement situation can be characterized by a task and an individual or group motivated to perform it toward the accomplishment of rewards and the avoidance of punishment. In such a setting, individuals and groups compete with each other, set levels of aspiration, and literally work and persist to produce and to solve problems. It is a matter of common observation that in such situations, presumably in some way determined by them, individuals display various signs of stress. Understanding the dynamics of the achievement situation, then, may help expose the details of an important source of stress.

Work

The oft-heard claim that stress is brought on by work or "overwork" is as commonplace as it is ambiguous and superficial. Stress is sometimes associated with reduced productivity as well as extraordinary labor. Thus, the stress reflected by work dissatisfaction may go along with inhibition rather than unrestrained output. Yet, especially compared with the state of non-work or idleness, the performance of tasks to reach goals has been regarded as a restorative and tension-reducer. Manifestly, one can lose oneself in work and become oblivious to the slings and arrows, or one can be enmeshed in work and feel intense pain with every arduous act. What makes the difference?

The value of external rewards contingent upon successful performance does not appear to be a decisive factor in the production of stress. More important, perhaps, is the magnitude of the loss or punishment that would be occasioned by failure. It is safe to say that the stockbroker who is working up to a decision as to where to invest his last remaining million is under heavier stress than he would be investing his first million. On the other hand, the receipt of large rewards for successful work does not necessarily obviate stress. If the large rewards can be lost, if success means an increase of responsibility and a threat to dependency needs, or if successful performance is regarded as a lucky break which threatens to expose the person as a mediocrity, highly rewarded work can be exceedingly stressful.

The ease or difficulty of the work as such—as opposed to the consequences of success or failure—does not seem to be an especially critical determinant of stress, although this depends on the particular measure of stress one has in mind. When doing a difficult task, like *The New York Times* crossword puzzle, most of us feel taxed, and probably there is an elevation of blood pressure. But the state of being fully concentrated, absorbed, and challenged is probably what we ought to classify as pleasant stress, if that is not a contradiction in terms. Let the individual be given the puzzle as a test of his IQ, or, at a less intellectual level, let the individual's manliness be measured by requiring 45 push-ups, then we move into unpleasant stress. In short, it is when there is a possibility of losing status that task difficulty significantly affects the magnitude of stress.

The existence of a deadline is commonly identified as a source of stress. It was reported some years ago in *The New York Times* that tax accountants have high levels of serum cholesterol and thrombin as the deadline approaches for filing returns. If the cause of stress is a discrepancy between where one is and where one has to get in a certain period of time, then procrastinators should show more intense signs of stress when they finally get to work, while individuals who start early should not be expected to be appreciably disturbed. If, more specifically, the cause of stress is the enhanced probability of failure created by the deadline, then individuals who know their ability, who know the job requirements, and who can pace themselves efficiently should not be bothered much by deadlines. Although deadlines as such are obviously associated with stress, it is probably more precise to say that it is the potential punishment for failing to meet the deadline which is the decisive factor. Potential punishment, of course, also depends upon the importance of the task. A deadline for a trivial task is a joke—just tell someone he has only four and a half seconds to shell a peanut.

It seems clear that to answer the question of what is stressful in work, we are obliged to come to grips with the underlying dynamics. Only when we know the motivations which determine the individual's competitiveness, persistence, and the quantity and quality of his performance, can we obtain an insight into the sources of stress.

Competition

Competition is widely supposed to be the cause of "nervous breakdowns," psychosomatic illness, character disorders, immature behavior, and other phenomena which implicate stress. But virtues are also claimed for competition, in terms of higher productivity, the development of a sense of purpose, sharpened standards of excellence, the feel of life, and so on. How can competition have detrimental effects and be psychologically salubrious at the same time? There would be no contradiction involved, of course, if it were recognized that competition is injurious only when it is excessive. Or, at a somewhat more complex level, it may be that when competitiveness is excessive, inappropriate, or indiscriminate, it results in some form of punishment by the social environment. According to this view, it is not the competition as such which is stressful, but the negative social consequences of it, or the internal tension generated by "competition conflict." A third possibility to consider is that only certain kinds of competition are more than normally stressful. Damaging effects may depend upon the particular constellation of forces and structures which determine the competitiveness. In order to get even close to deciding among these conjectures, it is obviously necessary to examine the bases of competitiveness.

Structural competition would seem to be an apt way of characterizing a familiar type. Here, the individual is constrained to act self-interestedly and against the interests of others by structural features of the situation. In spatial language, the pathways to the goal are so arranged that for any one individual to move forward toward the goal, the other individuals who have the same goal must be shunted aside or pushed in the opposite direction. At any given time, the goal can be entered only by one individual or group. Certain sports contests fit the structural category very admirably, in that the rules of the game specify the competitive actions between individuals (or teams) which are necessary for victory. In an analogous way, the physical structure of the task can force competitiveness. Of course, if individuals and groups are not motivated toward a goal, then structural properties are quite irrelevant as far as competitiveness is concerned. But given some amount of motivation greater than zero, competitiveness would seem to depend upon the degree of structural constraint involved in the conditions of goal achievement or in the physical nature of the task. If the degree of structural constraint in the task or goal is held constant, competitiveness should vary with the level of motivation toward the goal whose achievement is contingent upon satisfactory performance of the task. Of course, when both structural constraint and motivation vary, the amount of competitiveness depends upon the joint effect of both variables.

Two experiments may be cited to illustrate and support this structural constraint-motivational formulation. In the well-known study of Deutsch (1949), subjects were undergraduate members of a human relations course. In the non-lecture portion of the class period, the class members had to solve intellectual and human relations problems. In the condition which Deutsch calls the "contriently interdependent goal structure," each individual in the class was ranked according to how well he did on the problems. It was understood that the ranks he made would be a determinant of his final course grade. In a contrasting condition, called a "promotively interdependent goal structure," the class as a whole worked on the problems and was ranked in relation to other classes. Each individual received the same rank as the class, and this was understood to be a determinant of his final grade. These simple arrangements of how the students were to be evaluated had strong effects on a variety of behaviors. For example, students in the contriently interdependent situation showed less coordination of effort, greater redundancy of role behavior, lower volume of communication, less interpersonal liking, and other indicators of competitiveness than did those in the promotively interdependent condition.

The essential variable in the Deutsch formulation on competitiveness is the goal structure. Motivation to pass the course or to avoid failure was assumed to exist initially in students under both conditions to an equal degree. A demonstration of competitiveness as a function of success/failure motivation, where the structural constraint of the task is held constant, is given by the ingenious experiments of Mintz (1951).

Each subject in several small groups held a string to which a cone-shaped object was attached inside a large (common) jug. The instructions directed the subjects to extricate their cones within a certain time period or to remove them before they got wet from water slowly being poured into the bottom of the jug. The narrow neck of the jug—the task structure constraint—caused a few temporary traffic jams in some of the groups. Under conditions where the subjects were rewarded up to 25 cents for getting their cone out and fined up to 10 cents for failing to get it out, serious permanent traffic jams occurred in more than 50 percent of the groups.

Taken together, the data fit the motivation-structural constraint formulation nicely. But what about the relation between competition and stress? Since there were no conventional measures of stress in either of the studies, we can only conjecture that *relatively* more stress was experienced under the reward/fine condition than under the control condition (in which no incentives were employed). A more detailed picture of the possible connections between stress and competition can perhaps be exposed by a real-life example.

A mortal threat, like a fire in a theatre and the perception of an exit blocked by a tangle of people struggling to get out, are conditions highly likely to create panic—irrational, directionless behavior—among theatre patrons who become aware of such a situation. If there is one exit open, one would expect to observe extreme competitiveness over who gets out first. Surely, these are stressful circumstances. The essential source of the stress is the extreme danger and the perception that it may not be possible to escape. Similarly, in the jug experiment, the perception of traffic jams, that is, of competitiveness itself, presumably should cause some stress. Additionally, both stress and competitiveness can be regarded as results of the conditions of competition: namely the motivation with respect to rewards and fines, and the objective structural constraint represented by the narrow neck of the jug.

It should be noted more precisely, however, that it is not the competition-constraining structure of the task as such which contributes appreciably to stress, but the fact that the narrow neck constitutes a *threat* of a fine (or loss of anticipated reward). Another real-life example will make this distinction clear. In a ship fire, even where there are more than sufficient life boats to handle the passengers and crew—where the structure of the environment does not force competition over who gets out first—the fact that all the life boats are stuck because of rusted davits will generate considerable stress.

Another point about the Mintz study has implications for the precision of the motivation-structural constraint theory. Traffic jams occurred despite the fact that the subjects were perfectly clear about the necessity for coordination. Such compulsive irrationality suggests that more than the objective values of the rewards and fines contributed to the total motivation to escape. But, if the rewards and fines do not accurately nor fully describe the escape motivation, what then does compel the subjects to get mixed up in and to help form a traffic snarl? It may be proposed that threat of a loss of personal esteem or status was at bottom. In other words, a more precise accounting of competitiveness would require direct examination of the ego or self motivations to which the rewards and fines were connected.

In the Deutsch classroom experiment, involving a contrient goal structure, the significance of self-relevant motivation is more obvious. In the real-life counterpart it seems evident that competitiveness is not so much driven by grades as such as by the personal ego or social consequences of lower grades than some others and failure.

In addition to the question concerning the significance of external rewards and punishments, there are problems with the structural constraint component of the competition theory, which may have implications for isolating the sources of stress. Several observations go to the point as to whether structural constraint is a necessary condition for competitive behavior.

1. In real life, objective goal or task constraints do not always direct all individuals or the same individuals all the time to behave competitively. Not only are there instances of "resistance" to competition but cooperative behavior is shown. For example, coalitions and collusions—like cheating—are not uncommon in classroom situations where the instructor grades strictly "on a curve"—in other words, in contrient goal structures.

2. Goal and task structures are seldom uniquely contrient structures. Individuals are simultaneously engaged in different task structures or play different roles involving different goal structures. Even the same role sometimes involves the two types of structures. Thus, the businessman competes with other businessmen on the pricing of his goods but joins with them in various collaborative programs. It often seems that competitiveness depends upon the structural system to which the individual chooses to commit himself at a given time, rather than upon the direct influence of the structure as such.

3. Even in a situation in which there are *no* objective constraints in the goal or task, some individuals can be observed to behave competitively. In effect, they perceive structural constraints where objectively there are none.

The foregoing sketch of work and competitiveness points out the necessity to look into the motivational dynamics of such behavior in much greater detail. In particular, the role of the self as a motivational base requires delineation. However, specification of the relationships between the self and work and competitiveness is a complex matter, because apparently there are multiple self-based motivations by which the relationship is mediated. Before examining these, it should be emphasized that by motive we have no formal construct in mind. We use the term loosely and interchangeably with tendency. The ultimate aim is to separate and trace dynamic processes rather than to build a list of needs. In the following preliminary foray into the self, neither completeness nor accuracy of specification can be claimed.

Self-evaluation

According to "social comparison theory" (Festinger, 1954), uncertainty about one's ability can lead to competitiveness for the purpose of obtaining an accurate evaluation of the ability. If the performance coordinated to the ability cannot be evaluated by objective, physical criteria, the individual will use the performance of others as a standard of measurement. Specifically, he will try to raise or lower his performance so that it is close to the performance of others which he regards as reflecting a relevant standard. When such comparability with others is achieved, the individual is able subjectively to evaluate himself accurately. If, however, others are noncomparable, e.g., if they are experts, the individual ceases comparing. The need for self-evaluation can also arise when the performance level is slightly *above* the comparison group, but obviously in this case the individual does not have to compete to lower his score.

The foregoing implies that it is not the absolute level of the individual's performance or self-evaluation which affects the strength of social comparison processes like competitive bargaining, but the size of the evaluation or performance discrepancy. What does affect the comparison tendency is the *importance* of the ability about which the individual is uncertain. It is possible, of course, for the level of self-evaluation to influence comparison tendencies by way of its effect on certainty, but any such naturalistic relationship is not part of the theoretical specification.

In sum, the self-evaluation theory holds that competitiveness for obtaining a social comparison is a direct function of self-evaluation uncertainty. When the performance discrepancy between the individual and his standard of comparison is large, or when, for some other reason, the comparison group or individual is non-comparable, competitiveness will decrease.

The experimental work in support of the social comparison theory includes studies of competitive bargaining and persistence in setting level of aspiration. We shall confine ourselves here to the former.

Hoffman, Festinger, and Lawrence (1954) had groups of three, one of whom was a confederate, construct geometric figures for which they received points reflecting on basic abilities. Any two players could jointly construct figures which were worth more points than individual constructions. The formation of such coalitions and their durability could be taken in effect as measures of the competitiveness of the two players against the confederate. In both experimental conditions it was arranged surreptitiously to give the confederate a small, constant lead in number of points. In one variation, the two subjects were led to believe that the confederate was a basically superior individual (*Nonpeer* condition), while in the second, he was pictured as being in the same ability class as the subjects (*Peer* condition). In terms of the number of coalitions over the trials formed between the two subjects, the failure of the confederate to form coalitions with one of the subjects, and other measures, a greater degree of competitiveness was displayed in the *Peer* than in the *Nonpeer* condition.[1]

Uncertainty about self and stress

Since the social comparison experiments do not contain measures of stress, it is difficult to draw any conclusions about the role of self-evaluational uncertainty. There are, however, general considerations about the nature of the motive which have implications for stress.

One might assume that there is a functionally autonomous need for self-measurement developed very early in the socialization process of a human organism. Although failure to satisfy such a need would not have the same fatal consequences as failure to satisfy a metabolic need, discomforting and even damaging effects are not difficult to imagine. Thus, a person who does not know where he stands in any ability or personality attractiveness scale can be expected to have serious difficulty in setting levels of aspiration for rewards or understanding his competence for tasks requiring certain levels of ability. This is the kind of person who can be the proverbial square peg. Sometimes he cannot do the job; sometimes the job is beneath his capacity; sometimes he hits it just right. Obviously such an individual will sooner or later experience some form of social punishment at every turn. The anticipation of such consequences would be sufficient to generate stress.

But even if the individual did not live in a social world where accurate evaluation and utilization of ability are important, there probably would be some stress generated by his unknown self-evaluation. When, for example, there is uncertainty about an important ability, the exercise of which affects only himself—e.g., the ability of the stamp collector to identify the stamps of various countries—some stress can be expected. In such cases, the individual does not know whether he is able to pursue his interests in a satisfying or profitable way.

[1] Several considerations stand in the way of an unequivocal interpretation of these results in terms of self-evaluation motive—social comparison process. One difficulty arises from the fact that the comparability between subjects and confederate and not the need for self-evaluation, predicated on self-uncertainty, was experimentally varied. Indeed, subjects in the *Nonpeer* condition may have been made rather *certain* of their relatively low intellectual status. Consequently, it is not known if the smaller amount of competitive bargaining by subjects in this condition was due to the lack of comparability or to the absence of a self-evaluation need. Secondly, there is a problem as to whether noncomparability reduced competitiveness because the nonpeer was a poor source of self-evaluation or because one is not likely to beat a more intelligent player who already leads in points. Implied in the latter interpretation is that competitiveness is based on a need to win or to improve one's performance and is influenced by the probability of success, rather than based on the need for self-evaluation and influenced by the measurement-providing adequacy of the social environment.

Of course, temporary uncertainty about self-evaluation should not be expected to generate a large magnitude of stress. It is when the self-uncertainty *cannot be reduced* that the magnitude of stress should become sizeable. That is, to the extent that competitive social comparison processes are successful in reducing self-evaluational uncertainty, they should be associated with minimal stress. On the other hand, stress should increase as it becomes difficult to make an accurate comparison; it should be maximum when there is noncomparability and the individual has an unresolved need for self-evaluation.

Self- or status-enhancement

A second basis for work and competitiveness can be identified essentially as a motivation to raise (or maintain) one's self-esteem or one's esteem in the eyes of others, that is, one's status.[2]

Most frequently, this motive is activated in situations where success or failure can respectively raise or lower the individual's worth in terms of ability, personality, and so forth. We refer here, in short, to ego-defensive and -augmentative processes which are ubiquitous in test situations and which have been of interest to personality research for more than two decades. The tendency toward self-improvement or status-achievement is powerfully affected by the individual's existing level of self-esteem, relative to some normative ideal. A person's evaluation of himself in terms of ability or personality not only originates in how others have evaluated him directly or through standards they have defined but is also *reacted to* in conformity with this social evaluation. Generally speaking, in the case of abilities, the lower they are, the more negatively society evaluates them. This means that a person with low ability deviates from his own and society's ideal and is less attractive or more aversive to himself than a person who has high ability. One consequence of such a condition is that in an achievement situation where there is the possibility of loss or gain in perceived competence or status, he attempts to improve himself or to defend himself against any further loss in esteem.

How is it possible to distinguish competitiveness as a means of self- or status-enhancement from competitiveness as a social comparison process for purposes of self-evaluation? As already implied, competitiveness might be attributed to a self-improvement tendency or to a status drive if it is shown to vary inversely with the level of existing self-esteem. Social comparison, in such an event, would presumably be ruled out on

[2] Because self-esteem and status are highly interrelated causally we shall not attempt to distinguish them beyond pointing out a possible asymmetry. One can be motivated to seek status independently of self-esteem considerations, but one probably cannot enhance self-esteem without raising one's status in someone else's eyes or at least thinking that one's status has been raised.

the grounds that the greater the discrepancy between the individual's performance and that of a comparison group representing a normative ideal level, the *less* the competitiveness. However, such a distinction would be valid only within limits. If the discrepancy between the individual's self-esteem and the ability level defined as desirable by the group is too large, improvement of esteem may not be possible through competition and work. In other words, if competing and persistent hard labor cannot change the evaluation of the person's worth, he will tend to abandon such modes of coping with his self-aversiveness. Thus, one finds the familiar picture of the person of low confidence giving up and, in some cases, eventually changing his conception of what is a desirable evaluation so that he is more comfortable with himself. Such considerations suggest that a distinction between the self-evaluation and the self-improvement/status-achievement motivations, based on the effect of self-esteem level upon the amount of competitiveness, is not unequivocal.

The two motive tendencies, however, do seem to have been isolated in Dryer's (1954) experiment on level of aspiration. Each subject performed a sorting task and was fed back his own and the scores of peers. This information was contrived to place each subject either markedly above, at the average, or markedly below the peer norm. According to the social comparison theory, subjects above (as well as below) should perceive incomparability and cease setting levels of aspiration early in the series of trials. Indeed, those subjects above the peer norm did stop before any of the other groups. However, contrary to prediction, those below the norm persisted in setting aspiration levels as long as did those at the average level. The inference here is that the self- or status-enhancement tendency was operating most strongly in these subjects.

Another possible distinguishing characteristic between the self-evaluation and self- or status-improvement motivations focuses on the role of uncertainty. It has already been said that if a person is certain of his ability, if he knows clearly how good he is, there is no self-evaluation motive. If, however, an individual is certain of his low ability, he surely is no *less* self-aversive and quite possibly more so. So long as his self-esteem or status is changeable, the motive and its consequences should still be operative.

Some of the interesting research by Adams (1963, 1964) on the effects of dissonance on productivity can be interpreted, at least partially, in terms of a self- or status-enhancement motive. In one study, each subject in the experimental condition was told, in a rather pointed way, that he was unqualified for an interviewer job for which he had applied. The employer was represented as being in urgent need, however, and the unqualified subject was hired, "reluctantly," at $3.50 an hour. He had approximately two and a half hours in which to interview adults concerning their ability to identify automobile design concepts. The dissonance argument put forth by Adams is that unqualified subjects, in order to reduce the inequity occasioned by their being overpaid, interview more respondents per unit time than subjects who were told they were qualified. In fact, the average number of interviews was higher for the unqualified than for the qualified subjects. An obvious alternative to dissonance, however, is that increased productivity reflected the subject's desire to vindicate himself or to raise his worth in the eyes of the experimenter-employer. Another dissonance prediction is that if the subject works under a piece-rate system, a lack of qualification should make for *less* productivity. This derivation is based on the idea that the more money he makes, the greater the dissonance concerning his lack of qualifications. A second experiment involving both hourly and piece-rate conditions, did in fact show that, under piece-rate, qualified subjects do more; while under hourly pay, unqualified subjects do more (interviews). The question may still be asked, however, Is this due to dissonance reduction? By definition, piece-rate basis of pay emphasizes the quality of each unit. Unqualified subjects—in effect those in whom a low self-esteem was induced—are highly motivated toward self-improvement. In the piece-rate situation, success comes by taking more care and spending more time on the interview. Consequently, they accomplish fewer interviews of higher quality. In short, it could be argued that the kind of pay arrangement determined *how* the subject set about to improve his self-esteem or status.[3]

Stress and self- or status-enhancement

The Sunday supplements of the nation's newspapers usually carry a story about the harassed executive who daily takes an awful beating in the competition for advancement in his company. As a result of this "pressure of the job," the executive is a regular tippler, is nasty to his wife, has a spastic colon, and is looking into psychoanalysis, which he sees as a last resort for his unbearable tension. Similar sketches of heavily stressed businessmen have been made by more authoritative sources, of course. And at least one health survey (see Packard, 1962) bears out the surmise that there is a high rate of metabolic disorders, relative to other medical problems, among business executives. The picture is by no means uniform for all executives as a class, however. It appears that the maximum pressure is not at the very top of the organizational structure but in the junior echelons. Here is where one finds the legendary ambitious, ulcer-ridden, furiously-working fellow whose

---

[3] If an unqualified subject were to be told that his pay will be reduced in accordance with his poor qualifications, his productivity can be expected to be lower than that of an unqualified but overpaid subject. Under such conditions there would be no way for him to prove his worth to the experimenter, the latter having firmly categorized him as poor material. Dissonance theory makes the same prediction on the grounds that a pay reduction eliminates the inequity felt by an unqualified worker. (See Adams & Jacobsen, 1964, for confirmatory evidence.)

consuming goal is advancement up the managerial ladder of success. No doubt there are multiple determinants of this skewness of pressure stemming from job, home, and age. For example, it could be supposed that the unusual stress in the junior levels of the organization is due to the severe competition constraint in the structure at that place: junior executives are evaluated entirely against each other for promotion and other special rewards. At the top of the managerial hierarchy, on the other hand, a rank ordering is not the exclusive basis of evaluation. To some extent, top managers are evaluated against ideal or quasi-absolute standards. This is evidenced by the fact that often no one in the company qualifies and it is necessary to seek a man from the outside to fill a senior post. Moreover, at the top, there are more dimensions of evaluation; a more complex set of considerations is involved in the reward system. In addition to these structural properties which engender fierce competitiveness, the junior positions are relatively unattractive. Indeed, in terms of the explicit emoluments, perquisites, and overall prestige, the lower the rung in the ladder, the more negative it is. Hence, potentially stronger self-improvement tendencies are to be found in the junior portion of the hierarchy.

The derivation of appreciable stress from strong self- and status-improvement tendencies is not direct, however. It is necessary to consider the extent to which the motive is satisfied. Thus, we would assume that the magnitude of stress at a given level in the hierarchy is inversely related to the mobility from that level to the next higher level. By lack of mobility, of course, is meant not only external restraints, inherent in the contriency of the structure—for example, the fact that only one man out of a group of twenty is promoted each year—but internal restraints, like ability as well. In a random sample of executives, then, one should expect to find the greatest stress (a) among those in the lower levels of the hierarchy, (b) at the level where the organizational and administrative structure constrain the most toward competitive relations, and (c) among those who are least talented in those abilities upon which advancement is contingent.

The foregoing can perhaps be generalized by the statement that the magnitude of stress varies with the strength of the self- or status-enhancement tendency and the degree of restraint opposing it.

Self-validation

There is a third self-based motivation underlying competitiveness and work which can be considered to be a different phase of the self-evaluation tendency and an altogether different species from the self-improvement motive. As for the distinguishing properties, this "self-validation" motive *only* operates when the individual is reliably aware of what his ability or personality is and considers these characteristics unchangeable. Under these conditions we can identify a tendency in the individual to behave consistently with the evaluation he makes of his ability, personality attributes, and so on. More precisely, he tends to adopt attitudes and to behave so as not to invalidate his self-concept. For example, the self-validating tendency should cause the individual to select and strive for rewards in an amount proportional to his level of self-esteem. If the task or goal structure constrain the person to compete in order to achieve such commensurate rewards, he should compete more vigorously if he has high self-esteem than low. According to this conceptualization, self-validation differs critically from the self-evaluation tendency, in that the latter does not exist when the individual is certain of his ability and perceives it as invariant, while for the former this is a necessary condition. Invariance of one's evaluation also distinguishes self-validation from the self- or status-enhancement tendency, which assumes that ability, personality trait, etc., be changeable as a result of success or failure.

One of a recent series of experiments tested an interaction hypothesis involving the opposing effects of self-validation and self-improvement on individual persistence in dull and simple tasks. The reasoning behind the prediction follows the conceptual definitions of these two motives. Thus, if an individual's work and achievement have no implication for his self-esteem—that is, if he regards his personality as unchangeable— then a subject who feels positive about his personality will persist more on easy and routine tasks than a subject who feels less positive or negative about it. The amount of external reward achieved or the quality of productivity should be in rough proportion to the fixed self-esteem. On the other hand, if task productivity or goal achievement has definite implications for the person's evaluation of himself, then the person with the stronger self-improvement tendency—the person with low self-esteem— should persist longer and work harder on such tasks.

In one study, high and low self-esteem were induced by administering to each subject an individually credible but fictional personality inventory as part of a Psychology Department survey of the nature of volunteer subjects. With the aid of a scoring manual and other impressive-looking tables, the experimenter then fed back to the subject his scores and percentile ranks on three personality categories: *Personal Efficiency*— the individual's effectiveness in using native abilities, *Social Creativity*— the individual's effectiveness in dealing with the social environment, and *Personal Unity*—the individual's freedom from basic conflicts. High self-esteem subjects were placed at the eightieth percentile while low self-esteem subjects were told they were at the twentieth. According to personality trait scales on which the subject rated himself, the experimental treatments were in fact found to be successful. Following this preliminary manipulation, the experimenter put the materials away and told the subjects they would begin the tasks for which they had been recruited.

Two tasks were employed in alternating sequence so as to balance out order effects. One was moronically simple and tedious: to make Xs in the boxes of graph paper. The subject was given a large box containing strips of 125, 5 by 25 half millimeter cells. There were two experimental conditions. In the one, where no self-relevant goal was defined for the task, the experimenter simply said: "Place an X in the corner cell of the strip of graph paper, then fill in the adjacent cells until the entire strip is completed. If you wish to go on, take another strip from the box and continue working. You can continue working as long as you like and quit whenever you feel you have done enough." The experimenter made no explicit statement about his purpose; at most, he implied that whatever he was looking for was independent of the subject's output. In the condition which established a self-relevant goal, the instructions were exactly the same except for one rather cryptic statement: "Making Xs is a measure of various basic perceptual and motor tendencies—about which we'll give you more information after the session."

The second task required each subject to draw objects one at a time from a large trash can in which there were over a hundred pieces of assorted junk—nails, cork, combs, forks, picture frames, empty bottles, rubber balls, fuses, and debris. In the condition without a self-relevant goal, the subject was told to stand in a manner that did not permit him to see into the can, to take out the first object he touched, and to place it on the table. "You can remove as many objects as you wish and quit whenever you are satisfied you have done enough." In the self-relevant goal condition, the instructions were slightly, but importantly, modified: "As soon as three objects are on the table, begin sorting them into logical categories which represent the entire contents of the can."

There are two related measures of interest: productivity—the number of strips of graph paper filled in and the number of junk items taken from the can; and persistence—the time spent making Xs and time spent delving into the trash can.

The results can be easily summarized: Given a self-relevant goal, subjects of low self-evaluation produce and persist more. Without a self-relevant goal, subjects of high self-evaluation produce and persist more. The interaction term is significant for the X task. The same pattern is seen in the trash task, but the interaction misses significance.

Self-validation and stress

The results just described support the general hypothesis that if a person believes he is poor in some ability or possesses a negative personality trait, his behavior will reflect either an affirmation or a "defensive" denial of this evaluation, depending upon whether the ability or trait is changeable. If self-improvement is possible, the individual should show a high degree of persistence and competitiveness. If change is not possible, such an individual should show that amount of persistence and competitiveness which is proportional to his low self-esteem. We would suppose that stress does not accompany work and competition when they can be regulated so as to satisfy the validation motive. If, however, the individual behaves inconsistently with his self-esteem, some stress should accompany his attempt to resolve the inconsistency. For example, if a student who knows he is highly talented in physics and mathematics elects a program directed toward elementary school science teaching, he should experience a pressure to increase his aspiration. If he does raise his sights and takes appropriate action, he should become "unstressed," but if some other specific incentive—like wanting to live in the town where the normal school is—operates to prevent validation, the stress should remain unabated. The stress generated by invalid behavior or circumstance presumably works the other way around. Thus, a student who knows he is poor in science should try to lower his aspiration to fit his ability. In this case, however, one does not know how much of a self-defensive tendency is involved additionally. If a lowering of aspiration is prevented, stress will be maintained, and because of the possibility of failure, it should be of larger magnitude than in the case where the attempt to increase aspiration is blocked.

Conclusions

We have surveyed some of the self-dynamics involved in competition and work. We have focused on these behaviors because they are frequent companions of stress. The guiding assumption of the inquiry was that by exposing the determinants of competition and work we would gain insight into major sources of stress. Several implications and hypotheses about stress were drawn, and, at this point, some form of summary integration would be useful.

Three self-based motives were definitionally distinguished as working concepts. Experimental data supported the hypothesized effects of these self-tendencies when one was operating alone and the others presumably constant and when they were operating jointly in opposite directions.

A self-evaluation tendency is aroused in an achievement situation when the individual is uncertain of the evaluation of some part of himself. Since evaluation by objective standards is often not possible, he manipulates his performance so as to make it comparable with the performance of others which he regards as a measure. Work and competitiveness represent attempts to make such a social comparison.

A self-validation tendency is aroused in an achievement situation when the individual perceives that his ability, or other valued part of himself, is certain and unchangeable. Under this condition the individual aspires and achieves in amounts and ways consistent with his self-esteem. Competitiveness and productivity reflect the validation tendency.

A self-improvement tendency is aroused in an achievement situation when the individual perceives an opportunity to increase his self-esteem (or to prevent its further loss). The strength of this tendency varies inversely with the level of the individual self-esteem relative to some ideal level. Work and competitiveness represent attempts of self-improvement.

From the foregoing, it is clear that in any achievement situation the individual can be motivated by both a self-evaluation and a self-improvement tendency or both a self-improvement and a self-validation tendency. These motives can affect work and competitiveness in a mutually facilitating or mutually antagonistic way.

Stress, as measured by various physiological indices, may in general be regarded as an energy by-product of self-motivations. In an achievement situation the total magnitude of stress theoretically should be a resultant of the stresses generated from each operative motivational source. Considering any particular source of stress of the three we have mentioned, three stages corresponding to a scale of magnitude may be proposed:

Stage I: Activation.   The activation stage represents the period when a self-based motive is aroused. The stress that accompanies arousal is of a low order of magnitude.

Stage II: Conflict.   In the conflict stage, satisfaction of a self-based motive is prevented. Conflicts between evaluation, validation, and/or improvement and tendencies in opposition generate large magnitudes of stress. Examples of conditions which oppose self-based motive satisfaction include: incomparability of comparison norms, inadequate ability, competition-constraining task and goal structures, lack of mobility in a hierarchy, inability to lower aspiration and achievement, or more generally, inability to resolve self-inconsistencies to achieve self-validation.

Stage III: Conflict-Bind.   In the conflict-bind stage, the conflicts involving self-based tendencies cannot be resolved or, over time, have not been resolved. The magnitude of stress generated when a self-based motive is blocked escalates onto extreme levels when the individual perceives that the conflict is not resolvable. Sometimes this occurs when there is a change in the structure of the situation (e.g., the vice-president, who had favored an otherwise condemned executive and earmarked him for promotion, suddenly dies). Sometimes conflict-bind is the result of insight, as when the individual realizes that he does not have the ability to compete, but that he still has compulsive ambition. Sometimes a bind is reached when outside forces keep the individual in conflict. For example, the hostility and rejection which the individual engenders in others would normally cause him to attenuate his competitiveness. But the demands made by others (often the same others) keep the individual in the battle. Such chronic conflicts are devastatingly stressful.

Invited commentary

DAVID MECHANIC: It is quite evident from the papers and discussions so far that there is not really a general stress theory but many varied conceptions of stress and ways to study stress. It therefore seems to me quite worthwhile to do what Dr. Pepitone has attempted—that is, to ask such questions as "What can my particular area contribute to the study of stress?" and "What do we know about social psychological theory and social psychological empirical work which may have relevance for understanding phenomena often referred to as stress?"

One of the valuable contributions that his paper makes is that it introduces concepts which are no longer single person concepts but ones which have relevance for larger systems. Competitiveness does not make sense when you think of individuals unconnected with other individuals. Neither does the concept of social comparison make much sense unless you conceive of some kind of social system—or at least more than a one person system. Dr. Pepitone emphasizes only one aspect of social comparison processes evident in natural situations—how people vary their self-evaluations and aspirations as studied in certain kinds of experiments. I think it is important to realize that social comparison affects people in other ways as well. It not only affects the way people make estimates concerning particular tasks, it also affects their motivation. Through the process of social comparison—taking into consideration the kinds of motives other people have, the kinds of other goal setting activities people are engaged in—a person's goal setting activities are influenced. This can be seen in a global study like Shils and Janowitz' (1948) investigation of German troops who continued to fight, although they were well aware that the Germans were going to lose the war. The question was why were they fighting? Were they so loyal to the German cause? Shils and Janowitz found that they were not. It was rather group ties and comparisons with others within primary groups that made men continue to fight, although they knew that they were fighting for a lost cause.

Social comparison also sets the limits on what possible defense and coping techniques can and will be used by making clear the values relevant to how people can and should approach particular kinds of crises.[4]

Dr. Pepitone has generally concentrated on a few areas in social psychology which might be characterized as possible stress situations—work and competitiveness, uncertainty, need for self-improvement, etc. Of course, a very similar kind of argument could have been made for such other concepts and areas of research in social psychology as role conflict, social approval and disapproval, and acculturation or social change.

I am not sure that it is terribly worthwhile to identify sources of stress, because it is an endless process. The value of the approach that Dr. Pepitone chose lies in its emphasis on the self and social dynamics involved in stress response. As for his particular choices, the one that I find most interesting is his choice of social comparison. You find generally that in situations of uncertainty a person has a need to compare himself with others not only for the purpose of self evaluation but also to gauge how he is going to approach tasks. That is, he has to evaluate himself in terms of his strategies and the strategies other people are using, and he has to consider how he might change his strategies in order to handle the task more adequately.

Although experiments have primarily emphasized changes in aspiration in social comparison situations, it is important to recognize that social comparison in natural situations can be a rather important source of stress. In such circumstances it cannot be assumed that people will change their evaluations so that they don't compare themselves to others when these others are too far ahead of them. There are many natural situations where there are constraints operating—either external or internal—where a person is trying to achieve a particular goal. In the particular situation I studied, doctoral prelims (Mechanic, 1962), the fact that a student compares himself to another student and sees that the other student knows all sorts of things that he doesn't know, doesn't make him say, "Oh well, I'm not going to compare myself to you." If he feels he is less able than all the others, the laboratory experiments would suggest that he will leave the situation; that is, he has to give up his goal. Of course this isn't what happens. He gets very anxious and upset and he doesn't function very well for a few days, and then he starts avoiding these others who stimulate social comparison processes and anxiety.

There are also positive effects of social comparison. Comparison with others, as Dr. Pepitone has pointed out, may lead individuals either to raise or lower their comparison estimate so as to be closer to others. In many real life situations, the possibilities are more varied. When individuals compare themselves to others and come to the conclusion that others are slobs and that they are really competent, this often enhances their self-esteem. They may get considerable gratification from such estimates which make clear their excellence. So I certainly would not predict that individuals would lower their self-esti-

[4] See related discussion, p. 188 ff.

mates in order to achieve stability. Let me make it clear that I am not arguing against an experimental approach. I am suggesting, however, that very important mediating variables are often not included in the experiments dealing with social comparison.

Looking at stress in general, it seems to me that it is valuable to conceive of stress as characterizing the discrepancy between the demands impinging upon a person—whether these demands be external or internal, whether challenges or goals—and the way the individual perceives his potential responses to these demands. Generally, when discrepancies occur, they produce discomfort and concern. The extent of discomfort depends upon the importance of the demand or the extent of motivation, on the one hand, and the degree of discrepancy or failure, on the other. Such discrepancies between life demands and potential coping depend on self dynamics, and this is what Dr. Pepitone stressed—that is, goal setting, self-improvement, and so on. But they also depend very largely on the individual's preparation and skills. It seems to me that we have not given such factors enough emphasis. If we are to have an adequate conception of stress, we have to give more concern to problem solving and instrumental aspects of behavior. Stress theory must be more than some hypotheses about self dynamics. If we look at a simple-minded example of a stress situation, like that of a man who falls out of a boat, the main determinant of how much stress he feels is not going to be his defense system or the adequacy of the interrelationship of his cognitions but rather whether he can swim; and it seems to me that we tend to overemphasize the internal dynamics and not give enough emphasis to the skill or coping components.

As I see the problem of adaptation, there seems to be some advantage in separating the concepts of coping and defense, a point that others have also made in these discussions. Coping, as I use the term, refers to the instrumental behavior and instrumental capacities in meeting life demands and goals. It involves the application of skills, techniques, and knowledge that a person has acquired. The extent to which a person experiences discomfort in the first place depends on the adequacy or inadequacy of these skills or techniques to a very large extent. Defense, as I use the term, refers to the manner in which a person manages his emotional and affective states when discomfort is aroused or anticipated. Thus, dissonance reduction, the manipulation of self-evaluations, social comparison, and the like, tend to be primarily problems of defense and not problems of coping. Let me also say that social situations vary very widely in the extent to which they require defense reactions or coping reactions. If you survey the psychological literature, you soon realize that there is an overemphasis on processes like working through grief or responses to threats to esteem, which very largely call for psychological defense and where there is relatively little opportunity for the subject to manipulate the situation through instrumental skills.

One of the great inadequacies in the study of the social psychology of stress has been the persistent failure to give attention to the ways in which people use their abilities, skills, strategies, and information in approaching threatening situations. As I said before, I think too much work has overemphasized intrapsychic dynamics. Man has been treated as a relatively static entity, who responds to stimuli emanating from the environment rather than as an active agent who molds and structures the environment, who nurtures some alternatives and eliminates others, who selectively decides in large part to what stresses he will be exposed and at what pace.

The extent to which a person experiences stress in any situation, or conversely, a person's ability to achieve mastery, is dependent on his ability to mobilize effort when effort is necessary, the manner in which efforts are organized and paced, on psychological and instrumental ability and skills in dealing with tasks and people, and on the extent to which the individual has social and environmental supports. The mobilization of effort, assuming some level of motivation, depends on a variety of psychological techniques by which people direct themselves to particular tasks. Dr. Wilkins, for example, mentions the fact that the men in the Antarctic held a party when half of the winter was over. In most situations we have viewed, we find that people tend to have a need to break tasks—especially any task that takes a large amount of time—into smaller units which they attack a unit at a time. Long-distance runners do this, drivers do this, and writers do this.

The organization of effort may involve the manner in which a person anticipates situations, how he seeks information, the extent of practice in both the social and psychological sense, the rehearsal of problem solutions, and the manner in which efforts are allocated. We sometimes fail to give due emphasis to the obvious fact that successful performance is due in very large part to the way people learn to approach problems and learning from one's past experience and the experience of others.

The traditional approach has been to look at behavior and then go back and try to explain the behavior in terms of the developmental history of individuals. We all know that this has not been overly successful. It seems to me that a more productive way of approaching the study of behavior and of stress is to take a cross-sectional view, looking at the techniques individuals use and then correlating these techniques with effective performance. Most social psychology experiments do not really handle this problem adequately; investigators have not developed many approaches that give the subject leeway in manipulating coping devices in trying to produce a more effective performance. We have to develop experiments that can do this. Strodtbeck's (1951) revealed-differences technique, which he used to attempt to study how families work out disagreements, is an example of a very useful approach to the study of performance dynamics. We have to give much more thinking and emphasis to the ways in which subjects manipulate situations, as compared with trying to explain behavior in a developmental sense.

Discussion

Dr. Pepitone: My concentration on competition and work was not to imply that these are the only social conditions related to stress but simply because space would not permit careful treatment of additional variables. Such stress-generating conditions as direct depreciation and conformity pressure obviously require a detailed analysis.

As to the difference between our experimental situations and real life, it is evident that the latter typically permits a much greater variety of coping possibilities. In an experiment it is less useful to include many possibilities. On the contrary, one deals with a deliberate simplification, and one pays the price in that the ultimate applicability to real life situations is thereby postponed.

Dr. Haythorn: On the matter of methodology, I feel that when we talk about laboratory studies versus field studies we aren't making enough distinctions. I believe that there is a spectrum of research techniques, with different attributes at different loci along the spectrum.

We probably would agree that we are all interested in studying the nature of the real world, and I think we would all agree that what we want is a symbolic model of that real world—a mathematical model, scientific theory, whatever you want to call it—such that operations on that symbolic model would yield outcomes which would be consistent with outcomes of analogous operations made on the real world. On one end of our spectrum, then, we could place the real world, and on the other, a mathematical model. I think that Plato and Descartes knew—and we all know—that the real world is an hypothetical construct to which nobody has direct access. The best that we can do is make observations and measurements on it. Thus, moving along the spectrum from the real world, a first focal point to be identified may be variously called observational measurement, field studies, systematic collection of data in the field, in nature, in vivo, etc. I think this is as close to the real world as any of us will ever get.

If we go one step further along this continuum and make operations on the real world and measure the outcome of these operations, we may call this a field experiment. In many situations, not much in stress research—although HUMMRO did a certain amount of this—we try to represent in our laboratory as exact a replica of the real world as we can. We try to simulate in great detail and then study the situation—which is now in essence a replication of the real world but one where we, the experimenters, have control. Simulation, then, is the next point which can be identified along the spectrum.

Following this we might place the laboratory experiment, wherein we identify certain elements (though not all) of the real world and try to study the operation of these elements. Psychologists have so far only barely begun to move beyond this point, but it is possible to go much farther and to try to build mathematical models. We know that in our present state of knowledge mathematical models require so many simplifying functions that they are generally not obtainable for us, but there are two points along the spectrum that I think can be identified as approaches to a mathematical model having many of their characteristics. One is a deterministic model, such as economists use in linear programming, where you have a computer representation of a process, every point of which is deterministic. In essence you are saying, here is the way I think this process works, I'll make the computer work that way and see what comes out under different kinds of operations. A step back from this are the Monte Carlo or stochastic models which differ from the deterministic model, mainly in that we know that there are some things in the process that we don't understand or aren't interested in that introduce variance and we know about the variance so we put it in. We don't know or we don't care why we are getting the variance, but we do take it into account.

Looking at our spectrum of techniques, we can see large differences between information collection procedures at one end and information synthesis procedures at the other. Moving along the spectrum could be characterized as climbing up an abstraction ladder. Mathematical models are the most abstract and therefore the most powerful, so far as manipulation is concerned. They are also the most likely to produce problems in generalizing back to the real world. I think this is what we mean when we talk about the differences between a laboratory experiment and field observation. We have abstracted at one level, and in trying to generalize back towards reality we run into difficulty.

Perhaps this will help put methodological arguments into somewhat better perspective. Some work recently reported by one of Bavelas' students (Wright, 1962a) may lead you to discount all of this. He gave subjects a series of objects— paintings, for example—and told them that the art experts of the world had identified these paintings as falling into one of two classifications. He said he was not going to tell them what the classifications were but would tell them if they were right or not. He then proceeded to give the subjects a series of trials in which they were told whether they were right or wrong when they said this is an X or a Y type of painting. In fact what they were told had nothing to do with what they were saying. He used a noncontingent reinforcement schedule. What he found that is relevant here was that if he built subjects up to an eighty percent reinforcement schedule after say a hundred trials, and then asked them how they were making the distinction, he got fairly simple theories. He further found that under these conditions, the simple theories were subject to quick extinction after a few trials with nonreinforcement. If he built them up on a fifty percent reinforcement schedule, however, they developed very complicated theories that were highly resistant to extinction. If he built them up on approximately a twenty percent reinforcement schedule, they built no theories about the phenomenon at all but built theories about the methodology instead.

Dr. Korchin: Dr. Haythorn's sensitive analysis of methodological approaches recalls a concern I had when we discussed laboratory and field studies earlier. Too often, the two approaches are polarized and other alternatives neglected. In this dichotomy, the field study is characterized as investigating *in vivo* the phenomena with which one is *really* concerned. Thus, the stress of submarine life is studied in a submarine with real sailors. In this contrast, the laboratory experiment is seen as involving artificial situations, used because they can be created and manipulated in the laboratory, somewhat abstracted measures, and atypical subjects. Aside from other errors, this polarization obscures other choices.

One alternative, which we have favored in our research, might be called the "field or natural experiment." Here, circumscribed and at least partly controllable life situations are sought out because there are naturally occurring phenomena which we are interested in studying, but not because there is any interest in the situations *per se*. To illustrate: with the help of Dr. Haythorn's colleagues in the Obstetrics Department at the Naval Medical Center, we were allowed to interview "expectant fathers" waiting for their wives to deliver. We had wanted to study some aspects of cognitive functioning during relatively short but extended periods of rather intense anxiety. Rather than attempting to create such a state "experimentally," we used the natural "experimental" situation. Our interest, however, was not in learning more about expectant fathers, nor in developing techniques to help them in their suffering—the type of purpose which is often assumed to justify field research. However, it is pleasant to be able to report that the men welcomed the chance to wile away some time with the experimenter, and the experiment might have had more "therapeutic" effect than is usual with subjects in a laboratory stress experiment. In any case, without intending to contribute to obstetrics or the welfare of these men, we had the opportunity to study intense affect of a sort which could not be produced in a laboratory.

This brings me to a further point which was also stimulated by Dr. Trumbull's earlier comments (see p. 181). There is an ethical problem in laboratory research in which stressful situations are created and unpleasant and possible traumatic affects are produced. I am not sure that we are as attentive as we should be to the consequences of our actions. Are we really certain that people don't leave our experiments with lasting effects, with painful castration anxiety or lowered self-esteem? Have we checked adequately? We have the obligation to be continuously concerned. If we must cause pain, we must be certain that it is minimal for the purpose and that everything possible is done to avert lasting effects. Happily, the work of undoing may involve methodological gain. The effort to undo a procedure, particularly if deceit is involved, often gives further information about the value of the procedure and its effects. When we explain the purpose of the experiment, or apologize for any trickery that may have been involved, the subject becomes something of a collaborator and may be able to reveal more about his feelings and understanding of the situation than he could while undergoing the experimental treatment. But whatever the by-effects, we have a clear responsibility to avoid any damaging effects.

Dr. Back: Another kind of ethical problem should also be noted, though it is a curiously different one. We just made a study (Back & Saravay, in press) of the researchers who did research on the Kennedy assassination, and about forty percent of them felt some guilt on doing the research at that time.

Dr. Appley: I'll say "Amen" to the importance of ethical concerns and to the suggestions made by Drs. Trumbull and Korchin. I want to make two brief comments on Dr. Pepitone's paper. One to say that I am delighted to see his suggestion of stages or levels of stress, which I feel corresponds exactly to the model that Cofer and I have put forward (Cofer & Appley, 1964). The other is to comment on the importance of the time dimension again. One of the examples Dr. Pepitone gave was to contrast procrastinators and self-pacers in relation to getting tax forms in. He said that stress would occur as the deadline for filing tax returns approached for the procrastinators but not for the self-pacers. What was being described in essence, I think, was a difference between escape behavior and avoidance behavior. That is, an organism that learns an avoidance response reduces the tension. He has acquired a coping strategy, as it were—in this case to handle the effects of stress by spreading them over time. I think the importance of time and subtle but real differences between anticipatory behaviors and behaviors-at-the moment—when there is no preparation or no training—hasn't been emphasized sufficiently, although it has been implicit in much of what has been said here.

Dr. Lanzetta: Responding to Dr. Appley for a moment, the implication here is that you are terminating the tension or anxiety at the point of the coping response itself. What comes to mind immediately is the Kamin effect results in which there is a rather distinct performance decrement at some time period after the animal is removed from the situation. The decrement increases as a function of time out of the situation, reaches its maximum after about six or seven hours and then climbs back to the normal level. Further studies on this seem to indicate rather clearly that this decrement reflects an "incubation of fear" phenomenon (McMichael, 1965). It seems to me that in stress research we also have to worry about the possibility that the anxiety or fear actually incubates and may reach a maximum peak some time after removal from the stress or test situation. Performance decrements may easily occur in periods of time long after the stress has been removed. These are rather recent data but they strike me as being quite relevant for the study of stress phenomena.

Dr. Biderman: Dr. Pepitone's social evaluation theory parallels directly some principles I used (Biderman, 1963) in trying to account for the way in which prisoners of war misinterpreted the prevalent experience amongst their group and why the events surrounding prisoners of war in Korea had been generally misunderstood. Partly this was due to the misunderstanding of repatriate testimony and partly to the repatriates' misreporting in their debriefings upon their repatriation.

Now with respect to reporting prevalent behavior which was consistent with, or counter to, norms—patriotic norms or norms of group cooperation or norms of survival—there was very clearly a tendency to report that behavior by and large had been worse than the objective data we have seems to indicate was the case. Certainly the sum of individual self-testimony indicated behavior which was much more consistent with patriotic norms, etc., than the generalized statements of people about group behavior or the sum of statements of individuals about other individuals. So the principle we stated, and there were various evidences for it, was that for the person who behaved badly there was an advantage in saying "Well, what I did wasn't any worse than what was generally going on." This was a very common remark presented in exactly that way. For those whose behavior was somewhat better than average, the only way this could take place was by deliberately setting out to play the hero's part, a very, very difficult role at best under the circumstances. Because the differences in behavior tended to be not very clear-cut, stating that the level of the group as a whole was somewhat lower than it actually was tended to facilitate the self-evaluation of how well one had played the hero's role.

There were some exceptions to this kind of testimony and they were consistent with Dr. Pepitone's remarks on people who gave up the social evaluation process. These were of two kinds: people whose reactions had been, for example, what has been described as total collaboration, and others who defined themselves as being affected exceptionally because of their special circumstances. Also (although this was not completely consistent), more of the most extreme deviates in the negative conduct direction tended to give favorable comments about group behavior.

⁻There is a complication in all of this, however, and that is that these answers were the product of the standard kind of interviews that were given. These interviews forced upon the individual responses that were self-vindicating. Because we had some opposite biases of our own, which we acted on in interviewing a later group of repatriates, we tried different interviews of the same people which in effect permitted group vindicativeness as opposed to self-vindicativeness. With the interviewing structured in this way, the kind of testimony you got was different. The testimony was now colored by a tendency to elevate—to speak positively about—the norms of behavior among the group as a whole, rather than to deflate them.

Dr. Mechanic: One thing that was clear in my study of doctoral examination stress (Mechanic, 1962) was that when I followed people longitudinally—week by week—their description of the event which was taking place changed each week. It changed substantially from the period before they took the examinations to the period after they took them. In the period before they took them they reported that the examinations were unnecessary and that it was an attempt to degrade and intimidate them. After they passed them, their view of examinations became more pleasant. You can actually compare the statements of people before and after, and they are in some cases radically different. It would, of course, make a great deal of difference, if you were just going in at one point in time, at what point you approach your subjects.

Chairman's summary

KURT W. BACK: Much of the discussion during this meeting has dealt with two contracts, one of methodology and one between levels of discourse. The questions on methodology dealt with a range of different approaches, from laboratory experiments to field studies. It is fitting that the most explicit statements of the problem were connected with the discussion of Dr. Pepitone's paper, first of all because he treated the problem of work, a concept whose central position is shown by its ambiguous aspect. It can mean either physiological output or a central value in society. It also becomes relevant because Dr. Pepitone stresses that the meaning of work in the experiment for the subject depends on whether he uses self-evaluation or self-validation, according to the experimental manipulation. Work then becomes stress to the degree to which individuals give it the meaning of stress. If people take work as a meaningful kind of condition and if they think they are competent to do it, they do not undergo stress. This approach may be a purely social definition of stress, as our society values work and achievement highly. Perhaps other societies, where birth or religious excellence, or something like that, was valued, would not have the same concept. If society defines a situation as not distressful, apparently our physiological system is adapted to take a rather strong load without "realizing" it is stress. If society defines the same kind of thing as very tedious, or if one performs badly, the same kind of work can become stress and induce all physiological symptoms. So it becomes possible, on this topic, to contrast sociological and physiological reductionism.

As psychologists, we are interested in the *individual's* reaction to stress, and I think we can approach the matter from both sides. We know that there are certain physiological conditions which will lead almost exclusively to stress. In maximal situations, such as prisoners-of-war in Korea or in concentration camps, those people did not survive who were put into extreme conditions in which survival was impossible and there was apparently little effect of any psychological state on survival (see Chapter 9). However, in the middle range of seriousness, according to some of the papers presented, we can conclude that stress is centrally controlled. This means, in physiological language, that control of the meaning of stress comes from the CNS, or depends on psychological mechanisms, if we want to use mentalistic language. On the social side, emphasis is much more on control from outside of the person; but here again it is the meaning that a person gives to the outside pressures and to his social relations which may become decisive.

There is a connection between the question of the level of discourse and the problem of methodology. A methodological spectrum ranges from isolating a few variables in the laboratory to studying the structure of the situation as it is found; or, as it has been said, going from the laboratory to the real world. However, the laboratory is part of the real world too, and the subject is likely to attach some meaning to his laboratory experience. In fact, this may be a stress situation itself, and we have found in a series of studies that the relation of experiments to the life of the subject may produce differential reactions to the situation. For instance, it makes a difference whether the subject comes to this situation with friends or with strangers, whether he has been there before, or how he was recruited (Back, Hood, & Brehm, 1964; Back & Bogdonoff, 1964; Brehm, Back, & Bogdonoff, 1964; Bogdonoff, Klein, et al., 1964). These detailed analyses make the experiments not as different from the field studies as they may look at first glance. Substantively, we return to the position that reduction to one set of variables, either social or physiological, or to stimuli, cannot account for stress behavior, but that stress must be understood by the meaning a person gives to the situation.

Analysis of the different ways in which a person can relate himself to a task and view his personal involvement in it will give us much understanding of a person's stress in actual society—the interaction of social and physiological conditions—and can lead us to more fruitful research.

MARVIN K. OPLER   **8**

Cultural induction
of stress

Some years ago in the pages of the *American Anthropologist,* the distinguished physiologist Walter Cannon published a paper which he called, simply, *Voodoo Death* (1942). The article related cases scattered in the literature where members of nonliterate tribes who had broken a taboo or who were convinced of bewitchment literally wasted away and died. In analyzing the reports, Cannon was convinced that extreme forms of anxiety could produce loss of appetite, reduced intake of foods (and hence, fluids), and most of all result in loss of salts and bodily fluids through sweating. In effect, protracted dehydration processes occurred, so that, indeed, literal wasting away resulted in death.

In Nigeria, our phrase "being frightened out of one's wits" has some cultural sanction, for there are many cultural terms for cursing or bewitching. For example, the curse uttered within earshot of the victim is distinguished from a curse leveled against him when he is not within hearing distance, and each, in the catalog of mental illnesses, can lead to different disorders. An outstanding Nigerian psychiatrist, Dr. T. Adeoye Lambo, well trained in European and particularly British psychiatry, has regarded these syndromes as being paranoid reactions (Lambo, 1955); but we would insist, on the basis of cross-cultural comparisons, that they are hysterical, anxious states similar to those documented by Cannon with organismic compliance simply enacted. We are emboldened to make known this disagreement by the fact that Nigerian cases we have collected do not evidence fixed delusions unsanctioned by cultural understandings. The effects of bewitchment, once culturally sanctioned, are no more mysterious than various other social customs. The Navajo will not eat fish; the Kansas farmer might throw out, as moldy, a truly ripe Gorgonzola that a man from Milan would savor; and all three would be repulsed by the Eskimo use of vitamin-rich raw flesh of sea mammals or the Arctic delicacy of decaying birds. Mental compliance in Nigerians, somatic compliance in Cannon's cases, and either the flow of gastric juices or reverse peristalsis and vomiting, as the case may be, remind us that a continuous cognitive and emotional appraisal goes on in humans, producing mental reactions, somatic states, and physiological readiness of various types in all sorts of combinations and balances.

While most anthropologists prefer to discuss the cognitive and emotional balances achieved in cultures by a wholly cognitive definition of culture itself, usually referring to a body of custom, belief, practices, and artifacts, it is preferable, we believe, to include the emotionally felt, creatively understood values from the outset. In short, we prefer a cognitive-emotive definition of culture as being "what men live by." This is proposed in addition to the usual formal definition including customs, beliefs, practices, and artifacts (all those things engaged in or utilized by man as a member of a society), since it implies all the conditions of his existence which are meaningful and thus links culture with the vicissitudes of personality.

There is another reason for the inclusion of the emotional aspects in the definition of culture itself, and that is that the emotive life, or styles of emotion, themselves vary with culture. When a Masai warrior honors a youth who looks promising by spitting in his face, when an Andaman Islander greets a visitor or journeying relative by sitting down on his lap and wailing a tearful salutation, when a reprimanded Chinese schoolboy takes the scolding with cheerful (making a generous show of respect) grinning, and when both Navajo and Apache Indians lower the voice (not raise it) in a show of anger, we may well wonder whether emotional expressivity does not vary with culture. The Apache male, who lives in a dwelling contiguous to that of his wife's parents, is called "he who carries burdens for me" and refers to them in polite forms of the verb. His respect is further signalized by physical avoidance of face-to-face contact in the same visual space. Yet, given the clear statement of Apache affinal kin responsibilities, what could be a more certain insurance of continuing such duties than this formalized physical avoidance? Or if Navajo and Apache, both tonal languages, are found in a setting of mobile hunting and gathering encampments, and if friendly messages and communications are often shouted across space, what could signalize anger more than nearly inaudible remarks? To Chinese, a youth's smile connotes respect and agreement, to the Masai saliva is meaningful whereas a handgrasp is not, and to the Andaman Islander a real greeting requires tears of joy. We are not saying that the catalog of emotions is of a different sort, merely that the style and balance differ. This we should know from various traditions in art, in dress, in architecture, in music, or even in economy and political style.

There are those who argue that such variations are merely connation of cognate or connected qualities with only the slightest change from culture to culture. After all, the labeled emotions are the same. In answer to vicious racial theories, such sensitive early cultural anthropologists as Bastian (1881) argued for a fundamental unity of the human species, and indeed, the human mind. In America, Franz Boas, who trained and influenced most of the outstanding anthropologists of the twentieth century in the United States, popularized such European theorists as Wundt (1911–1920), who held that elementary forms of thought —the *Elementargedanken*—received in each cultural milieu a special stamp of variance, called the mode of folk belief, or *Völkergedanken*. Such theory was, of course, essentially correct in emphasis in the face of racist confabulations, since the human species is one by all biological criteria. Indeed, modern races are more admixtures, showing greater trends towards unification or similarity, than the relatively isolated types and regional variants, like Sinanthropus, Cro-Magnon Man, and the Neanderthals who preceded them.

But though ghosts of the White Man's self-glorifying "burdens" have been dispelled, modern anthropological theory has been moved to more sophisticated levels, far beyond the reach of crude racist theories. Though connotative life is the same, or generally the same, in all cultures, making rough translations of meanings and intentions similar, all we can say at this point is that the rubrics for constructing the forms of cultures are the same. That is, all peoples from one extreme of technology to another make provision economically for food and some sort of shelter, and either clothing or adornment, varying notoriously, for use to bedeck themselves. All seek answers to questions or develop *rapport* with the world and universe, be it in forms of science, philosophy, or religion. All regulate sexual behavior, have social organization as wells into which seep the notions of economic regulation, legal constructs, and social or ritual sanctions, or political streams of thought. All, likewise, provide a modicum of recreation in art, music, folk literature, and games. But beyond such universal culture patterns, as Clark Wissler (1938) termed them, the actual elaboration of structural form and function in cultures the world over varies so notoriously that equivalence in translation from one form to another is never exactly possible. It is here that the individuality and special characteristics of each culture assert themselves, on a level which is no longer connotative of species' unity but fully cognitive and emotive in its complete contours. While cultural evolution makes for further cross-cultural comparisons, a continuous cognitive and emotional appraisal goes on in cultures as it does in individuals composing the culture.

The proof of cultural differentiation, on grounds of cognitive-emotive theory, is to be found in social psychiatry. In 1956, the author was convinced that psychiatry was assuming a unity of human stresses the same for all cultures, of psychodynamic processes which were invariable, and of mental disorders which were presumed to be outlined for all peoples and all times in the diagnostic nomenclature of the American Psychiatric Association. In a volume called *Culture, Psychiatry and Human Values* (Opler, 1956), the cross-cultural literature and epidemiological findings for mental illnesses were presented continent by continent and in some historical depth for European psychiatry. Cross-cultural comparisons helped correct the conformist theories. For one thing, mental disorders had changed historically in Europe and varied cross-culturally. In the second place, the illnesses varied both in form or type and in amount or extent epidemiologically. Thirdly, concepts of mental illness had changed, and with them changes had occurred in the forms of treatment and organization of psychiatry. Finally, public attitudes had changed, making possible new forms of social or community psychiatry. In all of these transformations, it was important to note the social and cultural backgrounds reflected into varying types of mental disorder and the connections between psychodynamic processes and sociodynamic conditions.

Obviously, the relationship between social and cultural backgrounds and psychodynamic processes cannot be discussed exhaustively in a brief chapter. But required in each discussion is a concept of cultural stress systems producing psychopathology. By stress, in this context, no one can really mean psychological stress, pure and simple. Since Cannon, Selye, or Freud, total patterns of reaction, including physiological concomitants of emotional states, have been emphasized, making it impossible to limit psychophysiological stress down to some abstract psychological parameter. We maintain that the total organism and its reactive mechanisms, including limbic system, CNS, and so forth, constantly responds, sometimes adversely for its own survival, to the total conditions under which it exists. Individuals and even families maintain a balance or imbalance that connotes wellness or illness. In this sense, L. K. Frank's famous metaphor, "Society is the patient," contains a striking truth in that it means that individual or family functioning becomes maladaptive, distorted, and "sick" under certain social and cultural conditions (Frank, 1948). A psychodynamic process which is either maladaptive or well begins in the individual or family only when relating in some manner with others, whether the terms are reacting against, striving towards, coping, helping, or enjoying. One can extend the somewhat mechanistic energy-distributing paradigm of man, which Freud proposed, to signify maintaining some sort of balance or imbalance within a context. The typical context today is a combination of class and subculture, denoting the actual, real, reiterated conditions of existence. In the cultural sense, including cognitive-emotive areas, we mean *total conditions of existence*.

L. Wolberg's famous post-hypnotic experiment with three patients (Wolberg, 1947) indicates that experimental conditions can only work at best on previously conditioned adult human subjects. The patient who used conversion symptoms did not even see the negatively charged object (candy, in the experiment); the second subject, similarly warned of its negative qualities, reacted with sweating and faintness at the sight of the candy; while the third, with psychosomatic channels of reaction, utilized reverse peristalsis and vomiting only after eating it. Similarly, in the experiment reported by Schachter and Singer (1962), visceral responses and emotional ones related to environmental factors, including human cognitive meanings which were transmitted to the subjects and connoted social meanings as well. The adjustive and adaptive mechanisms in human behavior do not begin on some level of physiological response to fixed psychological stimuli. Sophisticated experimentalists, like Schachter and Singer, are aware in using environmental cues of the questionnaire sort, where the instrument in this case becomes more and more personal and insulting, that the stimulus conditions are really of a certain subcultural variety. Others, like the critical and exacting team of John Lacey, Kagan, and Moss of the Fels Research Institute of Yellow Springs, Ohio (Lacey, 1956), to mention only one group, are quick to point out the fact that variegated physiological display seems to accompany all behavior in the laboratory, including behavior in emotional or stressful situations. S. Sarason of Yale has noted that negative findings pervade the studies of relationships of anxiety to all manner of physiological indices.

Of special interest to the social psychiatrist today is the fact that while anxiety attacks, conversion hysterias, and acute confusional states open to rapid remission once plagued men in nonliterate cultures [such as are reported by Cannon in his cases, by Lambo for Nigeria, or by the author in regard to the epidemiology of the Ute Indians of Colorado (Opler, 1940)], their place is now taken in modern urban epidemiology by deeply rooted schizophrenias, often with paranoid reaction, or by scientifically attestable psychosomatic disorders (where organic impairment appears in ulcer, urticaria, asthma, blood sugar imbalances, essential hypertension, and the like). Where once shamans and curing cults handled conversion symptoms, often with marvelous cures, and where ceremonies involved some degree of family participation and concern for the patient, since Breuer and Freud (1959), psychiatry has made the organic dysfunction a matter of direct concern for patient and practitioner who prescribes for attestable organ injury. While we are commenting here on the total increased epidemiology of somatic reaction forms as a class, it is clear that mere hysteriform emotional outlets are becoming *passé*, although they still have a large prevalence, according to Dr. J. C. Finney of the University of Kentucky School of Medicine, in islands of rural white poverty in Southern Appalachian eastern Kentucky, where educational levels and aspirations are low (Finney, 1963).

These differentials in experience and in resulting personality patterning suggest that the psychologist, when dealing with adult subjects, should never assume he is dealing with Man with a capital M. Experimentalists dealing with rats, assuming that they are in a better position to deal with Rodent with a capital R, are today careful to avoid contamination of experimental strains or any other instrusive nonexperimental effects on the animals. Yet serendipity in the form of chance environmental effects intervened, as all know, in the instance of Harry Harlow's rhesus monkeys, or infant macaques (cf. Harlow, 1959). When his wife's sympathies for the isolated, nonmothered rhesus infants intervened and she contaminated certain subjects by playing with them, this led to interesting reparative behavior patterns. Her experiment was systematized so that nonmothered macaques were given opportunities for peer group play activity. (Harlow, H. & Harlow, K. 1962). Whereas nonmothered isolates, if female, are unable to enact maternal behavior in their turn, or if male to achieve normal copulation, peer group license to engage in play activity mitigated these symptoms and produced better social balances. A more complete picture of maturation processes after early infancy was produced (Harlow, H. & Harlow, K., 1962).

In like manner, S. Zuckerman's unadorned picture of competitive baboon behavior in the captivity of the London Zoo, with male dominance based on size and strength, and female sexuality used instrumentally in continuous presentations for food and other favors, is changed remarkably in S. Washburn's studies of great apes under field conditions (Washburn, 1961). No longer can one safely allude to Zuckerman's *Social Life of Monkeys and Apes* (1932) as a paradigm of male physical dominance and continuous female sexual maneuvers, since apes in African hordes have remarkable elaborations of protective functions for survival of the group, intensive group play activities of young, far less patriarchal arrangements in regard to sexual gratification, and often organized methods of movement, foraging, scouting, and standing off predatory beasts.

On the human level, of course, the analogs of such schemes vary notoriously, but our theme of going to cognitive-emotive levels, where stress is involved, can be continued. Experiments by Lazarus and Speisman (Lazarus & Alfert, 1964; Speisman, Lazarus, et al., 1964b), are both to the effect that different cognitive preparation for the same stimuli result in different physiological responses. The cognitive level of meanings and symbolic interactions in humans is the very level on which anthropologists begin their inquiries, and these have led away from *obiter dicta* about Man with a capital M to inquiries into conditions under which cultures operate and humans adapt, strive, cope, and develop.

The anthropologist or social psychiatrist therefore knows it is appropriate to begin his studies of stress in the context of field conditions. He claims that humans have too much spare adjustive and adaptive machinery, derived from their own personality balances as well as from adjustive or adaptive resources learned in cultures, to be caught as mere human organisms within the presumptive cross-sectional laboratory conditions of most experiments ignoring cognition and emotion. Instead, he seeks self-consciously for environmental contexts and categories in the conditions of existence which can be contrastive of variations in cultural stress systems. These points we claimed earlier (Opler, 1956) as a theory of the relational system obtaining in humans as a result of the natural interplay between sociodynamic happenings in cultural contexts and the psychodynamic stream of events influencing individuals. We urged, consequently, that such conditions of existence, as the combination of class and ethnic subculture, be used to select samples for study.

In a paper with J. Singer in the same year, (Opler & Singer, 1956), we used such socially and culturally distinct samples of Irish and Italian schizophrenics from our Midtown Manhattan Mental Health Research Study to show that in ten differentiating variables for types of schizophrenia, these sample groups, according to thirteen psychological test instruments and two years of intensive study of their behavior, were as different as day and night.

As an anthropologist, the author claims behavioral sciences have a proneness to eliminate conditions and contexts in favor of the empty hope that mixed samples will produce some magical uniformities simply because we use laboratories and don white coats. As a social philosopher, he would state that behavioral sciences, looking to physics and chemistry for models, have tended hitherto in the direction of faith, and even blind faith, in what is called "objectivity" uncorrected by *scientific* interest in such massive subjective processes in humans as are indicated in styles and patterns of cognition, of emotion, of culturally-induced irrationality, or what the phenomenologists would call human intentions, outlooks of modes of assessment that even the phenomenologists fail to recognize as being subjectively cultural in content. Scientific ontology, applied to humans, does not mistake subjective states for objective realities, but nevertheless such strange bedfellows as existentialist psychiatrists often do just that, and they do it along with the white-coated denizens of some of the best-regulated laboratories.

We claim, along with James B. Conant, in his *Science and Common Sense* (1951), that scientific verities are achieved by a ceaseless process of questioning and, indeed, construction of experiments to test hypotheses. But, as Einstein pointed out constantly, propounding the right questions is the most crucial element in the entire process. Thus, in behavioral sciences the penchant for defining parameters as neurophysiological and psychological may be constrictive and misleading unless cognition and emotional balances are traced in turn to their natural boundaries. What follows, from the author's own field experiences, are a series of comments on the parameters of cultural stress systems studied by the author over a thirty-year period.

In the 1930's, while studying Eastern Apache tribes in central New Mexico with Dr. M. E. Opler, the author was struck by two points, the persistency of Mescalero, Chiricahua, and Lipan tribes to maintain their culture (despite years of reservation living and a shunting around of some to such places as Fort Sill, Oklahoma), plus the emphasis in the culture on the values of mobility, vigor, and long life. Without describing these matters in detail, suffice it to say that aboriginal life was mobile, with extended family camps moving ceaselessly for hunting and gathering purposes; most Apaches as adults had individual supernatural power, many practicing ceremonies to cure ills and so maintain health and movement; and the life-cycle ceremonies, from first walking to elaborate adolescence rites—the Changing Woman ceremony, for example—were designed to achieve industriousness, health, and vigor through four stages of life. Nativistic rituals, such as peyotism and the Silas John Cult, were added to buttress older beliefs and rites in the constant attrition of Apache ways under reservation conditions.

An acculturation history of these changes cannot be given here, but slowly, almost glacially, the intrusion occurred. We recall, in the 1930's, the fact that one set of *gahe* dancers, curing supernaturals controlled by a shaman, had painted designs on torsoes applied by the reservation housepainter and that the aged shaman, who years before repeatedly kept these preparatory rites private, allowed pictures to be taken and joined in the jokes about where the whitewash for the color white had come from. Without presenting innumerable instances of such partial breakdown, let us add that these people, who so favored life and vigor, had equal sanctions and ritual observances against death, ghost "sickness," and physical contacts with death. Despite Hollywood versions to the contrary, we know of no people who feared death more than the Apache.

In the context of cultural breakdown, of rising rates of alcoholism, mental illness, and demoralization, suicide of a most dramatic and violent sort has emerged for the Apache. The method of choice is to swallow inflammable liquid, retain a portion in the mouth, and apply a lighted match. This curious method among Western Apache is not unknown in the east. Apparently, Apache sanctions against the concept of death have been among the last cultural conceptions to falter, but with cultural attrition occurring all along the way, when these last bastions fall, they do so with a thunder of violence. We find it most interesting, psychodynamically, that dead Apache are believed to contaminate the living and that family tensions and trials have of course increased in the present period. A related sociodynamic happening is that the young Apache—and suicides are by no means notable among the aged and infirm—are those most caught in the conflict of two cultures, have less reason for recourse to the older cultural traditions, and are those most prone to a weak and insecure position in intergenerational differences. Suicide by oral immolation is the magically manipulative, depressed, and anxiously hostile psychodynamic answer, an explosive one, to sociodynamic events, equally destructive in their own way.

Following our Apache fieldwork, we undertook an independent study of the acculturation of the Southern Ute Indians of Colorado (Opler, 1940). We shall not deal here with this study except to note that of three bands, two eastern and one western, with practically identical cultures to begin with, the two bands on the eastern periphery started accommodation to the surrounding White culture about a hundred years ago in a period of land sales, while the third western band, the Weminutc, attempted to maintain a mobile existence around Ute Mountain. Differences in economic history were reflected into rates of acculturation, more rapid in the East than in the West. In the Southern Ute case, one noted psychological problems of stress and strain in rapid acculturation, and again, nativistic cults developed more prominently in the more conservative cultural setting of the West to buttress and bolster up the older Ute ways. Though more poorly off economically, and suffering greater impairments in physical health, the Weminutc or western band were superior in mental health (less conversion hysterias, neurotic manifestations, and known psychoses). Their problems lay in the realm of tuberculosis and malnutrition, while alcoholism, conversion symptoms, and confusional anxiety states, often with violent outbursts, could be studied more readily in the eastern bands of the Consolidated Ute Indian reservation around Ignacio.

In anthropology, one can study cultural evolutionary series, such as the related cultures of Paiute and Ute, who are simple hunting and gathering tribes, contrasted with their cultural cousins, the Hopi of Arizona, who are village dwelling horticulturists, and the city-building intensive agriculturists, the Aztecs, who settled in the valley of Mexico. These are linguistically related but historically divergent peoples for whom the language stock, Uto-Aztekan, furnishes one proof of original connection. Other evolutionary series connect Athabaskan language-speaking tribes, of whom the eastern Apache tribes furnish the example of hunting and gathering mobile peoples, while Western Apache and Navajo, again linguistically related, furnish the examples of incipient agriculturalists and herdsmen.

The epidemiology of disorders, the modes of curing, and the changing concepts of health and illness are important to study in just such series, which we refer to as macroevolutionary developments. Beneath these levels of development, microevolutionary processes have also taken place, as in the differentiation of Southern Ute bands. But both macro-evolutionary series and microevolutionary processes in culture extend our notice to unfolding economies in total development, and also to the stresses and strains developed in cultural systems and in the psychologies of culture-carriers. As we have pointed out above, these provide us with living laboratories of particular conditions of existence, with more homogeneous samples on the microevolutionary level and with special experiences repeatedly encountered in a specific culture or subcultural variety of living.

A medical acquaintance recently mentioned that Tahitians are too exotic, that New Yorkers and Buffalonians are better subjects for study. Frankly, Irish and Italian schizophrenics in New York and Ute Indian or Kentuckian conversion hysterics are equally objects of science, as may be Tahitians in some other appropriate experimental design. One of the best studies of man in disaster is that by Dr. William Lessa of the University of California at Los Angeles who studied the natives of Ulithi after the typhoon struck (Lessa, 1964); it all depends where the typhoon strikes! At our University, a world famous physiologist, Dr. Hermann Rahn, has studied Korean and Japanese deep sea kelp divers (Rahn, pers. comm.), simply because human physiological response to pressure is of interest; here it depends on where, occupationally, great pressure in sea depth is a seasonal experience.

In the decade from the mid-1930's to mid-1940's, an attempt was made to extend these observations from settings of normative cultural operations to those in which cultural stress symptoms were still more implicit. As a professor at Reed College in Oregon, the author had, in Portland, the only federal hospital for Northwest Coast and Alaskan native patients (Indians, Eskimos, and Whites) found anywhere in the United States. At Columbia University, previously, we had agreed whole-heartedly with Ruth Benedict, R. Linton, and others that culture affects the psychologies of peoples profoundly. Benedict's *Patterns of Culture,* with generous allusions to pueblo peoples like the Hopi, standing in contrast to Northwest Coast Indians like the Kwakiutl, Tlingit and Tsimshian, had been published in 1934. Even before encountering Kwa-kiutl, Tlingit, and Tsimshian patients in Oregon's Morningside Clinic and Hospital (with generous contrasts of Alaskan frontier Whites, Eskimos, and Athabaskan Indians as well), we had felt that we had more disagreements with Benedict's brand of cultural relativism than agreements.

Granted that culture affects psychology profoundly, was the process, as Benedict claimed, wholly relativistic? Could the abnormals of one culture fit in normatively somewhere else, as she stated? In brief, was the problem of cultural fit with some given pattern in culture merely one of cognitive understandings and agreement? A sensitive anthropologist, Edward Sapir (1937), had already stated his criticism that no cultures were to be described as simply megalomaniacal or paranoid, or as obsessive, or passive dependent. Yet this was how the vignettes of Kwakiutl, Dobuan, and Pueblo Indian appeared in Benedict's account. Apart from the sharpness of her descriptions, the more important theoretical question Benedict raised was to be found in two of her central propositions, first that cultural pattern is infinitely variable ("anything" from paranoid to obsessive to passive dependent may appear), and secondly, that a process of purely "psychological selectivity," as she termed it, determined any pattern. It is clear that this latter proposition, presumptively causal, contains the former, or, obviously, if psychological selectivity can "select" any pattern among possibilities, then it follows any cultural pattern, no matter how extreme, may so evolve. In attacking the descriptive sharpness, and the labels, like "megalomaniacal" culture, Sapir merely disagreed on relatively weaker descriptive grounds. My own criticism, besides challenging the postulate that "anything could happen," added the more inclusive criticism that "psychological selectivity," since it grows out of culture itself, is a circular explanation. What determines such selectivity, if *not* culture?

In contrast to the "anything may happen" postulate, we suggested that the limitations set by culture, and determining its selectivity, were determined by processes of macroevolution and microevolution. As an evolutionist, we had doubts about absolute cultural relativity. Abnormals of one culture, as noted in Kwakiutl, Tsimshian, or Tlingit mentally ill, could fit in nowhere else normatively. The ill were indeed ill, but more important, their forms of illness and illness etiology reflected the cultural stress conditions they had encountered as Kwakiutls, etc. In place of absolute relativism, there is a fit between illnesses and cultural stress systems, whereas the normative cultures themselves were human modes of adaptation, obviously more or less adequate. This is, perhaps, a relational system between sociologically known sociodynamic happenings and psychologically known psychodynamic ones.

In an analog of Einsteinian physical relativism, it sees the world as finitely bounded, so far as human observers are concerned, by binding conditions of the culture or subculture, even the social class and ethnic group combinations of modern times. While these compose the typical conditions under which an individual copes, strives, hopes, and aspires, they may be set against the less finite and bounded (finite but unbounded) possibilities for development, where background conditions changed. Social psychiatry is, in effect, the least nihilistic and most willing environmentalist experimentation known to psychiatry or behavioral sciences simply because it combines determinism with a wider view of the possible cultural conditions of existence. While limitations are imposed by cultural conditions, modifications in this realm produce psychological change.

There are other positions which too rigidly limit culturally conditioned psychodynamic process. Kardiner et al., in the correctly titled *Psychological Frontiers of Society* (1945), while purporting to write of cultural influences, actually derived whole cultures and adult personality functioning from infantile disciplines. In our view, child-rearing disciplines are as epiphenomenal to culture as any other of its complexes, elements and factors. E. H. Erikson, in *Childhood and Society* (1950, 1963), continued the myth with Siouan culture derived from cradle-board restrictions and nursing past stages of tooth-eruption. The derivations, such as wandering unrestrictedly over the plains—a dubious picture of tribal territories and buffalo hunting at best—or occasionally mentioned Siouan cruelties towards women in a putatively male-dominated culture, are both negated in the Ute Indian experience where cradle-board and even later weanings are to be noted. The Ute, like their cognate peoples, the Hopi, were dominantly peaceful Great Basin people and their degree of equality between sexes and interdictions against cruelty are poles apart from Sioux. Further child-rearing derivations from zonal theory, like G. Gorer's toilet-training and weaning derivations of Japanese culture, illustrate the weakness in positions that detach psychological events from cultural ones.

Our own position (Opler, 1960) is that the developmental sequences of greatest importance lie in cultural evolutionary and microevolutionary series which aid in setting up comparative categories among or between cultures and generate hypotheses as to kinds of psychologies of people in art and creativity, or otherwise, in such pathological dimensions as the kinds and the epidemiology of mental disorder, the types of therapy, and the organization of the healing arts. While a cultural relativity which is not absolute, but rather comparative, in emphasis can begin to analyze specific forms of mental disorders, types of therapy, and organization of curative practices, it cannot ignore the microevolutionary processes that set the total conditions of existence.

In Morningside Clinic and Hospital, the histories of illness development differed from one cultural group to the next for Northwest Coast Indians, Eskimos, Whites, and northern Athabaskan tribes. The illnesses were maladaptive to the human condition as well as to the cultural context. Thus, one had maladaptations traceable to specific kinds of stressful cultural conditions. There were not only pathological individuals but also pathological families within these settings. In addition, as in the Eastern Ute bands, there were acculturation breakdowns making it difficult to be Kwakiutl, Tsimshian, or Eskimo. Vilhjalmur Stefansson, with whom we were privileged to work during portions of the northwest coast research reaching into Alaska, had pointed out in his experience that mental illness, alcoholism, and family pathology, which he encountered among Alaskan Eskimos, were virtually absent among the less acculturated Greenland Eskimos during his sojourns in both settings (Stefansson, 1913, 1922; Birket-Smith, 1936). While both acculturated and aboriginal Eskimo typically abandon crippled babies for both practical survival and because they believe in reincarnations from a former ill or maimed state, we might find an adult survivor from congenital or birth injury whose inability to marry or hunt was exacerbated by family neglect. Typically, greater acculturation meant more individualistic, competitive modes, uncongenial to Arctic survival. Acculturated Kwakiutl, similarly, who could neither find a place in our society nor in theirs, were, in D'Arcy McNickle's pungent phrase not only personally conflicted by "a foot in each culture" but culturally blocked from reparative solutions.

Illness typologies, according to types of culture, implied stressful cultural predicaments which set off one group of patients from another. For this reason, Morningside did not have the same kinds of illnesses, even when psychotic, that one could find in the nearby state hospital. While etiology of illness was similar within a group from case to case, it was variable between cultural groups.

I have discussed elsewhere (Opler, 1956) more broadly the regional and intercontinental variations in illnesses, as reactions to stress of differing types. If one considers *latah* (a confusional state psychosis with echolalia and echopraxia found in Micronesia and Malaysia), *imu* (among the Ainu of Hokkaido), so-called Arctic Hysteria (found in northeastern Asia), and Malaysian running amok, it is clear that these are related disorders with similar symptomatology, and often with distinctive age and sex distribution in the cultures where they occur. Echolalia and echopraxia may also, for example in *latah* and *imu*, be varied by negativistic acts. But whether helplessly imitating or doing the opposite (*latah* in Java may pun obscenely, for instance, on the words being used in polite conversation), the stereotyped and repetitive, uncontrolled and confused acts are commonly found in the series. Females, and older and socially vulnerable ones at that, are most noted in the epidemiology, which of course varies to males in the repetitive acts, again uncontrolled, of Malaysian men in running amok. In Hawaii, as reported by Enright and Jaeckle (1963), the Philippines male is again likely to react violently in contrast to the withdrawal behavior of Japanese psychotics, so that the one may retire quietly to his room and the other rush out into cane fields.

The excited confusional states described for certain African cultures, for instance for some Nigerian psychotic patients, may be neatly mirrored in modes of therapy such as the Nigerian use of *rauwolfia serpentina* (reserpine), plus shackling during the early stages of sedation, with family care and participation during the period the patient lives in the practitioner's compound, and aftercare membership in curing cults and group therapy organizations. Many of these aspects, both the illness types, like confusional states and simple catatonias open to remission, or the asylum with families (as in Gheel, Belgium), can be found in earlier phases of European psychiatry corresponding to peasant society and duplicated in peasant societies in other parts of the world.

Similarly, temporary disturbances in thinking or in affect, or the echolalias, echopraxias, and negativisms in action, all episodic *seizures* from nonliterate cultures and from nonurban Europe, were once more common forms of psychosis to be distinguished from the schizophrenias with paranoid reaction common today. Catathymic outbursts, open to remission among African peoples, are likewise part of the list. What we regard as startle reactions, Giles de la Tourette syndrome, catatonic negativisms, echolalias, and echopraxias are today hard to find clinically in urban hospitals of the West. But our psychiatric literature from earlier periods indicates how common they once were, and they are more indicated as symptoms even in E. Bleuler's classic on the variations in schizophrenias, written only a generation ago. Such syndromes were more common from the frontier regions of Alaska, as indicated in Morningside Hospital. Except under the most disastrous conditions of native acculturation, we are convinced further that the rates of psychotic illness are far less than in our modern, urban cultures. Melford E. Spiro (1959), after a careful census in the Micronesian island of Ifaluk, reported extremely low rates even following the turmoil of Japanese invasion in World War II.

Since culture is a whole species' mode of adaptation to the world, to fellow man, and ultimately to one's own fate, where in this cognitive-emotional series does one look for such differences as we have described in major illness typologies? Our suggestion of looking to specific cultural stress systems requires some general classifications within the series. If the illness typologies are monuments to man's relative degree of success or failure in making such adaptations or adjustments, wherein does the failure lie when success is not achieved?

In the first place, the struggle of psychiatry to achieve classification has been permeated with notions of illness entities as labels, diagnoses, fixed states, or, better, processes going on within the individual patient. As we have stated, the illness nomenclature has reflected recent Europe or America in the notion of continuum or gradient entering chiefly into the distinctions between organic syndromes, on the one hand, and the series from neurotic to psychotic, on the other. But continua exist in cultural stresses and in individual pathologies. Even psychotics are in and out of the psychotic state; and normals in the sleeping state have dreams which Freud typified as "primary process" psychotic-like phenomena.

Further, we find, processes going on within the individual patient are sensitive, always, in greater or lesser degree, to immediate milieus, types of interpersonal contacts, and connected associations. Most important, a continuity exists between normal reactions, neurotic, and psychotic ones so that most cases are admixtures, the more serious containing layers of earlier pathology. Such a series as anxiety reaction to obsessive compulsive and on to schizophrenic or depressive state reaction successively suggests a possible evolutionary series in psychopathology. But, as in cultural evolution, there is microevolutionary flow between one state and the next, and history is the term on both levels of analysis to refer to the actual ebb and flow of processes and events. What we have referred to above as balances and imbalances in the individual are the actual styles of striving and coping in the incessant selection of defenses which we see as a constant cognitive-emotional monitoring of inner states and outer happenings.

In this way, the cultural loadings of particular kinds of stress become significant. If Javanese etiquette is punctilious and sophisticated, will the attrition occur when the requirements for polite social intercourse most constrict the female *latah* so that obscene punning results? What of the general constrictions upon female role behavior, since they are the chief sufferers from *latah?* Surely the fact that the socially disadvantaged female is most likely to be affected is important. *Imu* rates affect unskilled women, often domestics, and also typically the unmarried or widowed whose lives are neither interesting nor rewarding. Frontier White catatonics from Alaska signified in private and ritual manneristic behavior, whether wax-limbed immobility or the symbolic obsessive rituals of rising, sitting, and turning square corners with Pinocchio-like half-wooden and half-human movements, that lives of unremitting toil on a hard frontier can deflect all tendencies to strive and cope. Alcoholism among Apache or eastern Ute bands at the point of no return, and lacking re-entry into the mainstream of surrounding American culture, may simply mean a waypoint in temporary escape. So-called Arctic Hysteria, with its aimless immensity of imitation, is prominent among the long acculturated tribes of Northeastern Asia, rises in rate with the most-in-contact maritime peoples, and represents, again, the hopelessness of those without horizons. The catatonias of peasant European communities are similar symbolizations. All are less defensive maneuvers in depth, certainly, than paranoid compensations of today. They are more open to remission when help comes—for good reason. At the same time, the conversion hysterias of many mobile nonliterate societies, Ute, for example, are dramatic outlets for both the endless requirements for vigor and mobility, and the close systems of authority sanctions—for instance the Ute insistence that age sanctions authority—in extended family organization.

The above accounts are merely descriptive and do not analyze the overuse of certain defensive maneuvers and their eventual outcome. Nevertheless, they show that forms of coping may become dysfunctional or maladaptive, just as a family system may contain particular hazards, or a cultural system contain stresses. The remainder of this essay will deal with two modern instances.

In 1943–46, the author served as Chief of Community Analysis (Social Science Analyst) in the War Relocation Authority, United States Department of Interior. His staff contained sixteen Community Analysts of Japanese-American extraction, plus secretariat, each of the former being a scholar trained in some social or behavior science and resident in the relocation center. Actually, staff also represented each sex and a range from young to old. They were *Issei* (first generation, born abroad, and consequently noncitizen), *Nisei* (second generation, born in the United States, and therefore citizens), and *Kibei* (like Nisei, citizens born here, but sent to relatives, usually grandparents, for reasons of filial feeling, and consequently Japanese in certain phases of rearing).

Constant staff reports on all aspects of center life, often two per week, were completed in a three-year period, each finally written by the author. In addition to matters of general concern, we made various anthropological studies and sociological surveys. The center hospital was studied in various reports, economic surveys of the residents' continual losses could be made, or long-range studies of their arts, recreation, rumors, reactions to incarceration, suicides, and even mental impairments developed. In 1946, *Impounded People* was published as a generalized book on these matters.[1]

The Tule Lake Center suffered the greatest losses through suicides and mental health impairments. We will therefore focus on its epidemiology.

The Center was the largest in size of population (18,000 men, women, and children), and existed for the longest period (three years) of any of the relocation centers. At midpoint in its history, and certainly against the advice of Community Analysis, it was designated a closed segregation center, so that thousands left for other centers and other thousands were sent to Tule Lake. The residences were partitioned segments of tarpaper theatre-of-operations barracks, surrounded by manproof fencing and armed watchtowers, with gate checkpoints manned successively by Army, Justice Department, and War Relocation Authority personnel. It re-

---

[1] Eugene Rostow, the Dean of the Yale Law School, has termed the removal and relocation "America's worst wartime mistake." The author has written affidavits, *amicus curiae*, on the duress and hardship occasioned by this removal of civil rights of over 100,000 Japanese-Americans from California, Oregon, and Washington, and he has published technical studies in G. Seward's *Clinical Studies in Culture Conflict* (Opler, 1958*b*) and in such journals as the *American Anthropologist, Southwestern Journal of Anthropology,* and the *Journal of American Folklore.*

quired three months of ceaseless effort by the author to achieve permission for kindergarten and nursery school children to visit the project farm across the Californian highway, whereas ten miles down the same highway a German prisoner-of-war camp with troop members from Hitler's Reich picnicked in the hills, cycled to the nearest town in "P.O.W." labeled dungarees, and freely roamed the countryside.

The degree of knowledge of this Center is indicated by dated reports which time and again predicted accurately. Predictions ranged from seriously-taken rumors that a murder would occur (and did occur in fact to the father of our staff artist because of his managerial post in the Community Co-operative which had come under strong attack), down to mass predictions that 6,000 citizens of Tule Lake would become involved in renunciation of citizenship proceedings.[2] Reports in government archives show that we surveyed economic loss based on knowledge of all remunerations and property payments as against all expenditures through Community Co-op, mail order, money order, taxes, etc., going out. Content analysis of rumors could be based on block and ward sample. The Center was one square mile, with monotonous uniformity in messhalls, food furnished by the Army Quartermaster staff, public toilets and showers, and decor achieved only with unusual ingenuity by utilizing wood from woodpiles, bleached and colored shells from the Paleolithic lake bottom on which the Center stood, or by woodcarving, paper-flower-making, etc. While we have written elsewhere of the creative and ingenious aspects of Center life, which indicates the soundness and vitality of the impounded people, it is obvious that mild personality malfunctioning could not withstand the rigors of Tule Lake incarceration over a three-year period and that epidemiology would reflect this.

The convenience of knowing about every obvious case of mental pathology, clinically labeled neurotic or psychotic, cases known to staff psychiatric social workers and physicians, Japanese-American or Caucasian, and further cases harbored in Center aberrant magico-religious organizations, allowed us to state that rates of exacerbated illness (acute illness states) related to certain protracted periods of center tension. The cases themselves were often dramatic or symbolized representations of these tensions. A *Nisei* wife married to an *Issei* husband, and hopelessly desirous of leaving the Center with her family, followed renunciation by killing two of three infants. The brains were smeared over barracks walls as being "the children's unspoken thoughts." Without giving in detail her feelings that the marriage and Center life were hopeless, we can state that there was protracted compliance to every whim of her husband and every pressure exerted in Center life, and

[2] The Department of Justice official, Mr. Burling, estimated "a dozen or so"; our estimate was correct, approximately 6,000 with a later correct estimate that thousands again would seek hearings and plead for restoration of citizenship!

reasoned agreement, in the face of economic loss, to the possibility of a
bleak future for these same children. A *Nisei* wife's subordination to
her husband, especially if *Issei,* is constantly enacted hourly and weekly.
The case, remanded to Stockton State Hospital as schizophrenic, drama-
tized other, nonviolent breakdowns. Outside of the Center, complete remission occurred in a matter of a few months!

Vulnerable categories, like *Nisei* wives of *Issei* husbands, had fewer
difficulties than *Kibei* wives. Yet *Kibei* bachelors were a predictable en-
clave in center population for high rates of suicidal behavior. In terminal suicide, gestural attempt, or threat, this population segment was
most vulnerable. If one analyzes the reasons for this accurate prediction,
it is based on the double jeopardy of *Kibei* status and the increase in
vulnerability produced by conditions of Center life. The *Kibei* separated
from parents were, in some cases, spoiled and narcissistic by indulgence
at the hands of grandparents. In general, Japanese child-rearing is in-
dulgent at first, followed by strong insistence, for pre-adolescent and
adolescent, on obedience and industrious concern for duties and obligations owed to parents, teachers, and the like. In *Kibei* as a class, separation anxieties were an added hazard, as was a sense of rejection at being
separated. On return from abroad, the *Kibei* often felt doubly rejected
by minority status in peer groups on the basis of speech, bearing, taste
in clothes, attitudes towards American female dress, youth dancing, and
the whole complex of the Californian bobby sox set. They were also
estranged from *Issei* fathers, whose notions of Japan dated back at least
a half-century. To separation anxiety and hostility, one can add those
factors of passive-dependent early spoiling and the later problems in the
realm of assertiveness, which affect certain *Kibei,* though certainly not
all. Our point, however, is that the Center magnified and repeated these
experiences. By rule, *Kibei* were sent to Tule Lake as a category. Their
status was the grounds for governmental rejection and suspicion. They
were least able to relocate by reason of such rules and by virtue of Japanese rather than American education in many instances. Double rejection became triple rejection. While some *Kibei* were notable among the
Center School's teachers, or were outstanding as scholars, artists, and
students, the vulnerability, in terms of hostile, anxious, and rejective
introjects, was revealed in male suicide rates and other forms of breakdown.

Where magical manipulativeness predominated, suicide might result. Where dependency and assertiveness were further compounded by
problems in anxiety control, schizophrenic withdrawals might be noted,
provided the anxiety was generalized or free-floating. Frequently such
patients had symptoms of depression, as did, of course, the suicides.
Problems of hostility control increased the potency of these trends, and
certainly the Center stimulated such response. From one Center to the

next in the War Relocation Authority, scholarly *Kibei,* who set themselves tasks, programs, and goals and retired, in a sense, from active
Center life, were constantly noted and reported. There were bachelor
Kibei apartments, distinctive from family dwellings in every Center. But
at Tule Lake, the governmental piling of one program upon another,
leading to confusions, allowed less opportunity for privacy in plan or
daily living. The periods of greatest tension and confusion were followed
by the essentially *magical* manipulation of suicides, and with acute
breakdowns of other types varying the bleak picture.

The rise and fall of suicides and schizophrenic breaks as a barometer
of Center tensions were, of course, not limited to *Kibei* males, though
they had, per capita, the greatest amounts of pathology. *Nisei* whose
futures seemed destroyed might suffer reactive depressions. Indeed, our
estimates of renunciants were based on careful assessments of the sense
of hopelessness and rejection—more realistic in quality than the Department of Justice's information—that an average *Nisei* of Tule Lake had
experienced. Our reports are replete with the prejudice they heard of in
daily news accounts (the burning of the Doi barn, the vandalism in their
cemeteries, the firing upon of volunteer sugarbeet workers, the looting of
property caches in Buddhist churches, or the insults encountered by
Nisei soldiers in American uniform, *inter alia*). Staff members had experienced such occasions (sugarbeet workers), or Center residents had
relatives in uniform visit.

The virulence of the Los Angeles press was a daily experience. These
were the days when Martin Dies inveighed against Japanese-Americans
in Congress and when crude slogans of sending them back "where they
came from" on Gripsholm exchanges were threatening. If *Nisei* sensed a
violent trend of rejection in ranting reactionary circles, it was reinforced
more directly by a southern soldier shooting a *Nisei* farm worker at
project gates, by repetitions of prejudice among certain Caucasian personnel, by tainted food from the Quartermaster, and by mismanagement,
which was reported by our office constantly for Center services.

At the time of one Center-wide demonstration, falsely called a
"riot," the allowed per capita cost of feeding had dropped from forty-five
cents per day to an average twenty-one cents. *Nisei* reactive depressions
had their realistic bases. Since some families had been moved six times or
more before arrival in the dubious haven of Tule Lake, deaths had occurred along the way, hardwon property was lost, careers were hopelessly
interrupted, families were separated, and second-class citizenship was
intensified. A *Nisei* insistence that citizenship rights be restored was
viewed as a "disloyal stand" in mass and rumor-ridden loyalty proceedings, and *Nisei* were either held at Tule Lake or sent there in the confusions of Center segregation proceedings.

Yet studies of arts and creativity at Tule Lake Center were among the most interesting products of our research. Resiliency under stress took forms of cultural revivalism. Tea ceremony flourished. *Issei* women, who had on isolated farms and settlements no time nor leisure, now studied dressmaking or Japanese flower arranging, while men blossomed into woodcarvers, painters, poets, or carved and painted wooden birds and made bleached shell jewelry and wall-plaques.[3] Nevertheless, a Community Activities project transformed one theatre-of-operations barracks building into a Japanese garden, complete with *papier-mâché* ornamental cherry blossom trees, paper grass and flowers, and humped bridged paths over rivulets of glass. On trees, each leaf was veined and properly serrated, in grass each blade folded, and in flowers each stamen in place. The paper garden had its analog in doorway lawns of perhaps a yard of real grass set in dirt brought in paper bags from project farmlands and "mowed" by hand with scissors. Dance, theatre, music (often on Center-made *koto,* violin, and *samisen*) flourished as a cultural reaction to stress, particularly among *Issei* and educated *Kibei* at Tule Lake. The *Nisei* penchants for Western style dances, baseball leagues, and talent shows had severe competition.

Within this total texture, epidemiology can be predicted on bases of psychiatric knowledge but not without knowledge of social, familistic, and cultural processes. The pattern of research, set at Tule Lake, was in this sense transferred in the decade of the 1950's to the Midtown Manhattan Mental Health Research Study where the author was named a principal investigator. In Midtown, New York City, the plan was to know both for ethnic groups and for social classes—since actually these factors work in combination—what the differential stress points were for various ethnic subcultures and how these might relate to psychopathology by providing bases for predicting epidemiology. Two communities, of eight ethnic subgroups, the Hungarian and the Puerto Rican, seemed most vulnerable. Predictions were made long before data-gathering that combinations of class and such specific ethnic group membership would be most highly pathogenic in these two groups. The predictions could only be made after intensive community studies among Italian, Czech, Slovakian, Irish, Hungarian, and German subcultures were completed and after the district boundaries were extended north to include the beginnings of Puerto Rican settlement. As predicted, in the diminishing Hungarian community and the newly settled Puerto Rican one, there were, in fact, disclosed the most sizeable mental health impairments, because of both the rapid and the disastrous features in their acculturation to the New York scene. This pinpointing of pockets of mental

---

3 The Russell Sage Foundation, through Allen Eaton, was encouraged to photograph this evanescent and passing cultural revival, so that the record still exists. The research staff was modified to contain, at all times, a staff artist or even cartoonist to catch the visual spirit of the Center. But much is lost.

health impairment followed an extensive series of community studies, like Tule Lake, including economic, social and cultural, political, historical, and even aesthetic organizations, again with block samples or other methods of survey being used. As with the economic surveys of Tule Lake, in the instance of the Puerto Rican community of our district of New York, every job history of every Puerto Rican was tabulated to learn why males in this male-dominant culture were less continuously employed, had been down-graded more drastically in positions, and had weaker union organization for strengthening their position. The shambles of Puerto Rican family organization, like the gradual attrition of the Hungarian community, destroyed normative supports in each instance, making accurate prediction possible.

I have cited these examples at some length to show how one can work methodologically from sociodynamic levels in the direction of greater psychodynamic knowledge. The starting point is cultural—the normative picture of the larger cultural context and the realistic conditions under which it operates. The Midtown Manhattan study moved from levels of intensive community studies to a later questionnaire of random sample representatives of the area, 1660 in number, through a census of all those in treatment and known to agencies, to psychiatrists and psychologists, and on to intensive studies of subsamples by class and ethnicity. We pass over these three initial stages of research in order to allude to a separate and derived fourth stage in the ten-year pattern of study. The fourth stage involved studies of hospitalized schizophrenics from the same areas and cultural groups of Midtown, namely Italian and Irish, German and Czech, and Slovakian, Hungarian, and Puerto Rican, and of course, Anglo-American. Various aspects of these studies have been published, (see Opler, 1956, 1957, 1958) and some, like the Irish and Italian, have been replicated by other scholars (see Fantl & Shiro, 1959). Whereas a third stage of research had utilized teams of anthropologists and psychologists, the former to study subsamples of Midtowners over a two-week period and the latter to administer five psychological tests in the home, our studies in schizophrenia which followed were designed by the author to study a patient for a two-year period, whereupon psychologists administered a larger battery of thirteen psychological tests in each case. The third stage therefore yielded clues of how both well and ill residents of Midtown looked when studied by the independent means of anthropological participant observation and psychological testing. The instruments, such as Rorschach, Thematic Apperception Test, Bender-Gestalt, Draw-a-Person-Tree-and-House, and Sentence Completion used in stage three research had to be expanded to thirteen, more sensitive to particular hypotheses for the stage four research on schizophrenias. Anthropologists were trained in our community studies in stage three research but were insulated from psychologists' test results. The same pattern of independent judgments and methods was preserved in research on schizophrenias.

We shall not attempt to define these studies further in this brief chapter, particularly since Italian-Irish contrasts in schizophrenias are readily available elsewhere (op. cit.), as are Puerto Rican studies in some clinical depth (Opler, 1958a). It therefore seems more appropriate to indicate that Irish and Italian studies have been continued in Buffalo, New York, using disturbed youth samples, and that Polish and German ethnic group studies were continued in the research on schizophrenias, using more simplified methods. In the Polish and German studies, samples of thirty male schizophrenics were selected for each group, making sixty patients in all. In place of the earlier more complex and lengthier research design, the study was limited to one continuous interviewing procedure, the initial interviews in each group being conducted by the author.[4]

While New York City studies had dealt with first and second generation patients, the Buffalo samples shifted to second and third generation. The samples were not selected from a single sector of the city, but constituted groups controlled, as in Midtown, for class, age-chronicity, education level, nonorganicity, sex, and where possible in the interethnic matches, for religion. As a gross simplification of Midtown methods, the intent was to see if more roughly designed methods could perceive ethnic contrasts in the schizophrenias. A summary of evaluations, prepared with Dr. E. B. Piedmont, is given below, based on nine contrastive criteria. While the nine criteria for schizophrenic stress reactions vary slightly from the ten used in the Midtown study, our interest at this point is less in the variables viewed separately but in the constellations that make up more catatonic stress responses in the Polish sample and more paranoid delusions and maneuvers in depth which characterize the more highly acculturated and longer urbanized German-American patients. In the light of our previous contrasts in this chapter, the village and peasant derivations of the first sample (Polish) are also contrastive with the urbanized backgrounds of the second (German-American).

Lacking in Table 8-1 are, of course, the whole series of sociodynamic conditions and events that determine outcome; yet the variables or parameters are arranged in terms of some temporal sequence and psychodynamic process. For example, German fathers were more domineering both in terms of cultural standards of male dominance and relatively earlier success as a community in establishing economic power and prestige. In Buffalo, the panorama of mayors and persons prominent in civic life goes from dominantly Anglo-American beginnings, through German and Italian mayors, and more recently, to Polish-Americans, and

[4] The interviews were continued with the assistance of Dr. Eugene B. Piedmont, then a trainee of the National Institute of Mental Health on predoctoral fellowship.

Table 8-1. Summary of evaluations (see text).

Parameter (1)	Dichotomy (2)	or	Differentiation (3)	Chi-Square (4)
1. Anxiety and hostility	Hostile (German)		Anxious (Polish)	$X^2 = 8.87$ $P < .01$
2a. Emotional expressivity	Present (Polish)		Absent (German)	$X^2 = 6.94$ $P < .01$
2b. Modes of emotional expressivity	Acquisitive-dependent (Polish)		Sado-masochistic (German)	$X^2 = 6.88$ $P < .01$
3. Orality	Passive-dependent (Polish)		Passive-aggressive (German)	$X^2 = 9.64$ $P < .01$
4. Sexual identity	Misidentity (German)		Nonidentity (Polish)	$X^2 = 9.19$ $P < .01$
5. Tendency toward alcoholism	Present (Polish)		Absent (German)	$X^2 = 5.08$ $P < .05$
6. Relations toward authority	Passive-dependent (Polish)		Passive-aggressive (German)	$X^2 = 19.28$ $P < .001$
7. Somatic and hypochondriacal features	Present and dependent (Polish)		Absent and aggressive (German)	$X^2 = 11.38$ $P < .001$
8. Delusional system	Present (German)		Absent (Polish)	$X^2 = 5.125$ $P < .05$
9. Overall psychopathological pattern	Catatonic (Polish)		Paranoid (German)	$X^2 = 6.79$ $P < .01$

SOURCE: Opler, 1966. By permission of Science and Behavior Books.

this despite the quite sizeable Polish population in the inner city. In regard to economic history, the Polish populace, from village and farm more often than from city, went from rural marginality to a most difficult seasonal employment in heavy industry, whereas more urbanized Germans found entrepreneurial placements or apprenticeships therein.

Polish cultural values of courage, honor, and hospitality were hard put in a setting of wage labor and factory seasonality far beyond their control, and the female roles of budgetary manager, household organizer, and child-rearing arbiter were greatly maximized. Cases in the Polish sample include those who were kept from entry into school at the proper age, those with highly overprotected childhood fears and phobic complexes, and often those for whom the fact of being favorite son was a thinly veiled disguise for being a compensatory male companion if a father were ill, an alcoholic, or morosely irritated by unemployment and bad luck. Anxious introjects are therefore, in the Polish sample, derived chiefly from maternal controls, whereas in German families paternal strictness and rigidity were only intensified by mother authority-surrogates.

The emotional expressivity is cognitively monitored in the emotional climates of the homes of the German-American patients, since culturally speaking, order, hierarchy, and rationalizing processes are inculcated at an early age. While there are Polish constrictions against unacceptable reactions or beliefs, these may be transformed and disguised in hysterical behavior, phobias, and naive symbolisms. One patient kept from school until eight years of age had a horse phobia as classical as that of Little Hans in Freud's documentation, but combined it with considerable concern with how the horses toss their manes; his father died of cancer with a similar toss of head, which then fell limply to one side. The patient later developed a painful functional torticollis which required considerable attention from the mother. By contrast, the picture of German climates of the home was best found in formal accounts of family meals, etiquette, rules, discipline, and orderly hierarchy.

Orality of a dependent and introceptive sort struck one in Polish sample patients, along with pallid doubts of male prowess and male courage. Here, anxious and hysterical accounts accompanied stories of time spent in armed services, but while German patients defended against homosexual trends with much ingenuity in rationalizations, the Polish were merely asexual but concerned about their fears, lack of assertiveness, and need for occasional alcoholic escape. The remainder of the balances and imbalances follow, with German patients and their families tending to see emotion as irrational and challenging to authority, with compensatory delusions replacing the somatic and hypochondriachal features of the Polish case.

Our interest here is to point out that the hazards implicit in styles of family organization and acculturation history are as clear in Buffalo as in Midtown Manhattan or in the Tule Lake Center of northern California. While it is not surprising that the catatonic is shy and anxious, and the schizophrenic with paranoid reaction is rationalizing and compensatory in a hostile and aggressive sense, it is important to note that in Polish families maternal controls and compensations were primary and allowed, in the absence of adequate male roles, to exert overcontrol and introjection of fears and anxieties. In peasant societies, the position of women, both historically and even contemporaneously in a comparative sense, may be so unprotected and lacking in social supports that catatonic symptoms were once prominent in European countrysides and can be duplicated in acculturating societies today.

On the other hand, the paternal role in urbanized societies may be

so lacking in the providing of real role models for the young that compensatory reactions to competitive role demands, so characteristic today,
may be required. In German-American families, paternal authority
though remote in daytime hours was a threat through the roles of female
authority surrogates, increasing the hostility reactions towards fathers
and undermining male role models in subtle ways.

At any rate, the strong suggestion is that psychiatry must work
through sociodynamic models, rather than exclusively through psychodynamic ones, if its activities are to be relevant to culturally-induced
pathology. In these comparisons, it is instructive to note that Midtown
Italian samples produced a third variety of schizo-affective disorder, and
Midtown Irish, while partially resembling the Buffalo German sample,
were still culturally distinctive as a group. The variations in culturally
indicated stress should not, however, tend to discourage us. They stand
in contrast to the neat pigeonholes for diagnoses and the fateful and
nihilistic prognoses which have been uttered in the past with all the
sonorousness of the voice of doom. Instead, they remind us that the worst
outcomes in the battle with stress have left patients with cultural and
human attributes to build upon, and in place of mysterious allusions to
possible organic defects, constitutional weaknesses, and twisted molecules,
there are tangible markers for the routes back to normal living in the
paths of departure.

Invited commentary

GEORGE W. BAKER: Dr. Opler has just shared with us more than a quar-
ter of a century of his rich and varied experiences as an anthropologist
with, for a number of years, a strong interest in psychological and psychiatric
matters. This in itself is useful, and, as Dr. Opler has ably demonstrated, it has
yielded a number of rewarding returns.

His paper approached the topic of "Cultural Induction of Stress" from a
delimited and specialized frame of reference. I had anticipated Dr. Opler's
statement with somewhat different conceptual expectations which I felt rather
naturally emerged from the assigned topic. Some of the reasons why I feel the
fit is somewhat unsatisfactory are the following: First of all, I would have liked
Dr. Opler to start with a much more detailed discussion of the culture concept.
We did have throughout the earlier papers somewhat comparable discussions
of psychological and physiological concepts. I think psychologists would find it
helpful to have the anthropologist employ at the outset a similar approach, if
we are to understand and appreciate the fundamental significance of the culture
concept. It is appropriate for the psychologists to ask: What is culture? What
holds it together? What are its component units? Does it have a structure? What

are its tolerances for stress—normally, I assume that there are some stresses always present in any on-going society or group. What are the points at which culture will break down in response to stress? These are the kinds of general questions I had hoped Dr. Opler would consider.

For understandable reasons Dr. Opler drew largely from his own experience. While this is demonstrably useful and highly interesting, it can seriously limit the illumination of pertinent matters. Dr. Opler identified his own particular theoretical orientation as an evolutionist at the macro-level. This is one of several theoretical positions one could take in anthropology. If you apply that one exclusively to a discussion of cultural induction of stress, you read out a lot of other material that could be of use to our understanding of Dr. Opler's topic.

Since much of Dr. Opler's recent work has been in the area of mental illness and epidemiology and since many of his illustrations were drawn from that area, it seems to me that he has eliminated or excluded from explicit consideration a number of facets of culture and its processes that also experience stress (for example economic development, family roles, and acculturation). Again, if his consideration of culture stress had been from the point of view of "pure anthropology" these things probably would have been included. I might say, in passing, that while Dr. Opler didn't make it explicit in talking about the relationships between culture and mental illness, I assume that he didn't rule out the influence of idiosyncratic behavior on mental illness.

In sum, there are considerations of culture and stress that are uniquely anthropological or socio-cultural. What are these? This is a matter that Dr. Opler can and should rise to in this conference. After these are identified, analyzed, and utilized, then I'd be more than willing to move on to the interdisciplinary effort on which I feel Dr. Opler has largely focused.

I had hoped to get in Dr. Opler's paper a theoretical and illustrative description of the ways in which cultures generally handle normal stress, as well as an analysis of their tolerance limits. Beyond this, he might have compared and contrasted a general culture-stress model with a few culture-specific models— maybe American, maybe Japanese.

Having started with criticism, I now want to indicate clearly that I have real positive feelings about a number of things in Dr. Opler's paper. I especially like his rejection of child-training and nursing practices as the explanation for all of culture, including cultural stress. About twenty years ago I met James C. Moloney during the course of a trip to Okinawa. When I returned that fall I discovered that Dr. Moloney had an article in *Psychiatry* (Moloney & Biddle, 1945) which explained the Okinawans' tolerance for extreme combat conditions. As I recall, he explained their tolerance for extreme stress almost solely in terms of child training. I felt then and continue to feel that this was neither an accurate nor adequate explanation of the pattern of stress resistance of the adult Okinawans. I saw, during my brief, nonresearch experience in this environment, a number of other socio-cultural variables (e.g., sibling roles) which accounted for the Okinawans' ability to sustain themselves under harsh circumstances.

I'd like also to underscore the significance of organizational units in cultural stress. Last fall, a man from France came to see me and others in North America with the expressed intention of getting background on American studies of human behavior in disaster. During the course of my half a day's informal exchange I attempted to identify what I thought were some important areas for his consideration if a disaster research program were to be initiated in France. I recalled Allen Barton's excellent sociological review of disaster studies (1963) and James Thompson and Robert Hawkes' fine chapter on organizational models (1962). From such American experience, organizational units are known to be important elements to consider in disaster studies. They don't always function rationally or as earlier anticipated. My visitor's answer was simple, confident, and unswerving. He reminded me that they have the Napoleonic code. It anticipates and will take care of organizational problems during a disaster!

At this point it is appropriate to recall that anthropologists have been contributing to the study of stress and have worked on cultural stresses for as long as there have been anthropologists. They were involved in some of the first colonial explorations. They certainly figured in the more recent British colonization programs, especially in Africa. And I would guess from the British point of view and others—French, Dutch—they operated successfully. They were used more recently during World War II in military government programs. During that same period they worked in our West Coast Japanese relocation programs that Dr. Opler knows so well. Currently they contribute to the Peace Corps Programs as well as others.

From the initiation to the close of the National Academy of Sciences-National Research Council's program for the study of human behavior in disaster (1952–1963), with which I was connected (1959–1963), anthropologists had an important advisory role. Perhaps they were not as active in research as the sociologists and psychologists. Independent of the NAS-NRC experience, there have been other very interesting anthropological reports on disasters in other cultures (e.g., David Schneider's "Typhoons on Yap" published in *Human Organization* in 1957 based on field work completed in 1947–1948).

It is my feeling that while anthropology, along with the other behavioral sciences, has already made useful contributions to the study of cultural induction of stress, anthropology's potential has not been fully realized. Some general recognition of the role of anthropology in this area was contained in *Man and Society in Disaster* (Baker & Chapman, 1962), one of the last publications supported by the earlier NAS-NRC program. The review by Margaret Mead which appeared in the *American Anthropologist* (June 1964) ignored much of the anthropological record which is of interest to this conference. We can hope that our conference will again illuminate new anthropological challenges. And these in turn lead to more sophisticated awareness of how cultural induction of stress is achieved.

Discussion

Dr. Opler: Dr. Baker enjoins upon me the task of representing anthropology in some fashion which he himself prefers to define. I must decline the invitation since I do not represent a professional group officially at these meetings. Since I do function as a professor of social psychiatry in a school of medicine, and at the same time am a professor of anthropology and a professor of sociology in the university's graduate school, my approach is bound to be multidisciplinary and my definition of culture one of multivariables. If one will consider the success of physics, for example, he will see that this science also recognizes multivariant conditions and in laboratory conditions controls with utmost care many variables simultaneously.

However, not only do anthropologists insist on their critical independence but they are adamant in insisting upon using their own concentrated field data to throw light on human behavior and culture generally. It is curious to me that Dr. Baker has missed this hallmark of an entire profession. Obviously, Bill Lessa's account of the typhoon on Ulithi (1959), which I use for illustration, is every bit as relevant as Dave Schneider's of the typhoon on Yap two years earlier. What Dr. Baker is illustrating is that anthropologists—whether Lessa, Schneider, or myself—go out into the field, develop some laboratory study *in situ,* and report it. In my own case, despite my own psychoanalytic training and years spent in research efforts with both psychologists and psychiatrists as colleagues, I am, indeed, committed to the same empirical tradition as other anthropologists (or as physicists, for that matter!). Therefore, I feel it helps but little to refer to some "delimited and specialized frame of reference" when interdisciplinary research is being discussed or to talk about classical definitions of culture, as in the Kluckhohn and Kroeber compendium, at a time when we are modifying these profoundly in interdisciplinary research. In the original draft of my paper, the poetic-phenomenological definition of culture as being "what men lived by" was developed to give scope to cognitive and emotional aspects of the total conditions of cultural existence. I have published on this definition over a dozen times in various contexts; consequently, I see no reason for further definition beyond verbal presentation or final draft on a totally different topic.

I do happen to sympathize with Dr. Baker concerning Margaret Mead's review of the book he edited with Dwight Chapman in 1962, a review which appeared in the *American Anthropologist* (1964). Prior to these meetings, the Chairman was good enough to circularize a simple outline of the speakers' interests, and I there expressed appreciation of this same book. In it, there is only one chapter by an anthropologist, Dr. John Gillin, and incidentally this is on a theory of "total sociocultural collapse" rather than on my assigned topic of the cultural induction of stress. These two topics and the processes involved in them are quite distinct. At any rate, concerning Mead's review of Baker, Dr. Baker can draw comfort from the fact that I have myself critically reviewed Margaret Mead's book on Ruth Benedict in the same pages of the *American Anthropologist* several years earlier.

Dr. Baker may further be implying that mine is a macroevolutionary approach of a special sort, that is, an oversimplified form of cultural evolution. If so, I don't think this is a correct assessment of my position. As everyone knows, macroevolution and microevolution are connected approaches, and I find both useful and indispensable. Dr. Leslie A. White of the University of Michigan sees psychology as epiphenomenal to a cultural evolution and therefore ceases to be concerned with it. But in my contribution to the Festschrift volume [5] to Dr. White, entitled "Cultural Evolution and the Psychology of Peoples," I tend

[5] See Dole and Carneiro (1960).

to distinguish macroevolutionary and microevolutionary levels of cultural development. Both concern, in my view, the psychological dimension of human behavior. Not only would one be wrong in assuming that a delimitation of the scope of science occurs in a use of macroevolutionary data, but as White has shown, in some contexts the opposite is true: namely, that evolutionary perspective expands the scope of the scientific enterprise. I happen to think, as do most other anthropologists, that this does not render behavioral elements irrelevant or psychology epiphenomenal in the microevolutionary dimension. In fact, if one scrutinizes the literature of anthropology in the last decade down to 1966, he will find that evolutionary anthropology and psychological anthropology have been remarkably productive fields, both separately and on occasion in concert.

I would like to say a few words about the importance of acculturative change. Let me take the Puerto Rican example. Our cases consisted of people of lower class status who migrated, within a few generations, from rural plantations or rural farm circumstances to the slums of San Juan and thence to New York. The slum as a cultural aspect has been described in the recent Rogler and Hollingshead book entitled *Trapped: Families and Schizophrenia* (1965), and I agree with the picture of poverty wholeheartedly. In our cases, there are similar circumstances too; there are instances of slum cultural effects. In one case, for example, one of the Puerto Rican schizophrenics from San Juan played the game in his boyhood community of being whaled by broom sticks, the whole game being to see how much pain one could stand. Now here is where they use pain, or use stress, certainly, as a game circumstance. I think words like "masochistic" are sort of pale to describe what is going on here. There are strong concepts of the male role—one could allude to role theory as a part of the ideal value-system in the culture which relates to concepts of masculine ability to carry through, to stand pain, to act like a man and not weep under these circumstances. And then, of course, there is the slum as a place where pain occurs.

In the discussion of Polish-German we talked about early learning phenomena as antecedent in a sense (perhaps even in an imprinting sense of coming in early learning experience) to the formation of character and temperament or even defensive psychodynamic styles which are developed. Some things that are added onto the personality structuring—even in the nine variables—I feel are obviously later additions. People reading either the Irish-Italian studies we have made, or here perhaps, the German-Polish, might think that we don't view this as life-cycle material in anthropology. However, we do. That is, the family style, the early learning, the sexual, social, and self-identification processes seem to me to be set down first. Later things, for example alcoholism in the Irish-Italian, may of course develop. In Table 8-1 (see p. 231), certainly, the overall psychopathological pattern as it is developing, and certain of the schizophrenic features, are attributable to acculturative factors. I certainly meant to emphasize role theory and acculturation theory as typical parts of the cultural approach.

Dr. Lazarus: I'd like to ask Dr. Opler about his interpretation of the increased suicide rate of the *Kibei*. He made the observation that the *Kibei* go back to Japan and are raised then in a setting which has an extremely high suicide rate. Evidently the culture of Japan favors suicide as a solution to certain kinds of problems. Why isn't it possible simply to say that the high suicide rate in these people is a reflection of this cultural background? These children grow up in a culture where suicide is a positively regarded art. When they return to the United States they retain this value system.

Dr. Opler: Dr. Lazarus seems to be suggesting a straight-imitation theory of cultural behavior. This comment is like saying that "monkey does as monkey sees"—only that monkeys and apes do not truly have culture in any completed sense, and one is, instead, applying this stereotype to human behavior. For me, much of human behavior is cultural behavior, and even where it is the pathological sort of human behavior, as in schizophrenias or in other mental disorders, I have been to some pains to prove that culture is still influential (see, Opler, 1957). Still, it would be incorrect to say that suicide is a value of Japanese culture. Rather, Japanese cultural values contained stresses that impelled persons in certain straits to use the ordained way out. In our journal, the *International Journal of Social Psychiatry,* we are publishing an article by a Japanese sociologist, Mamoru Iga, on the differential rates of suicide in various Japanese groups, and we have likewise published an article by Thomas Maretzki, an anthropologist in Hawaii, on the variable rates in group incidence of suicide for Okinawans. Indeed, social psychiatry typically uses differential rates to locate or pinpoint the source in social groups of a certain kind of pathology. Then the anthropologist may analyze what conditions in the culture cause these groups to succumb. To give several examples, Negroes in the United States live in a society in which the Whites have high suicide rates, yet Negroes have low rates. Or men and women live contiguously in our culture, with higher terminal suicide rates for men and at the same time, high threat and attempt rates for the women. Women attempt and fail more frequently, and the male terminal rates are higher. Or, as I once pointed out (Opler, 1959), Ute Indians had at one time high rates of conversion hysteria and low rates of schizophrenia. Such typical forms of pathology are not "imitated" or even freely invented as an act of free will but are based on cultural stress systems and occur inexorably in rates of prevalence or incidence as the case may be. This is why I always define culture, not as a mold but as a set of conditions.

Dr. Mechanic: To respond to Dr. Lazarus' question, one quite commonly finds, on looking at social disorganization indicators relevant to immigrant groups, that the first-generation immigrants tend to have rates that resemble the rates of the countries from which they came to a greater extent than the country to which they have immigrated. On the other hand, the second generation—their children—have rates resembling the rates of the country in which they have been reared. So I think that there is some basis to the hypothesis that being reared in another culture, as Dr. Lazarus suggests, has something to do with different rates of social disorganization.

Dr. Biderman: There are some comments on suicides in extreme internment situations in my chapter (see p. 249). Suicide rates are usually extremely low in situations of extremely oppressive captivity. It is not usually, as one might expect, a prevalent symptom of the oppressive circumstances. There are some exceptions, and some of these exceptions seem to pattern. One type of exception is illustrated by the high suicide rate of Polish officers who were captured by the Germans in World War II. The illustration here fits a generalization, which is true of some others, that suicides occur very early in captivity, where the situation involves the destruction of the entire social basis of the life of the person taken prisoner (i.e., in this case it wasn't only the Pole who was himself as an individual now a prisoner of war, but Poland had been destroyed, his entire society, his community had been wiped out, too. There was nothing outside any longer that he related to).

There are some explanations or conjectures as to why suicide rates should be low in the ordinary captivity situation. The two most common are (1) because of the challenging immediate demands of existence there is a great deal of mobilization on the basis of moment-by-moment requirements, and the larger context of hopelessness fails to get translated into a suicidal mentality, and (2) the general apathy that frequently characterizes these groups. Suicide involves a highly active decision and act, and consequently, people don't rise to this degree of mobilization in circumstances where they are debilitated and apathetic.

Dr. Mechanic: I would like to elaborate on Dr. Biderman's comment because his remarks seem to be particularly relevant and consistent with analyses of suicide rates. In general, there is considerable evidence to support the hypothesis that *lack* of constraint leads to suicide to a greater degree than *constraint*. Persons of higher status (and presumably exposed to lesser constraints) tend to have higher suicide rates than persons in lower status groups, as evidenced for example by the higher rates among army officers as compared to enlisted men and the higher rates of whites as compared with nonwhites. An hypothesis that Henry and Short (1954) have attempted to develop is that constraint leads to aggression outwardly, while those under lesser constraint are more likely to express aggression inwardly. In short, suicide seems to be correlated with a lack of constraint rather than oppression and constraint.

Dr. Biderman: A corollary here is that there is a very high rate of suicide among released prisoners of war.

Dr. Levine: Dr. Opler spoke about the variety of schizophrenias. Another broad category, that of depression, was alluded to only in its extreme form, namely suicide. Undoubtedly there were multitudinous cases of varying degrees of depression, and I would like to hear something about that.

Dr. Opler: Just to tie this together with Dr. Mechanic's good point about the Negro, we have published some papers in the *International Journal of Social Psychiatry* on the lack of depression in the Negro group which point to the social solidarity items within their community and contrast with Dr. Biderman's example—the Durkheimian, actually Anomic circumstances—where there is no community to go back to, where it has all been killed off. It is interesting that Southern Negroes have been reported as being low in rates of psychotic depression states, because of their social solidarity. I very much agree with these two comments as being important. Besides, Durkheim—to give sociology its due—there is the very interesting Italian study by a follower of Durkheim who isn't heard about so often, which also indicated that suicide rates varied inversely with degrees of involvement in a social structure that was satisfactory or marked by social solidarity.

Dr. Appley: It is too bad that we are not able to relate these quite general comments, and I think very meaningful ones, back to the problems of individual as well as cultural determinants of vulnerability and ultimately to intra-individual criteria of stressfulness.

Chairman's summary

SAUL B. SELLS: Dr. Opler's interesting and indeed profound discussion of the diverse and multifaceted influences of the total environmental situation, including human organization, customs, beliefs, practices, products, and behavior of other persons and organizations, on the efforts of men to cope with their life circumstances is a needed emphasis and important contribution to this Conference. Although, as Dr. Baker has properly commented, Dr. Opler has not presented an explicit theoretical model for the cultural induction of stress and his choice of content focuses principally on *abnormal* behavior rather than on reactions to *normal* stress, his paper seems to me to assert a number of generalizations which are the basis for a theoretical model that links anthropological and psychological analysis in a productive manner. These generalizations parallel closely arguments that I have presented in support of an ecologic emphasis in psychology (Sells, 1963, 1965), and perhaps my readiness to perceive them reflects a selectivity that Dr. Baker does not share. Nevertheless, I would like to state more explicitly the model that I believe Dr. Opler has implied, and in fact, included, among the discursive illustrations in his presentation.

First, Dr. Opler has emphasized that the customs, beliefs, practices, artifacts, and values that characterize any culture are not matters of arbitrary choice but rather the products of what he has termed macro- and microevolutionary processes in the history of particular peoples coping with particular environmental circumstances. Second, these constitute fundamental models, with variations among subgroups, that guide the development of individuals, who learn concepts, skills, values, attitudes, patterns of coping, and self concepts, each individual in interaction with the particular circumstances of his unfolding life experience. These response repertoires enable individuals to respond with characteristic effectiveness to the accustomed patterns of circumstances for which they have become programmed in the cumulative growth and development interactions described. However, and third, as life circumstances change drastically and sometimes suddenly, accustomed responses may prove ineffectual, required behavior may conflict with deeply held values, and required roles may conflict with self-concept to a degree that would properly be designated culturally-induced stress.

In my opinion, and I believe that Dr. Opler would agree, no substantive distinction is made in this model between those influences in behavior that are customarily regarded as "culture" and other effects of the continuing interaction with the environment; nor is there any need to provide an additional model to account for *normal* stress in the environment. However, the inclusion of the wide range of social and cultural determinants of behavior in the analysis of the problems of *stress* appears to add both a necessary and an important dimension to the formulation.

The type of question raised by Dr. Lazarus, with reference to the sources of the high suicide rate of the *Kibei,* is not answered by this model, as it represents a level of analysis more detailed than the more general treatment presented by Dr. Opler and expressed in the principles outlined above. Either of the interpretations mentioned and even both, operating together, are possible, but the question requires specific evidence not presently available.

I have been impressed with the wide range of experience cited in Dr. Opler's presentation. If this represents selectivity reflecting his personal experience, I believe that we have been fortunate to have this topic discussed by an anthropologist of his unquestioned breadth.

ALBERT D. BIDERMAN

9

Life and death in extreme captivity situations[1]

Some definitional comments

Most societies have some institutionalized arrangements of internment, custody, or incarceration. All of these involve some restraining of persons from exercising freedoms enjoyed by ordinary members of that society—particularly freedom of movement but also freedom of social intercourse, privacy and autonomy in the choice and scheduling of activities. But it is very difficult to form a universal, absolute definition of terms such as *imprisonment* or *captivity,* in that in some degree almost all members of any social order are held captive—to locales, groupings, and activities—by various powerfully restraining moral forces and ultimate sanctions. While custody statuses are clearly apparent at their oppressive extremes, such as punitive solitary confinement, only marginal, nominal, and subjective discriminations delimit many such states from others that we are more inclined to label as segregation, or isolation or ostracism or vertical status differentiation. Internment statuses can be defined only with reference to the special definitions placed on some persons relative to other persons by an authority, by a group consensus, or by the observational standpoint taken by the observer of that particular social scene. For example, an observer may be able to detect only marginal objective differences between the freedoms possessed by the soldiers in the barracks as compared to those possessed by the prisoners in the guardhouse. But the social and the subjective significance of the status differences may be vast.

[1] This paper is based in part upon work supported by the United States Air Force Office of Scientific Research under Contract No. AF 49 (638) 727.

The life conditions of prisoners exiled to Siberia under both the Czars (Kropotkin, 1887) and the Bolsheviks (Ciliga, 1940) in many instances didn't differ a whit from those of free laborers in the same areas, and the two were commonly intermixed in many economic activities there. Penitentiary trusties, prisoners of war, or high status persons under conditions of house arrest are very frequently unguarded. Individuals commit themselves to mental hospitals. These illustrations show that attempts to define imprisonment or captivity in terms of coercion or volition, or even nominally, have very limited scope.

Custody arrangements serve a variety of latent and manifest functions whose performance depends upon the isolation or special control of individuals. These functions include (1) punishment, (2) the insulation of persons perceived as posing a threat of injury to a group or contamination of it, (3) the facilitation of the material or social exploitation of people, (4) psychological manipulation that is directed towards effecting personal change, (5) the marking of ritual transitions of persons to other statuses, (6) the symbolic affirmation or display of the lost or degraded status of an individual or group of individuals, and (7) sometimes simply a limbo state for human beings to whom some controlling group can ascribe no other appropriate status.

Custody arrangements, from a cultural and social evolutionary point of view, become increasingly required for the performance of all of these kinds of functions with the elaboration of the scale and complexity of social and cultural organization. Correspondingly, killing or avoidance of contact—which are alternative modes for doing the same kinds of things—become less adequate for coping with persons outside of normal in-group modes of interaction. There are an increasing number of situations which involve the deviant member of the in-group, the stranger enemy, the social nonperson, the conversion of humans into exploitable resources, or elaborate needs for reshaping egos and social identifications of persons so as to have them fit transformed social arrangements, or to remove those who cannot be made to fit these transformations.

In very rudimentary forms of social organizations one doesn't find institutions like the slave or the hostage. The criminal or political prisoner or the patient are even less characteristic of these groups.

Social scientists during the present century have been increasingly preoccupied with one particular kind of captivity situation on which we will concentrate here. But much of this is generalizable to other similar arrangements (e.g., penology, slavery, the mental institution), which have well-developed literatures of their own and will not be dealt with here. I will focus instead on those episodes that have involved imprisonment of people because of political conflict—particularly the prisoner of war, the concentration camp, and the civilian internee. And, following the orientation of the literature to these events, I will concentrate on those instances which were most extreme—extreme in terms of the intensity of deprivations, the rigidity of the incarceration arrangements, and so forth.

The literature on captivity situations

The greatest volume of material on extreme captivity, and probably the most influential, has been the literature on the German concentration camps from the period 1935 to 1945. While there have been some important investigations of relatively more benign recent situations, such as that of the Japanese-American relocation and internment (Grodzins, 1946; Leighton, 1945; Spicer et al., 1946; see also Chapter 8) and the more or less enforced confinement of displaced persons in camps in Germany and throughout Europe after World War II (Murphy, 1955), the greatest attention has been to the particularly extreme oppressive and deprivational circumstances. The range of oppression—or of stress, if you will—to which human beings can be subjected and still survive is quite vast. Its breadth can perhaps be illustrated by a review of the literature that we did (Biderman, Louria, & Bacchus, 1963) in which we attempted to estimate, for a variety of episodes characterized by overcrowding, the degree of crowding in terms of an objective index—the number of people per square foot (or per cubic foot if one counted the stacking of people vertically). Relocation camps and even the assembly centers during the Japanese-American relocation involved by far the most lavish allocations of space of all of the situations that we surveyed.[2] They were on a scale all by themselves when the situations were arranged in histogram form. Yet they were very extreme stressful situations (see Opler's discussion of Tule Lake in Chapter 8). This indicates how wide the scale is. One even has to get off the scale if all human situations are included. Taking space as a crude index, if one considers something like the Middle Passage of the African slave trade, particularly the illegal slave trade, in the early eighteenth century, one finds an order of crowding (and of deprivation) that was greater than in any except the worst circumstances of the German concentration camps at the end of World War II and during the disorganization of Germany.[3] This litera-

---

[2] We estimated the barracks space in the relocation camps as about 62 square feet and 437 cubic feet per person. In a Belsen concentration camp barracks for which we had data, it was 3 square feet and 22 cubic feet, while testimony on the slave trade Middle Passage described an alleged voyage during which a group of women and girls were packed to where each had available a space less than that of the displacement of an adult male—1.1 square feet and 1.3 cubic feet. (Biderman, Louria, & Bacchus, 1963, pp. 7, 10.) (In New York City, a legally-loaded subway car affords 2.2 square feet and 20.8 cubic feet per person.)

[3] The interesting thing about the slave trade, of course, is that the slave traders had an economic interest in preserving the lives and health of their cargoes and the extreme crowding and the extreme curtailment of indulgences of any kind were

ture, then, provides a very good index as a corrective for the understanding of what constitutes stress, what constitutes the extreme in the range of ordinary experience.

The study of oppressive captivity situations

Moral indignation and the dramatic nature of oppressive captivity situations doubtless account for much of the attention such events have received from social scientists. But they have also been of interest on purely scientific grounds. Exposing objects to extreme conditions is a fundamental technique of the sciences for determining their basic properties. Isolating objects from interacting elements with which they are always found associated in the natural state is another such method. Moral limits on experimentation with humans restrict to a narrow range the environmental conditions which can be investigated in a laboratory. For much of our knowledge of human nature, we are consequently dependent upon experiments of nature—including those naturally occurring situations in which people are subjected to extremes beyond those which can be produced under controlled conditions or which isolate people from environments in which they are usually observed. Now, "occurring in nature" here simply means occurring outside the laboratory. The experiment of nature may be as much a product of human action and human design as the scientifically-controlled experiment. The human action of which it may be a product is governed by other limits than those that restrict the activities of the scientist, however. So, much of the interest in the scientific study of captivity situations involves this view of them as highly significant experiments of nature.

This orientation, if you look at it, however, isn't very much removed from folk wisdom regarding the significance of the knowledge of human behavior in crises. There is a close relationship between the meaning of such words as *trial* and *test* in science and the denotation of crises by these words in common speech. Folk wisdom regards crises as providing critical tests of the moral worth of an individual—as trials of his physical mettle and as revealing his true and fundamental nature. However objective has been the approach, scientific writings on stressful captivity situations almost invariably have focused on aspects of behavior which have the same kinds of significance for human values, as in this folk use of the terms *trial* and *test*. Even investigations of the question of life and death among oppressed prisoners have less frequently been an examination of the physical limits of viability of the human organism than a seeking of answers to questions with much greater moral loadings.

---

regarded by them as economically rational, that is, consistent with delivering the most number of bodies to the New World after a passage of time.

Many questions, if not most, about the necessary environmental conditions for the biological survival of the human organism can be answered by experimentation with other organisms having similar biological requirements and similar equipment for biological adaptation. There is some point, then, in the concentration on questions regarding the distinctively human in exploiting these experiments of nature for knowledge. Many of the questions that have been asked by students of stressful captivity can be directly classed as of this type: through what range of conditions will a human being continue to display the characteristics of a person? Physical deprivation is one aspect of the model of captivity that has been of central concern.

From a social psychological standpoint, however, the deprivational environment assumes special significance in the context of the peculiar captor-captive relationships of the situations with which we are here concerned that aren't present in other extremely deprivational situations, such as the aftermath of natural disasters, famines, and shipwrecks (Wallace, 1956). The influence that captors have on the definitions of the situation by the prisoners and the modes of adaptations open to them is a pervasive differentiating factor in captivity situations.[4]

There is a rather elaborate amount of doctrine to which almost everybody in fairly developed societies, and particularly in Western civilization, is exposed, that deals with captivity situations and what is appropriate behavior in these situations. This lore has been changing fairly rapidly and has affected behavior in these situations (Biderman, 1964).

Some factors affecting adaptation in captivity

Many of the problems we are studying here can be ordered by examining the requisites of organized behavior that are missing initially among the prisoner populations in these situations. Adaptations of captives can be analyzed in terms of reestablishment of these lost elements or innovations or substitutes for them or compensations for the lack of them (Abel, 1951; Bettelheim, 1960; Bloch, 1946–47). There is, first of all, very limited and highly erroneous content in pre-existing definitions of the situation that can be derived from precapture exposure to mass communications, song and story, and so on. A fundamental problem facing the captive is that of working out definitions of his new social and physical environment. These definitions have to be relevant to a viable position he can occupy in this environment. Some of the con-

[4] This is a topic that I have treated at considerable length elsewhere (Biderman, 1964). This paper dealt with the effects that the lore, the information, the preconditioning through the culture, have on the behavior of people initially upon entering a captivity situation.

ceptualizations that are advanced for this process are adult socialization and cultural innovation (Cressey & Krassowski, 1957; Goffman, 1957).

Captor control measures vary in the degree of autonomy they allow the captive society and their inmates. These can range from the total control of external relationships only, as in the case of early arrangements of American Army-run camps in World War II (Lewis & Mewha, 1955; Tollefson, 1946), through semi-authority such as that allowed prisoner authorities in the Nazi concentration camps (Abel, 1951; Kogon, 1950)—Burney used the title *Dungeon Democracy* (1946) for his book on the concentration camp experiences—to the Communist attempts at total control of the situation wherein they attempt to direct every aspect of the lives of the prisoners (Lifton, 1961; Hinkle & Wolff, 1956).

Continued interaction of captor and captive personnel leads to a breakdown of action on the basis of formal, official, and stereotypical role models. Sets of complex understandings and a normative structure develop at the levels of direct contact between captor and captive personnel that are necessary for sustaining vital mutual relationships but which conflict with official norms applicable to both groups concerning their appropriate roles vis-à-vis each other (Ciliga, 1940; Jacobson, 1949; Johnson, 1941; Weissberg, 1951). These conflicting pressures are experienced by prisoners frequently as involving loyalty crises. A great deal of literature has attended to these loyalty crises that arise out of the difficulties of the prisoner's working out a *modus vivendi* consistent with viability in the situation [5] (Biderman, 1959, 1960b; Einsiedel, 1953; Grodzins, 1946; Hinkle & Wolff, 1956; Misconduct in the . . . , 1956; Schein, 1960; Tollefson, 1946; West, 1958; Wolff, 1960). Differences in the personal characteristics that have been found associated with this kind of conflict have been primarily analyzed in terms of a differentiation between people who adapt to it in a passive, withdrawing fashion as opposed to an active, coping fashion (Schein, 1957; Segal, 1956; Singer & Schein, 1958).

Without going through the rather broad-scale discussion required to cover this very rich literature, I can say that I find that only limited kinds of answers are derived consistently to these questions with strong value implications. In part, the limited understanding of prisoners' adjustment to the value and behavior conflicts of captivity arises from very different kinds of value significances that are experienced by participants in the immediate situation from those that are felt to be appropriate when any kind of outside or retrospective standpoint is taken. And the major need, I think, if people are going to address themselves to these kinds of loaded questions—like the questions of differential survival—is a

[5] I do not believe that this reflects the intensity with which such crises are experienced in the situation, but rather the kind of preoccupation of the literature itself with the value-loaded question.

need to be able to come closer to taking the attitude of participants in the situation; to grasp the immediately-experienced meaning of stresses in the situation.

Let us turn now to some more general considerations concerning survival in extreme captivity.

Physical deprivation and death

Utopian philosophers have sought to imagine the characteristics of the good society and the good life. The ideal type that is the implicit model in studies of punitive captivity is the antithesis of these imaginings. The study of captivity is concerned with how humans function, as well-being, welfare, freedom, love—all things that humans need and value—approach the minima that are consistent with existence. A central characteristic of the situations under consideration is deprivation.

Many of the questions posed in the captivity literature examine deprivations of the simplest character—physical deprivation of the material requirements of life—in relation to the grossest criterion—life or death. At first glance, these questions appear in the realm of biology and as such should be beyond the purview of social scientists. Even this type of question is raised in such a way as to concern the social scientists, however. A number of important variables intervene between environmental scarcities and perils and their impact upon the biological survival of captives.

Several classes of these variables concern us particularly:

1. Humans, like all living beings, are not passive participants in their environments. Their survival is dependent upon alternatives created by their behavior. What, then, are behaviors associated with survival and nonsurvival in extreme situations, and what are the determinants of these behaviors?

2. Humans adapt by group effort, as well as by individual effort. One consequence is that where the sustenance that an environment is capable of providing may be less than that necessary to maintain all the members of a given group, some may nonetheless survive, and even prosper, while others perish. In what ways are organization of group adaptive efforts, and the allocations of sustenance that occur within a group, linked to the survival of particular members of a group of captives, as well as to the survival chances of the group as a whole?

3. Some imply that death is a psychic, as well as a physiological, event and that a meeting of psychological requirements of living is necessary for survival. Included among these requirements, according to many interpretations, are the purposiveness and psychic support pro-

vided by social groups. What are these psychological and sociological bases of "the will to live"?

4. As in most features of captive life, the captor plays a key role in determining and mediating the impact of environmental scarcities and hardships on the prisoner. Our perspective toward understanding the dynamics of survival in extreme situations is altered when we look upon the interaction of captor and captive, as contrasted with a view of the captor as a constant feature of the demanding environment to which the prisoner must adapt. What are the determinants, then, of captor action that increase or decrease the likelihood of prisoner fatalities?

The norms of human perishability

Examining the most general of these questions regarding the survival of captives—the literal question of just how perishable humans are—we find accounts and interpretations of captivity phenomena in conflict. Some writings convey the impression that people constitute a highly perishable and fragile commodity; others imply that they can be stored tightly and negligently and endure a vast range of abuse without perishing or even suffering permanent deterioration.

In accounts of Americans captured in Korea, these conflicting judgments are in evidence. On the one hand, writers such as Kinkead, as well as former prisoners themselves, record their surprise at what appeared to them the frequency of deaths from apparently trivial causes.

The Army found that almost all prisoners were unable to adjust effectively to a primitive situation. . . . Very few appeared interested even in providing themselves with the basic necessities of food, warmth and shelter. . . . (Kinkead, 1959, p. 77)

On the other hand, we find the five U.S. Army physicians who survived captivity in North Korea writing:

. . . . it is amazing, not that there was a high death rate (among American POW's in Korea) but that there was a reasonably good rate of survival. (Anderson et al., 1954, p. 121)

The same conflict appears in accounts from Nazi concentration camps. On the one hand, we have views like the following:

Death in a Nazi concentration camp requires no explanation. Survival does. Detailed knowledge of the techniques of torture and extermination has made us "understand" the outcome of nine to ten million deaths. What bewilders us are the survivors. Through the flogging and the shooting, the cold and the hunger, the sixteen hours working day and the epidemics, through individual tortures and mass murder, thousands of them live for years, three, five, eight, and longer. What was it that enabled them to survive? Death reached out for them ever so often. How did their urge to live win over the wish to die? What kept them from suicide and fatality? (Bluhm, 1948, p. 3)

On the other hand, we have the speculations about the "sheep-like" manner in which men permitted themselves to be herded to their death by the SS (see, e.g., Cohen, 1953; Bettelheim, 1960, pp. 250–251) and the total inability or unwillingness of those called "Muslims" to engage in the struggle for existence in the camps.

The medical and physiological sciences have developed a great deal of knowledge regarding the requirements of life. There is excellent information on the limits of toleration of the human organism for variation in those parameters of the environment that are significant for survival—e.g., heat, pressure, oxygen, and carbon dioxide content of the atmosphere. Fairly good estimates are available of the nutritive requirements of the human organism. While the matter is considerably more complex with respect to many of the other factors necessary for maintaining the elaborate homeostatic equilibria that constitute life, reasonable predictions can be made of circumstances that will result in death (see, e.g., Bruce, 1960; Biderman, Louria, & Bacchus, 1963).

This scientific knowledge about death and survival is of interest to us here only as it figures in the action systems, social and psychological, of captors and captives and as a basis for evaluating the nonscientific concepts that animate behavior in the prison camp. Death has intense emotional and moral connotations. For understanding the motivation of the person in the extreme situation, the specific content of cultural norms that involve death must be considered.

Important among these are the conceptions of both captors and captives as to the circumstances under which it is possible for a man to survive or as to the survival chances that exist under varying sets of extreme circumstances. These conceptions are obviously not completely consistent with objectively determined knowledge of the survival requirements of the human organism. Consequently, while the objective facts regarding the perishability of the person are not of direct interest to the social scientist, those sections of the literature of captivity that address themselves to this question are of importance. The factors that lead some former inmates and observers to comment on what they regard as the remarkable endurance of individuals, or that lead others to comment on the remarkable vulnerability of individuals, are perceptions of the captivity situation that are at least similar to the perceptions of the actors within it. This makes these important documents for understanding behavior in extreme captivity situations.

Captor's norms regarding survival requirements

At the level of generality at which rules for prisoner treatment are formulated by international agreements, individual governments, and by the large bureaucratic formations that formulate prisoner policy for nations, regions, or armies, the explicit concept for at least two centuries has generally regarded prisoners as worthy of preservation. Preservation of prisoners has been accepted as doctrine either because of humanitarian considerations or instrumental reasons, such as avoiding reprisal and encouraging desertions among the enemy, or some combination of both instrumental and humane motives (Flory, 1942).

There always have been exceptions. Historically, orders have been issued for the liquidation of prisoners as a device for terrorizing opponents, for provoking opponents into committing reprisal atrocities that may serve the instigators' propaganda purposes, and for forging bonds of solidarity through shared guilt among one's own forces, as well as for the more simple objective of leaving one's own forces physically and economically unencumbered by an unwieldy number of prisoners. The extent to which the extermination of prisoners has been the exception rather than the rule has been obscured in recent times by the rationalized bureaucratization of irrational malevolence that was epitomized by the Nazi *SS* (Adler, 1958; Soupault, 1946).

Within the broad boundaries set by the concept of the captive as one whose life is to be preserved, there is a broad range of possible variation.

Conceptions regarding the requirements for survival are important determinants of the behavior of captors toward captives, as well as the latters' behavior in the extreme situation. In many situations, these attitudes of captor personnel define for them the line between killing prisoners and holding them prisoner. Some concept about the minimum necessary to sustain the lives of captives has frequently been the standard employed, explicitly or implicitly, in the provisioning of camps. As in the case of the prisoners themselves, objective considerations regarding the physical requirements of life form part of these captor concepts, but important elements of moral judgment figure in them as well. It is the latter type of concept which finally delimits the captor's conception of his responsibility—whether he or the prisoner is "to blame" if a prisoner dies or if a given proportion of prisoners die (see Spaight, 1918, pp. 265–273).

At any given level of the hierarchy of the captor organization, discrepancies are common between what objectively are survival needs and what are conceived as such. The distinctions captors make between "needs" and "luxuries and frills" derive from many nonrational cultural and sociological sources. In handling prisoners of war and civilian internees during wartime, there is always the reluctance toward according enemies a more favored situation than that being experienced by one's own soldiers. While formal international practice makes the living conditions of the formations having actual custody of prisoners the measure of what the latter should be accorded (Geneva Conventions, 1950), comparisons are inevitable with groups of one's own fighting troops who face death and privation. In the United States during World War II, most publicity regarding POW's held here was concerned with the issue of "POW coddling" (Tollefson, 1946).

An impressionistic generalization suggests that certain types of needs are more likely to be regarded as essential by captors than are others. Thus, rations of sufficient caloric value and sufficient water are rarely denied prisoners over so long a period as to result directly in death. Less attention is likely to be paid to the quality of these provisions, so that deficiency diseases and diseases from polluted rations or water are common (see Biderman, 1960a).

Further, the value of a ration cannot be considered apart from the adaptive demands confronting prisoners (Hinkle, 1961). The impression from the literature is that prisoners are unlikely to die from the direct effects of starvation, but rather from starvation making adaptation to the other privations of the environment impossible.

The provision of food seems to have a ritualistic quality to it, so that it is frequent to find rations continuing to be provided to prisoners who are being forced to endure conditions that are fatal in other respects (Cohen, 1953). Both World Wars I and II produced many stories of bread and soup being brought to boxcars full of prisoners who had already frozen to death or suffocated.

The importance prisoners themselves attached to meeting various of their needs also does not follow completely rational criteria of survival. For an understanding of the motive force of survival in behavior, knowledge of what people regard as essential to their survival and of the differing impacts on individual consciousness of different types and degrees of deprivation must supplement objective knowledge regarding bodily requirements.

Prisoner perceptions of survival requirements

While there are many variables of the environment which cannot vary beyond certain limits without death occurring, most of these limits are much broader than those which are actually encountered during the life of the ordinary member of civilized society, and, consequently, are much broader than most newly captured prisoners imagine are tolerable. This, in itself, has important consequences for survival, as well as for behavior in general during the early stages of captivity. Death rates among prisoners are usually much higher during the earliest stages of captivity.

New prisoners usually despair of being able to survive what to them appear to be absolutely hopeless circumstances. There has been considerable discussion of this reaction producing a psychological state which itself results in death—"fatal surrender" (Nardini, 1952) or "give-up-itis" (Anderson, C. L., et al., 1954; Mayer, 1956); "bamboo disease" (Katz, 1950); or the "Muslims" of the Nazi *KZ*'s (Kogon, 1950). Less debatable is the fact that these reactions of despair interfere with vigorous efforts toward self-preservation that are usually necessary for survival in the extreme situation.

The tendency for the uninitiated person initially to take a dimmer view of survival possibilities of a given prison environment than is objectively true also has important consequences for prisoner society. It helps contribute to the frequent attitude of prisoners that their only chance for survival is dependent upon their somehow being exempt from the common lot of their fellows. Such phenomena as divisive and hostile tendencies among prisoners and collaboration and favor-currying with captors may be traceable in part to this kind of perception of the environment.

It is important not to overlook the cases, and these are far from rare, where the belief by the prisoner that he has little or no chance of surviving is an accurate estimate of the true circumstances. Death rates of ten percent per day and greater have occurred for extended periods of time among many groups of prisoners in recent history—the groups having survived as groups only because of continuous replenishment by new internees and by the survival of the few who occupied favorable positions. Another facet of conceptions of captivity is illustrated by some writings on these situations. It is not infrequent, as I have earlier noted, for there to be an implicit moral condemnation of those who failed to survive situations that, from a medical standpoint, would not have permitted survival (see, e.g., Anderson, C. L. et al., 1954; Bloch, 1946–1947; Bondy, 1943; Katz, 1946; U.S. Congress, Senate, 1957). The moral loading that different types of persons place upon survival and nonsurvival in differently defined types of captivity situations is an additional source of our interest in these documents by survivors.

The vital role of "nonvital" factors

There is a variety of reasons why needs for survival and well-being do not correlate with a person's motivational system in complete correspondence with their physiological importance, even in the extreme situation. First of all, the sensory apparatus of humans registers disproportionately great distress for some deprivations and little or none for others. In addition, there is a great adaptation to some sources of distress and little or none for others. Further, people's intelligence and cultural training leads them to exaggerate some threats and to minimize others, and cultural definitions make certain things essential or urgently desired that are not actually essential for physiological survival.

Thus, with respect to the sensation of privation, pain and distress signals are highly developed with respect to perils of the ordinary animal environment and undeveloped for those which occur relatively rarely in nature. To illustrate, strangulation evokes among the strongest of distress reactions, but there is little or no distress reaction to a dangerously depleted supply of oxygen in the air. As a consequence, on many occasions in history, prisoners have been packed so tightly into "Black Holes" of one kind or another as to die or suffer permanent injury from heat or oxygen starvation (see Biderman, Louria, & Bacchus, 1963; Amin, 1958). Since the distress from cold is generally greater than that from inadequate ventilation, prisoners enjoying the relatively "plush" conditions of well-constructed quarters and a supply of fuel have in this manner occasionally done themselves in. Thirst, and to a considerably lesser extent, hunger, can be tyrannical needs. As an obvious consequence, prisoners on many occasions have eaten or drunk from infected sources and perished, while they might not have suffered, or suffered only briefly, had they remained temporarily hungry or thirsty (Grant, n.d.).

On the other hand, physiological hunger in other situations has not been tyrannical enough to overcome cultural habituation regarding what is appetizing. Although the force of these cultural standards in some individuals becomes weakened almost to the vanishing point with progressive need, many prisoners have shed standards of what is edible too slowly or insufficiently to avoid starvation, where, from a purely chemical standpoint, enough food was available to sustain life (Grant, n.d.). A factor in some cases has been the vanishing of the press of hunger, either by a process of adaptation or by the loss of appetite associated with gastro-intestinal disease(s)—the latter being a frequent concomitant of serious food deprivation. Anorexia is one of the most frequently reported symptoms in starvation situations (Biderman, 1960a). Another example of the conflict between cultural standards and bodily needs has been the occasional unwillingness of prisoners to conserve body heat by "bundling" where this was possible and perhaps essential.

The survival of a group is dependent precisely on the fact that the press of biological needs is restrained by social and cultural proscriptions, however. Extortion, theft, betrayal, murder, and cannibalism have occurred when social and cultural controls have been sufficiently weakened.

Conflict between levels of behavior organization

Explicitly or implicitly, theories of conflict between various levels of the organization of behavior—culture, society, group, personality, and biological organism—characterize many of the interpretations of the behavior of persons in the extreme captivity situation (see, e.g., Bettelheim, 1960; Bloch, 1946–1947; Bondy, 1943; Cohen, 1953). Two explanations of the high death rates among prisoners to which we have alluded are of this kind.

One of these is the constantly repeated observation of former prisoners and observers that "men become like animals" under the press of extreme privation. With the advent of the social sciences, more sophisticated terms like *deculturation, desocialization,* and *depersonalization* (cf. Foreman, 1959) have supplemented the older phrases about reduction to the animal level, but the meaning remains much the same. In conditions of starvation, for example, the quest for food is said to become the all-consuming drive, and all social restraints and codes of morality lose their force in the fight for bread. According to accounts of conditions like those in the Nazi concentration camps, even the most fundamental taboos, like those against cannibalism (Kogon, 1950), give way, if the privation is sufficiently prolonged and extreme. Primitive urges for survival, according to this view, dominate all learned patterns.

These breakdowns of social, intellectual, and cultural controls are said to contribute toward high fatalities by precluding the cooperative functioning of prisoner groups that is the requisite for the survival of any considerable proportion of their members. They also hinder the use of intelligence, foresight, and insight by the individual for his own survival.

At the same time, among all large groups subject to chronic, extreme privation, some proportion is reported as perishing because of the loss of "the will to live," rather than as a direct result of starvation or organic disease. The most common interpretation of such "fatal surrender" (other than pejorative, moralistic interpretations regarding the "weakness of character" of those who succumb in this fashion) is that the behavior necessary for biological survival demands violations of cultural norms that are intolerable for the person (Bettelheim, 1960; Cohen, 1953). Many prisoners fail to survive because they fail to become *deculturated* and *desocialized*—because they choose not to live, rather than to live like animals.

The primitive urge to survive, according to this view, is not so powerful as to overcome acquired moral standards. Indeed, in reports on American prisoner behavior in Korea and accounts of a number of other episodes, the survival drive is interpreted as not being sufficiently powerful to penetrate relatively less significant learned standards (e.g., U.S. Department of Defense, 1955). Not only were some prisoners unwilling to snatch, cheat, and steal to get food, but in various situations they were reported to be unable to put aside cultural habituation regarding food, and, consequently, sank into starvation states rather than eat the perfectly edible but strange foods that were available (Grant, n.d.).

The perspectives of the social sciences impose axiomatic considerations that conflict with the theories of atavism as a survival mechanism. The major adaptive abilities of humans, social science axioms tell us, are not biogenic mechanisms. To the extent that demands for adaptation are severe, requiring drastic behavioral alterations, adaptation, the axioms lead us to expect, will be largely socio-cultural adaptation. Any *deculturation* or *desocialization,* if gross quantitative terms can have any meaning, would be more than matched by *reculturations* or *resocializations* where adaptation takes place.

In these respects, the literature confronts us with fatality resulting both from the press of biological needs becoming ascendant and failing to become ascendant over sociocultural values and restraints.

Physiological death and the viability of social and personality systems

The human personality, social groups, and the cultures they bear are all systems. Various requirements for their coordinated functioning are remote from the biological needs of the organisms that are their vehicles. Psychological and sociological analysis has the task of identifying these critical system-sustaining needs through an analysis of the conditions under which social groups and personalities are viable or not viable.

In applying the criterion of survival to the extreme situation, however, analysis must go beyond this. The dependence of the biological survival of the individual upon the maintenance of a given degree of personality organization must be identified. The same is true with respect to the dependence of the individual on psychological support and on physical nurturance and defense from organized social groups.

Clearly, generalizations regarding behavior and survival in the extreme situation require a more integrated conceptualization of biological, personal, social and cultural factors than those which posit the primacy of one or the other of these levels of the organization of behavior for survival. All these levels present possibilities of adaptation and maladaptation to privational circumstances.

The social scientist has a special burden, however, when the criterion he employs is the death of the individual. Death is a physiological event, and, as various classes of inmates of our mental institutions testify, the social and cultural destruction of a person can occur without his physiological death. While the former can be a part of a short and direct chain leading to the latter, the task of the scientist is to define and trace these connections. Much of the writing about the death of prisoners begs these questions with sociological and psychological mystiques.

There is indeed a tendency in many writings by social scientists, and laymen as well, to jump from evidence regarding the destruction of bases of the personality and social organization of prisoners to conclusions regarding the reasons for their physical destruction. In these interpretations, there is confusion of the *person* as an element or carrier of social and cultural systems and the *human being* as a living, functioning, self-sustaining organism. It is clear from many captivity situations, if the evidence from these is needed, that a drastic disintegration of social involvements and culturally relevant behaviors can become a necessary condition for the simple survival of the human being. In many situations, a correlation appears to have existed between the survival chances, health, and recuperation of a captive, on the one hand, and the ease and rapidity with which he could disinvolve himself socially and shed much of his cultural equipment, on the other.

In some extreme situations, these processes of *deculturation, depersonalization,* and *desocialization* have extended quite far along the scale toward almost completely vegetative states. There are many striking cases of individuals who, by extreme curtailment of physical and psychic activity, have been able to survive for long periods under conditions incredibly below ordinary conceptions of what the physical requirements are for sustaining life (see, e.g., Lilly, 1956b; Small, 1900; Frankl, 1959).

The thesis of many writings on captivity is simply the enunciation of the fact that survival is dependent upon the meeting of psychological, social, and cultural necessities. They affirm that the individual requires for his very existence emotional integration with primary groups, identification with supra-individual cultural values, the maintenance of self-esteem, etc. Given events like those in the prisoner camps in Korea in 1950–51, involving the death of half of those imprisoned, the social scientist is prone to accept the social dislocation and the frustration and destruction of personal values as sufficient to account for the "loss of the will to live" of prisoners and to pay little attention to the organic factors. Such interpretations by social scientists and psychologists and psychiatrists who are survivors of such situations may be suspect of being biased by something akin to a tradesman's chauvinism. Just as tailors are apt to believe that clothes make the man, or dentists that teeth are among our most vital organs, social scientists estimate highly the importance of psychic, social, and cultural factors.

Overgeneralized applications of these perspectives in interpreting experiences in extreme situations have exaggerated the significance for survival of continuity of personality, as opposed to the needs for adaptive change, and the significance of active and aggressive adaptive modes relative to passive and withdrawing ones.

In the opposite direction, there has been equal exaggeration of the extent and frequency to which men "sink to a purely animal level of existence" in the extreme situation.

Atavism as great as implied in the more extreme of such statements is inconsistent with survival, except where the body needs of the prisoner are ministered to as are those of the thoroughly depersonalized mental hospital inmate. There are indeed parallels to such situations in captivity experiences—the prisoner held in complete social isolation with barely marginal subsistence in a dark dungeon being one set of conditions in which rather radical regression may favor survival and is quite apt to occur (Small, 1900). Where active adaptation to the social and physical environments is necessary, a considerable amount of the cultural repertoire of the prisoner must be drawn upon and serve as a basis for further adaptation to the camp, including acculturation to the prisoner culture. Yet, it is in the latter type of situation, where there is a high degree of social interaction between prisoners, that prisoner behavior seems most frequently to be characterized by prisoners and observers as "like animals." The dungeon victim will frequently say he "lived like an animal"; but it is the prisoner in a large group who is more likely to remark "we became animals."

It is not a disappearance of culturally determined behavior, a withdrawal from social interaction, nor the loss of identity that is most likely to be characterized as "animal-like behavior," but rather sharply different forms of social and personal organization and changes and inversions of cultural forms that come to exist. Only with considerable detachment, however, is it possible to recognize in extremely predatory forms of organization, such as captive societies frequently evolve, that elaborate social organization exists, that coherent roles are being performed, and that complex, distinctively human behavior is taking place, rather than animal-like behavior. Even where there is an apparent abandonment of all social standards, or perhaps, even where a large number of these standards become defined as irrelevant to the situation by the actors in it, a considerable amount of socio-cultural restraint remains. At times, this may be hidden by an inversion of customary social forms, as in many camps where the use by an inmate of the verbal courtesies of the "outside" like *please* and *thank you* evoked more intense indignation than does the failure to use them in normal life (Bettelheim, 1943; Cohen, 1953; Kogon, 1950). In the Nazi camps, for example, the obscene epithet is said to have replaced *sir* as the standard mode of address. The inversion of cultural forms, or their perversion, is quite different from their abandonment, however. For appreciation of the sociological meaning of these situations, an important fact is that the affective regard of prisoners for one another and the forms of their interaction with one another remain a matter of great significance to them. In sociological terms, their fellows remain significant others.

As another illustration, there is the frequent remark on the fixation of prisoners' attention on food. Many accounts of this total preoccupation

with food involve talk of food among prisoner groups and quarrels arising because of ambivalence toward futile, tantalizing discussions of food.

Where deprivation becomes integrated with the social interaction of
the prisoners, including negative interaction, it is not an illustration of
the biological bases of behavior becoming dominant over the socio-
cultural.

The more nearly deculturated, desocialized, and depersonalized
specimens that have occurred in groups of prisoners, as, for example,
those called "Muslims" in the concentration camps, were less likely to be
targets of the impression that they were "behaving like animals." They
intruded and competed minimally with others as contrasted with those
who fought "tooth and claw" for survival.

Distortions in survival data and interpretations

The moral significance prisoners attached to each other's
behavior apparently underlies their definitions of what constitutes "animal-like" behavior. For our analytic purposes, these moral connotations
must be separated from evaluations of the extent to which behavior is
complex, culturally based, socially relevant, and in continuity with previous action patterns of the individual. The animal analogy obscures,
rather than illuminates, these questions, particularly as it is applied by
former victims of captivity hardships.

Some, but far from all, who have written from personal experience
in the more extreme type of captivity situations, recognize the considerable problem of objectivity confronting them by the very fact that they
are survivors of situations that few others survived. Comments to this
effect have been a common feature in prefaces to autobiographical accounts by survivors during the past hundred years. There is first of all
a selective factor operating in that motivations toward survival may have
been more powerful determinants of the behavior of those who survived
to write of their experiences than of the mass. Even where surviving such
a situation was due largely to favored accident, a basis exists for problems
of guilt and for the need to justify one's own survival where most others
perished. This is particularly likely to be the case where survival was
possible only through actions departing radically from standards of
ordinary life. Such problems of conflict are particularly likely to be experienced by prisoners who had roles demanding of them self-sacrificing
ministrations to the needs of others—for example, physicians, clergymen,
ranking officers among a military group, and family heads among civilian
internees.

From accounts by survivors, then, the impression may possibly be
derived that survival was a more powerful motivating force than it was

in the behavior of most persons encountering the same situation. Survivors may also tend to attach greater moral significance to surviving than do others.

For reasons discussed earlier, similar emphases on survival values are also likely to characterize accounts written from the perspective of the captor.

PRISONER ORGANIZATION AND EVALUATION OF DEATH RATES

Group organization in submarginal situations

These evaluations are of particular interest in view of the prominent role played by interpretations of the high death rate among American prisoners of war in Korea in both scholarly and popular discussions.

As has been cited earlier, the high death rate among American prisoners during the Korean War was attributed to failings of the men themselves, rather than to treatment they received at the hands of the captor. The failure of the groups to maintain military organization and discipline in captivity was regarded as a major one of these failings. Kinkead (1959) and other writers see a lack of the ability to organize and a general lack of discipline of the American prisoners in Korea which they interpret as manifestations of failings singularly characteristic of American youth.

Other students of these events have disputed these interpretations. They placed greater weight on deliberate measures of the captor to prevent the development of any organization among the prisoners, other than that which served the captor's exploitative and control objectives. These measures included the segregation of prisoners according to rank and the removal and punishment of emergent leaders (Schein, 1956, 1959).

While there is disagreement on the reasons for disorganization among the prisoners in Korea, and regarding the extent to which organization was in fact present, there is general consensus that a greater degree of group organization would have improved survival chances. The survival needs of the group as a whole are further posited by all observers as a rational objective for motivating the subordination of the individual to an organized group in the extreme situation.

In reviewing other historical incidents of extremely deprivational captivity, the degree of disorganization is found to vary generally with the rate of fatality. In Korea, as elsewhere, it is a difficult problem to determine which was cause and which effect, however.

A general conclusion from examining various episodes is that group

survival is a natural object toward which prisoners may organize themselves in situations which they tend to perceive as marginal, i.e., where
all seem to have a good chance of surviving providing there is concerted
action toward the goal of group survival. Organization of the entire
prison community on such a basis does not evolve, or quickly breaks
down, where conditions are actually submarginal or where they are perceived as submarginal by any sizable proportion of the group, i.e., where
it seems apparent that there is just not enough for all. Under conditions
in which the dominant question is perceived as "who shall survive,"
organization resting upon some carry-over of legitimacy from the larger
society cannot contend either with clique organizations or general disorganization. The usual pattern under such circumstances can be appreciated from the well-known Andersonville and German concentration
camp models. "Official" inmate organization loses control by its inability
to control major rewards and sanctions—a process accelerated by the
capture of key positions and material by clique groups. The latter may
have the basis of their organizational identity in similarities of any of a
number of types: ideological, social class, seniority, proximity, physical
ability, or personality.

A number of such cliques generally arise which contend with each
other and with the "official" inmate organization. One group or some
coalition may achieve total and uncontested control, either by capturing
the key positions and the symbols of legitimacy of the "official" inmate
organization, or simply by *de facto* incontestable power. On the other
hand, more than one group may continue to contend throughout a
camp history in a "balance of power" situation. In either event, the
mass of inmates remains unorganized. They become progressively less
able to counter the dominant factions as their energy becomes progressively depleted by sub-subsistence living. At the same time, the organized
groups appropriate the food, weapons, and barter goods which increase
their physical strength and power positions. The situation in various
camps has indeed approached the "state of nature" of Hobbes' conception.

A predisposition toward psychopathological ruthlessness does not
appear inevitably necessary for the membership of the cliques which
succeed in such circumstances, but it is not necessarily a hindrance (cf.
Wolf & Ripley, 1947). Groups of criminals have come out on top with
frightening regularity in such situations, although there have been some
major exceptions. The submarginal situations in which noncriminal
groups have succeeded have generally been those in which they have
operated according to an equally ruthless doctrine, but one justified in
terms of some more selfless social value. The Communists, and some
other political groups, which gained control in some of the German
concentration camps (Kogon, 1950), are illustrations. The tendency of

such groups to allocate terror and starvation more rationally and less promiscuously than criminal groups may allow them to succeed to power on occasion despite initial advantages the criminal groups may have.

Whether the motives are selfish or altruistic, Marxian and other political-economic "iron laws" hold in submarginal situations. Elites, to survive or to pursue some larger purpose, must be willing to appropriate a disproportionate share of food and other material. In starving communities, the elite may do this by default of the mass, but only under special circumstance can they do it by general consent. Those who serve the purpose of the controlling organization, or simply its maintenance of power, must be provided with a super-subsistence ration. This involves more-or-less deliberate decisions to force others to accept starvation, cold, going without medication, the performance of debilitating work, or, in the case of the German concentration camps, the filling of the quotas for the gas chambers. It also frequently involves developing a collaborative relationship with the captor.

Leadership which can exercise control over a prisoner group in a submarginal situation requires as its basis, therefore, a commitment to some objective other than the survival of the group as a whole. Such values as the maintenance of an escape organization, resistance to the captor, or providing for the survival of some differentiated, elect group among the prisoners (elect on class, political, or nationality bases) have provided principles for such leaderships. Such principles provide bases for the subordination of both leaders and followers to some group interest and for differentiation of allocations of scarce values among the members of the camp population. For this to be the case, there must be principles toward which leaders are willing to sacrifice others and sacrifice themselves.

Organization of prisoner populations toward such objectives as escape and resistance arises more typically in situations of relative abundance than in the submarginal situation. Among populations where conditions change from the former to the latter, an already established organization can continue to function toward such objectives. In situations such as Americans experienced in Korea or in the Philippines, where problems of immediate survival were critical from the outset, it is much more difficult for such organization to evolve.

In comments about the Korean episode, discussions of social disorganization are oriented toward explaining the failure of positively valued social organization to develop and the consequences thereof. Not all forms of social organization are usually applauded, however; and, as has been noted here, this is particularly the case in the submarginal captivity situation. While there was to some extent the development in the Korean camps of gangs and organizations of a predatory kind (see Misconduct . . . 1956), these were less prevalent than seems to have been the case in situations of comparably acute deprivation. The failure of well-organized, amoral groups to develop and prosper by theft and extortion from their fellow prisoners in Korea differentiates the Korean case from situations such as developed in various Civil War prisons, the German concentration camps, and Russian prisoner-of-war and slave labor camps.

Since the analyses that were conducted of social disorganization among American prisoners in Korea were quite exclusively oriented toward explaining the deficiency of "good" organization, it is only possible to speculate regarding the reasons for the relative lack of development of the predatory forms of organization that have been typical of captivity situations equivalently submarginal. Possible factors differentiating the Korean case from the more typical one might include the following:

1. Control measures by the captor suppressed such developments.

2. The opportunity was not present for alliances between predatory prisoner groups and corrupt captor personnel that have frequently developed elsewhere.

3. Moral controls continued to be exerted by the prisoner group, or as internalized by individual prisoners, although in informal and unfamiliar ways which were not recognized by participants and observers as the presence of control.

4. During the worst period of their existence, the Americans in Korea lacked energy or skill for organizing for any purpose, whether selfish or altruistic.

The domination by predatory groups of a prison camp existing in submarginal circumstances can markedly accelerate the rate of death of the mass of prisoners, since even very small losses of rations, clothing, or shelter can prove fatal. It also can create an atmosphere that increases greatly the proportion of the entire group choosing by conscious or unconscious act not to engage in the "fight for survival" at all—those who succumb because of the apathetic "fatal withdrawal" frequently noted in submarginal captivity.

The press of submarginal privation can also motivate the participation of prisoners in another type of socially disapproved organization—that which seeks to gain favor or provide services to the captor in exchange for extra rations and privileges. Unlike predatory organization, collaborative organization sometimes can markedly ameliorate the lot of the group. Participation in such organization was widespread among American prisoners in Korea. In terms of the proportion of active participants and the thoroughness of the cooperation of prisoners with such organization, collaborative activity among prisoners in Korea was not as great as in some other historical situations of extreme privation. Collaborative activity has been greater both in situations characterized by more extreme conditions than those in Korea, for example, among World War II prisoners in the Soviet Union (see Einsiedel, 1953; Goll-witzer, 1953), and by less extreme conditions, e.g., Japanese prisoners of Communist armies (Rigg, 1951; Yamamoto, 1952).

The survival of an individual, or survival rates among a group, pro-vide no neat bases for valid evaluations of the virtuousness of their be-havior in terms of any social standards.

Invited commentary

JOHN T. LANZETTA: A most impressive feature of Dr. Biderman's pa-per is the light it casts on the relative value of the natural experiment as a source of reliable data. Dr. Biderman, I think, more than anyone else in the United States, has devoted considerable attention to an analysis of this literature, and unless I am misreading his remarks, he is rather discouraged about the conclusions one might draw from the "captivity" literature. It is a bit discouraging because the energy and effort involved in studies of this nature obviously are enormous. Maybe the lesson to be learned is that our level of as-piration has to be lowered a bit. Although we all recognize the inadequacies of more controlled environments for producing the conditions we would like to investigate, unless we can get better access to the data of these natural settings, we are very likely to find ourselves essentially investing considerable effort and time with very little payoff.

The points Dr. Biderman stressed relate to the appraisal process and to Dr. Notterman's concept of the closed-loop problem (p. 122). Dr. Biderman emphasized the need for understanding the appraisal process, both at the level of assessing the "stressfulness" of the situation and how cultural and at-titudinal variables can affect perception of what are the minimal conditions for survival, for personality integration, etc. This point has been made by several participants in these discussions. The interesting additional suggestion contained in Dr. Biderman's remarks, however, is that the same appraisal process operates on those people who impose the stressful conditions; here is the closed loop. I couldn't help but think of the urban "blight" situation. To a large extent the kinds of conditions that we allow to exist in our social systems must reflect our appraisals of what are the minimal conditions for integration and survival of the human organism. As these evaluations change, social action tends to try to keep pace with the changing expectations of these minimal con-ditions.

Dr. Biderman emphasized the need to examine the appraisal process with respect to adaptive actions. That is, the extent and accuracy of one's assessment of the kinds of action required to survive in a situation such as captivity will have a strong bearing on survival probability. Possibly of equal importance is the extent to which this appraisal generates conflict. If the assessment suggests instrumental behavior which itself has strong affective components, conflict may result. I wonder to what extent some of the results on stress could be accounted for in such terms? As an example, to look at the situation described earlier by Dr. Lazarus (see Chapter 6), is it possible, for instance, that the major distress in that situation is really the response conflict generated by it? Dr. Lazarus was, in effect, showing subjects a "dirty movie." We have all sorts of affective loadings associated with looking at pictures of this sort. A response conflict may easily be generated in such a situation—between an expectation that the experimenter, having sat the subject down and showed the film, obviously expects him to look at it for some reason or other and the knowledge that society doesn't especially approve of this kind of viewing behavior. It is possible that the cognitive manipulations, then, have their effect by virtue of reducing this response conflict. The moment that one tells a person that it is legitimate to look—to take the view of an anthropologist, for instance—there is no guilt attached to the looking process and therefore no distress associated with the response called for in the situation. So cognitive variables may operate not only in terms of modification of our perception of whether something is stressful or not. They may operate to reduce or engender response conflict *vis-à-vis* the adaptive mechanism. I'm sure there are certain complex stress situations wherein the required adaptive response, the one that would be most efficient, can very easily be one that has strong social sanctions attached to it. This kind of means-goal conflict which has been demonstrated to have strong emotional concomitants and affective concomitants will be reflected in the "stress" indicators. Dr. Biderman, I think, very forcefully brings this home in his discussion of survival in extreme situations, where one of the critical variables seems to be exactly this sort of conflict. Survival might depend on your ability to take from others a scarce resource, but there are social sanctions against this kind of behavior. Much of the apathy and distress noted in such situations may actually be a response to the conflict *per se* rather than to the "stressful nature of the situation."

Discussion

Dr. Oken: There is beginning to be some growth of interest in the problem of population and the effects of such variables as overcrowding on birth rate and on survival of young (see Christian & Davies, 1964). Data also suggest that, in general, there may be decreased survival under conditions of overcrowding. Focusing on the physiological level rather than on the behavioral level (although it is not clear what the mechanisms involved are), one may recall the data reported by Curt Richter (1957) of Wild Norway rats which were initially enclosed in a cloth bag, then had their whiskers clipped, and were put in a prolonged swimming situation. Death was rapid—often immediate. There seemed to be a rapid "giving up" in terms of any attempt or effort to stay on the surface, just a rapid sinking down and then drowning. Richter talked about the affect of hopelessness and giving up, and related this to Cannon's (1942) publication about "Voodoo Death" describing people who, under certain circumstances, gave up and then seemed to die within a few days. He speculated that the mechanism for death might be some sort of parasympathetic, over-discharge leading to cardiac arrest—something like vaso-vagal syncope—although I think he really had little if any data to support this speculation.

I am reminded also of the fact that in some studies of depressed patients by Board et al. (1957), there was some suggestion that patients who had had depression of extreme length had less elevated hydrocortisone levels than those observed in the more short-term, acutely depressed patients. It seemed that after prolonged depression, a state of adrenal exhaustion or decreased response occurred. I am also reminded of George Engel's (1963) classification of "primal unpleasure" affects into a "fight-flight" group and a "depression-withdrawal" group, and his suggestion that depression-withdrawal, representing a more extreme response—a kind of giving up—may have some long term survival value in its energy-conserving function. Perhaps—though again this is a massive oversimplification—one might in some way get back to this notion linking parasympathetic activity to intake and energy conservation functions and sympathetic discharge to active mobilization, etc., although I think dichotomization is in the strict sense an over-simplification to the point of inaccuracy.

I am struck by Engel's comments about the tendency of research people not to study grief and depression. I think what may be even more interesting is the fact that there are few, if any, *experimental* studies of depression. Of course this may be partly due to practical difficulties—it is very hard to induce depression experimentally as compared with anxiety or anger—but it is also true that ethical considerations preclude our producing depression experimentally—certainly this is true of suicides. But we are faced with this question: does being depressed have survival value in lowering energy output, in conserving energy? Might it also diminish survival through some other physiological mechanisms? We really don't know much about the physiology of depression.

Dr. Cohen: Bruce Welch, a biologist at William and Mary College, has been doing ecological studies, including evaluation of the catechol amines (see Welch & Welch, 1966). He has been interested in the effects of overcrowding on the synthesis of catechol amines in the brain and has been raising rats in isolation and comparing their brain catechols to those raised in groups of twenty. There was a relationship between the level of brain catechol amines (adrenalin and noradrenalin) and the rate of synthesis of those substances and the environmental conditions in which the animal was raised. The isolated rats were more excitable and had higher levels of brain noradrenalin. The major point is that there seems to be a correlation between social-environmental conditions and brain catechol amines.

Dr. Sells: John Christian at Einstein Medical School also has shown endocrine effects (see Christian & Davies, 1964). In fact, this is a very interesting connection.

Dr. Levine: With regard to this pronounced state of apathy I was also struck by the fact that there was a low degree of other kinds of neuroticism. Pronounced apathy may be regarded as a form of neuroticism and indeed an adaptive one and the adaptation may not be to save one from death; one knows that death is almost inevitable, but an apathetic state is more comfortable than being highly anxious.

Dr. Korchin: Somewhere, I read a report of a kind of situational paranoid psychosis occurring among prisoners of war who could not communicate either with other prisoners or with guards. I think it involved isolated Hungarian soldiers, imprisoned with German or Austrian troops by the French during World War I. The essential condition was isolation because of a language barrier. The incidence of paranoia was high among these men, although following release they returned to more or less normal functioning. Similarly, deaf people are more given to paranoid feelings. Such pathology seems to be facilitated by an inability to know or be known, to communicate, despite social proximity.

Conditions of incarceration have various dimensions such as the degree and kinds of communication which are possible, crowding, the kinds of social organization, and the like. I wonder whether there are any data on the effects of imprisonment as they might vary with such social psychological factors.

Dr. Lazarus: I would like to make two points, with respect to Dr. Lanzetta's comment about appraisal. If the findings on the influence of reorienting instructions were limited only to the Subincision film, I would be more uneasy. But we can produce the same kind of result with a film which doesn't have the social constraints associated with a "dirty movie." We have repeated them with a movie which involves ordinary woodshop accidents. I think that while Dr. Lanzetta's general point is sound, it does not apply specifically to the research I have reported.

The second is with respect to the interesting comments of Dr. Biderman about survival rates. I wonder if his lack of enthusiasm about the inferences that survival rates are related to psychological processes concerns mainly the conclusiveness of the evidence. Consider the observations made by Bettelheim (1960), for example, about the Jehovah's Witnesses' ability to withstand imprisonment because of certain psychological characteristics. Are there any grounds for doubting this conclusion of Bettelheim? Can someone definitely point to differential treatment which might account for the survival rate?

Dr. Pepitone: It seems to me that one of the values in Dr. Biderman's broad gauge analysis of captivity is that it shows what is not too important as well as what might be important. It strikes me, for example, that while such physical characteristics as crowding and sheer physical deprivation are rather constant over a great range of captivity situations, the effects on people do differ obviously from one situation to another. What makes the difference? Possibly of causal significance is the degree to which the situation degrades, demeans, and activates shame in the individual. Dr. Biderman did allude to this peripherally, but such conditions may be very central in producing the devastating effects of captivity and may well be of greater significance than physical circumstances.

Dr. Opler: I think all of these questions converge. If, for instance, one goes way back to overcrowding behavior, the St. John-Calhoun-Norwegian rat kind of approach, you get this welter of maladjustive symptomatology occurring. People talk about a homosexuality approach to the infant rat, failures in feeding and caring, spontaneous abortions, and things of that sort. This is very suggestive of the human problem to me, but not quite on target. I think the kind of content that Dr. Biderman gave (which I feel is a corrective of Bettelheim's simple regression formula) alludes to many additional variables in the experimental situation too—slavery, for example. I was recently reading *The Masters and The Slaves* (Freyre, 1963), about the brilliant slave women who were concubines in luxurious apartments in Brazil. Or, if one talks about Kwakuitl Indian slavery, they were not really slaves, in the sense of our own South. They bought their way out of slavery, they worked in a cohesive social group with the highest ranking free and noble Kwakiutl and lived under the same roof as he did. But I wonder whether one should not be very careful in discriminating sexual functions, social functions, and self-identity functions, as these may be put under stress or be placed in hazard. There is much literature of this sort, too. For instance, Harry Wilmer works with small groups in prisons where the communication function is maximized. Mexican prisons, for instance, recently had the visiting wife or the mistress, and there are other examples of this phenomenon in Latin American countries. When I take these reflections and put them side by side with what I read about concentration camp survivors—the lady, for instance, who with others was made to stand up in February outside the barracks through the night and has nightmare recalls of this kind of experience, I am told that one of the things that helped save her in the situation was some remnant of a sense of social identification carrying her through, that others were suffering with her, that she was not suffering in absolute isolation. I wonder if data do not exist to examine the kind of hierarchy that may exist amongst self, sexual, and social identifications. If the data are clear that when apathy occurs, when "lose fight" means self-perpetuation motivations are no longer available, perhaps this is the key point, the final point in attrition. I am wondering then about the sustained values of social identification and sexual identification, as well as self-identification.

Dr. Biderman: One of the primary things I was trying to illustrate was a dilemma in the study of natural events that have intense dramatic significance. This is the dilemma between studying those things that really are most important scientifically in these situations, which offer an opportunity to study peculiarly human kinds of phenomena on the one hand and the temptations, in treating these phenomena, towards overdramatic and value-biased interpretations of them. One of the things that has struck me continually in looking at this literature is the tendency to use very dramatic or mysterious interpretations for phenomena that, outside of this dramatic context, would be perfectly understandable and where you would not be seeking for a bizarre or dramatically-loaded or a value-loaded interpretation. I think this is illustrated particularly well by the initial accounts of physicians—these are not psychiatrists, they are just ordinary physicians—who return from oppressive captivity. They tend to make psychosomatic diagnoses of ills where they would never dream of looking for a psychosomatic explanation for the same kind of disorder occurring in a patient in ordinary practice who had been exposed to similar kinds of circumstances. The literature on apathy is full of descriptions of people you would expect to behave in no other way, given the degree of water deprivation, of food deprivation, of just sheer debilitation, if they were, say, in a hospital setting. You wouldn't expect a person who was that badly off to behave in any other way but apathetically. Where would the energy come from for any other kind of behavior?

I am really quite critical of the literature on this subject where I think death and survival are quite inappropriately used as criteria for evaluating behavioral adjustments, when there are very obvious physiological reasons for expecting people to succumb. Indeed, we should be rather bewildered at the few exceptions to death in these circumstances.

The same kind of thing leads me to be somewhat suspicious about similar kinds of interpretations of experiments, like Richter's (1957) where you are working with animals and the interpretation made is very heavily loaded with moral significance for human behavior. If you want to do experiments of this kind, I think that there is a requirement for a considerably greater attempt than is usually made to exhaust the possible interpretations for these observations, to look initially for those things that have as little dramatic significance as possible, rather than to see immediate confirmation of the tempting, morally-loaded hypotheses.

I don't know very much about rat social behavior, but in terms of the indicators that are used in some of the crowding studies, such as reproduction rates, I see a possibility of some parallel to Zuckerman's observations of the London Monkey Hill Baboon Colony (1932), where a situation of overlordship developed. In my view, this pattern was accentuated by the way the sex ratio was set up initially in that Colony to keep the population from multiplying too rapidly. I think some analogous consequences of unnatural initial sex ratio compositions may affect these rat experiments. The way you initially constitute a rat population, whether you have an original breeding pair or build into the colony some particular sex ratio, is presumably going to have a lot to do with how the colony then develops. At any rate, I would think that, given the range of possibilities for the observation of seemingly strange and dramatic effects in these experiments, before jumping to the very tempting morally relevant conclusions, some attempt should be made to exhaust all the possible parameters. This is particularly necessary because of the strength of the temptation of a dramatic interpretation.

That is one of the reasons for my dissatisfaction with the entire literature I discussed: that it usually has jumped all of the intervening questions to the most apparent, dramatic, value-loaded interpretation. It has not been sufficiently workmanlike in its approach to the source material. Now that it has been with us long enough for all of these temptations to have been yielded to and just about every conceivable parable exhausted, perhaps the literature can be gone back to with a workmanlike orientation to it.

I could elaborate, although it would take a great deal of elaboration, on Dr. Pepitone's question about social structural matters. I mentioned this earlier in relation to the development of social organization under the pressure of different degrees of privation. Here, too, one tends to get a distorting mirror in accounts because they are colored by all participants by their particular social situation relevant to others in the camp society. And the special bias of survivors of the most extreme situation is to attach moral significance to survival. One of the things that is true of survivors is the need to justify their survival where most perished. This is particularly true of those who survive with very intact egos. As I earlier noted, advantages may be enjoyed by an individual because of the way a camp society was initially constituted. There is the advantage that very frequently adheres in being there first, for example, or of having an identification with or being a member of a group which established positions of power within a camp society, or of having a presituation status that lends itself well to continuity with a viable role in the situation.[6]

To understand the influence of social structure, reports of survivors have to be reinterpreted on the basis of some independent perspective as to the dynamics of the situation.

Dr. Ruff: I would like to comment on Dr. Biderman's observation that restriction in imprisonment is a relative thing—that there are small degrees of it as well as large degrees. If one considers freedom in terms of the range of decision an individual can make about his activities, it isn't just a matter of how a prison or a totalitarian regime may restrict him. There are so many educational and economic conditions which restrict the decisions a man can make that the amount of freedom most people have is limited. I think this is a source of stress for some people, although others have become acclimated to it.

Dr. Weybrew: With reference to the so-called captivity studies, I am reminded of Captain Nardini's cautionary note in interpreting behavioral observations made under these conditions without taking into consideration factors related to general health (Nardini, 1952). He used something like the term *vital incapacitation* to describe behavioral decompensation that sets in as the result of, among other things, organic illness, starvation perhaps. But more than this, Nardini's anecdotal account of the gruesome Bataan death march, it seems to me, contains some useful suggestions as to the most relevant group process accounting for individual differences in the ability to adjust reasonably well under these incredibly severe stress conditions. Apparently, some people not only survived but were able to withstand the duress and maintain some sem-

---

[6] The physician is one example of this—he can continue to act the part of a physician most of the time, can carry his precapture identity into the situation, as opposed to a lawyer, for example, who can't; a carpenter and a cook usually have very favored skills and a good deal of continuity is possible for them, although here it is a segmental as opposed to a total life identity and is less satisfactory. There is a tendency again, for these kinds of statuses, to provide a differential, value-interpreted outlook on the situation for the people who are reporting.

blance of psychiatric intactness. Others developed acute psychopathology, even died without any overt symptoms of acute organic disease. What accounts for these differences? I think I agree with Nardini that a crucial pair of concepts involved here are role structure and group identification. He argued that positive group identification (with propitious interpersonal attitudes) was tenaciously maintained by those who remained psychologically intact throughout the ordeal.

Along similar lines I am reminded of an ONR-supported study of group structure of the crews of fleet-type submarines (Scott, 1952). Utilizing complicated multivariate techniques, this study showed rather clearly, I think, that the quality of a submarine crewman's adjustment to the confinement, the stale air, and to the other stresses of prolonged submergence, was related to the degree of "role congruence," defined by this researcher as the consistency of the man's perceived role with respect to the role imposed by the Navy system. Too, we have some recently-collected, unpublished data from nuclear, atomic-missile submarines. These data appear to argue further for the relevancy of the role congruency concept. Thus, the adequacy of the adjustment of a submarine missileman, for example, is directly related to the degree to which he perceives himself as occupying a significant role in a clearly-delineated group or subgroup which imputes explicit status to that role. Torrance (1961) has made a very similar point.

Finally, in regard to the question of conceptual levels for the mechanisms, hypothetically, at least, related to stress adjustment, I personally feel that the most useful point of view for stress researchers generally, and particularly for those interested in psychophysiology, is an interactional one.

Dr. Appley: I want to make three brief comments. First to appreciate Dr. Biderman's caution against overinterpreting data in terms of intra-individual characterological or psychological variables. However, I think that this is a two-edged problem, namely, that by throwing out intra-individual variables one might be missing some significant classes of variables for which there may be no measures available at the moment. For example, psychoendocrinological or hormonal readiness changes over time in these restricted environments need to be studied, as should psychophysiological determinants related to control versus noncontrol of input from the environment. I was thinking here of the Walter Reed studies (Brady, et al., 1958) of psychophysiological changes associated with whether the individual has control (or even the illusion of control) over his environment. Only the beginning of research has been made on this most significant area.

I want also to comment on Dr. Ruff's mention of freedom, of how much freedom we do in fact have in any situation. Actual freedom is probably much less significant a variable than is the amount of illusion of freedom that we have, and it is the latter which, it seems to me, is what is being manipulated and affected in most situations.

Finally, I could not see a generalizable model in Dr. Biderman's presentation for the social disintegration or the social reorganization he describes. The one that appeals to me is some type of homeostatic model, in which the individual, failing certain types of support in the environment, may re-order his life around other forms of support. What seems to be happening is that the individual, when familiar props are removed, finds others or selects from those available the ones he is best able to use. When none are available he invents his own, in a sense, by assuming artificial roles. An extreme example of this is seen in the social structures that formed in concentration camps. This environmental restructuring through assuming unusual and even imaginary roles might well be applied also to the psychotic world, which could be seen as a world peopled in order to retain a kind of integrity for the organism. These are not different processes but lie on an adjustment continuum.

Dr. Prescott: Knowing what we do of life experience in prison and captivity in recent human history and of individual differences under stressful situations, could one now write a manual on prison situations and captivity situations specifying the kinds of behavior which would lead to survival of either the group or the individual?

Dr. Biderman suggested that deculturation is essential for survival under certain kinds of captivity situations, but then he stressed the maintenance of social organizations as one essential condition of survival in other situations. Is there a contradiction here?

Dr. Biderman: We have sometimes been asked to provide policy advice on training people for survival as well as policy advice on what actions on the part of the military service would be appropriate for improving both the survival and the integrity of the behavior of military personnel should they become prisoners. I think there is some wisdom to be derived from the literature I have been discussing that can contribute to these decisions, and I think we have been able to provide some advice which was heeded.

But there are several difficulties in this. I recall, during a period in which there were some Americans imprisoned in the Far East, that there was a rather elaborate attempt to predict how these people would behave. This was attempted on the basis of an intensive review of records available in service files on the men who had been captured and by interviews with their parents and other people who knew them. The predictions were very good except for one thing, namely, that assumptions were made about what the stresses would be that they would be encountering in China that were highly erroneous. Their life situations had been different from the models of life situations that entered into the attempt to make clinical predictions about their behavior before they came back. And this indicates the major problem—the problem of the tremendous variations in the nature of the situations that might be encountered. This is in addition to the variation in the ways in which different kinds of people can adapt to these different kinds of challenges.

Now to relate this to Nardini's recommendations on the basis of his own experience as a prisoner after the Bataan collapse. Nardini emphasized the need to maintain an identification with the outside, with one's past life and role. This was fine for Nardini and was apparently the basis for his own adjustment in the situation. But Nardini, again, was a physician, and he had a precapture role that allowed him, as I indicated earlier, to behave consistently with his past identity and to change minimally to meet the demands of the situation. With other people with different precapture identities there is an altogether different kind of emphasis in the recommendations that survivors make about what you have to do in order to adapt. There are many survivors who say you have to forget about your past. The demands for them require tremendous personal change. The person who is unwilling to change, to commit himself to this situation, to fight tooth and nail to survive, to do these very different things and to become an altogether different person than he was in the past is the person they feel will not survive intact. So there is at least an apparent conflict—between recommendations which at a general level say you have to maintain continuity of personality and to resist pressures from the environment that tend to change you fundamentally in some way, to maintain your hopes by clinging to your social identification with the past, and a contradictory set of generalized recommendations that you have to change, to adapt, to immerse yourself in the immediate present.

Dr. Oken: This last discussion suggests to me that the issue here is that the response is dictated by the *meaning* of the situation as a transaction between the stimulus and the individual who is responding, a conclusion we have returned to many times in these discussions.

Let me return, for a moment, to the issue of depression. I have indicated that, for one thing, depression may have survival value. It may have very positive qualities. (I think, incidentally, that the ethical issue is irrelevant here since the depression is not being induced by the investigator.) I believe that we must study empirically whether there *is* depression under these stressful circumstances. Secondly, we should study what the physiology of depression is and what significance this has. There may be marked differences between depression as an active state and apathy.

I would take strong exception to the statement about these people being "too sick to respond"—the starving, beaten down, malnourished, etc. I don't think this is a "physical thing." For one thing, inhibition of behavior may represent as much energy expenditure, in a physical sense, as activity. To take one example—the maintenance of homeostasis that goes on during illness, starvation, etc.—while there may be depletion of fat stores, there is glucose in the blood, and its level is not so low as to prevent someone from getting up out of bed. If a fire were to start, in a surgical ward, for instance, you'd be surprised how many patients would jump out of bed and run out. I think that this behavioral withdrawal has to be seen in behavioral terms.

We talk about regression, for example, as an adaptation to the state of illness. I think it has to be viewed as a psychological parameter. It can be seen in part as an indirect result of the physical changes in terms of a perception of the physical changes, though not necessarily consciously. And it is partly the behavioral adaptation *per se.*

Dr. Trumbull: I would be interested in Dr. Biderman's further comments on the dynamics of change of concepts of stress. He was commenting on the slave holds. Now we are living in another period in which we have concepts of space requirements of people in different cultures (cf. Hall, 1959), we now air-condition all of our electronic equipment, we even pack our bananas a different way. Would a slave hold today be different from one that was present in those times because of these changes in our culture? Dr. Biderman mentioned the fact that perhaps the primary concern there was economic, slavers being concerned to deliver as many slaves as possible. We still see economics as an important determining factor. When we put a vehicle into space it is more in terms of what we can lift off the ground with a given thrust. We don't start with the man and really compute the square footage we think a man needs. What reflections do we have of this as really being a cultural sort of thing?

Dr. Biderman: Well, in another line of endeavor, we looked at sea transportation over the years, and I think for the sort of time orders you are talking about there hasn't been very great change. There wasn't very great change, for example, in the standards for loading troop ships between World War I and World War II. But there was considerably more liberality in loading troop ships in World War I than there was in the convict deportations to Australia a few years before that. Part of this depends upon a definition of the status of the person, and in these situations of enforced privation, there are notions about the amount of claim on life and on other things that vary considerably and reflect various ideas in the culture about how important different things are (see Biderman, Louria, & Bacchus, 1963). The prisoner of war, for example, is defined as somebody whose life is legally worth preserving, but preserving at a given amount of cost. And in any social arrangements that we have, we don't attempt to guarantee 100 percent survival. There is a risk element even in normal provision. There is a tremendous range in the absolute amount of provision that is made on the part of different people acting out this cultural doctrine of what is required, and there are also relative allocations to different classes of people.

Dr. Back: On the question of methodology: one of the difficulties apparent in using extreme situations or panic situations for the purpose of any scientific knowledge on different kinds of stress is that most of them—such as the ones in the concentration camps—include many stresses (e.g. social, ego threat, hunger, thirst, and crowding), so it is a cumulative process. Actually one should look at the data the same way as in a factorial experiment. That is, look at situations where there is hardly any feeling of discomfort but extreme social disorganization, or no social disorganization and considerable physical discomfort and other changes, or excessive ego threat and shame but nothing else, and then see what happens on those. I still think the natural situation is better in some cases, because an experimenter, for ethical reasons, won't go that far. But if one could look for these situations, and sometimes they are obvious, he might get farther.

Dr. Baker: I would agree with Dr. Trumbull's comment on the need for more careful study of human space needs. This area, sometimes called the social psychology of housing, has received very little sustained and basic attention from the behavioral scientist during the last ten years or more. Earlier, in the late forties and early fifties, a modest amount of useful work was accomplished (c.f. Merton et al., 1951; Festinger, Schachter, & Back, 1950).

In my current work, evaluation of proposals for new laboratories and other research and graduate training facilities, I'm often reminded of the meager character of our knowledge of human space needs. Our evaluation efforts focus on the institution that submits a laboratory request, its relevant research staffs, and their research and graduate training programs. In this context I generally ask behavioral scientists about their space requirements. They usually respond in fairly specific terms about laboratory instrumentation, but they have few ideas or facts about such gross design features as size, shape, color, materials, or configuration. Since our proposals come from some of the nation's best scientists we can be sure that this knowledge gap is real.

Chairman's summary

SAUL B. SELLS: As suggested by Dr. Lanzetta, Dr. Biderman has presented an illuminating analysis of the complexity of factors involved in the survival of people thrown into various forms of captivity, which appears to cast much doubt on the value of the "natural experiment" in the study of complex human behavior. It is indeed discouraging to see so little in the way of useful knowledge result from investigations reflecting the energy, effort, and expenditures, such as many of those discussed in this paper.

I must object strongly, however, to the alternative that Dr. Lanzetta would have us accept, as implied by his mention of the Notterman closed-loop problem. Students of stress have made discouragingly little progress, in relation to investment, toward the understanding of complex stress, such as is encountered in natural situations. Without disparaging the importance of exact laboratory study and control, it must be recognized that useful generalization will be achieved only when scientists develop the capability of coping with field conditions, since it appears doubtful that these can be simulated in the laboratory.

It may appear that we have here a dilemma represented by proponents of the two types of error, both of which must be rejected. However, I hope not. I do not reject the laboratory completely, and certainly many of the fine laboratory studies presented at this Conference justify the use of this approach. But we must not be blind to the limitations of these studies. Despite impressive expertise in execution, they are pathetically meager as substantive contributions to knowledge. Their chief value is in the formulation and testing of part hypotheses that must eventually be brought to the field situation.

This brings me back to Dr. Biderman. He has demonstrated a level of critical scholarship that is long overdue in facing many of the social and moral complexities encountered when working with real people in real life situations, complexities with which the laboratory scientist is typically unequipped to deal and which he characteristically prefers to eliminate.

Dr. Opler and Dr. Biderman have offered a good deal of evidence on various effects of different cultural systems in the development of norms, rules, sanctions, and other examples of behavior that function as alternatives in the environment that an individual has for choice of possible responses to particular situations. The importance of early learning antecedent to character formation, temperament, and perhaps personality style has also been emphasized. These have been illustrated to us in terms of a number of cultures, and we can also see the effects within our own culture.

When we look at problems of experimental design, it is very easy for an experimenter to take subjects more on the basis of availability than on the basis of the very important programming aspects of their backgrounds which have effects on the generalizations that can be made from the experimental data. Hence, I think that if nothing else, we have at least brought to light many of the important implications for research in stress of these different background effects.

Secondly, we have had some productive discussion of the implications of value problems. We have undoubtedly demonstrated the effects of various value systems on definitions and interpretations; we have had them pointed out in relation to the ways in which people react to situations and the ways in which investigators interpret their data. I think that this is perhaps a much greater problem than we have recognized up to this point.

I have been impressed by the different endpoints that have been used in the study of stress problems. It is important to take special note of this, because when we go from the endpoint of physiological arousal, as in Dr. Lazarus' study, to that of survival, as in the kind of material that Dr. Biderman presented, we must realize that the behaviors are different, the criteria are different and perhaps different theories are needed in dealing with them. Although we know better, there is a strong tendency to put all of these under one broad rubric and call it stress.

Dr. Biderman's example of density of space, of number of people per cubic unit, was only one example of the importance of collecting normative data on the nature of the environment and on the kinds of behaviors which are important in the lives of people and in the kinds of research that we are discussing.

One of the most important things that we can do is to understand behavior with reference to social and cultural norms. One of the examples that Dr. Opler has used on a number of occasions is the behavior that is considered socially acceptable at funerals of different ethnic groups. If you go to a funeral where loud grief and lamentation is expected, then anything less than this is disrespect to the deceased. We need to have normative data carefully planned over a wide range of expressive behaviors, values, and cognitions, representing the response repertoires that are considered norms for different groups and sub-groups within our own society and also across cultures. Dr. Lazarus' (Chapter 6) comparison of the Japanese and Americans with regard to GSR response is another example of this.

Dr. Biderman's conclusions illustrate more than anything else the difficulties that are involved in field studies. The observations that he has attacked in his analysis are from studies which illustrate the wrong way to go about this kind of research. There is no question that many of the situations that have been represented are of vital importance for us to understand.

Many examples can be cited from disaster research which illustrate how much can be accomplished by careful planning, training of observers, and having readily available and qualified field teams standing by for opportunities to make observations.

Another problem is that we live professionally in a culture which has given economic as well as academic support to a tradition of evasion of discomfort. In many cases, it seems that the way to get a doctor's degree in psychology is to do a study which, above all, is neat, rigorous, and convenient, and which will not delay the student unduly. Psychologists have shown little taste for facing danger in their research, they appear to avoid travel and hardship, and they typically choose problems in which they do not need to work too hard to collect their data. We are essentially laboratory-bound by the nature of this culture-web in which we live. We also run into problems of privacy. People are deterred from asking questions that will get them into trouble. People refuse to answer questions that they consider a violation of their privacy.

And yet there are examples (not all excellent ones, by any means), of efforts that have been made to cope with these problems. I cite Kinsey's monumental investigations of human sexual behavior (1948, 1953), for example, as at least an acceptably successful solution of the privacy barrier. I think that the work of Roger Barker and his group at the University of Kansas (1963) has shown the possibility of developing effective observational techniques in life situations.

Two years ago there was a dissertation under Dan Sheer at the University of Houston, which was carried out at Lackland Air Force Base with very massive military support. The student, whose name was Zinner (1963, pers comm.), undertook to observe common behaviors in different life situations to see whether there is any consistency across situations in the extent to which people perform routine behaviors, e.g., scratch their noses, stretch, sit down, knock out their pipes, pick something up, and the like. He had about forty different behaviors that were observed, and the Air Force provided him with a very large group of observers whom he trained and who were stationed at various places—in the barracks, in the dining hall, in various work and training places. He made excellent reliability studies and carried out observations for something like fourteen hours a day over a sixty-day period. The results of his study, which involved massive multivariate analysis, were very interesting, because they showed that there were situationally-dependent behaviors and there were a number of relationships that one would not have predicted in advance simply because this kind of work had not been done, but which were quite rational when they were examined at the end of his study.

I regret that these are not better examples, but I feel that they do illustrate that there is a possibility of working out arrangements for studying life where it occurs. And I think that psychologists need to come out of the ivory tower and go into the world where life actually takes place and not simply reject it on the grounds that it is too difficult, or too expensive, or that there have been a lot of people who have tried it and it hasn't worked out. The problem is rather one of looking on this as a challenge for which we need to mobilize our efforts. There is no lack of ingenuity. More than anything else it appears to me to be a matter of apathy.

WALTER L. WILKINS

10

Group behavior in long-term isolation

We turn now to the examination of some factors involved in naturally stressful situations in which groups have found themselves and for which it may be possible to obtain some measures relevant to group behavior.

Some of our recent insights into group adjustment under stress conditions go back a long way, even to such sources as Homer or the Bible. Despite the temptation to illustrate the extent to which this is so, I shall refer to only two or three situations from the natural history of groups, and these will be in the twentieth century. Nor will I discuss the account of groups in involuntary situations, such as prisoners, disaster victims, etc.

I want to limit the discussion to groups involved in *voluntary* isolation—although again avoiding the definition of what a volunteer is, even on a sliding scale. And a further limit is brought about by exclusion of deliberately experimental groups in favor of nonexperimental or natural groups.

There are many accounts of instances of natural group isolation situations—that is, of groups not formed purposefully by some experimenter but occurring as a result of the need for group effort to survive, or to reach some worthy goal, or to accomplish some mission. Sometimes these are historical, but anecdotal accounts of men at sea, like Lieutenant Bligh and his men in the small boat after the mutiny on *H.M.S. Bounty* (Nordhoff & Hall, 1934), or the Scandinavians on the raft *Kontiki* (Heyerdahl, 1950), or Captain Rickenbacker in the Pacific (1943). On shore, such small groups of men hiding out after a conqueror's invasion, as the American guerrillas in the Phillipines during World War II, have been described. A recent dramatic example of a purposeful group under stressful conditions was that of the scaling of the highest peaks in the Himalayas (Lester, 1964). More prosaic voluntary groups working for a useful purpose are illustrated by the groups manning the Distant Early Warning (*DEW*) and Ballistics Missile Early Warning System (*BMEWS*) lines (Eilbert & Glaser, 1959; Braun & Sells, 1962).

Purposes of groups

But I wish in this discussion to concern myself with the adjustment problems and behavior of men in the Antarctic. Here we have groups of men who are generally of diverse social and cultural backgrounds but also of skill in scientific or technical phases of a task, dependent upon each other not only for the successful conduct of their technical tasks but even for physical survival and avoidance of harm; whose personal, social, technical, and physical resources must complement each other's; who are faced with a perilous and harsh physical environment which requires constancy of vigilance for a period of six months or more, during which time they are almost completely dependent upon the individual ingenuity and resources of the members and the collective resources of the group.

The purposes for which groups may voluntarily put themselves into isolation may be military, religious, social (or sometimes asocial), adventurous, economic, political, scientific, perhaps even esthetic, and often a combination of many of these. Some of the situations are compounded of adventure and hazard while aiming at goals which are military or scientific, (the most glamorous of these is, of course, space exploration). Of the accessible places on the surface of the earth, where ordinary physical conditions are such as to provide a real hazard and under which a relaxation of vigilance is probably fatal, the Antarctic continent has no equal. Man can make his way to environments more hostile than the Antarctic—in outer space and at the bottom of the sea—but to exist in such places man must carry a good bit of his environment along with him. So far as we know it is patently impossible to "live off the land" if you are at the bottom of the sea or on a Mars fly-by. In these circumstances even the oxygen for survival must be manufactured or brought along (Hartman et al., 1964; Weybrew, 1963*a*). But in the Antarctic one can manage to survive. Sir Ernest Shackleton, with only the tools from his crushed and sunken ship and the small boats he hauled over the ice with him, managed to keep his entire command alive and in reasonable spirits during a vigorous winter (Lansing, 1959).

The Antarctic as a laboratory for study of groups

Nowadays, the combination of National Science Foundation, U.S. Antarctic Projects Office, and the U.S. Navy has so routinized the living at the U.S. Antarctic bases that year after year men come and go and their performance can be assessed and evaluated in terms of the achievement of tasks assigned, the personality resources of the men, and the *esprit de corps* of the group.

This natural laboratory, where we have been privileged to gather some data, represents a physically demanding place. Outdoor temperatures range from approximately 30 degrees Fahrenheit at the highest down to —110 degrees; altitudes from sea level to 9,600 feet above sea level, for just the manned stations. The wind can be fiercer than almost anywhere on earth; and the period of total darkness, at Amundsen-Scott station on the geographical South Pole, for example, is six months. One just goes "overnight" if one winters over there.

But the demands do not end with the weather; they include work—hard, physical labor for long hours throughout the sunlit summer months, building and repairing, receiving and storing fuel, foods, and other supplies, and setting up instruments for data collection. With the onset of harsher weather and then of darkness, outdoor activity diminishes to the barest essential. Activity goes underground (under snow), replenishment ceases, and except for the radio with its essential transcriptions of the scientific data and logistic information and for the occasional phone patches to home, there is isolation from the other groups and from the world generally.

The number of men comprising the wintering-over groups varies from ten or twelve to thirty-five or forty (see Table *10-1*); (Data from the Air Facility at McMurdo with its 200+ have been used mostly for control comparisons).

The effect of the variety of demands produced by the physical and social confinement in the small stations is further increased by the fact that only one or two persons of a single occupation will be found in any of the groups, producing a sort of occupational isolation. Mean age for civilian scientists and technicians is about 26 and of the Navy personnel about 28, so the participants of both types are a young group. There are features that distinguish the two groups, however. Civilians have a good deal more education than the sailors, whereas in job experience the sailors have a good deal more experience than the civilians. My colleagues, in a series of papers (see Gunderson, Nelson & Orvick, 1964; Nelson & Gunderson, 1963; Nelson & Orvick, 1964), have reported detailed aspects of demographic and attitudinal factors typifying these groups.

Table 10-1. Station descriptions.

Location	Byrd	Eights	McMurdo	Palmer	S. Pole
Terrain	On inland ice	On inland ice	On volcanic ash	On bedrock (near S. Amer.)	On inland ice
Latitude	79° 59'S	78° 18'S	77° 51'S	64° 45'S	90°S
Air distance from McMurdo	885 miles	1,525 miles	—	2,360 miles	820 miles
Feet above sea-level	4,971	1,500	102	25	9,184
Method of supply	Air	Air	Air, sea	Sea	Air
Number of buildings	15	11	70	2	11
Mean annual temperature	−19°	−13°	0°	+20°	−57°
Approximate number of winter personnel:					
Civilian	9	5	7	5	7
Navy	17	6	260	4	13

I do not want to discuss the motivations for hazardous duty nor the characteristics of men who get involved in such duties, except as these may throw some light on the interactions of members of the group. We should mention that dissimilarities in background can provide a breeding ground not only for misunderstanding but also for hostility, which is a very contagious emotion, especially in an isolated setting. Sometimes a difference of only two or three years in educational level or a preference for, shall we say, string quartets versus Anglicized Tennessee hillbilly rhythms loudly played by Liverpudlians, can provoke a tenseness that a mere difference of one or two orders of magnitude in pay can not produce. Fortunately, it seems not to result in homicide.

Criteria of effectiveness

Now what are the criteria of effectiveness in these group situations? Of course, survival is first—all other considerations are secondary. If you do not live, all the rest is irrelevant. For men in outer space or at the bottom of the sea, a guarantee of survival is still to be achieved. In the Antarctic, however, the combination of knowledge, skill, vigilance, and discipline has, without any reduction in the inherent dangers of the environment, made bare survival no criterion. Death, serious accident requiring evacuation, or mental breakdown have been each so infrequent as to be statistically meaningless.

The human organism possesses a truly remarkable capacity for adjusting to stresses and strains in the environment. Just recently we have been looking at the general level of physical fitness in Underwater Demolition Team trainees at the end of their arduous "motivation week," and the celerity with which these men recover, given twelve hours of sleep, from their five days and nights of constant physical exertion. The ability of the UDT man (or the trained athlete anywhere) to maintain an internal environment which varies little even during exertion is well known, yet new evidence of the effects of physical conditioning impress us. After running eighteen miles in sand or paddling a rubber boat all night these men are fatigued, and look it, but they maintain a steady state, internally, and their neurological condition is quite normal.

What kinds of people comprise these wintering-over groups? Because the unusual and the adventurous attract the young and conscientious, for very good reasons (cf. Hebb 1955b), the Antarctic has, since the beginning of deep exploration with Scott, Amundsen, and Shackleton, during the first decade of this century, been attractive. The selection of the American teams for the systematic, continuous work on the continent, which began with the International Geophysical Year (IGY) in 1956, produced a superior group of individuals. Since then, although the glamour of being first in establishing permanent stations has gone, selection has continued to provide sailors who are measurably superior to the average in a considerable number of characteristics, some of which should be mentioned.

Experience during the first year or two of IGY strongly suggested that age was an important factor. Scrutiny of diaries and logs for examples of disruptive behavior and testimony suggested that the very young men were impulsive—a mighty poor characteristic in a hazardous situation. Furthermore they did not seem to have the stamina to be able to do their share of the work. Since social acceptability is highly dependent upon the perception by others of one's usefulness, the youngest expedition members in these early years were criticized by the older ones.[1]

The instability in day-to-day performance of men under 25 makes them poor risks, and of course those of us over 45 cannot do the work any more. So psychological maturity interacting with physical stamina gave us an optimal age range of somewhere between 25 to 45.

Age is related to more than stamina and stability. General experience

[1] Visitors to the South Pole have remarked with what reserve they are received. Visitors do not do their share of the work, even the simple maintenance tasks involved in food and warmth, and are not really members of the group. The concern for sharing responsibility (work load) may be basic to the in-group/out-group differentiation made by sociologists. At the South Pole any person (in- or out-group) who does not do his share of the common work jeopardizes his acceptability (McGuire & Tolchin, 1961; Rohrer, 1961).

in living, perhaps indefinable except in the loosest of sociological terms, is perceived by those presumably less experienced as a worthy thing, and in a situation of danger or of the unknown, specific relevant experience is perceived and accepted as even more worthy, whether it be experience in cold weather living and in the specific dangers of the Antarctic or the experience of the man competent in his job—cook or radioman, weatherman, or physician.

In any group subject to military discipline, one's rate (i.e., rank) and rating (i.e., occupational specialty) are relevant to one's relation to the group. The Antarctic is a nonmilitary situation by treaty, but the support of Navy and Air Force, through their logistic and other capabilities, is essential, and the Navy men who winter over are, as all servicemen, subject to authority. For the most part, status in these groups is directly related to rate or rank. Yet it is much affected, as status is in most special groups, by the factors of competence and relevant experience. In other words, one's rank or rate is important, but without skill it loses its significance. A first-class radioman as first-class petty officer will have the esteem of his colleagues, but if he is first class only in the chevron on his arm and not as a radioman who guarantees the continuity and timeliness of communication, he may rapidly lose such esteem.

In these very small groups there may be only one specialist in any one occupational category. Two radiomen and two meteorologists are needed at each station generally, but for the rest, one of a kind is all that can be afforded. At the present time, at Amundsen-Scott Station at the South Pole, for example, there are seven civilians—three meteorologists from the U.S. Weather Bureau, one man from the National Bureau of Standards who is working in ionospheric physics, one from the Coast and Geodetic Survey in geomagnetism, one from Bartol Research Foundation doing work in cosmic rays, and one from the Arctic Institute of North America in aurora research. The servicemen include a physician (who is a Lieutenant, Medical Corps, and is the officer-in-charge); an hospital corpsman; two radiomen (who this year work on a twelve-hour-on and twelve-hour-off schedule, but in other years had other schedules, even two hours on and two hours off); one cook; one electronics technician; two electricians; two mechanics; one carpenter; one plumber; and one heavy equipment operator. At the smallest station, called William Eights, there are four scientists and one meteorologist who are civilians, and six sailors who are radioman, plumber, hospitalman, etc. Now what I suggest here is that each man must do his own task, as all others depend upon him for his unique contribution to the group's mission—indeed for its survival. This fortunately leads to each man's acceptance not only because of his worth as an individual but because he is a worker with useful, even indispensable, competencies.

What happens when these men are teamed up?

With a mixed bag of occupational experts, some of them military in orientation and training and some civilian, there is some chance of a lack of compatibility. So we have been looking at some aspects of compatibility among work associates. Paul Nelson of our laboratory has reported some features of this (1964a). In his formulation, a group composed of compatible or mutually attractive members has advantages in eliciting member support for its goals and in realizing effective communication within the group. A group so composed does not have to spend a great part of its time and energy resolving group maintenance problems which arise from interpersonal tensions.

Using demographic and self-descriptive data we have constructed some measures to try to maximize homogeneity on age, rank, and similar variables. We have not, however, manipulated these groups in an experimental fashion at any of these small stations. While there are enough volunteers for these jobs, how the choices are made is based upon considerations other than our recommendations. For some occupations there are more than enough volunteers, for others there are far fewer. So far as the Navy Sea Bees are concerned, for example, the chances of a Sea Bee eventually spending part of his time in the Antarctic are excellent.

We have examined achievement needs for the men and for leaders, too. The bases of compatibility, as analyzed by Nelson—who in this matter takes a lead from Roby (1956)—are (or may be) quite different from one situation to another, depending upon the sort of task the group is engaged in, the length of time isolated, and so on. In the Antarctic groups studied, Nelson (1964b) has reported that men evidenced greatest compatibility during the latter six months of their year, when all summer workers and visitors had long departed. This compatibility was not that which is dependent upon similarity of interest, although heterogeneity of interests is no predictor of compatibility, either. Compatibility partly depends upon role structure, because these are, after all, formally constituted groups. What one has to have in many of these situations is a very careful definition of roles and yet a great deal of possibility for relaxation of them, because status leveling is a very important consideration.

The study of group structure as affected by isolation has had a long history, and the patterning of interaction tendencies has been reported for prisoners in North Korea (Schein, et al., 1961), station-keepers in the Arctic (Braun & Sells, 1962), fall-out shelter trappees (Rasmussen & Wagner, 1962), Greenland traverse parties (Seaton, 1964), and Air Force personnel in survival training (Torrance, 1957a, b, 1961). These groups, seen under conditions of varying stressfulness and composed of different sorts of people, show some similarities and some differences. Faced with the demands of a stressful and fairly unpredictable environment, men attempt to increase the stability of the interpersonal or group structure, and the changes in such structure may indicate some change in function or mission of the group, or worse, the possibility that the adopted structure is failing to cope with the needs of the group.

As a means of studying the relationship of work and its significance to the social situation, men completed, at various times during the Antarctic year, independent job descriptions which aimed at telling not only exactly what work they had been doing and how but also with whom, who helped, and how, who asked the individual for advice about his specialty (this included not only questions about health and fitness asked of the medical officer but also all those questions asked of any group member about his occupational specialty). The men responded to items concerned with sources of information about task mission, scientific goals and procedures, military problems, and a sociometric type of inquiry about off-duty preferences in companionship.

Results certainly suggested that the greatest number of interpersonal relationships occur between work partners. I suppose this sounds routine, since many of us bowl or golf with laboratory, office, or shop colleagues. Yet in the Antarctic it was not this simple, for the pattern of actual choices revealed that individual X who preferred Y was not preferred by Y, who preferred Z, and so on. There were comparatively few reciprocal choices and the structure of the group revealed considerable complexity—with a good many group members linked through different degrees of interaction. Preferences in work interaction are such that almost no man is an isolate, for nearly everybody works with someone else. In off-duty choices, however, it is interesting to note that as the isolated group gets smaller, the proportion of isolates—that is, men not mentioned as preferred off-duty companions—*increases.* An interesting problem in the change of structure in groups in isolation, as compared with groups in ordinary social living, is that any restructuring must, of course, be accomplished with the same population of individuals who comprise the group. When groups are very small, it happens that only one man or perhaps two will have the same jobs so that there is minimal task-role overlap. This tends to conserve work structures that depend on complementarity of skills.

Distance between leader and group in an isolated situation is difficult to maintain, and sometimes to achieve. There are anecdotes about a couple of Antarctic leaders, in different years and different stations, whose personal styles required a large amount of "standoffishness." They experienced some reactions from the men which were designed to reduce their haughtiness. The status-leveling which physical and social propinquity engenders promotes a problem which, again Torrance (1957a) has commented on with perspicuity—that the leader must, probably in a variety of ways, and willingly, reinforce his position as a leader. Torrance's six ways in which a leader can do so are certainly corroborated in the Antarctic. They are: expertness, demonstrating competence, especially in troubled situations; willingness to share danger and discomfort, willingness to take risks, willingness to make decisions and take action; to act outside authority, to care for men, and willingness to require discipline—for cleanliness, social order, etc.

Importance of the goal

How important is the goal for groups of this sort? Some mission or goal must be the reason for a group of men to enter a situation involving isolation from their fellows. How important is the group's mission? Aside from survival, task performance is the paramount criterion of the effectiveness of the group, and commitment to the group's goal and pride in its performance are important.

What about individual or group behavior which is not directly related to mission accomplishment? Gunderson (1964; Gunderson & Nelson, 1964, 1965) has studied the recreational, avocational, and personal interests and attitudes of men when first being selected for Antarctic duty, and then during the isolated time on the ice. Young men who have a strong need for avocational, extra-work, recreational activities should not go to small stations, where such opportunity is lacking. In point of fact, their general adjustment on the ice is less satisfactory than it might be. On the other hand, men who express such activity interests perform *more* satisfactorily if they are at the large station, McMurdo, where, indeed, recreational facilities are available. In this sort of isolation, therefore, the fun-loving, gregarious lad will probably show poor adjustment in a place where outlets for activity do not exist. Satisfaction with the work and the total experience through the year is related to several factors beyond this one, however. In his scale of job dissatisfaction, developed by Gunderson for exploring such satisfactions and dissatisfactions, he found that for the long, hard winter's pull, the ambitious, achievement-oriented individual was the one most likely to have his satisfaction with himself and with the group and the task erode.

Emotional components of both physical fitness for the task and effective performance of the task are also important and should be assessed. Isolation in itself is not a disease nor an inevitable producer of mental ill health. In the Antarctic, the presumed individual or social effect of isolation, in Nelson's words, is blunted. These men, as sailors, expect to be assigned to tasks away from home for considerable periods of time—at sea or on remote shores. Many of the younger scientists and engineers also expect to work and dig and build in out-of-the-way places.

The quality of emotional responsivity in group isolation is related to the immediate boundaries of daily living—facing and mastering the hostile physical environment, getting through the day's work demands, and the social boundaries. On the last item, it should be emphasized that a small group in isolation for a long period of time actually finds itself in a condition of enforced socialization. When pressed in upon itself by the physical conditions, the group may be isolated but the individual may cry out for a little privacy.

Emotional symptomatology over the Antarctic winter has been reported upon by Gunderson (1963). While such symptomatology is certainly less than some observers have feared, there is no doubt that the prolonged isolation and confinement are related to increase in symptoms, the most marked of which are sleep disturbances, depressive feelings, and irritability. From 50 to 70 percent of the men had sleep difficulties during the period of greatest isolation. From 25 to 50 percent had depressive feelings, even if indicated only in an expressed wish to be alone, or in feeling blue. From 25 to 50 percent of the men experienced episodic feelings of hostility toward another member of the expedition, although such feelings rarely eventuated in behavior beyond grousing or an occasional cathartic expletive. All of such symptoms may be related to fatigue and sometimes to boredom.

Learning to expect, to recognize, and to tolerate such feelings in others and in one's self is an important matter of mental health. Toleration of such expressions of feeling is one of the lesser marks of maturity, perhaps.

Boredom commonly sets in when the work day collapses from between sixteen and eighteen hours to four to six hours, and is enhanced by the constant cold, preventing change of scene, the utter bleakness of the visible world, and the monotony of unvarying days and unvarying demands (Palmai, 1963). Part of the problem is the difficulty of structuring time by setting intermediate goals. Some successful leaders have kept morale high by setting tasks which have realizable, tangible effects on work and recreation.

Time, and the group's perception of it, is of great relevance, although our cultural orientations may make it of greater importance than it need be. One can compare, on this time dimension as a factor in group adjustment, the behaviors described by the anthropologist Gladwin (1958). The Trukese, who set out on long ocean voyages in slight canoes, with primitive navigational knowledge, treat as routine a voyage of obviously great hazard—and they avoid personality decompensation and group disintegration. For the Trukese time is a matter of minor importance; it is useful in relating one's self to the seasons and thus to some realities of nature. Civilized man, however, is more time-bound.

Year after year, the diaries of station leaders have shown how tensions in groups of wintering-over people are related to the passage of time, stressing the excitement just before the last plane leaves; then the relief that only the in-group members remain; the shakedown and adjustment, involving even getting rid of the last sniffles; the work roles getting straightened out; the mid-winter excitement with the realization that the worst may be over; then the tension just before the first plane arrives; and the breaking of the seal when newcomers arrive.

In summary, there are required of men who comprise task-oriented groups isolated for long periods these three characteristics: (1) task motivation, with a complete commitment to the group's goals and the skill and pertinacity to carry them out; (2) emotional composure, involving tolerance for the variability in other people's conduct and sensitivity to how one's own conduct may bother others; and, finally (3) social compatibility. The leadership requires a nice balance between social distance —sufficient to maintain the group's perception of who the leader is—and an ability to meet and mix and work along with any colleague.

There is no reason to doubt that with available knowledge and tools we can identify the minimal physical, intellectual, and emotional qualities needed. On the issue of motivation, I should like to put in a little plea. Nowadays the most respectable of all motives is the advancement of knowledge, preferably if we can put it under the guise of scientific inquiry. But physical adventure, carried out for its own sake, and shared with peers on whom one can rely to share the hazard as well as the glory, is also a very powerful and, I think, a valid motive. I wish, as psychologists, we would design a study to demonstrate such a motive.

Invited commentary

ABRAHAM S. LEVINE: One point which intrigues me is what happens to a certain portion of these men emotionally during the long wintering-over period in the Antarctic. Dr. Wilkins has reminded us that the human organism has a remarkable capacity for adjusting to stresses and strains in the environment. But it is also interesting that when healthy (presumably better than average) men are placed in such extreme conditions as being confined together in close quarters during a six-month Antarctic Winter certain cracks begin to appear. It is true that florid psychosis rarely appears any more and that crippling neurotic behavior is rather unusual. But when we consider milder emotional disorders, such as sleep disturbances, apathy, feelings of boredom or glumness, all of the symptoms which we associate with mild depression, we see that the situation is different—perhaps 50 percent of the total are so afflicted for varying periods of time. These are mildly neurotic symptoms which are not incapacitating when the occasion for work arises. Nevertheless, this finding points up the fact that when the environmental situations are rough enough, these types of symptoms appear where there was no previous history of such occurrence. It suggests that in these circumstances we need not look to Freudian or endogenous factors or, at least, their role can be minimized.

Dr. Wilkins raised many interesting issues which should be discussed. Goal-, mission-, or task-orientation seems to be an extremely important variable. In highly stressful environments, there is little question that commitment to the group's goal, where every man is needed and skills are complementary, is demanded. Pride in one's performance is a necessary precondition.

The remarks regarding time leave one a little hungry for more data. Granted that it is one of our cultural orientations and that civilized man is time-bound, what are some of the countervailing techniques, if any? Will pre-mission orientation or certain leadership techniques alleviate the felt rigors of a long winter? Perhaps certain types of group composition, as well as compatible avocational interests, may be useful. Are age and experience factors in reducing this kind of variance? These are all researchable questions and have important implications for prolonged confinement of small groups of men. Dr. Wilkins has told us, for example, that the optimal age range for such missions is between 25 and 45. Is the upper part of this range less susceptible to the ennui and other depressive symptoms of long confinement with a small group of men?

Dr. Wilkins mentioned homosexuality but not heterosexuality, which I suspect is an important issue in long-term isolation. It is reported that this topic is suppressed, even as one for academic discussion, during the long winter's night. That is, these men avoid talking about this problem even though it is, ordinarily, a favorite barracks room topic. If this is correct it may have implications for the way psychic defenses operate.

The whole problem of group composition is of obvious importance, particularly where selection of small groups to perform important missions is concerned. Nelson's hypotheses, that trait similarity among work associates would be most conducive to compatibility in regard to achievement, while trait complementation—that is heterogeneity—would be more conducive to compatibility in regard to the need for interpersonal dominance, seem reasonable. But these hypotheses require more research. Perhaps some of the results coming out of Dr. Haythorn's laboratory will have bearing on this question.

Research at the U.S. Naval School of Aviation Medicine has indicated that volunteers for hazardous duty (exposure to extreme cold or to cosmic radiation) and volunteers for astronaut training were superior in aptitude, performance, and motivation in the flight-training program compared with nonvolunteers. In the accelerated Polaris Fleet Ballistic Missile submarine program, no decrement was observed in the above average aptitude level (Navy Basic Test Battery) of volunteers admitted to the program over an eighteen-month period. These observations bear out the contention that in stress research involving groups in prolonged isolation, we are generally dealing with better than average men. This should be taken into consideration when we consider the incidence of work-decrement or of psychiatric disturbances.

It should come as no surprise that volunteers are apt to be single or divorced, since they are not concerned about a family back home. More important is the fact that after the novelty and glamor of these programs diminished, the quality of volunteers has remained high and has perhaps even improved. Such findings are reassuring in view of the practically complete reliance upon volunteering in a number of vital national programs, such as those for nuclear submarines and space.

In a study of biographical information, reported from Dr. Wilkins' laboratory, the two items which held up best for personnel in relatively large Antarctic stations were rank and pay grade attained. This suggests that conformity or adjustment are consistent predictors of performance if such attributes are accepted as criteria of following accepted job norms through time. I believe that the results generally agreed with those for small station personnel. Does the generalization follow that the men that perform and adjust best (whatever best may be) to the stressful conditions of the Antarctic situation are the kinds of people who do so under ordinary conditions? Or are specific stresses more stressful to certain kinds of people? Dr. Wilkins made the point that careful study of the environmental qualities of a situation involving isolation is required in order to prescribe the modes of compatibility required or desired. So group composition variables, as complex as they are, may indeed have to be related to specific environmental situations. Of further relevance in this context was the point that the demands of a stressful—and fairly unpredictable—environment influenced men to increase the stability of the interpersonal or group structure, and that changes in such structure may indicate some change in function or mission of the group. Putting these bits together, I get the impression that men are picked in terms of their past job and adjustment histories for stressful missions and then teams or groups are composed rather carefully in terms of the demands of mission. There is nothing novel in such an observation but it does imply that a lot of knowledge and a good selection ratio is necessary.

Dr. Wilkins' observation regarding social distance and leadership was, I think, most important, namely that social distance between leader and group (which has been found useful if not necessary in stressful situations) is difficult to maintain in the Antarctic situation. Leadership there is reinforced by providing the expertness necessary for group survival. This is reminiscent of Air Force crews during World War II in which fraternization among officers and enlisted men in a crew did not jeopardize the pilot's leadership because of his vital expertise.

Discussion

Dr. Ruff: An obvious comment should be made on the selection problem. There is no question that the best way to pick a person for a job is to take someone who has done well in that job in the past. If nobody has done a particular job in the past, the next best thing is to pick someone who has done well in whatever he is doing—the more similar to the new one the better.

Another comment relates to the matter of cyclical emotional symptoms. Little research has been directed to this phenomenon, although it is quite common. For example, those who work with basic military trainees can predict almost to the day when their situational depression will begin to lift.

Finally, others who have been involved in the South Pole expeditions have mentioned the kind of ennui and the inefficiency which appear during the winter period of boredom. I would suggest that this may reflect a kind of sensory deprivation phenomenon. The extreme case of sensory deprivation is water immersion, with severe reduction in sensory input. A more mild form is reduction in patterning of input. Finally there is something like the South Pole with reduction in variety of sensory experience.

Dr. Wilkins: I appreciate Dr. Ruff's comments on emotional symptomatology. We need more normative data on all sorts of group situations where responses seem to be cyclical. With regard to the changes during the year, Eric Gunderson (1963) has speculated about the possible analogies between waxing and waning of emotional symptoms and the sensory deprivation reactions. There is certainly some relationship there. We are very much interested, in various of our studies at the present time, in the transient nature of many types of emotional symptoms that can be found in reasonably healthy young people.

Boredom is related, in our opinion, to the effectiveness of one's work and one's job, and the Antarctic offers an interesting illustration. So far as I know, for example, no man has ever carried a correspondence course to the Antarctic and finished it.

Dr. Sells: I believe there is a great deal of consistency between the results reported in the Antarctic, where there are volunteer personnel, and studies that have been made in the Arctic where people are conscripted and sent there by direction. This applies to selection as well as to other factors.

Dr. Wilkins has pointed out that competence is an important variable in adjustment, and I agree, but if I understand the argument correctly, very active individuals make better adjustments at large bases than at small bases. The astronauts are active people. Does this imply that the astronauts would not make a good adjustment in an extended duration, multimanned space crew, over a long period of time?

Dr. Ruff: I think that on the variable of activity the astronauts would have more difficulty on a long-term mission than some others. But there are other variables, too.

Dr. Opler: The Antarctic is an excellent kind of laboratory in which to study cycles or continua and fluctuations in behavior. I think it is obvious in psychiatry that there is a tendency to look on the psychoses as steady states—maybe not the manic depressive or depressive state phenomena so much, because they are so obviously cyclical—but generally to forget that psychotics are "in" and "out of it"—they are back to the neurotic baseline defense kind of structuring when that works, and then when this wears thin, they move into psychotic states again. This is the suggestion to make about studies of the psychotic level as these are influenced by prolonged periods of stress. About the normal level, one is reminded that in terms of diurnal phenomena we are all in pseudo-psychotic states so far as dream states are concerned; and if that isn't persuasive there are at least the life-course variations in terms of which I think very few honest people would say they have never been neurotically troubled or have never experienced anything like *any* psychiatric illness. I am just commenting on a continuum in psychosis and a continuum in normality.

Dr. Prescott: The finding of emotional disturbances as a function of an unvarying environment is highly consistent with the findings of Hauty (1962), which I commented on earlier, and the role of Circadian biological rhythms in the maintenance of emotional stability and of performance. If it were at all possible to monitor, on a continuous basis, some basic information, such as heart rate and temperature, one might be able to predict that individual's who show disturbances in synchronizations in such periodicities might be the ones who would be most disturbed. Dr. Wilkins has pointed out the practical difficulty of such measurements under the primitive conditions of life in the Antarctic, but perhaps this could be made before the men go into isolation by placing them in sensory deprivation situations and monitoring their biological functions; disturbances in Circadian rhythms and functions in this constant environment might then be correlated with degree of disturbance under Antarctic conditions.

Dr. Arnold: Perhaps we have been too quick to ascribe these difficulties to sensory deprivation. It may not be sensory deprivation that leads to such emotional disturbances but the lack of significant activity. While any activity may be better than none—men allowed to do physical exercises in sensory deprivation experiments are not nearly so disturbed as those who are not allowed to do anything—activity may have to be related to the job that is being done as well as to the men's interest before it will prevent apathy or disturbance. Would it not be possible to select people with strong interests which could be followed even at the South Pole? Another possibility would be to select men with a strong motivation to succeed in this particular situation. There is evidence that motivation can be assessed successfully (see Arnold, 1962). We have found high correlation with achievement in demanding occupations, as well as with achievement in elementary school, high school, and college.

Dr. Mechanic: I think it would be incorrect to assume that the environment is unchanging. It is plausible to believe that during the winter social relations would be very salient and that sociometric networks would be changing. I don't therefore quite see how these data pertain to Circadian rhythms, as Dr. Prescott has suggested. But I would really like to ask if there is any evidence as to the amount of mood fluctuation in this situation as compared with others. Are the mood fluctuations observed any different from those observed in situations which are not extreme by any criterion?

Dr. Wilkins: The remarkable thing to me is that, given this hazardous situation, there are so surprisingly few adjustment difficulties. The difficulties I've mentioned are within normal ranges. Obviously, there are some deprivation factors in the situation—not only the temperature, which everybody can feel, and sex. I might say, incidentally, in reply to Dr. Levine's comment, that there has been no active homosexual behavior, but there is no lack of academic discussion of sex (if you can assume that what a Sea Bee talks about when he talks about sex is academic). On the contrary, there is plenty of sex conversation, though the presence or absence of spectacular pinups has been the function of the attitudes of particular commanding officers.

Dr. Appley: I think Dr. Wilkins' comment on the success of the mission—in the sense of lack of breakdown—is a very important one. Can we gain some information from this situation that might apply elsewhere? One feature, for example, is the fact that each man has a job and every man has a different job. I compare that with the reports of laboratory studies of isolation where subjects are given artificial jobs—jobs for which they were not trained but simply assigned in the laboratory setting. I don't mean to denigrate the laboratory-type study by these remarks, but rather to say that the stress effects may be quite different when the task is not one for which the man is trained or in which he is especially competent, as compared to a task in which the man is an expert (and in a setting where his expertise is appreciated). There might be other features worth examining, if we take the Antarctic setting as a successful isolation experience. The size of the group for instance, is different from some of the other experiences to which some transfer of information might be useful.

We know that there are certain "flat" periods in the conditions down there. Are any attempts made to manipulate the environment? Dr. Wilkins spoke of space capsules and undersea areas being artificial in that men must bring most of their environment with them. Can one not bring some cycle-related environment to the Antarctic? One could imagine introducing stimuli that might put peaks back into this flattened-affective situation? One could plan parties at particular periods, or do outdoor light-cycling, for example, so as to create artificial day-night differences. One might also carry on sensitivity training sessions with the men.

Dr. Wilkins: There have been attempts at environment manipulation, but I must admit they have been uncontrolled in the sense of measurements related to them and sometimes they go astray because of the composition of the people in the group. We have reports, in the Medical Officers' diaries, of how many such matters were planned and how they worked out—sometimes effectively, where tension was released and everybody got to be friends again.

As to sensitivity training, we have not had an opportunity to provide such training, but we have attempted to translate some of these notions to the medical officers, who are the senior officers on the small stations, so that they have some awareness of this. But the young general practitioner, fresh out of his internship, who is in his first three weeks of Naval duty, has enough to do to learn his basic job without going into sensitivity training. However, these ideas would be useful.

Dr. Back: One contrast between the situation in the Antarctic and those described by Dr. Biderman is that the Antarctic people know how long they are staying, and that is probably one of the most important things—if you can see the end of something you can tolerate it better! Time perspective seems to be one of the more important variables.

Dr. Biderman: I would assume that in this situation there develops a culture about behavior, including ideas of pathologies, to which people in general and special groupings of people are subject. A culture of pathology—and also a culture of acceptable pathology—leads the group to expect to observe certain things, and presumably as a consequence these do occur in accordance with the expected pattern. In prison literature there is a lot of this kind of evolution.

Dr. Wilkins: An example of this might be the wide-spread insomnia or "big eye" originally reported by John Rohrer (1961) at the end of the first IGY, which was widely experienced by the first people, especially apparently if they get into a period of social ostracism. But this is much less frequently reported now that the routine of living is stabilized after five or six years.

Dr. Trumbull: A few years ago we placed 37 Naval Officers in a fallout shelter without advance warning (Trumbull, 1966). Two observations from that experience may be relevant to the discussion here. In a typical fallout shelter emergency, it should be noted, of course, one doesn't have a full structured crew, and it thus presents a quite different organizational problem than that in the Antarctic. In an emergency setting, the first thing that happens is that searching for some organization starts immediately. In our particular instance it was interesting to watch how fast the group decided who the senior officer was, because that information was of course available to them. This has dangers obviously, since the ranking officer may not be the best leader of the group in a case such as this. This would be comparable, let's say, to a fallout shelter under a big building in New York City, where the manager in that building all of a sudden became, *ex officio,* the fallout shelter leader. This might not be what you want at all. But people tend to gravitate towards symbols of leadership in a stressful situation. The symbolic significance of a uniform, for example, appears to lead people to accept directions or expect guidance from persons in *any* kind of uniform in emergency or disaster conditions.

The second observation of relevance is the attitude toward time that develops. The very act of searching on the part of these people to try to determine when they were going to be allowed to get out of the place was remarkable. They tried to find a cue in anything they could see around them. Just by pure chance somebody gave them a little extra serving of jelly to put on the crackers they had at one lunch time, and they decided that this was a good enough indication that the shelter period must be terminating that day. They were actively seeking some time measure on which to orient. Time is, I believe, and as others have emphasized, a very important factor for us to study.

Chairman's summary

KURT W. BACK: The discussion of the Antarctic station and similar experiences performs, I think, a very valuable function in the study of stress. It remedies some of the biases which have resulted from the common research approach which equates stress with breakdown. Normally, to do research on stress we introduce, or observe, a condition—a stressor—under which we can find a distinct deterioration of performance or emotion. It becomes tempting to conclude that the stress condition leads to severe disruption. It is valuable, therefore, to remind ourselves that people frequently function under very severe conditions and perform very well. The present discussion illustrates a case in point and we can try to distinguish the features which make for efficient functioning in such situations.

Pulling together all the specific features which might occur to us, we can say that functioning depends on the whole place which the stress situation has in the life of the person. We have just discussed the meaning of time perspective in the different settings. From a larger point of view, time perspectives become important because of the way the situation fits into a person's life. A professional who wants to make certain observations for half a year on the South Pole can give a meaning to his experience. This is also true of a specialist rating in the Navy who volunteers to spend part of his service time under this condition. It would be different to take the same people suddenly, perhaps as a punishment, and then send them to the same place without giving them a definite timing so that they can tie up this experience with their future. What I am trying to say is that we cannot look at the stress experience as an isolated part in a person's life. If we do so, and especially if we make it an isolated experience, then this by itself will produce greater stress. This may help us in producing strong stress conditions for a study but contributes little to understanding how people cope with stress they encounter in their lives.

We can see from the South Pole experience how important this fitting into total life is. In managing this situation, a few facts stand out. Selection becomes important in finding those people who are most likely to see the experience in a comprehensive framework. The fact that people with higher rank and pay perform better means not only that they are higher conformers but are better adapted. These men can also be assumed to have more commitment to their career in the service and kind of occupation, and therefore, are more likely to see this experience as part of their life pattern. A striking fact of this paper, as well as of Drs. Ruff and Korchin's paper (see Chapter 11) was the great emphasis which all participants put on being professional, a "real pro." As this experience has meaning only in terms of a work career, it would be this aspect which can be fitted in best, while the interplay of personalities can be relegated to some other time. In line with this, I would think that sensitivity training for this group would be a waste and may even be detrimental. These men did not volunteer to find friends or to have a group experience, and emphasizing this aspect may make them less able to structure relationships in terms of their work. This structure is the way the organization functions best. The disruption which occurs when guests are at the place, which means when purely interpersonal relations are called for, shows how emphasis away from the work may be threatened.

The importance of the time structure within the tour of duty itself has also been discussed. It is again the possibility of scheduling the whole experience in relation to plans for the future which makes timing so important. The importance of time schedules in crisis situations has been documented in a recent book by Julius A. Roth (1963). He takes another stress situation where timing is not well defined, namely, hospitalization, and shows how desperately patients try to make up a time schedule of their own progress. This kind of scheduling can also be compared to occupational careers, or in general, to the course of one's life. It will be advantageous to look at stress situations as having these kinds of connections with the past and future and especially with the time perspective the individual brings into the situation. Stress is not something which impinges on a person suddenly and with which he copes right then. For the living organism, stress is a condition of life, and he relates each individual stress to his past and future in order to be able to incorporate it into his whole life space.

GEORGE E. RUFF

SHELDON J. KORCHIN

11

Adaptive stress behavior

Stress occurs when an organism is forced into strenuous effort to maintain essential functions at a required level. Because a load is placed upon the organism, it must modify its activities. This involves the concept of adaptation—a compensatory response which permits continued functioning in spite of the load.

Adaptation can be described in terms of a model of the organism as a system with inputs and outputs of energy and information. Each system tends to maintain steady states of many variables through homeostatic mechanisms. These confine within a limited range the variables which are crucial for continued existence of the system. Inputs which force the variables beyond this range are stressors. Adjustments made to restore equilibrium constitute the process of adaptation. This involves the reorganization of certain subsystems to prevent failure of other subsystems required for survival.

Stress can be defined by inputs, outputs, or both. *Input* definitions involve underloads or overloads of energy or information which produce stress within the system. In a sleep-deprivation study, for example, stress could be defined by total hours of wakefulness. *Output* definitions are based upon variables which are displaced from equilibrium under stress. Performance tests are commonly used for this purpose, with a decrement beyond a certain level being taken as an index of stress.

When used alone, each of these approaches has disadvantages. Input definitions involve either past experience, which demonstrates that certain conditions are stressful, or *a priori* decisions about what conditions are expected to be stressful. They may be inadequate in biological research, where responses to the same input vary from individual to individual and from occasion to occasion. On the other hand, output definitions may also be misleading. For one thing, performance decrements may occur without stress—as when motivation decreases. And, if compensatory responses are effective, performance may be maintained at a high level even while the subject is under a heavy load.

While definitions based on adaptive mechanisms avoid many of these problems, they also have disadvantages. Most involve a psychophysiological approach, where physiological variables are used as indices of the organism's state of activation. However, these variables may give contradictory results and may change in response to conditions not considered stressful. For example, many occur with stimuli which simply attract the attention of a resting subject. Unless the concept of stress is broadened to include all instances of increased arousal, demonstration of the adaptive mechanisms alone may not be sufficient to establish the presence of stress.

The most complete definition of stress is given by the combined use of input, output, and adaptive considerations. First, the experimenter specifies which inputs are the stressors and describes as well as he can the mechanism by which they produce their effects. Next, he measures one or more output variables which fall within a specified range under ordinary conditions but cannot be maintained under stress conditions. Whenever possible these variables should be part of the subject's natural, ongoing activities. Finally, indices of adaptive or compensatory processes are chosen. Insofar as possible, patterns of autonomic change are selected which have been found to characterize stress responses under the specific experimental conditions employed.

It would appear desirable to conceptualize all of these steps according to a single frame of reference. In psychological stress research, input, output, and adaptation should be presented in behaviorally-relevant terms. For example, if the input is information that a subject has failed at some task, the output could be a psychological function displaced from its usual range, such as the affect state or performance, and adaptation should be described as a psychological defense mechanism. Physiological processes measured concurrently may be of interest but should be conceptualized on a separate level. In experiments where inputs are described psychologically, and outputs are described physiologically, the contribution to our understanding of the psychological processes may be minimal.

SOME PROBLEMS OF STRESS RESEARCH

Of more practical concern are the problems of a suitable experimental setting. The investigator usually has the choice of two broad strategies: either to study stress where it is naturally encountered or to create a model in the laboratory. Unfortunately, this choice may amount to a dilemma. Where conditions are naturally stressful, the possibilities for controlled investigation are often limited. Studies carried out under field conditions may be hampered by the exigencies which make these conditions stressful in the first place. On the other hand, constraints binding the investigator who seeks to create stress in the laboratory often give rise to procedures which approach his problem tangentially, at best.

Among the natural stress experiences which lend themselves to systematic study are those of military training, students before examinations, and patients awaiting surgery. Although many military training situations are not notably stressful, an exception is airborne training. Thus, Basowitz, Persky, Korchin, and Grinker (1955) studied psychological and physiological responses of paratrooper trainees while jumping from towers and planes. Students taking examinations are readily available, at least to those of us who live with the "natural stress" of academic life, but this may not be the kind of stress the investigator seeks to explore. The many factors which make an examination stressful for the student may or may not, for example, overlap the many factors which force the psychiatric patient into a psychosis. Another group which is often accessible consists of surgical patients. However, the focus here is inevitably on threats of bodily harm—a vitally important source of stress, but not necessarily the one the investigator prefers to explore. No one kind of experience can serve in the exploration of all stress behaviors.

Where the chosen interest of the investigator is matched by a natural experience involving the proper set of threats and amenable to systematic study, there should be no impediment to productive research. Naturally-occurring stressful events, particularly where controllable measures can be made, make possible "natural experiments," which combine many of the advantages of field and laboratory research. The paratrooper studies just mentioned and the work with the astronauts described below are cases in point, but such opportunities for stress research are rare. For this reason, or because of a desire to achieve better control over relevant variables, many workers choose to develop an artificial stress procedure in the laboratory. Unfortunately, this task is seldom approached with a firm notion of the kind of stress which is to be studied. The investigator chooses to do research on stress and attempts to devise a procedure which should be stressful. All too often he achieves a gimmick which alters subject behavior in some fashion but contributes little to our understanding of the psychology of stress. For example, a rigged situation in which the subject is convinced he has failed in a simple task may be an appropriate means to test a formulation regarding self-esteem. But simply as a means to produce stress in some nonspecific sense, it accomplishes little.

A problem for a particular type of stress research is the difficulty of producing laboratory analogs of the stress processes which are seen in psychiatric patients. The belief is commonly held that although external conditions may precipitate mental disorder, they do so by producing internal conflict. Although it is recognized that psychoanalytic and other formulations centering around this impression should be subjected to experimental study, it has proven difficult to devise a method which will consistently arouse inner conflict. The experimenter usually employs a laboratory procedure which confronts a subject with an external threat. This has been done by various methods, including fear-producing motion pictures or stress interview techniques, where threats can be "custom-made" to arouse whatever conflict appears important for a given subject. However, unless a procedure is included which demonstrates that the desired conflict *was* elicited, interpretation of results may be ambiguous.

A STUDY OF THE MERCURY ASTRONAUTS [1]

Many of these concepts and problems are illustrated by a study of the Project Mercury astronauts. From a research standpoint, Project Mercury had many advantages. First, it offered a chance to study men who had demonstrated particularly effective modes of adaptation to stress. Because the astronauts had been extensively tested at the time of selection (Ruff & Levy, 1959) and would be followed for a period of several years, it would be possible to study each individual carefully over time. Most important, they would be facing real stress which could not be simulated in the laboratory and which would be encountered under conditions allowing systematic observation.

The Project Mercury study involved simultaneous measurement of psychological, physiological, and biochemical variables in response to training and flight activities. It was carried out in three phases: (1) personality assessment; (2) repeated measurements during training; and (3) evaluation of response to flight.

Phase 1: Personality assessment

This stage involved reevaluation of each of the seven astronauts to investigate personality mechanisms relevant to stress behavior.

[1] We are grateful to the National Aeronautics and Space Administration and to the National Institute of Mental Health for making this study possible. However, the opinions and conclusions expressed in this article are those of the authors and do not necessarily represent the views of the National Aeronautics and Space Administration or any other governmental agency. Portions of the work reported here were presented to the American Association for the Advancement of Science, Philadelphia, December 28, 1962, and published in a volume reporting the proceeding of a symposium jointly sponsored by AAAS and American Psychiatric Association (Korchin & Ruff, 1964; Ruff & Korchin, 1964).

The data consisted principally of interviews with the astronauts individually. In addition, the extensive material from the original assessment program was included in the analyses. To make it possible for the men to speak frankly without compromising their chances to be chosen for future flights, it was understood that details of the study data would remain confidential until selection was no longer an issue. To maximize reliability and the coverage of different areas, each of us interviewed all men in two one-hour sessions. All interviews were tape-recorded and transcribed for later study. The analysis and findings based on this material derive from independent study of the tapes and transcripts by the two psychological investigators and the convergence of their clinical judgments.

In the initial interviews, and amplified throughout the subsequent course of the study, the following general areas were investigated:

Motivation for project.   Each man's motivation for joining Project Mercury, and the needs subsequently served by participation, were explored. His goals and aspirations for the future were examined.

Self-concept and concept of the astronaut role.   Self-esteem and self-attitudes, in general and in connection with the astronaut role, were considered. Concepts of the "ideal astronaut," and the competence, values, and other aspects of behavior believed relevant were discussed.

Emotional activation and control.   The variety, intensity, conditions for activation, and control of various emotional states were studied by examining behavior in situations of psychological threat and objective danger. The somatic representation and behavioral consequences of anxiety, anger, and depression were described. On the positive side the sources of pleasure, feelings of competence, mastery, achievement, and other conditions of well-being were also determined.

Type and strength of defenses.   Efforts were made to discover the typical modes of dealing with threats to psychological equilibrium. The efficiency of these mechanisms in coping with stress was assessed.

Social behavior.   Relations to family, to the other astronauts, to management, and to other persons were examined. The social organization of the group, as a group, was described.

Other aspects of personality.   Impulsivity and lability, energy level and fatigue, reactions to potentially disruptive agents, such as alcohol, and other qualities were reviewed. These included such dimensions as activity-passivity, dependence-independence, trust-distrust, and needs for affiliation, achievement, and autonomy.

Phase 2: Repeated measurements during training

During training, a small battery of psychological tests was given on repeated occasions over a two-year period. Paired measurements were made before and after centrifuge simulations of suborbital and orbital flights, environmental control system runs, and selected prelaunch activities. In addition, the battery was used during more relaxed control occasions. The primary purpose of this phase was to develop a baseline against which the same measures made at the time of flight could be evaluated. A "P-technique" model was used, where comparisons were made across occasions for each man individually. The areas of psychological functioning assessed and the measures used included:

Measures of personality and emotion.   The emotional state on each occasion was described by self-administered adjective check list (Clyde, 1959), self-rating scales, and a brief questionnaire which inquired into the astronaut's perception of the adequacy of his performance and asked him to describe any special circumstances which might have influenced his behavior on that occasion. Where scheduling permitted, interviews exploring these matters were also included.

Performance measures.   In order to assess possible changes in psychomotor and intellectual functioning caused by training or flight stress, three tests developed for studies requiring repeated testing of the same individuals were used (Moran & Mefferd, 1959). These procedures had been administered to the astronauts at the time of the original selection program. The tests were (1) Aiming, which requires that the subject dot the center of connected circles as rapidly as possible; (2) Number Facility, a mental arithmetic task; and (3) Perceptual Speed, a number-cancellation procedure. All of these are timed tests of familiar-overlearned functions, which should be stable in repeated testing, except for changes resulting from stress or states of disorganization.

Phase 3: Study of flight behavior

The third phase of the study consisted of more intensive evaluation of five of the men who made suborbital or orbital flights. The battery of measures described above was administered immediately before and after each flight. At the same time, there were brief interviews evaluating the astronaut's condition just prior to and following the flight. There was a longer interview two days earlier to review each man's experiences since the last contact, to explore in greater depth his feelings and anticipations and to determine fears or doubts he may have had. Similarly, two days after flight, there was another long interview to review the flight experience itself. Observations were also made during debriefing sessions and other less formal contacts. In addition to the primary and back-up pilots, interviews were held with all other astronauts who were available during the pre- and post-flight periods.

Personality qualities of the Mercury astronauts

In order to understand the pattern of adaptive response observed, it is necessary to know something about the men who were studied. Although each of the astronauts has distinct and separate personality traits, certain features were found to be common to all. Some of the more salient personality characteristics which are relevant to the understanding of stress behavior are summarized:

General characteristics. The Mercury astronauts had high levels of intelligence, were concerned with problem solving, and had the ability to focus on the essentials of issues which confronted them. They tended not to be abstract or speculative but to think concretely. Facts rather than theories were emphasized. What was unknown and uncertain was handled by efforts to make it known. Details irrelevant to their areas of primary concern were avoided.

These men were not introspective and tended to have limited fantasy lives. However, they could describe their inner processes when asked to direct their attention toward them. They were oriented toward action rather than thought, preferred action to inaction, and disliked assuming a passive role. At the same time, they were not overly impulsive, and could refrain from action when it was not appropriate. In most of their behavior, evidence of emotional stability was apparent.

Although attachments within the group itself were not intense, the men shared a common purpose. The most important bond between them was their common background as test pilots. Strong emphasis was placed by each man on values related to professional competence.

Motivation. All the men were professionally motivated to contribute to the space program. This was part of their strong drive toward mastery and achievement. In each case, this tendency became apparent early in life and was eventually expressed in a desire to fly. Not infrequently, the heightened drive toward mastery once served to reduce self-doubts. However, in most cases it later functioned independently of the need for such reassurance.

The astronauts felt the challenge of their work and enjoyed the opportunity to use all their capacities. They derived a sense of satisfaction from participating in something they considered important—something on the frontier of their field. Along with this, all had the conviction that they were making an important contribution to the national interest.

The men had no special wish to face danger, although they were willing to accept the risks demanded by their job. Where danger was present, it was not a motivation for their work. Although a few men enjoyed certain types of risks, this had little to do with volunteering for Project Mercury.

Frustration tolerance.   Since the astronaut's drive for achievement was strong, their potential for disappointment was great. Nevertheless, they displayed striking resilience in the face of frustration. The most important sources of disappointment were delays in the schedule and failure to be selected for a particular flight. In general, both were dealt with by looking beyond the immediate obstacle and deciding that the problem would be resolved in the future. Whenever a course of action suggested itself, they embarked upon it as quickly as possible.

Psychological response to training and flight

Effects of training and flight stress on performance.   Each of the three performance tests yielded two scores: (1) the number of items correctly completed within the time limit; and (2) the number of errors made. Since these two scores are essentially independent (Moran & Mefferd, 1959), both were considered separately as measures of behavioral efficiency. On all these tests, each man showed improved functioning after the training events, such as centrifuge runs and simulator trials. By contrast, from before to after flight there was a drop in total trials and a rise in errors. But in general, pre- to post-differences were small.

One finding is worthy of special comment. The preflight scores for all tests were above the general level of performance. The reverse might have been expected, since this measure was made at a time when preflight anxiety might be highest. Furthermore, preflight testing was done in the early morning hours, when most subjects are less efficient. That performance was so good at this point suggests a state of activation. The anticipatory anxiety such as might exist not only did not lessen but seems to have facilitated psychological functioning in the immediate preflight hours.

Emotional reactions.   As part of the test battery, along with the psychometric procedures, a mood scale consisting of 53 adjectives was administered. The astronaut was asked to what degree—on a four-point scale—each adjective described his mood at that moment. On factor analysis, Clyde (1959) had extracted six factor variables from this list: (1) "Friendly"; (2) "Energetic"; (3) "Clear-Thinking"; (4) "Aggressive"; (5) "Jittery"; and (6) "Depressed." The score for each of these is the sum of the ratings for the adjectives found loaded on the factor. Since each factor score is based on the sum of a different number of adjective ratings in the original scoring system, they were recalculated on a mean-per-adjective basis to simplify comparison.

On all occasions, the men described themselves more in terms of the positive than the negative emotional states. Thus, the highest ratings were obtained for Friendly, Energetic, and Clear-Thinking; the lowest ratings were for Aggressive, Jittery, and Depressed. As with the performance variables, pre- to post-changes were greater than those produced by training events. Following flight, there was a general tendency for the "Energetic," and "Clear-Thinking" scores to drop and for greater anxiety to be admitted. There was a parallel increase in "Friendly." Thus, compared to their state prior to launch, after flight they tended to be somewhat less energetic and clear-thinking, somewhat more anxious, and to feel more warmly related to people. However, it should be noted that most of these change scores are small, and that both before and after flight the men described themselves as alert and attentive and generally without fear or disturbing affect.

Clinical summary of stress behavior.   Throughout the study, adaptive behavior was observed under various potentially disturbing conditions. As in any job, there were day-to-day problems. But because of the particular qualities of the project, the number of delays and frustrations was necessarily large. These were often enhanced by a sense of functioning in an unfamiliar organization. Procedures and responsibilities were often unlike those in the military services in which the men worked for years. Furthermore, the national importance of the project focused public attention on the astronauts and their work, none of whom could continue to live in accustomed anonymity. Both the novel technology and the unusual social conditions were potential sources of difficulty.

In spite of such considerations, few adverse reactions were noted during the development and training phases of the program. The astronauts were usually able to maintain a level-headed, realistic approach to their problems. For most, not being chosen for the first flight was the greatest threat to their self-esteem, since it carried the implication that they had somehow failed and were not functioning as well as they had assumed. In response, they analyzed possible faults in their performance and worked the harder to overcome them. Eventually each was able to believe that his day could come. Once chosen for a flight, schedule changes and delays had little impact, despite fears voiced by the press. Once decided, the issue of "when" was secondary.

Until the day of flight, the astronaut's major concern was with achieving a state of readiness. Discomfort was evident until the man felt "on top" of things. In the days and hours before flight, all of the men felt ready to go and competent for the job. Conscious thoughts of danger and possible death were infrequent, and suppressed as they arose. The men were preoccupied with operational details and showed little anticipatory anxiety. When it appeared, it was experienced as mild tension or "edginess." It was similar to that felt in combat or other earlier stress and, being familiar, was not disturbing. In most cases, anxiety seemed more related to an intense concern with the success of the mission than to fear of injury or death.

All of the astronauts had considered the risks. They were convinced that their past experiences and intensive training in the project had prepared them for any emergency. Much of the ability to control anticipatory anxiety resulted from confidence in their preparation. Considering every eventuality and doing all possible to prepare for it, they saw little point in worrying further. When thoughts of danger did arise, they were displaced by review of the flight plan or other technical aspects of the flight. In one man's words, "Whenever I think of something that may go wrong, I think of a plan to take care of it."

In the period just before lift-off, men reported being on edge and interpreted this as a positive sign. There was excitement, anticipation, and readiness to go, of the sort athletes describe before the race, but no instances of severe or potentially disabling anxiety. If tensions mounted, the response was to stop, take stock, and decide what to do to bring matters under control. Conscious mechanisms of self-control—a quality valued by these men—were available in all cases during the immediate prelaunch period.

So, too, during flight, thoughts centered on procedures needing execution and on the experiences of being in orbit. Successful launch and well-executed flight induced feelings of exhilaration, which were further reinforced by the pleasant sensation of weightlessness. Anxiety never went to excessive levels, and even when objective dangers arose, functioning was effective and disturbing affect held in check.

After flight, there was uniform elation coupled with fatigue. Elation came from both a sense of a difficult job well done and from a sense of relief that the long-anticipated flight was over.

In conclusion, it might be said that the most striking finding of this study is the effectiveness of adaptive responses based on past experience and professional competence. Given a group of men with repeated success in accomplishment of hazardous duties, followed by training which led to highly organized, efficient patterns of behavior, evidence of disruptive stress behavior was minimal.

Invited commentary

GEORGE MANDLER: I am particularly pleased by the methodological stance which this paper represents. For many years, one dominant attitude in psychology has been that the way to learn about human beings is to study the abnormal, the hyponormal. The trend has been: "Let's find out about the schizophrenic, and then we'll know all about basic processes of human behavior." Very rarely have we been given data on the hypernormal. This paper gives us an opportunity to see what adaptive behavior looks like when the organism has not been deliberately selected because he cannot adapt to stress. The subjects here were specifically chosen because they could adapt to stressful situations. Before discussing some general problems of adaptation to stress, I would like to make two specific comments.

First of all, I found Drs. Ruff's and Korchin's outline and discussion of the stress paradigm most helpful. Rather than waving some particular theoretical flag, they have given us an overview which, for a change, most of us can adopt. I think all of us can live with such a basis for discussion without having to worry whether we really do agree with this or that definition of stress.

Secondly, one general comment on the interpretation of the data. Psychologists have only recently been concerned with the demand characteristics of test and experimental situations. What are the subject's hypotheses about the test situation, and how do these expectations affect his behavior? What does he think is expected of him and why? Particularly in the kind of situation that has been described here, such problems may be quite important and should be carefully considered.

What I would like to discuss at greater length is the question of how the human organism adapts to stress and the relevant alternatives that may be available to him. I believe this problem is related to the general problem of planning, to the cognitive structures that the organism has available at the time he is placed in an unusual, stressful, or unexpected situation. Recently I have been much concerned with the organization of behavior, the development of organized labor sequences, and the effect of interruption of organized responses on behavior in general (Mandler, 1964; Mandler & Watson, 1966).

By organization I refer to the development of unitary sequences of behavior which, once they are initiated, run off smoothly and present an inevitability of completion. Some organized sequences—which we usually call consummatory responses—are built into the organism and need not be acquired. These include swallowing, drinking, sexual behavior, and so forth. Other, learned organized sequences include—at a very simple level—walking, typing, rowing. Exactly the same kinds of sequences develop at a more complex level. We may, for example, execute a very well integrated or organized sequence of driving or walking to the office. Organized behavior not only occurs at the overt level—in terms of observable behavior—but once behavior has been organized it is cognitively represented. The cognitive representation of organized behavior is equivalent,

I believe, with what Miller, Galanter, and Pribram, (1960) have called "plans."

Parenthetically I might note that within such a system it is not particularly useful to talk about goals or about organisms striving toward goals. Behavior sequences, once initiated, persist and end up with responses at a point which is usually called a goal. But the goal is part of the sequence and can be considered as a stop rule for a particular sequence. Rather than organisms striving toward a goal we may say that they execute a particular path with the goal at the end, a "goalpath."

Where does all this become relevant to stress? Stress results in a condition—or is one of the conditions—which interrupts these organized behavior sequences. Any event that prevents completion of an initiated sequence produces ANS arousal, which in turn sets the stage for emotional behavior (cf. Schachter & Singer, 1962; Mandler, 1962).

Now, to turn to the problem of adaptation. What can the organism do when a plan or an organized sequence has been interrupted? I have suggested three general reactions: persistence, increased vigor, and substitution. One well-organized sequence most of us have available is that of putting a key in a lock and opening a door. If it does not work the first time, we try again. Persistence frequently will complete the sequence and therefore undo the interruption. If it does not, we might try a little harder and increased vigor also may short-circuit the effects of interruption. Or we might break the key, in which case the effect of interruption would be more intense and prolonged. More central to the problem of adaptation is the third choice—substitution.

If a particular plan or sequence has been interrupted, one can avoid the emotional consequences by finding an alternative sequence or response which will complete the original plan that was laid down. The problem of substitution was effectively discussed years ago by Kurt Lewin and his students (1935).

The major point I want to make for present purposes is that interruption produces emotional arousal and that this arousal will, under certain circumstances, produce anxiety or distress. A subjective state of distress will be the emotion of choice if no successful alternate sequence is available, if the organism is helpless. In the animal literature, Mowrer and Vieck (1948) for example have shown that rats who were able to control the onset of shock were much less anxious than those who could not do so. Watson and I (Mandler & Watson, 1966) have discussed the problem of control, and Dr. Watson has shown that subjects in a simple task will perform much better if they can control the sequence of tasks than if they cannot. We also know that the control of onset and offset of shock is much less disturbing to human subjects than lack of control. Dr. Haggard (1943) presented data to that effect some years ago, and more recently Elliot (1966) has replicated some aspects of his findings.

Stressors are stimuli which frequently fit very neatly into the organization-interruption paradigm. They interrupt a plan or an ongoing behavior sequence. And the most adaptive response to stress is to have alternate responses available.[2] There is something that the subject can do with the situation in which his plan is interrupted.

The astronaut, as cited by Drs. Ruff and Korchin, illustrates our theoretical

[2] Such availability is, by the way, closely related to Dr. Lazarus' concept of "coping."

notions very well: "Whenever I think of something that may go wrong, I think of a plan to take care of it." This is a very neat description of a man who, in anticipating possible interruptions, lists for himself a variety of alternate behaviors. He says: "If something goes wrong, I can do A or B or C or D." He anticipates the possibility of interruption and subsequent emotional arousal and prepares for bypassing the emotional consequences by having alternate completions immediately available. He *plans* for interruptions.

In discussing frustration tolerance, Drs. Ruff and Korchin noted that the astronauts are easily disappointed. I think this is to be expected. They have well-developed, highly dominant and smoothly operating plans. If these are interrupted, disappointment is an obvious emotional consequence. But disappointment does not grow into disruptive helplessness if good alternate plans are available at the time of interruption. The organism can still complete a relevant sequence. Apart from the availability of alternate responses, I have suggested elsewhere (Mandler 1962, 1964) that frustration tolerance involves the ability to "hold." If one can hold or delay in the face of interruption and rising arousal, then the longer the delay lasts the more likely it is that the situation will change, the more likely it is that one will be able to discover some alternate response that will permit completion. In this sense frustration tolerance is the ability to stop and consider the situation instead of engaging in persistence, for example, which frequently may not produce completion. The astronauts have this ability; they are practical, they are realistic—which means they have a veridical view of the situation; they can properly evaluate their environment, and they know what could be done if interruptions occur; they are highly adaptive, i.e., they have good alternatives available.

I have mentioned earlier that planning for interruptions is highly adaptive. Sometimes this is difficult; for example when shock is used to interrupt behavior. This stressor, beloved by psychologists, frequently interferes with planning, it does not permit the subject to think about much other than the pain. If, however, the subject has a plan to deal with shock—"When shock occurs, I will do such and such"—then the shock becomes part of the plan, interruption is attenuated, and the degree of disruptive emotional behavior is reduced. I am similarly convinced that when a plan does include the occurrence of and coping with a noxious event, then the *absence* of that noxious event— a new interruption—will also produce arousal and emotional behavior. But in this case the condition under which the arousal occurs is not one of helplessness, and positive emotions, such as euphoria, will be produced. If you expect to be shocked and are not, the interruption will also produce emotional behavior but positive, rather than negative, in tone.

Finally, I would like to relate some of these notions about organization and adaptation to some other problems that were raised by others earlier. Dr. Bovard (p. 64) mentioned that positive reinforcement inhibits stress. Positive reinforcement is the condition that produces consummatory behavior, i.e., well organized responses. Kessen and I (1961) have discussed the role of organized responses in inhibiting distress, and Kessen has demonstrated this phenomenon in the neonate. Positive reinforcement involves the completion and execution of well-organized behavior and is therefore stress inhibiting.

A point that Dr. Sells made earlier (p. 145) fits rather nicely into the picture of adaptive behavior I have drawn here. The confirming outcome of expectations implies that sequences are completed, dissonant outcomes imply their interruption.

Again let me say that I am glad that we are spending some time with the hypernormal astronauts, if for no other reason than that for the counter example to the abnormal hyponormal is so rarely available. I believe that we can learn much that is useful from the individual who has well-developed skills in dealing with stress, maybe more than from those who only show the debilitating effects of interruption.

Discussion

Dr. Haggard: What is known about the adaptive history of the astronauts, especially with respect to their development of various types of stress tolerance? We usually assume that stress is inherently bad—because it taxes the system and involves discomfort. But there is a good deal of evidence which-questions this assumption. For example, young animals, if not given too "good" a diet, grow up to be stronger and more vital than animals that had been fed "better." Exposure to stress can also have beneficial effects in another sense, as training under combat conditions may have survival value when the man actually goes into combat.

In our society I think we tend to trim the wings of our adaptive mechanisms. When the temperature increases to a point of discomfort, we turn on fans. If they do not cool us off enough, we may go to a room which is air conditioned. Or, if the room were to get cold, we turn on the heaters. This minimizing of the role of our adaptive mechanisms is not shared to the same degree by all cultural groups. For example, the Finns, who adore to take the sauna, first make themselves as hot as they can, and then make themselves as cold as they can, and thus maintain their ability to adapt to a wide range of temperatures with relative comfort. What about the history of the astronauts from this point of view? What types of stress situations had they gone through to develop the sort of adaptive mechanisms which contributed to their performance as astronauts?

Dr. Korchin: In one of our reports (Korchin & Ruff, 1964), we consider their early histories and what inferences can be drawn from them. Their histories are interesting, and they share a number of qualities. They grew up in relatively small, well-organized communities, with considerable family solidarity and strong identification with the father. They still refer to their fathers as vital persons in their lives. From early in life, their high intelligence and fine constitutions served them well. Their environments did not challenge them beyond their capacities on either score. Nor, at the same time, did they internalize aspirations which were beyond their reach. They went to schools and colleges in which they could do well. One can visualize histories of successive crises and resolutions—which is one way a strong ego might develop—but in the case of these men we saw instead a relatively smooth growth pattern in which they could meet available challenges, increase levels of aspirations, succeed and gain further confidence, and in this way grow in competence through a kind of positive feedback.

They had very few failures and few decision crises. Events seem to flow naturally from stage to stage. For example, many went into service during or shortly after World War II, functioned successfully, and stayed on. They didn't suffer through the torturous decisions which seem so characteristic of our world. In retrospect, it is hard for them to recall life crises. This is one kind of life history which one can visualize as being a basis for adult competence, although not the only one. Another might involve the overcoming of barriers and difficulties, successive crises and resolutions, which is the pattern which perhaps was implied in Dr. Haggard's question.

I would also like to comment on Dr. Mandler's remarks, because, along with Dr. Ruff, I am pleased that he saw some of the essential themes which we intended in the study. Aside from the possible contribution to the space program, we undertook the study because of the opportunity to study unusual men, unusual in their competence. Moreover, it involved methodology which I believe is important in the field of stress research. The study might be termed a *natural experiment*—the men were studied in natural, rather than laboratory, circumstances, but in a limited and defined situation which had a definite onset and termination, and definable events during which more or less precise experimental measures could be made. The project also combined personological and experimental approaches—individuals were studied in some depth prior to measurements made in response to specific stress situations, over a period of two-and-a-half or more years. For these various reasons we welcomed the opportunity to do this study.

Dr. Mandler's formulation correctly describes an important aspect of the adaptive behavior of these men, but I wonder if it is prototypic of adaptive stress response generally. These men had stable self-concepts in which, as was pointed out, professional values were clearly and sharply defined. They have clear criteria for right and wrong, and for what is likely to be more effective and what is likely to be less effective. We can envy them that because our world doesn't provide such clear standards. They also have two other important qualities. They have a high level of competence. They know what they can do, and they can do a lot well. And they are men of hope. In the Lewinian sense, they are oriented to a positive future. They have the conviction that if one has knowledge and does the correct things, all will turn out right.

Now, when these three qualities are put together—sharp criteria for action, actual competence (and the feeling of competence), and basic hope—then the specific stress behaviors described are understandable and might be characterized by Dr. Mandler's alternate-plan mechanism. Other mechanisms, of a more classic defensive sort, might be used. *These* men are capable of making a plan, noting a problem, shifting to an alternate plan, if blocked, and carrying out the psychological acts required in Mandler's schema. I believe that this is a particular kind, and a very effective kind, of stress response. It may not necessarily be the model of all adaptive stress reaction, however, although it represents the functioning of men like these who are planful, reality-oriented, have clear criteria for decision-making, and the other qualities already described. But these same qualities keep them from being particularly creative people, at least in the sense that the term has been used in recent writings on creativity.

Dr. Pepitone: Before we close the door on the attributes involved in the astronauts conducive to their adaptability, I would like to raise a question about a variable which may have a lot to do both with the performance effectiveness and the general adjustment of these individuals, namely the fact that they are participating in and making history. Not only are they playing an historically unique role as navigators and adventurers in the cosmos but they are aware of it. I wonder whether the fact that they will go down in history has anything to do with their extraordinary handling and avoidance of stress.

Dr. Ruff: The interesting thing is that while most psychologists will agree that this is important, most of the astronauts didn't look at it that way. In fact, their tendency was to deemphasize this aspect of the project and to treat it as just another mission. I don't mean to say that they were so unrealistic as not to recognize the uniqueness of what they were doing. But they responded by putting it into the framework of their accustomed professional activities.

Dr. Sells: Another part of the background of these men is that they are test pilots and have lived for a number of years in an environment in which the social system is organized adaptively in terms of backup systems or correctives. This is also a characteristic of the Mercury program and of every one of these men in the spaceflight organization. Every space shot has been organized with double and triple backup systems to a point where it is just built in as part of the culture, that this is the way you operate. Going back historically, you might say that this is one of the geniuses of organized aviation, and these men are also products of this system. This is an important thing to recognize.

May I also add a footnote to Drs. Ruff's and Korchin's observations. Robert Voas (1964) in a paper he prepared for me on "Performance evaluation in the Mercury Flights" described what I think was a most ingenious method, which demonstrates the possibility of going out and making rigorous measurements where the behavior is being performed, as distinguished from the laboratory. What he did was to get continuous recordings of eye movements, from which he was able to infer on which instruments the men's eyes were focused. When this was transmitted down afterwards against the flight plan, he could determine whether they were doing what they were supposed to be doing at any particular time. The record is very clear and supports the report of the very high level of performance in orbit. Most important, it represents not only the major things that were on TV but the continuous performance all the way through.

Dr. Haythorn: I was struck by Dr. Ruff's comments on the men being active versus passive and concrete versus abstract which I think is related to the field-dependent versus field-independent dimension (cf. Chapter 3). These two personality dimensions are generally found to be poor prognosticators of adjustment in isolation. Would the same kind of selection procedure used with the astronauts work if one was dealing with a long space mission, say a Mars flyby?

Dr. Ruff: That is a good question. There are many reasons to think that the kind of man who did well in this acute situation might not do well in a chronic one. However, if given enough time and enough work with simulators, he might well learn to adapt.

By the way, we put all of these people in isolation as part of our selection program. It was just a short procedure, three hours, and they liked it—showing low levels of arousal on all measures we used. We felt this was not only because of the brevity of the procedure but because it came during a hectic week when they were being tested night and day. To be put in a room with nothing to do was a welcome change.

Dr. Haythorn: For three hours you can sleep. In Myers' (1964) and Zubek's (1964) studies, the critical time seems to be three or four days. I wonder if these highly active, relatively concrete, stimulus-oriented men wouldn't have considerable difficulty in very long periods of social isolation and stimulus reduction.

Dr. Ruff: I think you're right in that they probably would have more difficulty than certain other kinds of subjects.

Dr. Lanzetta: I am concerned about two points, the first is purely methodological. What happened to the control group? I think there is an awful lot being said about these few men when it could very easily be that they are not very different from, say, test pilots in general. As a matter of fact, you would probably find them not very different in personality structure from any of the group of fighter pilots, as I gather from some earlier data that Paul Torrance (1954) reported. I am not sure I would want to attribute too much to the personality analyses based on these people.

But, more important is my concern that we are slipping away from our theoretical conception of what is stress. By everything that has been said, the Astronauts were not experiencing stress; and therefore, in terms of the definition of stress offered in this paper, I am not sure that anything was said about adaptive reactions to stress. Apparently the main function of their prior experience was to prepare them *not* to see this as a stressful experience. By any of the criteria already elaborated as minimum criteria for saying people are in a stressful situation, they were not stressed since they showed none of the expected reactions.

Dr. Ruff: The only control group would be the other candidates. They were also in the elite category of test pilots and might have done as well. There is no way to test this.

As to the comparison with fighter pilots, I would say that these men have gone a lot further than most fighter pilots. We have data on fighter pilots, and Dr. Sells has a lot more. The two groups have both similarities and differences.

Dr. Trumbull: I think these men provide a beautiful illustration of personal history building to the point where the experience they underwent was not stressful. Sitting here on the outside, we may say, "That is really a stressful situation," and we then tend to expect the subjects to respond according to our evaluation rather than their own. It is quite conceivable that these men do not think of the publicity side nor the hazardous side of this. Again we come to the point that stress may be a function of how a situation is perceived by the men themselves. The same may have been true about Lindberg. He was called a "flying fool" at the time, but he knew more about all the dangers and all the possibilities of that flight than anyone else. Similarly with Byrd's isolation in the South Pole. We have to keep coming back to asking how this man himself views it, does he feel he is competent to deal with exigencies? Let us remember the astronauts' history as test pilots, where such evaluation of probabilities is a daily thing.

Dr. Mechanic: What we really seem to be saying is that stress is a condition which exists when individuals' capacities and strategies are not compatible with the kinds of demands they face. In essence, stress is a discrepancy between peoples' resources and skills and life challenges. We have to be more productive in developing research which allows us to think in terms of stress situations rather than in terms of personality. Different kinds of demands require different coping capacities.

If you look at the psychological literature dealing with stress you find that what are frequently discussed and studied are psychological crises of one sort or another. Neurotic conflicts are just one kind among many sources of stress and, therefore, the study of neurosis is not a very adequate model for studying stress situations in general. It is difficult to specify the sources of neurotic conflict and the kinds of instrumental skills and abilities most relevant to dealing with such crises. In contrast, most situations that many peope find stressful are situations where we can specify instrumental skills and abilities and kinds of behavior patterns which make a great deal of difference in how these situations are perceived and experienced.

Psychological experiments in the study of stress are not often designed to allow an opportunity to view the ways in which people approach problems, the ways they organize their efforts and their instrumental capacities for dealing with situations, and therefore, these experiments emphasize defense or are limited to psychological reactions to stress. We need more designs that allow us to study the coping process, how people plan their strategies, how they approach problems. This would add to our general understanding of stress processes.

Dr. Oken: I wonder if some of the dilemma about this question of whether there is stress or not can be helped by looking at a temporal issue and broadening the temporal view. On a number of occasions we have talked about anticipation. I wonder if it doesn't make some sense to look at the other end too, i.e., after the stimulus situation has terminated. I am struck by the "fatigue" or "let down" after the flight and the same sort of thing mentioned in Navy fliers. It may be that this after-reaction [3] is the sign of stress. And it may also be that one way to look at adaptation or at least one kind of adaptation to stress may be the capacity to postpone the reaction: not just the way of handling it during

[3] Evidence of this kind of "end phenomenon" is discussed in Basowitz et al. (1955).

the time the stimulus is present but simply the capacity to postpone any kind of detrimental response until after the need for performance is over, until after the stress stimulus is over.

One other point I would like to make is referable to the point Dr. Mandler raised about interruption of behavior and the development of substitute behavior. I think we have to also look at behavior which is not specifically substitutive but is distractive. There is no question that behavior which is not simply related to the task can be responsive or at least stress-response-reducing. Probably this is more dependent on external availability of distraction than on more internal cues compared with other kinds of defensive responses. I think it is an important issue, not simply conceptually but because of its relevance for methodology. For example, testing procedures introduced during any kind of stressful occasion may be viewed, in one sense, as a distraction. You can joke about a busy soldier being a happy soldier, but there is no question that if you give somebody a task—and we have seen this all the time—they feel better while you are testing them. This effect can be an important artifact, I think, in the kind of research Dr. Ruff reports.

Dr. Prescott: Regarding Dr. Oken's observation on the postflight letdown, I see a similarity to Brady's (1958) demonstration of "executive monkeys" in which the gastric acid secretion did not occur during the work situation but afterwards during the rest period. This needs more attention.

Dr. Stern: I am a little concerned about the suggestion that the astronauts were not stressed in the flight experiences. If you look at the physiological measures on them during flights I am sure that it would be agreed that they were stressed. In addition, there were a few behavioral slips—to put it delicately—that were made by some of the astronauts during flight as well, which would also indicate that they were responding under stress.

Dr. Ruff: Once again, I think it depends on which definition you use. Dr. Lanzetta's is perfectly reasonable, but by our definition, the astronauts were under stress. We speak of strenuous effort required in order to maintain functioning, and suggest that you consider the input, output, and compensatory mechanisms. There were high heart rates and similar indications that the men were making strenuous efforts.

Dr. Kubzansky: What we seem to be disagreeing about is the question of what is an appropriate conceptualization of stress. It would help if we could at least agree that stress has to be defined as more than performance decrement, in terms independent of response *per se*. Otherwise, we get into other kinds of trouble.

Dr. Back: To return to the matter of selection, I would wonder if the men chosen were indeed the best ones for the job or whether they simply correspond to a cultural definition of a hero? If one would give a questionnaire to a representative sample of people asking them what their ideal astronaut should be like, we would get a layman's paraphrase of Drs. Ruff and Korchin's personality profiles.

These people were selected, and the selection process is a product of the social system which did the selection. Dr. Korchin has said that they were completely adapted to the society. They are really typical "all-American men," and they cope with stress in the stereotyped way of culture. It may be that in other cultures astronauts would be selected according to different processes, representing coping with stress in that culture. A comparative study of different selection processes might give a very different look at behavioral responses.

Dr. Haggard: On this matter of definitions, I suspect our difficulty in articulating a single definition of stress stems from our divergent research value systems and theoretical approaches.

Also, in terms of the discussion about models, I think we sometimes forget one of the points emphasized by the philosopher Peirce (1931 ff.) who had a good deal of influence on methodology in modern science. He emphasized the importance of what he called an iconic relationship between the phenomena and the characteristics of the model: there should be maximal correspondence between the model we develop and what we are talking about. We sometimes, perhaps, use a model which, for the sake of convenience or of tradition, is easy to use; we don't always check its correspondence with the phenomena under consideration.

Related to this point is our tendency to ignore the practical settings or questions that may generate the propositions with which our models eventually must articulate. In my view, the kinds of research questions that are raised by military field commanders, for example, can be most important. It has been argued sometimes that the practical, realistic setting "isn't science" and doesn't necessarily provide meaningful grist for the mill of our research. I question that argument. I wonder whether many of the practical situations might not prove to be some of the most potent sources of research ideas, partly because they can provide a focus of important variables, just as the problem of the astronaut's adaptation does. Also, this problem area is interesting because it is vital, because something real is going on. In this type of situation conflict and stress are not patched on with scotch tape, and the decisions are not about trivial matters. It's harder, of course, to deal effectively with problems of this sort.

Dr. Weybrew: Many of the questions raised by the field commanders—submarine skippers with whom I have dealt, for example,—are indeed meaningful and often provocative. Many of the submarine captains are concerned, for instance, with their men's appraisal of the submarine environment, i.e., how harmful do the men think the carbon dioxide and other substances in the atmosphere are for them. Questions such as this seem to be researchable ones having to do with the relationship of submariner attitudes to adjustment. Similarly, I suspect flight instructors often make cogent suggestions for control and display designs which, when tested, result in certain insights into the most effective modes of adjustment to the stresses of flying. One could, for instance, posit the hypothesis that perceived stress or threat is directly proportional to the number and severity of specific stressors which can be verbalized. For example, we have asked submariners, "List everything that bothers you about submarines." Years ago, Cason (1930) published a check list of things that annoy a person: body odor, excess heat, noise, and so on. A test instrument like this could be used to obtain indices of the relative intensity of various stressors, and I would predict that there is a rather strong inverse correlation between the number of annoyances specific to the environment in question (the submarine in our work) and the probability that a man will reenlist in the service, a very important prediction for the military by the way.

Finally, I would like to advise caution in deleting from our stress repertory the concept *activation level* or for that matter activation theory in general as suggested or implied by Dr. Lacey. Both for animals and humans, it seems to me, adjustment to stress, coping behavior or whatever, involves energy mobilization, channelization, redirection, or suppression, and these energetic or activation concepts, particularly if operationally definable, could serve to clarify some of the mechanisms of stress adjustment. In short, I feel if activation theory goes by the wayside, we will need a replacement for an important theoretical formulation.

Dr. Bovard: Let me get something off my chest that's been bothering me since the earlier discussions of this conference. It seems to me that if we are going to inquire into what people experience in the way of mood by means of a verbal check list, or observe their behavior under stress, we should take into account the fact that the locus in which such experiential and behavioral events occur is the central nervous system. The circumstances under which such events occur certainly include and must include the microevents in the nervous system which completely determine such behavior and experience.

It is very difficult for me to see how we can expect a sensible definition of mood without reference to recent studies by Dr. Carl Sem-Jacobsen (1963) and others involving experimental production of mood changes through electrical stimulation of the conscious human brain. I find it difficult, if not impossible, to understand the behavioral effects of stress without reference to the neural mechanisms mediating these effects.

Attempts to compare the brain to a computer, comforting as they may be, or to explore cognitive behavior of the rat (presumably he consults with himself as to what to do next under stress!) are merely evasions of the obvious fact that our behavior and experience is the product of systems that have evolved over two billion years. This evolution is so specific that, for example, individual cells in the retina are able to follow a bug across the field of vision in case of the frog. What we call mood changes can be evoked at will by electrical stimulation of specific regions of the brain, and there is no evidence that such experience represents anything but the activity of these regions, which include the temporal lobe.

Psychologists like ourselves have a tendency to verbalize and get as far away as we can from the actual locus in which psychological events occur, from where they are in fact located in respect to both space and time. This location is, of course, the brain and spinal cord. Without the almost unimaginable density of relationship obtaining among the ten or so billion neurons of the central nervous system, no psychological events could take place.

Dr. Arnold: The neurologist may quarrel with the way in which the psychologist tries to correlate neural functioning and behavior. But that such a correlation will have to be established is surely implied in the aims of both neurology and psychology. Cells in the brain may be programmed to account for inherent appraisals, leading to instinctive actions. But such genetic memory cannot account for the millions of adaptive reactions to new situations that are necessary in the life of every animal. Still less can genetic programming account for the wide range of human activity, from tilling the soil to artistic creation or scientific discovery.

Dr. Altman: I have found a very recurrent theme implicit in what has been said by Drs. Ruff and Korchin and by Dr. Arnold (Chapter 5) and perhaps related to some of the confusions that are apparent in trying to correlate different physiological indicators of stress. This is the fact that the processes, whether we are dealing with them on the independent, intervening, or dependent side, are dynamic with respect to time. These are temporally occurring and temporally-bound processes. I am a social psychologist, and one of the main criticisms that I have been levelling about modern social psychology is its lack of concern with social psychological phenomena as they occur through time. To add to Dr. Ruff's reflections on the laboratory process, in social psychology we have been studying very complex phenomena in the context of fifteen-minute or one-hour laboratory situations. I think these tend to take too short a cross-sectional view of the phenomena in which we are interested and provide no opportunity to observe developments and change in the phenomena through time. There may be some extremely long lag times, as reflected perhaps in the astronaut situation. At the physiological level, they apparently did show some reaction to the stress, which may not have been manifested in their performance until after the flight had been completed. We make a mistake if we assume that all behavioral effects are simultaneous—happen all at once—and can be studied through an examination of different forms of behavior in a cross-sectional slice. I suspect that many of the low correlations between physiological indicators, for example, might be a function of the fact that these processes develop in time and there may be sequential effects.

Dr. Nowlis: Dr. Mandler's comments on organizational behavior and the letdown reminded me of Seymour Epstein's (1962) work on sport parachuting. While the beginner tends to have his highest anxiety just before he is to jump from the plane, the experienced parachutist has his highest level the day before, or on the morning of the jump. There seemed to be a suggestion of the same kind of early peaking in the astronaut data as well.

Dr. Ruff: This is an intriguing comment. For some of the astronauts it was clear that the flight was less stressful than certain phases of the preparatory period—even to the point where the flight might have come as a relief.

I would like also to make a comment on Dr. Bovard's remarks. This is a philosophical issue which has been with us since the beginning of psychology and won't be answered here. It has to do with whether it is worthwhile to formulate principles of behavior. I suspect most of us have concluded that it is important. Incidentally, Seymour Kety (1960) has provided a very good discussion of the issues raised.

Dr. Bovard: Well this does get into philosophical issues, but I think that the tendency of psychologists and some psychiatrists to neglect or ignore the current rapidly expanding experimental work on the human brain, including deep electrode stimulation of the brain in patients undergoing neurosurgery, suggests very clearly why the present frontiers of scientific research remain in brain research and molecular biology, rather than in psychology.

Dr. Lazarus: I want to add to Dr. Ruff's comments that I don't think Dr. Bovard could fully understand the neurological system he is talking about without some adequate referents at a behavioral level. For example, he cannot talk about anxiety, fear, or anger at the physiological level alone since these terms have psychological meanings. If the psychology is bad, then the physiological inferences that are drawn will also be bad. Psychophysiology depends on sound analysis at both levels.

Dr. Trumbull: I would like to make an observation about something Dr. Ruff was saying concerning anticipation. We had an experience in our high altitude balloon studies where we were doing some biotelemetry. Pulse rate and blood pressure were both being recorded in a plane that was to accompany the men in the balloon. A decision had been made that the balloon would be ripped and brought back to earth by remote control from the plane when these physiological measures got above what the medical men felt was a feasible level for them, both in terms of rate and pressure. While the balloon was being filled on the ground, with Ross and Prather in the gondola, both the pulse rate and blood pressure indices rose suddenly far beyond the level that had been set for aborting the entire flight! They were asked what was going on—had they checked their instruments, was something wrong, were their contacts in good position, etc. They checked them and all was in order. They were just preparing for the flight. Apparently merely in anticipation they had already exceeded the critical levels (which in fact they never did again during the entire flight).

Dr. Korchin: Drs. Oken and Altman have again drawn attention to the importance of the temporal dimension, which is so often neglected. The question may be not whether or not a given response occurs but at what point it occurs. What might be maladaptive at a particular moment might be less critical if delayed to a later time. The importance of considering a temporal dimension was brought home to me in our studies of paratroopers in training (Basowitz et al., 1955). We preselected two groups of men, on the basis of initial hippuric-acid excretion level (a biochemical measure previously found to be related to anxiety), to be more and less likely to become anxious under the stress of jumping. The group expected to be less anxiety-prone did in fact function better and expressed less anxiety throughout the training period. But the daily measurements were continued to the day *after* graduation from the training program, and on that day the "low" group showed decidedly higher levels of anxiety and related physiological and psychological measures. Apparently, they had the capacity to block disturbed response during training, which is a different matter from not responding at all.

Dr. Appley: I would like to comment on the time variable again. It seems to me that we are treating stress as if it were *the* phenomenon, when it may indeed represent only an index or reflection of change processes going on, that is, of the establishment of coping procedures. For instance, as has been noted, the peak of a stress reaction often occurs in anticipation of a noxious event in experienced people, while it occurs at the time of the event in inexperienced people. In effect what may be happening as a result of training or experience is that the response moves back in time, suggesting that a kind of covert adjustment procedure is going on, following which the individual is better prepared for the actual stress experience. A similar temporal shift appears, I believe, in the acquisition and extinction of avoidance responses. I recall a study of avoidance learning in cats in which a distinctive EEG pattern was shown to emerge at the time the learning was being established—a clear anticipatory change—which showed up long before behavioral responses began to appear and then disappeared once the overt response began to be established and the smooth avoidance behavior occurred. This EEG pattern was not present during the avoidance performances, but reappeared during the development of extinction behavior and then disappeared again when the extinction took place. What I am suggesting is the notion that the stress phenomenon—and observed changes in physiological measures in stress—may simply be indexing the process of a change in coping device, "down-time" as it were, while a search goes on or while a new pattern is being introduced. The timing of responses, and particularly any shifts in temporal patterning of responses—covert or overt, physiological, endocrinological, neurological or psychological—is a very good clue to what might be happening. Timing is, to my mind, as I have said before, an extremely important dimension.

Dr. Haggard: The last two or three comments bring to mind an incident that occurred many years ago when I recorded GSRs in connection with a conditioning experiment involving electric shock. One subject in particular became very tense—controlling and postponing, in the sense of Dr. Korchin's usage—and his skin resistance showed practically no change at all. Then for some reason he gave a sigh and seemed to relax, and without any change in his basal level there was a recurrence of the spontaneous fluctuations in resistance which we call the GSR. He couldn't tell me what happened, and I don't know what happened. But obviously some mechanism was involved which had served to control his anxiety, and upon its release he began to respond in a way which was qualitatively different from how he had responded before its release. There is also evidence that mechanisms of this sort may function adaptively under severe stress conditions, such as combat (e.g., Haggard, 1949).

Dr. Korchin: An additional thing one should expect is that where a number of systems operate together, the temporal relations need not be the same for each. One could conceive having an elevated pulse during an event and conscious affect afterwards. Think, for example, of the commonplace experience of being in a near auto accident. In such a situation, there is likely to be such displacement, although the amount and type of displacement would likely differ with all the factors we have been discussing.

Dr. Sells: I thought when the Mercury program was getting underway that each succeeding shot would be less stressful than the previous one because the unknowns were being reduced. Then, later, they went on TV. Some mention was made earlier of the fact that "you are making history," and so on, but I think that perhaps performing a mission like this on TV may make it even more stressful than doing it where you are not performing under the microscope all the time. I wonder if Dr. Ruff could say whether there was any long-term trend that could be observed over the different Mercury shots.

Dr. Ruff: That's a tough one, because as you well know, at the same time the unknowns were being reduced, the flights were getting longer.

Dr. Biderman: Since we have had a radical reductionist statement introduced into our discussion by Dr. Bovard, I think we ought to make an equally radical one in the opposite direction. Drs. Ruff and Korchin's paper was instructive to me as data for the sociology of knowledge. It indicated to me how, through the processes of selection and administrative decision based on particular ideas of the kinds of demands and challenges that are faced in this kind of operation—and particular *a priori* ideas that follow regarding what kind of person is needed to perform the operation—a culture and social organization are established in which persons displaying particular characteristics fit very well. These original decisions were not based upon experimental knowledge—there was no control group, as Dr. Lanzetta says—but rather upon a blend of notions of the subcultures having a legitimate involvement in the activity—military aviation, engineers, and certain brands of R & D scientists. Now I think this can be particularly instructive to us if we are interested in phenomenological approaches. That is, I think this does tell us a great deal about, first, how our society singles out certain things for definition as stressful; second, what it defines as appropriate mechanisms for coping with stresses, and third, how it defines people as having differential abilities to handle these stresses. We then go about organizing these activities in line with these kinds of concepts about them—choosing and instructing the cast of characters, elaborating the language regarding their work, setting the tests and criteria by which they are evaluated, building the hardware they use, etc., all in line with these initial concepts.

It is quite possible that the same instrumental goals could be better effected by a radically different system involving very radically different kinds of people—perhaps juvenile delinquents, chairmen of chapters of the League of Women Voters, or jelly bean salesmen might be able to perform many of these kinds of things equally well or better, provided the activities were differently organized.

I think one instructive thing is that most people in our society do perform very demanding and hazardous tasks quite regularly. Driving an automobile on a country road is objectively extremely hazardous. It can be rather elaborately demanding in terms of the decisions that confront the person, the split-second timing he has to execute. And there are slum dwellers and subway riders who daily encounter situations as noxious and deprivational as those on submarines. We could elaborate such examples at great length, but they don't relate to the definitions we have of special stress and the kinds of events we study under the notions of stress. I think we ought to pay very strict attention to the kinds of definitions and concepts about stressful phenomenon that are shared or distributed among special people within our culture, and to how we organize activities in accordance with our ideas of what is stressful in their performance.

Chairman's summary

ERNEST A. HAGGARD: The theoretical position taken by Drs. Ruff and Korchin regarding how phenomena associated with stress should be conceptualized is sound and fruitful. This position holds that the input, the adaptive, and the output factors must be considered in concert, that marked deficiencies or excesses in one or more of these factors (in relation to the others) result in what we call *stress*. Furthermore, the authors are to be commended for their skill in utilizing the space program as a natural laboratory to delineate the astronauts' general background and personality characteristics, as they bear upon adaptation to the special situation of space flight. But an unresolved question is whether these men, so skillful in their active adaptation to current reality, would fare as well on extended space flights. The Mercury astronauts almost appear to require constantly challenging environment; certainly they sought and found one. But how would they adapt to relative monotony, with many of the usual environmental supports removed? It may be that for missions of extended duration, astronauts of a somewhat different sort would do better (see also Haggard, 1964).

Dr. Mandler's discussion of the development and organization of complex behavior sequences, and of the individual's ability to extend his repertoire of adaptive responses at vulnerable points in the sequence, may be extended with respect to the astronauts' life histories. The fact that they seem never to have been pushed beyond their capacities, or to have been scarred by traumatic failures, but rather moved step-wise to increased levels of competence in the important areas of their life, appears to have enabled them to retain their non-anxious, flexible, and effective approach to current problems. These findings reinforce again the importance of background factors in shaping the style and range of the adult's adaptive capacities.

One of the dominant themes of the discussion had to do with the time dimension, particularly in relation to individuals' ability to cope with inherently stressful situations. Apparently, as an individual becomes increasingly able to function effectively in a stressful situation, most of the symptoms of disturbance usually associated with it tend to precede or to follow the crucial period. It is as though the individual's adaptive mechanisms come to work best when they are needed most, and that he permits himself to suffer many of the disturbances when it doesn't matter so much. Parachutists, balloonists, and others are mentioned in this connection, as well as the astronauts. A theme which was not emphasized has to do with the range of psychophysiological changes that accompany adaptation to social groups (see Welch, 1965). Presumably the importance of such considerations will increase as the flight crews become larger and the flights become longer.

Throughout the discussion, it was obvious that different members of the Conference approached questions of adaptation to stress from divergent vantage points, which included the neurological, physiological, psychological, phenomenological, sociological, and anthropological. While such divergence can be stimulating, it also indicates that we are a long way from a common conceptualization of *stress* and the factors associated with it. But until a common framework is developed, we might as well reconcile ourselves to the fact that we will continue to work along the lines of our personal preference and of what makes the most sense to us. Also, it may be that exposure to others' views will help us to broaden our own.

BENJAMIN B. WEYBREW

12

Patterns of psychophysiological response to military stress[1]

In the preceding chapter Drs. Ruff and Korchin have examined the relationships between a number of background and personality characteristics and astronaut performance during exposure to the stresses of simulated and actual space flight. This chapter broadens the focus to cover a wider range of environmental stressors while at the same time narrowing the focus upon a more restricted area of stress responsivity, namely, those responses characterized as psychophysiological.

The range of content included in the stress symposium edited by Wolff in 1950 and again in the Army symposium at Walter Reed in 1953 attests to the all-inclusive scope of the literature loosely classified under the stress rubric. Indeed within the behavioral sciences, at least, it is difficult to identify the nonstress literature, so broad has the concept become. The voluminousness of the stress literature, of which perhaps ten percent or more originates from the military, is indicated by two bibliographical compilations on the topic, one of 2400 entries, edited by Miller et al. in 1953, and the other of 2600 entries, edited by Appley in 1957. Moreover, the fact that the 1965 Documentation Incorporated Catalogue of Life Sciences Research shows the Department of Defense and the National Aeronautics and Space Administration as currently supporting more than 200 contracts listed as stress research attests to continued interest in this area.

This chapter will not review the stress literature as such, but has the

[1] The opinions or assertions where they appear in this paper are those of the author and are not to be construed as the official views of the U.S. Navy Medical Department.

rather more narrow objective of reviewing some of the major military studies which focus upon psychophysiological measurement involving mainly human subjects under laboratory or field conditions, interpreted for the purposes of the experiment, as stressful or stress-inducing.

In the military stress literature are studies of two general classes: (1) those emphasizing stressor identification and delineation with a view towards controlling or eliminating the environmental situations producing the stress responsivity, and (2) those studies focused upon measurement of response patterns including responses both proximal to the stress situation as well as those involving long-term, cumulative, and often pathological effects.

The psychologist's use of the term *stress*, particularly in military studies, has typically included both stress-inducing factors and patterns of response to them, interpretations being given in terms of the interaction of the two. An extension of Cannon's usage of the term *homeostasis* underlies most interpretations of data, particularly those involving psychophysiological measurement. Measures collected during basal conditions, or at least prior to stress induction, are used as base line data for comparison with the subsequent stress response profiles. Often post-stress or recovery data are collected for additional comparison. In short, stressors are seen as factors or agents—external or internal to the person—which cause acute or chronic homeostatic imbalance, whether at a physiological, psychological, or psychosocial level. Inevitably, then, such stress studies fuse inextricably with studies of frustration, acute emotionality, anxiety, conflict, and psychopathology.

ORIGINS AND OUTCOMES OF STRESS RESEARCH IN THE MILITARY

Where do the ideas for stress research in the military originate? What incentives are operating in the military to maintain research output? Who does—or what organizations do—the research and what are the outcomes of the research? The schema in Figure *12-1* provides some answers to these questions.

It may be helpful, in interpreting stress data arising from service studies, to examine their sources. It is my impression, for example, that most data originate from Source 1, especially insofar as the in-house effort in the submarine service is concerned, and next from Source 2. An example of such studies would be the recent confinement of three men in a helium-oxygen chamber at seven atmospheres pressure, to ascertain if any remarkable physiological, psychological, or other effects would result (Weybrew, Greenwood, & Parker, 1964). A similar study was

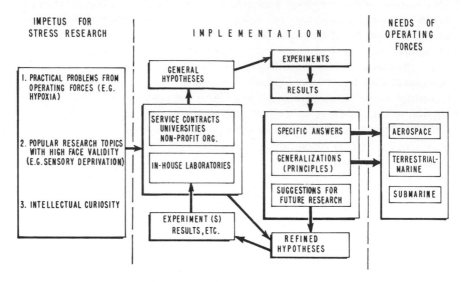

FIGURE 12-1.   Schema describing the machinery of stress research in the military.

requested in connection with the first prolonged submergence of *Nautilus* in 1956 (Weybrew, 1957), to provide data on man's reaction to some anticipated operational problems. It is reasonably certain that many of the research problems associated with weightlessness, acceleration, and similar variables investigated by aerospace research teams arose in response to such requests for information on anticipated problems.

This is not to argue that some—if not most—of the ideas for stress research should not originate from operational problems. Often, however, the military stress researcher, in the haste of getting an experiment underway, ends up measuring less-than-the-most-desirable variables under less-than-desirable conditions, a fact that contributes, equally often, to less-than-desirable research outcomes. Along a similar vein, in connection with high-altitude monitoring of blood pressure, pulse, and respiration, one review publication devoted an entire table to depicting the wide time ranges between data-collection points characteristically found in military stress experiments (Simons, Flinn, & Hartmann, 1963). These researchers stated the predicament nicely: "In each of these examples of acute psychophysiological stress, the problem of obtaining interpretable physiological data eclipsed considerations of more refined methods of analysis and psychophysiological interpretation. The problem to date has been to obtain any data at all. Refinements have had to wait" (p. 133).

Class 2, and less so perhaps Class 3, appear to constitute the major idea sources for most stress studies supported by government contract. While it is suspected that Class 1 and certainly Class 3 ideas produce the most reputable research, it may be that answers to specific questions asked by field commanders are not being delivered frequently enough to maintain adequate rapport with the operating forces. Instead, much of the outcomes of military stress research are "suggestions for further research" resulting in the closed loop in Figure *12-1*. While in many studies this circular situation is unavoidable and, possibly a necessary preliminary to serious research, it tends nonetheless to evoke strong negative comments from high-ranking officers facing budget-limitations but at the same time left with a residue of operational problems demanding immediate solutions.

Further, it is suspected that research stemming from the Class 2 situation—what Appley (1964) has called the "bandwagon effect" and what I call "public image" research—results in a great deal of work which may be repetitious and often inconclusive. This appears to have been particularly so in stress research. Perhaps the point is belabored, but it is felt that the conflict between basic and applied research goals affects in a very real way the kind and quality of stress research produced by the military.

INTERACTION PATTERNS OF RESPONSE TO STRESS

Though stressor characteristics and stress responsivity seem to be inextricably interrelated in most stress experiments, we find it useful in our work in submarine psychology to distinguish primary and secondary stressors, in a manner analogous to that often used to dichotomize needs in the motivation literature. Primary stressors, in our descriptive frame of reference, involve environmental impositions, trauma, or insults which directly strain or stress the adaptive capacities of the neuro-physiological system. An hypoxic or toxic submarine environment, high level radiation, or excessive heat or cold would be examples of such primary stressors. Secondary stressors would include those environmental circumstances that impose immediate or anticipated barriers to ongoing goal-directed activity. Task failure or threat of status loss would be classified as secondary stressors. Moreover, situations resulting in acute conflict of social or other derived motives would be secondary stressors in this system. The response patterns to the two classes of stressors often may be quite similar, though the primary stressors frequently result in more extensive physiological displacement, with coping mechanisms being affected only indirectly. The reverse emphasis is presumably true for secondary stressors.

Military studies of stress responsiveness have included a wide gamut of physiological, psychophysiological, and psychosocial measures, all presumably enjoying some useful validity as indices of stress or stress adjustment. The particular classes of stress responses emphasized depend upon (1) the reasons for conducting the research (Class 1, 2, and 3 in Fig. 12-1); (2) the situation in which the study occurs (in a simulator, e.g., centrifuge, escape training tank; in a laboratory, e.g., isolation hypoxia, etc.; or in the field, e.g., in combat, a submarine, a space capsule); and (3) the duration of the study (e.g., acute "one-shot" imposition of stressors versus chronic stress exposure over protracted periods of time).

Accordingly, I have reviewed what was thought to be a representative sample of the military stress literature, noting the relative frequency and presumed relevance of the major classes of responses characteristically measured during the studies. Generally speaking, with the exception of scattered laboratory studies of acute stress (e.g., Mackworth, 1952) and particularly in field studies during combat, prolonged marine submergence, or space flight, the trend seems to have been to measure as many variables as feasible, hoping that meaningful "stress effects" and variable interactions would become apparent. Table *12-1* is an attempt to show the

Table 12-1. Relative weighting given to the major classes of stress responses characteristically measured in military research.

STRESS SITUATION

GROSS CLASSIFICATION OF STRESS RESPONSES	Field Acute	Field Chronic	Simulator Acute	Simulator Chronic	Laboratory Acute	Laboratory Chronic
Physiological*	++	0	++	?	++	+
Psychophysiological	+	?	++	?	++	+
Psychological	+	++	+	+	++	++
Psychiatric	+	++	?	+	++	+

* Including endocrinological and biochemical measurements
++ Heavily weighted
0 Seldom or never measured
? Weighting not estimable
+ Measured, but not heavily weighted

relative significance of four gross classes of response variables typically measured in such military studies.

Two major points may be made concerning Table *12-1*. First, in the chronic studies (long flights or prolonged periods of marine submergence, for example), psychological and psychiatric data collection is emphasized. Second, most of the physiological and psychophysiological stress data, on which this chapter is focused, are obtained in acute experiments carried out in laboratories or simulators. Examples of studies involving acute stress are those by Pettit et al. (1958), who showed blood pressure and pulse rate increases during centrifuge-induced stress, and by Cook and Wherry (1950), who found increases in urinary 17-ketosteroid production in submariner candidates being trained in the submarine escape tank.[2]

Directly or by inference most military stress researchers, regardless of the particular class of measures emphasized in their studies, have searched for major mechanisms by which individuals adjust to environmental stress. The complexity of the interaction of physiological, psychological, and psychophysiological processes studied by military stress researchers is suggested by the schema in Figure *12-2*.

The hypothetical coordinates depicting adjustment as a function of imposed stress at the upper right of the schema represent the operational situation upon which much of the military stress research appears to be focused. How confident are we of our predictions of individual differences in quality of adjustment to multiple stressors imposed over time in the aerospace or submarine environment when much of the data on which the predictions are based are derived from studies of acute stress (e.g., the high G-load in the centrifuge or the hyperbaric conditions of the submarine escape tank)? More to the point, which class or classes of response patterns have the most predictive validity for this purpose? Are there, in this mass of variable interactions, some functional unities that provide a rational basis for some of our predictive hypotheses?

Easily recognized in the lower left of the schema is the neurogenic-hormonogenic interaction complex proposed by Selye as the General Adaptation Syndrome, a theoretical conceptualization allowing for the possibility of predicting stress adjustment from indices of adrenocortical reserve. Closely related are the hypothalamic-hypophyseal-adrenocortical and adreno-medullary-hypothalamic axes as they relate to the part which autonomic regulation plays in homeostatic maintenance, as proposed by Cannon thirty years ago. The measures usually classified as psychophysiological (pulse, blood pressure, etc.) then are intrinsically related to systemic response patterns and are regarded as usefully reliable indices of neurophysiological—particularly autonomic—function as it relates to stress adjustment.

From such complex stress response interactions, monitored during an acute (or, less frequently, a protracted) stress experiment, coupled with as much detail as possible regarding differences in adjustment potential (predispositional factors in Figure *12-2*), the military stress researcher is typically called upon for scores or indices predictive of individual differences in the quality of human stress adjustment. Though basic questions regarding the mechanisms underlying stress adjustment are often dis-

---

[2] Specific findings from additional studies involving psychophysiological measurement will be briefly discussed later in the chapter.

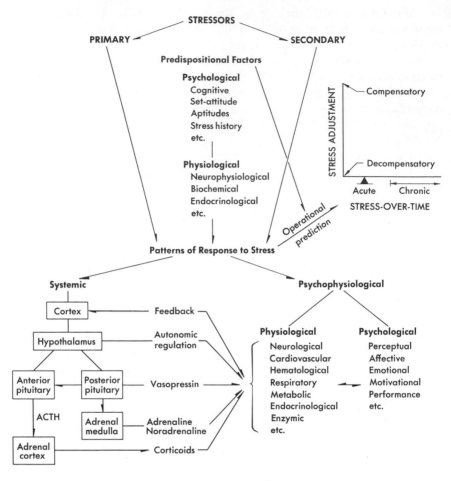

FIGURE 12-2.   Schema showing the complex variable interactions affecting adjustment to stress.

cussed in military publications, a review of this literature suggested that a considerable amount of the work produced in military laboratories is concerned in some way with problems of selection, evaluation, or assessment of individual differences in potentiality for stress adjustment. Typically, the psychologist or psychiatrist is asked to screen out those persons who might tend toward decompensatory or pathological behavior as stress is imposed over time. Similarly, he is asked to identify those persons who tend toward compensation rather than decompensation, whose coping capabilities increase at a faster rate than the stress effects accumulate, who "stay on top" as it were, in terms of the quality of adjustment as stress increases.

Having indicated some of the origins of stress research interests and requirements in the military, and some of the difficulties in doing and applying military stress research, let us turn now to those studies emphasizing psychophysiological measurement. We will look first at their possible contribution to the fund of knowledge regarding mechanisms of stress adjustment and, secondly, at their predictive validity with respect to the adjustment criteria available to us.

STRESSOR ANALYSIS AND CORRELATED PATTERNS OF PSYCHOPHYSIOLOGICAL RESPONSE

As indicated in many of the preceding chapters, environmental stresses seldom occur one at a time. Rather, real life situations characteristically involve multiple stressors, often imposed simultaneously or in some cases sequentially. However, it is feasible, and indeed helpful, to group primary and secondary stressors into classes according to environmental conditions peculiar to the experiment or field situation under consideration. Moreover, by surveying the literature for evidence of psychophysiological response patterns unique to one or another stressor class as well as common to several, some impressions as to the existing stressor-response correlations can be obtained. Though admittedly incomplete, Table *12-2* presents gross yet suggestive information regarding these interrelationships.

Judging from the number of question marks it should be readily apparent why the interaction complex in Table *12-2* might be called an "ignorance matrix." It will be noted that many often-used autonomic measures, such as salivary pH, dermographia, sinus arrhythmia, and certain adrenogenic substances, are omitted in the Table. These omissions reflect their relatively infrequent use in military stress experiments.[3] Equally obvious is the overlap between the stressor categories—for example, acceleration stress may involve pain, isolation, noise, vibration, and so on. Moreover, primary and secondary stressors are not independent, inasmuch as primary stressors, by straining the physiological adaptive capacities, may—and likely do—affect awareness of the threat aspects of the total stress situation by means of feedback effects presumably of great relevance in understanding stress adjustment (Darrow & Henry, 1949, p. 427) (see Figure *12-2*). In short, comprehension of the processes of adjustment to primary stress situations must in most cases take into account the interaction effects of superimposed secondary stressors. Secondary stressors, on the other hand, may or may not involve a primary stress component, depending upon the military situation.

[3] For a recent summary of psychophysiological measurement techniques in common usage, see Ruff (1963).

By examining the rows and columns in Table *12-2* for evidence of relationships between psychophysiological variables and the major classes of stressors listed, it is possible to estimate which variables are most highly correlated with a particular stress situation (rows) and which indices are most significant over the arrays of stressors (columns). Accordingly, it appears that indices of cardiovascular response (pulse, pressure, and volume), breathing rate, and skin conductance are most frequently measured and show some relationship to most of the stress situations included in the Table. Least often measured and, when measured, showing least significance across the stressor classes, are (grouped in decreasing order of "apparent" significance), corticoids and catecholamines (urinary usually), skin temperature, electrolyte balance and protein metabolites, metabolic rate, blood cell counts, EEG amplitude and frequency variation, skeletal muscle indices, and finally, EEG scores, some derived from alpha-blocking variations.[4]

Looking at the rows in Table *12-2* should provide some general information as to similarities and differences in psychophysiological response patterns between the various classes of stress. These descriptions, by stressor class, follow.

Weightlessness and acceleration.   Two comprehensive summaries of the literature involving psychophysiological and other measurement under zero-gravity and hypergravity conditions are now available (Loftus & Hammer, 1963; Chambers, 1963). As suggested by the pattern of indices in Table *12-2,* increases in heart rate, blood pressure, skin conductance, and magnitude of GSR are reported before and during weightlessness as well as under high G-load conditions (Zuidema, 1956; Schock, 1960; Von Beckh, 1959). One investigator has shown that GSR lability is inversely correlated with ability to tolerate high "G" stress as indicated by blackout level (Pettit et al., 1958). That attitudes may affect the response patterns to gravitational stresses of this kind is suggested by Webb (1958) who showed that change in pulse rate under acceleration stress is positively correlated with anticipated G-level. Along similar lines, Zuidema (1956) found that the magnitude of GSR prior to the imposition of high G loads was inversely related to the quality of performance during acceleration.

In general, the psychophysiological effects of weightlessness and acceleration reported in the current literature suggest a diffuse sympathetic reaction as being characteristic, at least at the outset, of the exposure to these stresses.

---

[4] Although not found frequently in the psychophysiological literature, this measure was nonetheless included because of the relationship of alpha-blocking time to hyperbaric gaseous atmospheres, a finding relevant for submarine stress studies (Bennett & Glass, 1961).

Table 12-2. Patterns of psychophysiological response to stress

Legend:

- **+** Facilitative effect
- **−** Inhibitive effect
- **±** Either facilitative or inhibitive
- **?±** Tentative relationship
- **?** Unknown relationship
- **A** Applies
- **NA** Does not apply

Classes of Stressors	Military Activity — Aerospace	Terrestrial-Marine	Submarine	Autonomic — Heart Rate	Blood Pressure	Skin Conductance	GSR-Lability	Skin Temperature	Vascular Volume	Breathing Rate	Metabolic Rate	Endocrinological/Biochemical — Adrenal Corticoids	Catechol Amines	Electrolyte Balance	Protein Metabolites	Eosinophiles	Lymphocytes	EEG and Neuromuscular — EEG (Potential/Frequency)	EEG (Alpha Blocking)	Muscle Potential	Psychomotor Control
Primary:																					
Weightlessness	A	NA	A	+	+	−	±	−	−	+	?±	+	+	?±	?	?−	?−	?	?	+	−
Acceleration	A	NA	NA	+	+	+	±	?−	−	?±	?	+	+	?±	?	−	?	?	?	+	−
Hypo/hyperbaric atmosphere	A	NA	NA	?±	?±	±	±	±	±	±	?	±	±	±	±	+	?+	±	±	?	?−
Atmospheric composition	A	A	A	±	±	±	±	±	±	±	±	+	+	−	+	±	±	±	±	?	?
Extreme temperature variation	A	A	A	±	±	?±	?	±	±	±	±	−	−	−	±	±	?	?	?	?	?
Sleep deprivation – fatigue	A	A	A	?−	−	−	?−	−	−	±	±	+	+	+	±	?	±	±	+	±	−
Pain exposure	A	A	A	?±	?±	+	?	−	−	±	?	?	?	±	±	?	−	?	?	?	?
Deprivation (hunger, thirst, etc.)	A	A	A	+	+	?	?	?	?	?	−	+	+	−	?	?	±	?	?	?	?
Radiation	A	A	A	+	−	+	?	?−	?−	+	?	?	?	?	+	±	−	±	?	?	?
Noise, vibration	A	A	A	±	±	+	?	?−	?−	−	?	+	+	?	?	±	?	?	?	±	?
Diurnal flattening	A	A	A		±	±	?	±	±	±	±	±	±	±	±	±	?±	±	?	?	?
Secondary:																					
Isolation/confinement	A	A	A	?±	?±	?±	?±	?	?±	?±	?	?±	?±	?	?±	?±	?±	±	?	?	?
Threat to "life & limb"	A	A	A	+	+	+	+	−	?±	?±	+	+	+	±	+	−	−	?±	?	?±	?±
Threat to status/self-esteem	A	A	A	+	+	+	+	?−	?±	?±	+	?	?	?±	+	?	?	?±	?	?±	?±
Sustained performance	A	A	A	±	±	±	?	±	±	?±	±	+	+	±	+	−	?	?±	?	?±	?±

333

The search for possible mechanisms underlying these response patterns observed during weightlessness and acceleration leads directly to the question of the relevance of gravity-sensitive receptors as a source of autonomic stimuli. In the first place, the relationship between proprioceptive feedback and motor performance under normal gravitational conditions is well known (Young, 1961, p. 292); however, it is not known to what degree the modified sensory input occurring during acceleration and weightlessness affects the emotional response to the stress.[5]

Secondly, some animal experimentation by Gellhorn (1957) may have some bearing on the matter. This worker has demonstrated some important relationships between kinesthetic and vestibular sensory input on the one hand and hypothalamic activity with correlated autonomic reactivity on the other. These results, taken together with the knowledge that the intensity of kinesthetic and vestibular sensory input are increased during acceleration and decreased or eliminated during weightlessness, suggest the possibility of hyperexcitability—if not dysfunction—of the hypothalamic and autonomic systems, resulting from protracted exposure to these two classes of stressors.

Hypo-hyperbaric atmosphere and atmospheric composition.
As might be expected from pressure and gas laws, the patterns of psychophysiological response to decompression and to compression of atmospheric gases are intrinsically involved with gaseous composition. For example, in submarines, in aquanautics, and in space flight, an increase in either partial pressure or concentration of carbon dioxide results in adrenal cortical stimulation, with increase in heart rate and blood pressure (Faucett & Newman, 1953; Schaefer, 1959). In addition, an enhanced oxygen supply to the brain results from the vasodilatory effects of CO_2 upon the cerebral blood vessels. In turn, chemo-receptors and baro-receptors in carotid and aortic glomera provide feedback effects upon both the parasympathetic and sympathetic nervous systems (Gellhorn, 1957). Quite possibly, some of the changes in psychophysiological indices seen in Table *12-2* are accounted for by mechanisms of this nature.

Additional findings regarding the effects of carbon dioxide are now indicating that high CO_2 tension modifies adrenalin secretion rate, affects electrolyte balance, and increases EEG alpha blocking time (Navy Bureau of Medicine and Surgery, 1956, p. 335 ff.). Similarly, high partial pressure nitrogen results in the same general effect upon alpha rhythm, though a normal tracing is restored by replacing the nitrogen by helium at the same ambient pressure (Bennett & Glass, 1961). Increase in voltage and slowing of alpha activity in EEG tracings results from hypoxia, but

---

[5] There is a well-integrated review of the problems involved in obtaining psychological and psychophysiological test data during acceleration (Galambos, 1961).

the addition of small amounts of carbon dioxide lessens the effect of reduced oxygen (Finesinger & Brazier, 1946). Possibly interrelated with these findings is some recent evidence for covariation of barometric pressure of weather air with the low frequency, high amplitude waves characteristic of drowsiness or sleep (Webb & Ades, 1964).

Another problem has to do with sensory insufficiency to gaseous buildup. Apparently, in some instances the person is not aware of the psychophysiological effects of the gaseous conditions, possibly because the changes are too subtle and slow-moving. For example, Colonel Simons (1958) during his mile-high balloon flight failed to notice and make corrections for an increase in CO_2 level resulting in a threefold increase in breathing rate. Numerous examples of nitrogen narcosis or "rapture of the deep" are reported for marine divers at extreme depths (Hoff & Greenbaum, 1954). In short, there are a number of gaseous conditions (e.g., toxicity from high concentration of oxygen) which provide examples of primary stressors directly inducing physiological homeostatic imbalance, which, in turn, may affect the total emotional or stress response to secondary stressors should they be superimposed. Finally, attitudes of submariners toward the danger of injury from the submarine atmosphere appear to be a relevant consideration in predicting adjustment to prolonged submergence (Weybrew, 1963a).

Extreme temperature variation.   Cannon's (1932) experiments with sympathectomized animal preparations demonstrated rather clearly the significance of the autonomic system in adjustment to cold and heat. One mechanism involved in the autonomic response to cold is rather extensive vasoconstriction with a concomitant decrease in plasma volume (D'Amato & Hegnauer, 1953). Skeletal muscular activity (such as shivering and brisk movement) increases metabolic heat production, while the autonomic responses of piloerection and vasoconstriction decrease heat loss. Moreover, changes in thyroid, adrenal, and pituitary function have also been implicated in the organismic response pattern elicited by cold (Hendler, 1963; Kayser, 1957). While these and other autonomic and endocrine mechanisms provide some explanation for the effective adaptation to cold stress frequently reported in the literature (e.g., Burton & Edholm, 1955), there is further evidence that the magnitude and persistence of the psychophysiological responses to cold are affected to a considerable degree by the adapting person's interpretation of the cold environment or if in the laboratory, his attitudes toward the experiment (Joy, Poe, Berman, & Davis, 1962). It is assumed that the same general relationship would exist for heat exposure also.

Taken in the context of the above discussion of response to cold, the pattern of psychophysiological indices in Table 12-2 suggests that the inhibitive (—) pattern would be characteristically found during cold exposure. On the other hand, the facilitative response pattern (+ in Table 12-2) typically results from prolonged exposure to excessive heat. Insofar as these peripheral response patterns are specific to heat and cold, they tend to support Gellhorn's (1943) suggestion that heat stimulates the parasympathetic and cold the sympathetic system. However, the more recent literature (see Hendler, 1963) dealing with autonomic responses to heat and cold tends to support the concept of synergistic rather than antagonistic function of the two systems. For example, extreme heat results in rapid and extensive peripheral vasodilation; cold results in vasoconstriction. Both vasodilation and vasoconstriction, however, are mediated by sympathetic cholinergic fibers in the first case as an inhibitory effect and in the latter as a facilitative one. Too, the pilomotor response to cold results from sympathetic stimulation but again involves cholinergic nerves. Finally, loss of heat resulting from sweating results from parasympathetic (cholinergic) stimulation, but emotional sweating during heat exposure is a sympathetic response though mediated by cholinergic fibers (Shelley & Hurley, 1953).

In sum, the psychophysiology of heat and cold stress is not simple, and any interpretation of the autonomic and perhaps of the endocrinological and biochemical indices as specific to either heat or cold is not supported by the literature. Nevertheless, deep space and deep sea exploration demand firm data having to do with the processes related to extreme temperature adaptation and adjustment under a wide range of conditions.

Sleep deprivation and fatigue.   As sleep deprivation progresses, low frequency, high amplitude brain wave tracings (the delta wave pattern) tend to replace the low amplitude, relatively high frequency patterns associated with relaxed wakefulness (Johnson, Slye, & Demont, 1964). At the same time, autonomic indicants of activation level become enhanced during deprivation, though autonomic responsivity to stimulation apparently decreases. Corroborative evidence that sleep has drive properties is found in the systematic relationship between activation level (as measured by electromyograms, breathing and heart rate, body temperature, and palmar conductance) and the duration of the deprivation period (Malmo & Surwillo, 1960; Armington & Mitnick, 1959). Moreover, biochemical data are accumulating to provide an additional indicator of the stress effects of sleep loss (Luby et al., 1960). Considerable evidence is also found for loss of psychomotor control with extreme sleep deprivation (Kleitman, 1960; Oswald, 1962). Finally, the ability to maintain vigilance and sustained performance following protracted sleeplessness appears to be systematically related to motivational intensity specific to the measurement situation (Wilkinson, 1960).

Though the pattern of psychophysiological changes indicated in

Table *12-2* occurs during protracted sleep deprivation, there appears to be rather convincing evidence that these indicators are not systematically related to subjective symptoms of fatigue.[6] Taken alone, however, the pattern of autonomic and endocrinological indicators found in the chronic fatigue and sleeplessness of combat and prolonged flight suggest a diffuse sympathetic pattern, the persistence and perhaps the magnitude of which depend upon the severity of the stresses involved and upon individual differences in adaptability as time progresses (Pace et al., 1956; Simons, Flinn, & Hartman, 1963). While adaptation to fatigue-inducing flights and the like seems to be the rule, there is little doubt as to the severity of this stressor class, at least as inferred from urinary indicators of adrenal hyperfunction (Marchbanks, Hale, & Ellis, 1962; Murphy, Grafton, & Cleghorn, 1954). Along similar lines, eosinopenia is characteristic of simulated submarine cruises (Faucett & Newman, 1953) and is related systematically to the judged rigors of different flight assignments (Domanski, 1954).

Pain exposure.   There are a number of comprehensive reviews of the literature related to adjustment to chronic pain (e.g., Edwards, 1950; Barber, 1959). The use of noxious or physically painful stimuli as a stress-induction technique is common, particularly in laboratory studies (Holtzman & Bitterman, 1952). However, most of the literature pertaining to the effects of chronic pain as a stressor originates from the dental and surgical treatment wards of military and civilian hospitals (e.g., Holmes & Hawkins, 1956; Price, Thaler, & Mason, 1957) and from the recorded observations during prolonged internment (Farber, Harlow, & West, 1957).

The neuroanatomical evidence for the involvement of the thalamus and hypothalamus in pain perception as well as in emotional behavior generally (Penfield & Rasmussen, 1950; Bard, 1928), coupled with the observations regarding the emotionality of a few congenitally analgesic humans (Cohen et al., 1955), suggest the likelihood that psychophysiological components of emotion would be affected by long-term exposure to pain. It is not surprising therefore that for the array of indicators in Table *12-2* acute pain results in a peripheral response pattern characteristic of a sympathetic overflow similar to a fear pattern. Accordingly, both in the anticipation of pain and as a result of immediate pain, skin conductance rises, blood pressure and pulse increase, skin temperature drops, breathing rate increases, and EEG patterns change (Barber, 1959).

There are many general as well as specific factors related to individual differences in pain sensitivity. Evidence can be inferred from the experimental literature (Schachter & Singer, 1962) and from observations of

---

[6] Studies bearing on this point have been integrated by Trumbull (1965, p. 39ff.)

the chronically ill (Holmes & Hawkins, 1956) that a number of social factors affect psychophysiological response to stress in general and to pain exposure in particular. The organic and psychologically debilitative state resulting from wartime incarceration apparently resulted in some cases in a cataleptic-like indifference to pain and in others in an exaggerated sensitivity to the slightest pain or threat of pain (Nardini, 1952). Moreover, laboratory studies of pain sensitivity have shown that the tonicity of the skeletal muscular system at the time of stimulation is systematically related to pain sensitivity (Hardy, Wolff, & Goodell, 1952). Finally, individual differences in the psychophysiological response patterns observed during high-intensity pain are dependent upon past experience with pain, the perceived threat of the pain-inducing situation, the motivating circumstances involved, and the prestress emotional condition of the subject. (op. cit.)

Prolonged hunger and thirst.   Most of the military reports of prolonged food and water deprivation are anecdotal, the stress involved having occurred on life rafts, on arctic ice caps, and in detention camps (Gibson, 1953; Scott, 1953; Farber et al., 1957). Extreme attitudinal modification, at times pathological, appears to represent the most remarkable effects of primary deprivation of this kind. Moreover, ethical standards typically deteriorate—for example, food may be obtained from inmates in somewhat abject ways (Wolf & Ripley, 1947; Friedman, 1949; Nardini, 1952).

Although the mechanisms may not be well understood, the interactional effects between hunger and thirst motivation resulting from deprivation of either has been known for some time (Morgan & Stellar, 1950). Moreover, there is evidence from the older literature for the effects of reduced diet upon perceptual and ideational processes and as they relate to sex and other drives (Miles, 1919; Keys et al., 1950).

Wolf (1958) has provided a broad coverage of the literature pertaining to the neurophysiology as well as the psychology of thirst and drinking. Stemming largely from animal studies, evidence has accumulated to indicate that there are centers controlling eating and drinking in the hypothalamus, these centers being affected by blood sugar, body temperature, and possibly by hormonal agents originating from the pituitary, adrenal, and thyroid systems (Teitelbaum & Epstein, 1962). Both food deprivation and water deprivation result in eating and drinking but the drive strength and appetite specificity appear to involve hypothalamic structures, oral and gastric stimulation, and possibly social factors (Bruce, 1941).

This brief review failed to reveal any substantial literature focusing upon psychophysiological measurement during protracted deprivation conditions. Indirectly, however, the findings that hypothalamic and endocrine processes are complexly related to thirst and hunger suggest that biochemical and metabolic by-products in blood and urine may be sensitive to this kind of stress (Grossman, 1955). Moreover it appears that indices of autonomic function may be affected by food and water deprivation since animal experimentation has shown that adrenergic chemicals cause eating behavior and cholinergic substances stimulate drinking behavior when injected into the lateral hypothalamus (Grossman, 1960).

Radiation.   In an excellent review of the literature pertaining to radiation and behavior it is stated that men under ordinary circumstances on the planet earth are exposed to approximately 1/100 of the amount of radiation considered as a permissable dose (Tobias, 1963). Also, the probability of harmful effects of radiation exposure during prolonged submergence on a heavily-shielded nuclear submarine is indeed remote (Ebersole, 1960). However, there appears to be some disagreement as to the possible biological effects of excessive ultraviolet (Haber, 1952) and cosmic radiation exposure of the astronauts during protracted space flight (Leavitt, 1958; Simons, 1958).

While the literature contains very little direct information regarding the psychophysiological changes resulting from radiation exposure, there is some evidence indirectly suggesting these effects. Most of the data dealing with the biological effects of radiation exposure of humans originates from pathological laboratories involved in radiation therapy and from scattered accounts of radiation accidents and the bombings of two Japanese cities in World War II. Most of the experimental data on the other hand originate from laboratory studies using rats or monkeys most often as subjects. Both of these kinds of literature are reviewed by Tobias (1963).

Several studies involving both humans and animals indicate that the latency and magnitude of conditional reflexes are affected by relatively low radiation dosages (Livanov & Kondratéva, 1960; cited in Tobias, 1963, p. 412). This effect is best substantiated for conditioned salivary responses, which are more difficult to condition following radiation (Lyman, 1933).

Though sparse, there is some evidence pertaining to the effects of radiation upon CNS activity. Apparently discrimination learning by primates is not affected by moderately high radiation dosages (Harlow, Schrier, & Simons, 1956). However, relatively small dosages significantly increase audiogenic seizure susceptibility in mice (Miller, 1962). Possibly related is the finding in the Russian literature that cortical excitability, as measured bioelectrically in rabbits, is increased following a single radiation dose (cited in Tobias, 1963, p. 412).

As radiation dosage increases from 0.075 roentgen (maximum allowable monthly dose) to 400–500 roentgens, the lethal dose probability increases from 0 to 50 percent. Also increasing with dosage is the incidence of frequency of symptoms of radiation sickness, nausea, vomiting, and blood cell changes (op. cit., pp. 406). Though this review failed to disclose any literature bearing upon the question of the autonomic and endocrinological effects of radiation dosage in humans, one would expect at the very least that these severe physiological symptoms would contribute feedback effects upon the quality and intensity of psychophysiological response to the total stress situation. The frequency of question marks appearing in the row dealing with radiation in Table *12-2* reflects the obscurity surrounding the matter. One review publication suggested that the insidiousness of radiation effects may be a source of anxiety for astronauts and thus may indirectly affect their health and adjustment (Smith & Altman, 1961, p. 20).

Noise, vibration.   A recent publication has provided a succinct summary of the performance effects of noise and vibration (Trumbull, 1965, pp. 17–22). Though studies which focus exclusively on the psychophysiological effects of these stressors are somewhat sparse, Plutchik (1959) has integrated a considerable amount of related literature pertaining to high intensity sound while Nadel (1963) has done the same for vibration.

Noise and vibration both constitute a source of distracting, unwanted, and often competing stimuli, which, if excessive, induce a number of physiological changes as well as significant performance decrement (Trumbull, 1965). One writer suggests the etiological involvement of noise and vibration in what is called *aeroneurosis,* which is described as a chronic mental disorder of aviators (Reinartz, 1943). Similarly, an earlier literature review presents considerable evidence for acute emotional changes resulting from prolonged exposure to these stressors (Coermann, 1938).

In general, sound intensity of 100–116 decibels or more causes considerable pain (Study of. . . . , 1958). Moreover, both constant and intermittent sound in the same intensity ranges have been shown to result in increased pulse, blood pressure, and electromyographic activity (Corso, 1952; Plutchik, 1959; Davis, 1957*b*).

There is evidence, however, for partial adaptation to high intensity noise, though presumably at a high physiological cost as judged by the general activation level resulting from the exposure (Helper, 1957). Under conditions of protracted noise exposure most people show symptoms of irritability, aggression, and fatigue (Murray, 1959); however, personality and motivational variables appear to be involved in the differential susceptibility to noise demonstrated in several studies now in the literature (Jerison, 1955; Corso, 1952).

Depending upon the amplitude, frequency, and duration of the imposed vibration, the effects vary from intra-abdominal bleeding and chest pain, to the nausea, vomiting, and dizziness characteristic of motion sickness (Nadel, 1963; Fraser, Hoover, & Ashe, 1961). Moreover, muscular tension characteristically increases during vibration, thus enhancing the transmissability of the vibration (Guignard, 1959, cited in Trumbull, 1965, p. 22).

In sum, data to support the pattern of psychophysiological indices in Table *12-2* originate both from animal and human studies and indicate that while intense vibration results in severe physiological disturbances, moderate vibration but of long duration results in increased heart rate and in lowered blood pressure and respiration rate. Body temperature and blood cell counts are affected by vibration, but the literature is contradictory as to the direction of change (Goldman, 1948; Hines, 1958).

Diurnal flattening. There is now a sizable body of literature pertaining to behavioral periodicity, which, if interrupted, presumably results in considerable stress (Greenwood & Weybrew, 1964). Periodicity has been demonstrated for a number of physiological functions some of which are described as circadian, i.e., approximately synchronized with day-night cycles (Burns & Kimura, 1963). Heart rate, blood pressure, skin conductance, and body temperature show definite circadian rhythm. There is also some indication that urinary indices of corticoid and catecholamine production, lymphocyte counts, and sodium/potassium ratios are also periodic, though perhaps not diurnal.

Years prior to the first manned space flight, concern had been expressed regarding the performance and adjustment effects resulting from the removal or desynchronization of the diurnal-nocturnal (or other) cues associated with the physiological functions known to be rhythmic (Strughold, 1952; Schaefer, 1959). In general, this so-called diurnal flattening is thought to be a contributing factor for the fatigue symptoms reported during long periods of confinement to a submarine and a space cabin simulator (Faucett & Newman, 1953; Steinkamp et al., 1959). However, for submariners (Kleitman, 1949) and for SAC crews (Hauty, 1963) performance decrements not attributable to changes in motivation failed to appear.

It has been assumed for some time that the effects of manipulation of day-night and other "time-givers" may be indirect, resulting from sleep deprivation and not from disruption of the cyclic functions themselves (Utterback & Ludwig, 1949). There are a number of military studies in which work-rest cycles were systematically modified, e.g., six hours on two off, four on four off, four on eight off, etc. Though the studies are not wholly consistent, it appears that heart rate, skin conductance, and body temperature appear to synchronize, but respiration rate tends to maintain its circadian periodicity (Hauty, 1963; Passey, Alluisi, & Chiles, 1963).

The significance of individual differences in the tendency to resynchronize to imposed schedules is remarkable in these and in similar studies. For example, one study taking place in polar isolation involved the issuance of watches desynchronized with respect to real time. It appeared that performance decrements were observed only for those men whose physiological functions failed to resynchronize to the "pseudo" clock time (Lewis & Lobban, 1957). In addition there is some evidence that numerous personality factors are involved in the already complex interaction among cyclic physiological functions, performance, and time cues (Colquhoun, 1960).

The nature of the neurophysiological mechanisms underlying these individual differences is not clear. However, it is hypothesized that there may be functional differences in the way the sensory input produced by the environmental time-givers (stimuli) synchronize with the innate rhythmic phase relationships of the reticular formation and hypothalamus (Halberg, 1962a). An example of the persistence of the early-established rhythmicity of the cortex is the evidence that the 59-to-90-minute infant sleep rhythms can be detected in adult EEG tracing taken both during sleep and wakeful periods (Kleitman, 1960; Kleitman, 1961). Finally, spontaneous autonomic activity as a measure of autonomic lability appears to be related to differences in adaptibility to temporal changes in the stimulus conditions (Johnson, 1962).

Though the severity of the stress effects of diurnal flattening may be questioned, some workers in the area of sensory deprivation suggest that aperiodicity of circadian and other cues may be one of the most important factors in adjustment to prolonged isolation and confinement (Schaefer, Clegg, Carey, & Weybrew, 1965; Burns & Kimura, 1963). This literature will be discussed next.

Isolation and confinement.   Since the McGill experiments (Bexton, Heron, & Scott, 1954), the literature in the area of sensory deprivation, as it has come to be called, has increased markedly (Solomon et al., 1957; Wheaton, 1959; Weybrew & Parker, 1960). Much of the earlier literature is anecdotal and consists of personal accounts of shipwreck, survival, arctic isolation, and the like (Byrd, 1938; Slocum, 1900; Tiira, 1955). Perceptual and attitudinal abnormalities, often hallucinatory and delusional, were frequently reported in these accounts.

Most of the measures obtained in the isolation or sensory deprivation experiments have been psychological in nature (Solomon et al., 1957). However there have been a few military studies in which a rather wide gamut of psychophysiological measures were taken and included autonomic, cardiovascular, hormonal, biochemical, and neuro-bioelectric indicators (Ruff, Levy, & Thaler, 1959; Passey, Alluisi, & Chiles, 1963). Apart from the tendency for the cyclical characteristics of the blood pressure, pulse, and temperature curves to persist, few additional findings were reported in these experiments.

Heron, Doane, and Scott, (1956) reported EEG alpha slowing and voltage increases during confinement. This change in brain wave tracing persisted three and one-half hours after termination of the experiment. Somewhat similar EEG changes were reported for immobilized (but not isolated) subjects, however, thus raising the possibility that restriction of skeletal muscular movement may be confounding some of the isolation and confinement data (Zubek & Wilgosh, 1963).

The pattern of psychophysiological changes, most of which are hypothetical (i.e., coded "?" in Table 12-2), are based upon tentative relationships suggested in the literature (e.g., Burns & Kimura, 1963). However two examples of studies in which psychophysiological measures were made successively during confinement will be mentioned. Hanna (1962), in an Air Force study, reported heart rate, skin resistance, and blood pressure changes indicating a sympathetic pattern response early in the experiment, some evidence of a parasympathetic pattern midway, and a reversion to a sympathetic pattern at the termination of a fourteen-day confinement at simulated high altitude. Similarly, three submariners confined in a recompression chamber and breathing helium at seven atmospheres pressure for ten days showed palmar conductance levels and changes suggestive of autonomic patterns similar to those reported by Hanna (Weybrew, Greenwood, & Parker, 1964).

Activation and arousal theory suggests U-shaped function between activation, e.g., as measured by autonomic indicators and intensity of stimulus input (Malmo, 1959). It seems plausible then that acute sensory reduction should result in pattern changes in certain of the psychophysiological indices in Table 12-2. Perhaps consistent with activation theory is the growing animal literature showing well-established operant curves, a short burst of light or sound being the reinforcement for lever pressing (Fox, 1962). These findings suggest that a need for exteroceptive stimulation may have drive properties and as a result may be reflected in arousal or activation indices. The possibility also exists, however, that stimulus invariance rather than level of stimulation itself is most crucial for adjustment to isolation and confinement (Weybrew, 1963a, pp. 93–94).

Threat to "life and limb."   It should be obvious that most, if not all, of the stressor classes in Table 12-2 may involve threat of injury or death, though the expectancy of occurrence may vary from one situation to another. Most of these studies in the military involve simulated air casualties, nuclear radiation, demolition, and so on (Berkun et al., 1962), pre- and postbattle combat measurement (Pace et al., 1956), parachute maneuvers (Basowitz et al., 1955), or simulated submarine escape (Cook & Wherry, 1950). Holtzman and Bitterman (1952) have integrated this literature rather well, particularly as it relates to combat pilot selection and screening. These reviewers concluded that although individual differences are significant, all pilots experience anxiety before and after combat missions. Moreover, based largely upon psychophysiological symptom patterns similar to those indicated in Table 12-2 and upon subjective symptomatology, anxiety proneness is related to two basic factors: (1) the lability or susceptibility to emotional arousal and (2) control or ability to function under emotion-evoking circumstances. In addition they bring to bear strong supporting evidence from the aviation literature (e.g., Anderson, 1947) to indicate the important relationship between stress tolerance and motivational variables, in particular what they call ego-involvement.

Coleman (1956, p. 241) has brought together literature to support the general conclusion that the frequency and severity of psychosomatic symptomatology as part of the so-called combat neurotic syndrome increased between World War I and II. The specific autonomic indices involved are indicated in one Air Force study showing that the combat neurotic characteristically had less salivary output, shorter dermographic latency, reduced lymphocyte count, less tidal air variability, higher metabolic rate, and smaller pupillary diameter (Wenger, 1948). In addition, simulated ditching of aircraft and accidental radiation exposure resulted in reduced circulating eosinophiles and an increase in the production of urinary 17-hydroxycorticosteroids (Berkun et al., 1962).[7] Also, an increase in 17-ketosteroid output was reported during simulated submarine escape (Cook & Wherry, 1950). Finally, additional supporting evidence for profound adrenal response to combat stress came from data obtained during the Korean campaign (Pace et al., 1956). It is important to note in all of these studies that not only are the changes considerable (though generally not debilitating) but also that the indicators of adrenal cortical hyperfunction persist for hours and even days following combat.

Temporal factors therefore seem to be crucial in interpreting data pertaining to the psychophysiological responses to the stresses of combat. The point is made in several places in the literature that the emotional response to the stress situation may be delayed minutes or even hours, occurring only when the troops are well behind the battle lines or when the plane has returned to the aircraft carrier (Davis, Elmadjian, et al., 1952; Grinker & Spiegel, 1945). These findings suggest that the timing for collection of urine samples or measurement of peripheral responses must be taken into account when interpreting psychophysiological and perhaps other data obtained from stress situations of this nature.

---

[7] The study also showed that steroid production was greatest for the simulated "hazards" which were most realistic, or, as the authors stated it, for those with the most "perceptual support" (p. 7).

Based upon data obtained largely from paratrooper trainees, Basowitz et al. (1955) have delineated certain dynamic processes, hypothetically at least, underlying the psychophysiological and endocrine symptomatology reported in the majority of combat studies. These writers point out that two sources of anxiety may be involved: (1) *harm-anxiety,* i.e., deep concern regarding threat of physical harm, or death, and (2) *shame-anxiety,* i.e., fear of depreciation in self-esteem or status. Evidence is presented that harm-anxiety in the main may account for the acute endocrine and psychophysiological changes reported (see also Persky, Gamm, & Grinker, 1952). On the other hand, shame-anxiety may account for some of the more subtle but often chronic effects of stress. This last-mentioned class of stressors will be discussed in the next section.

Threat to status or self-esteem.   With the advent of the nuclear age the need for highly-skilled military personnel increased greatly. With technological specialization came a restriction of role and associated status within a submarine crew or aerospace team. Previously, a man's status was contingent upon his proficiency in a range of skills within his area of specialization, but the status of a modern military man is dependent upon his ability to operate and repair a specific missile or a particular fire control system. As a result of this specialization, his adjustment has become increasingly affected by the degree of consistency existing between his narrowly-defined role and the status imposed by the system (Navy, Army, or Air Force). There is some older literature suggesting the strong relationship between what has come to be called role congruence and the quality of adjustment to the submarine environment (Scott, 1952). More recent literature suggests that role conflict, with its underlying dynamics related to status, ego, and self-esteem, may be a contributing factor to stress adjustment under a wide range of conditions (Rohrer, 1959).

Moreover, the aptitude standards imposed and the arduousness of training in a technological era increases the likelihood of failure, often with severe consequences for the man's self-perceived status and esteem. One review of the Air Force literature resulted in the judgment that the most serious stress effects result from two causes: (1) failure and (2) the complications, distractions, and annoyances of task performance (Lazarus, Deese, & Osler, 1952). Similarly, in a review of the submarine literature, Haggard (1949) emphasized the relevance of early experience with failure and frustration for predicting emotional response to stress. Terms like ego-threatening and ego-defensive have been used by some writers to describe the helpless, depression-like condition often seen in acute stress reactions (Appley, 1964). But what psychophysiological changes result from stress of this kind?

It is almost a truism, as was earlier noted, that the subjective probability of status or esteem loss occasioned by failure, injury, or death is an intrinsic component of most of the stressor classes in Table *12-2* (i.e., exposure to weightlessness, radiation, and so on). Lazarus (1963) has recently similarly discussed the relationship between so-called psychological and physiological stress.

This review disclosed relatively few psychophysiological studies in which threats to self-esteem and status were the major experimental variables in the study. In one instance, it was shown that urinary 17-ketosteroid output increased when submariner candidates were realistically threatened with failure in an academic testing situation (Cook & Wherry, 1950). Though heart rate was not affected, skin potential decreased more when the person occupied a successful role in a three-man group than when he occupied a failure role (Shapiro & Leiderman, 1965). Moreover, skin potential adaptation (decrease in level over time) was more likely to occur for those in contrived success roles than in failure roles. Finally, subjects occupying single roles, successful as well as unsuccessful, showed more adaptation than when they were part of the small experimental groups (op. cit.).

Forty submariner candidates were severely paced on an aiming task which was thought to be ego-involving for most subjects (Weybrew, 1962). Hand steadiness and palmar resistance measures were obtained continuously during the 22 trials. Factor analytical patterns showed that decreases in palmar resistance and absence of change in hand steadiness were associated with subjects who received favorable adjustment ratings from their peers.

It appears that responses to psychiatric symptom questionnaires frequently yield scores that correlate with psychophysiological indices of arousal or activation, particularly in studies involving a high degree of threat (Mandler et al., 1961; Berkun et al., 1962; Weybrew, 1964). These findings may be interpreted to mean that personality factors, in particular those related to the experience history of the person, may be meaningfully related to indices of autonomic and endocrine function. This covariance in turn may account for a sizable portion of the individual differences reported in most stress studies.

Sustained performance.   Colonel Simons' high altitude balloon flight, orbital astronautics, prolonged submarine cruises, and DEWLINE vigils are examples of this stressor class. Darrow and Henry (1949) in an excellent review of the psychophysiological literature related to submarines [8] discuss two general types of stress, the first resulting from the straining of the physiological adaptive capacities of the organism by

[8] Additional reviews of related literature are available. For a good overall coverage of the fatigue literature, see Tidwell and Sutton (1954), and for an excellent integration of studies related to pilot and driver fatigue, see McFarland (1953).

environmental insults (gases, pressure, heat, etc.—our primary stressors) and the other type described in the authors' words as

. . . that due to demands placed on the performance of the organism. These are the stresses attributable to the rigors of performance of duty, such as effort, fatigue, hunger, loss of sleep, etc. . . . Again, both the physiological consequences of the activity involved in performance and the emotional reaction to those effects may secondarily affect the central nervous system. . . . (p. 418)

Add to this list of stress factors group morale, boredom, attention satiation, motivational conflict, and threats of various kinds, and the complexity of this stressor class may be placed in proper perspective. Thus, depending upon the situation in which the observations or experimentation take place, a number of the stressor classes in Table *12-2* may be contributing to the effects of prolonged flights, submergence, and the like.

Most of the relevant military literature is grouped by the generic term *operational fatigue*. Chronic malaise, apathy, depression, exhaustion not relieved by rest, restlessness, boredom, and irritability are frequently reported symptoms describing this condition (Darrow & Henry, 1949). Though contradictory evidence was found in the field studies reviewed, in general, prolonged performance of pilots (McFarland, 1953), truck drivers (Jones et al., 1941), and submariners (Faucett & Newman, 1953; Weybrew, 1957) results in increases in muscular tension, decreased vigilance, and increased reaction time. Moreover, decreases in eosinophile counts and increases in corticoid excretion were reported during an eight-week simulated submergence (Faucett & Newman, 1953) and during protracted flights (Murphy et al., 1954). Additional field studies reported changes in a number of blood and urinary substances, in metabolic rate, in blood pressure, in heart rate and subjective symptomatology, all measured during sustained performance in a variety of operational situations (see Darrow & Henry, 1949; McFarland, 1953). It may be tentatively stated from this review of field studies of this kind: (1) in general, psychophysiological changes do not correlate significantly with performance decrements, (2) psychophysiological changes do not occur in all persons in a given stress situation, (3) if changes occur, often they are not in the same direction for all subjects at a given time, and (4) in some instances, the direction of change may not be the same for a given subject measured successively over a period of time in a given stress situation. Concepts proposed to explain these wide ranges of individual differences in response to stress vary a great deal; however, there are some workers who apparently feel that most of these differences in response to operational stresses of this kind result from differences in the subjects' knowledge and expectations regarding the duration of the task or mission as the case may be (Fraser, 1954; Jerison, 1958).

There are also a number of laboratory studies related in a general way to the question of the stress effects of long-duration performance. For example, Adams and Chiles (1961) obtained repetitive measurements from pilots confined for fifteen days to a cockpit simulator under a variety of work-rest schedules. The results indicated that heart rate declined, skin resistance decreased, and errors on an arithmetical task increased as the experiment progressed. The relationship between psychophysiological measures of activation and muscular tension were examined by another experiment involving an auditory tracking task (Pinneo, 1961). Heart rate, EMG frequency and amplitude, respiration rate, and palmar conductance, together with tracking performance, were all inversely correlated with muscular tension induced by a hand dynamometer. Although other studies are contradictory (e.g., Moeller & Chattin, 1962), the majority of the evidence tends to support the finding of a positive relationship between activation or arousal level and performance efficiency. However, the inverted-"U" function between performance and arousal proposed by Malmo (1959) remains problematical.

A generalization, perhaps rather obvious, emerges from this survey of the literature in this complex area, namely, that the psychological and physiological effects of stress are inextricably interrelated and the intermediary system between the two is the autonomic nervous system. Others, commenting earlier on similar literature, have emphasized the same general point (e.g., Mason, 1959b; Darrow & Henry, 1949). Since the majority of psychophysiological measures characteristically obtained in stress experimentation involve autonomic indicators, we would expect that naturalistic or experimentally-induced psychological and/or physiological changes will be reflected by such indicators. The changes in autonomic indices, increases in vigilance and motivation, and increase in performance efficiency resulting from the use of energizer drugs like amphetamine in sustained performance studies seem to be a demonstration of the functional relationships between the psychological and physiological realm as mirrored by the autonomic system (Hauty, Payne, and Bauer, 1957).

ISSUES IN STRESS RESEARCH AND SOME PRELIMINARY FINDINGS

It seems from our review that the majority of questions being asked has to do with some one or another aspect of the problem of assessing individual differences in potential for adjustment to the chronic stresses of the military, aerospace flight, prolonged marine submergence, and so on. At the same time, most of the opportunities for experimentation seem to be limited to acute stress situations in the laboratories and simulators.

In considering the question of whether the military studies involving the measurement of psychophysiological response to stress are providing any substantial answers to the adjustment question as posed, we find a considerable amount of psychophysiological data (Table *12-2*) which is useful in a descriptive sense, but the data appear to shed little light on this applied question. However, studies involving urinary and blood hormonal measurement and measures of autonomic balance (e.g., Wenger, 1948; Davis et al., 1952; Berkun et al., 1962) do point out some of the physiological mechanisms involved in adjustment to combat stress, thus suggesting the predictive possibilities of these indices. More specifically, the now somewhat outdated Air Force experiment showing the potentialities of EEG patterns as predictors of anxiety-proneness of flying personnel stands as an example of a study focused upon one aspect of the stress adjustment problem (Ulett et al., 1952). Using ratings as adjustment criteria during a sixty-day completely-submerged cruise of one Fleet Ballistic Missile submarine, for example, several scores derived from palmar conductance changes to laboratory-induced stress yielded some sizable (though not cross-validated) multiple Rs (Weybrew, 1964). (See Table *12-3*.)

Table 12-3. Multiple correlations and beta weights for selected tests and palmar electrodermal conduction (EDC) scores with respect to adjustment ratings obtained during a sixty-day submerged cruise of a Fleet Ballistic Missile Submarine.

Variables	Beta Weights	Predict- ability (Percent)	Multiple R
% EDC change during hyperventilation	−.507	17.2	
% EDC recovery during breathholding	.489	12.2	.543*
Neurotic Symptom Questionnaire	−.221	4.9	.586
% EDC change (discrimination conflict)	−.143	2.9	.610
Verbal intelligence	.087	1.2	.620

*Calculated from Beta Weights, the multiple R's are based upon combination of the variables in the row containing the coefficient plus those above it. (N= 170), Wherry-Doolittle method.

Failure to use the most appropriate methodology for analyzing psychophysiological data may be one limitation to military stress research. It is felt, for example, that the methodological possibilities of P-technique of factor analysis may have been overlooked, specifically in connection with isolation studies. The relationships indicated in Table *12-2* permit the inference at least that changes in patterns of autonomic, endocrine, cortical excitatory, and neuromuscular indices do in fact occur in a number of military situations. Moreover, there is evidence (cf. Lacey & Lacey, 1958b) that these psychophysiological patterns *between* individuals within a given stress situation differ disproportionately more than the same pattern *within* a given person but over an array of stressors. This probably contributes to the characteristically low communalities reported for psychophysiological measures interrelated over arrays of persons but within a given stress situation (e.g., Wenger, 1948; Holtzman & Bitterman, 1956). One would argue, therefore, for greater emphasis upon intraperson-over-time variance analysis in the search for organizing principles and functional unities underpinning psychophysiological change patterns. For example, one might analyze the co-variance between a number of psychophysiological indices from the same person or between group statistics for the same measures, both collected successively over an array of measurement occasions. The sample "N" would then be the number of measurement sessions within a given stress situation or staggered over a series of different stress situations.

Unfortunately we have not obtained reliable psychophysiological data from the same men for enough measurement occasions during submerged cruises to do a correlational study of this nature. However, we did factor analyze the co-variance between the arrays of the means of fifty submariners' self-ratings of fifty-five adjectives and ten atmospheric

Table 12-4. Factor loadings for the adjectives and behavioral statements rated daily during the world circumnavigation of the submarine *Triton*.

Variable number	Loading*	Content [†]
7	.88	Morale low
22	.76	Fed up
10	.70	Irritable
37	.68	Homesick
15	.65	Don't feel like talking
13	.64	Annoyed
24	.64	Disinterested
41	.64	Feel like giving up
11	.63	Mouth dry
4	.59	Bored stiff
5	.58	Don't feel like doing anything
19	.58	Daydream a lot
40	.58	Headachy
43	.58	Uncomfortable
50	.56	Frustrated

* Factor has been reflected.
[†] Takes into account the sign of the loading.
SOURCE: Weybrew, 1963a, p. 106. By permission of Free Press.

variables over an array of eighty days submerged during the Triton circumnavigation (Weybrew, 1963a). Table *12-4* shows the loading configurations for the most meaningful factor extracted.

These adjectival ratings were obtained daily from fifty men by means of a ten-point, multicategory response scale. Though these subjective data are somewhat irrelevant to the psychophysiological focus of this review, their presentation, nevertheless, helps to demonstrate the methodological possibilities of this "hybrid" factorization technique in stress research. Moreover, there are suggestions in the literature that the relationships between subjective indicators and psychophysiological responses may be highly relevant to the problem of stress adjustment as a whole (Berkun et al., 1962; Weybrew, 1963b). My discussant, Dr. Nowlis, has had a great deal of experience with subjective data of this kind and may be able to make some comments about their incorporation into psychophysiological stress experiments.

Factor scores were estimated from the loading pattern in Table *12-4* and plotted for each of the eighty days submerged (Figure *12-3*). Low positive or high negative factor scores indicate absence of the symptoms or indicators contained in Table *12-4*. With this in mind, it is possible to infer some cause and effect relationships from the concomitance of the peaks and troughs with changes in the stress conditions plotted over time as the abscissa in Figure *12-3*. The analysis of a similarly-derived matrix of psychophysiological indices might suggest functional unities of

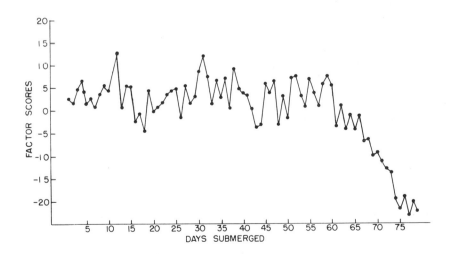

FIGURE 12-3.   Factor scores computed from the factor matrix in Table *12-4* and plotted by day during the submerged circumnavigation of the world by the submarine *Triton*. (Modified from Weybrew, 1963a, p. 107. By permission of Free Press.)

relevance in comprehending some of the processes of adjustment to stress.

Not at all unique to the military are problems of construct validation for psychophysiologists involved in stress studies. What theoretical
constructs underlie—and thus provide a rationale for—the measurements
obtained in our studies? For example, Selye's (1956) theory of the General
Adaptation Syndrome would suggest the validity of measurement of
pituitary and adrenogenic hormones. Wenger's (1948) Autonomic Balance
concept suggests utilization of peripheral autonomic indices with high
factor loadings (factorial validity). In this context, one concept which may
be worth examining involves the necessity to interpret stress responsivity
in the context of the prestress state of the organism. [Gellhorn's (1957)
autonomic tuning notion is of relevance here.] Along similar lines, and
with the problem of predicting submarine stress-tolerance from peripheral autonomic indices in mind, we have proposed a simple notion,
which we call stair-stepping, to describe an autonomic pattern hypothetically predictive of low stress tolerance (Weybrew, 1965).

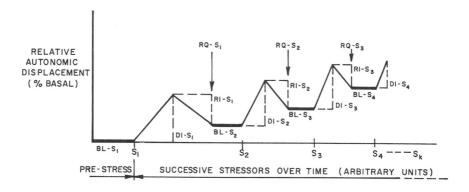

FIGURE 12-4.   Schematic representation of the "stair-stepping" hypothesis showing incomplete recovery from autonomic displacement
resulting from the imposition of successive stress situations (S_1, S_2,
. . . .S_k). BL-S_1, DI-S_1, RI-S_1, and RQ-S_1 refer to Basal Level, Displacement Index, Recovery Index, and Recovery Quotient (RI-S_1/ DI-S_1) respectively associated with S_1, and so on for S_1, S_2. . . .S_k). (Modified
from Weybrew, 1963a, p. 116. By permission of Free Press.)

The stair-stepping idea involves the imposition of a series of stressors
in the laboratory (e.g., trials on a paced motor task). The individual
differences which interest us should appear as the variance in relative
recovery as the successive stressors are imposed. Based upon Freeman's
(1948) recommendations, the operational measure for recovery, following
a given stressor exposure, is the Recovery Quotient (RQ) computed from

the ratio of the Recovery Index (RI) to the Displacement Index (DI). Individual differences in the slopes of RQs plotted against sequential stressors over time may provide a usefully valid predictive index, positive slope predicting compensation and negative slope predicting decompensation under field stress conditions. However it is obvious that the Law of Initial Values (Wilder, 1957) is intrinsic to this formulation and unless appropriately handled statistically, may pose a serious limitation to this approach.

There are still additional validation problems for the psychophysiologist working in the area of stress. The patterns of stress indices in Table *12-2*, for example, may be valid indicants of the direct effects of a primary stressor (such as weightlessness) or might reflect the effect of the person's perception of the stressor. Both are undoubtedly involved and it is important to determine the relative significance of the two kinds of processes under different stress conditions. Moreover, we must learn how psychophysiological response patterns are modified when stressors occur in combination (e.g. high G-load and excessive heat) as compared to their effects singly. Are the effects essentially summative, interactional, or counteractional? Some investigators have proposed encompassing conceptual models in order to systematize this complex multivariate situation confronted in most stress studies (Howard & Scott, 1965).

Similarly, using present methods, it has not yet been established whether different patterns or degrees of psychophysiological response are associated with different acute stress situations. It would be difficult for the psychophysiologist to rationalize the relevance of psychophysiological stress indices to particular stressors if essentially the same response patterns appear for radically different stress situations. There is some evidence, for instance, that a typical adrenergic response pattern occurs in acute fear, extreme cold, and following exogenous introduction of adrenaline. It is important to clarify this and other fundamental issues as soon as possible.

SUMMARY

An attempt has been made to provide an overview of some of the findings and unique problems of stress psychophysiology in military settings. Some illustrative examples were offered from the submarine service. In the following chapter, Drs. Haythorn and Altman move from the emphasis upon psychophysiological measurements of this chapter to center upon the psychosocial processes related to the adjustment of small groups of military men confined to highly circumscribed environments.

It has been suggested in this chapter that the most significant class of applied problems for military stress researchers is to develop stress response indices, psychophysiological or otherwise, which are usefully valid criteria of individual differences in what has been called stress tolerance. Such proposals as Ax's (1965) concept of Physiological Learning Aptitude (see p. 38) offer interesting possibilities. Siegel and Wolf's (1963) computer-simulated model, the input parameters of which include stressor dimensions, indices of an hypothetical man's adjustment potential, and differentially-weighted response patterns as adjustment criteria, also indicates a step in the desired direction. As a function of time-in-stress, the logic of this model calls for a reiterative interactional analysis of these parameters to provide, as output, actuarial predictions of the quality of adjustment of individuals and groups under stress.

One serious shortcoming in military research dealing with the problem of stress tolerance is the discrepancy between the limits imposed by ethical considerations regarding stress experimentation in contrast to the extreme limits in real life settings. Adjustive capacities determined within these strictures will necessarily be limited in their application to wider ranging natural stress conditions.

Invited commentary

VINCENT NOWLIS: To ask a man to review in a period of one hour the widely scattered literature on military stress is to request what is nearly impossible, yet Dr. Weybrew has just given us that review. His organization brings us new insights and his account of difficulties inherent in this area of research provides useful background for evaluation of this research.

What are the major difficulties? First, for the reviewer, there is the fact that both the term *stress* and the term *military* are used so imprecisely that the domain to be reviewed has no clearly recognizable boundaries. Second, for the researcher in the military situation, there is the constraining fact that his research study may be initiated under urgent circumstances which preclude an orderly approach to the basic problems. Third, the environment which presents one important factor inevitably presents or develops still other stressful features, which may be ignored or unrecognized. Finally, the psychophysiological items comprising the pattern of response to the stressful environment have such complex interrelationships that any one item, used as index of response, may obscure rather than clarify the ongoing phenomena.

Weybrew shows why, for theoretical, practical, and empirical reasons, we must be interested in the long-term effects of stressful environments. Using as model his eighty-day study of fifty submariners on the *Triton* during its circumnavigation cruise, he would now introduce into such studies repeated measures of psychophysiological responses in addition to measures of subjective responses and of environmental variables. Since each individual thus yields many successive measures of the same set of variables, a factor analysis can be carried out for each individual. A similar model has been used by Cattell (1960), by Wessman and Ricks (1966), and by others.

Wessman and Ricks found that the factors identified for any one individual differed from those obtained for others and that the composition of the factors was useful in interpreting other information available for the individual. We can expect an increasing number of studies which obtain records daily or even more frequently from individuals over periods of a month or more. However, in order to select the most appropriate psychophysiological indices for such long-term studies, Weybrew has wisely decided first to study shorter temporal series of responses to stressors in the laboratory, with analysis based on his "stair-stepping" hypothesis. Continuous records of multivariable response to stressors over shorter periods have also been used by other investigators in this area of stress. We increasingly find that an understanding of behavior requires adequate knowledge about the structure of behavioral sequences involving periods of seconds, minutes, hours, or days. The search for such knowledge requires good theory, and it is encouraging to note that the Miller, Galanter, and Pribram (1960) book was only the first of the more recent attempts to develop such theory (cf. Mandler, pp. 307–308, this volume).

Let me turn briefly to a few of the issues concerning the use of subjective responses in psychophysiological research. First, because the term *subjective response* is so thoroughly ambiguous, we might rephrase the problem thus: "Is verbal behavior useful in psychophysiological research?" Or still more precisely we can ask whether or not relationships between verbal behavior and intraorganismic processes are or can be made dependable enough to justify the use of verbal behavior in psychophysiological research. In this way we do not restrict the term *subjective response* to just two of its many important referents—private events and the verbal report of private events—but extend it to any verbal behavior potentially useful in the study of intraorganismic processes and events.

Next we should note that three completely different classes of intraorganismic processes can be identified: phenomenological processes, hypothetical mediating processes, and physiological processes. These are depicted schematically in Figure *12-5*, modelled after the kind of diagram which Kurt Lewin has made popular.

At the lower level, we have the general class of physiological processes, involving the activities of the nervous, endocrine, cardiovascular, and other organic systems. In the middle, we can place the hypothetical mediating processes—that general class of theoretical or dispositional constructs and intervening variables which Hull and Tolman first taught us to use and which are now indispensable in much psychological research. At the top level, we place that problematic class of phenomenological processes, sometimes called private events, which include conscious feelings, images, ideas, and the Jamesian stream of consciousness.

It is obvious that the logical status and empirical status of processes in

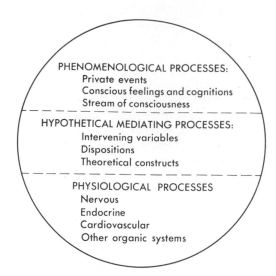

FIGURE 12-5.   Schematic representation of classes of intraorganismic processes.

any one class differ radically from those of processes in the other classes. But it is also becoming clear that the prediction, control, and understanding of behavior require adequate knowledge about all three classes of processes. To obtain this knowledge we search for and identify empirical relationships among various subsets of intraorganismic processes, of environmental events, and of behavior. In principle, then, verbal behavior in the presence of any specific subset of environmental events may be found to be significantly related to intraorganismic processes in any one, two, or three of these classes.

Investigators are usually interested in some limited aspect of only one class of intraorganismic processes, and when they use verbal report it is examined only in relation to the specific focus of their interest, whether psychophysiological or theoretical or phenomenological. What is needed are some studies which simultaneously examine the relationship of verbal report to selected processes in all three intraorganismic classes.

In an early stage of our research on mood at Rochester, we recognized that the existing literature ambiguously applied mood terms to all three classes of intraorganismic processes. Most writers associated mood, as state of mind, with certain conscious affective and cognitive events, others referred to mood as a complex set of dispositional mediating processes, and others dealt with mood in terms of general bodily functions and of inherited or constitutional traits of temperament. To gain some grasp on one part of the domain of mood we decided to restrict our conception of mood temporarily to that of a complex set of hypothetical mediating processes—that is, following Ryle (1949) and Skinner (1953, 1957), to regard mood terms as dispositional terms. Thus we expected that in any one mood a person is more strongly disposed to emit one repertoire of behaviors, including verbal behaviors, than when in any other mood. We searched therefore for verbal responses which varied in probability of occurrence with variations in mood. The adjectives carefully selected for the *Mood Adjective Check List* (*MACL*) (1956, 1965) may be regarded as operants rather than as respondents or tacts—that is, as behaviors which the person has learned to emit in a social environment when in one mood or another. Intensity of any dimension of mood (or temporary strength of the disposition) is then assessed through the frequency of occurrence of certain words in a free situation, or more feasibly, by the frequency with which certain adjectives are checked on the *MACL*.

Others will criticize our restricted approach and insist that private events, such as affective feelings and certain cognitions, are essential for the study of mood. This is only partly true. It is not unusual for a subject to check through the *MACL* and, upon rereading it, discover to his surprise that (1) he has checked all such words as *angry, belligerent,* and *rebellious,* and (2) that he *is* angry! Only by noting what you are doing or about to do or have just done do you identify how you are presently disposed. Private events are only part of the total repertoire of occurrences which vary with mood. But the basic criticism is valid, since even verbal report on the *MACL* is partly influenced by the concurrently occurring private events, as well as by other features of the organism and the environment. To include these private events in the study of mood produces a number of difficult problems. Whereas the *MACL* assesses strength of disposition through the frequency of checking certain adjectives, with private events as a focus we will have to develop methods for assessing the frequency of their occurrence, the intensity of the conscious affect and, if conscious cognitions are also used, develop mood scales based on various formulations of these cognitions. In any case, as in the study of mood as disposition, we will again have to use verbal behavior in the study of private events as indices of mood. Again we recognize the importance of learning how to study selected aspects of two or more classes of intraorganismic processes *simultaneously.*

Only a decade ago it would have seriously offended many psychologists to propose that we pack our model organism with three classes of processes and events; phenomenologists wanted only private events, the theoretical experimentalists wanted only intervening variables or hypothetical constructs, while the psychophysiologists wanted neither the mental nor the theoretical but only that which seemed physical or somatic. Now we are more disposed to cooperate and to widen our domains of special interest. Accepting the fundamental methodological principle of behavioral science, we are interested in predicting behavior on the basis of adequate knowledge about all three classes of intraorganismic processes. This means that we seek functional relations involving (1) environmental features, private events, and behavior; (2) environmental features, intervening mediating processes, and behavior; and (3) environmental features, psychophysiological process, and behavior. A present and future task is to examine, when possible, how the empirical relationships which involve factors in any one of these three sets do or do not coordinate with those which involve factors in the other two. In all three sets verbal report, when regarded as behavior, is a legitimate and potentially indispensable component of the research enterprise.

Discussion

Dr. Trumbull: Dr. Weybrew's matrix (p. 332) indicates his disposition to such an extended, inclusive model and concern over the present deficiencies. We all look forward to its completion through better research in the future.

At the level of physiological processes, we know that we test 17-ketosteroids as we pick them up in overflow. We test blood pressure by restricting flow in the arm. The temperature center is somewhere else but we use thermometers in certain places. Very few of our measures of processes in the lower part of Dr. Nowlis' diagram are really direct and to the point. However, we have found different ways of obtaining them. Could we similarly go through a list of affect characteristics at the phenomenological level of Dr. Nowlis' diagram and show how the check lists, questionnaires, statements, verbal reports, etc., sample affect either directly or somewhere peripherally, the way we do on the psychophysiological level? Would one be picking up secondary or primary responses? If one were to say "I'm done in!" it might be a representation of the 17-ketosteroid overflow. But how does one know that when two people use the same expression it means the same thing any more than does the 17-ketosteroid overflow in two people mean the same thing? We also know that the person doing the measuring —and the way in which his role is perceived—makes a difference in the effect being measured. The conditions under which the measuring is done also make a difference. It seems to me that affect is one stage removed from measures already too distant from the source and more susceptible, then, to these other influences. It would be profitable to run through an analogue of affects in terms of level represented and then attempt correlation with the other sections of the diagram.

Dr. Nowlis: Yes, the basic methodological problem is to establish functional relationships involving each of the three sets of intra-organismic processes and events and then to see how, with a given environmental input, a functional relationship involving one set of processes does or does not coordinate with those which involve one or both of the other sets. Within this framework the empirical information would then let us, among other things, determine the extent to which private events correspond to concurrent psychophysiological processes and the extent to which we do need information about private events in our attempts to predict, control, and understand behavior.

Dr. Korchin: I am delighted that somebody spoke of private events because they often get lost in the shuffle of behavioral and physiological measurements. We ought also to keep in mind that the subjective feelings which should concern us are not only those referable to the affective state of the subject but also those related to his physiological state. The physical symptoms a subject can report—what Dr. Mandler and his co-workers have called "autonomic feedback"—are important data, and of the same sort as statements about one's mood. When anxious, we may feel as if our hearts beat faster, muscles tense, stomach contracts, and the like, although these may or may not be related to measurable physiological changes, as Dr. Mandler has shown (Mandler & Kremen, 1958; Mandler, Mandler, & Uviller, 1958). Moreover, these symptoms are idiographically organized, seem to be consistent over time, and may be used as personal indicators of emotional states. In one of our experiments (Basowitz, et al., 1956), subjects were interviewed as to their characteristic somatic reactions in strong emotional states. On a later occasion, a small dose of epinephrine was infused, and many subjects reported the same somatic experiences which they had earlier described. These differed from subject to subject but were individually consistent. I would suggest, therefore, that we not forget the aspect of subjective experience which has to do with bodily symptoms as well as that related to psychological or emotional state and that Dr. Nowlis' diagram should be expanded accordingly.

Dr. Ruff: This discussion raises the problem we all face when we try to measure affect. An adjective check list will readily indicate what kind of a feeling state is there—it shows the difference between a subject who says "energetic, elated" and the one who says "tired, downhearted." But it's difficult to measure intensity of feeling in that way. What we do is sum the ratings for all the adjectives in a given category. A subject who checks "definitely feel this way" for each item will have a factor score four times greater than one who checks "definitely don't feel this way." But it would be hard to demonstrate that his feeling is necessarily four times as intense. And so, the investigator tries to use psychophysiological variables to measure intensity. He hopes that the degree of the feeling state will be indicated by the height of the basal skin resistance, the heart rate, the number of muscle potentials per unit time, etc.

The appeal here is that each approach would seem to complement the other. Psychological variables may indicate the nature of the affect but not the degree. Physiological measures may indicate the degree but not the nature.

At the moment, however, the psychophysiological approach also has its disadvantages. We can't say that when skin resistance falls by half the subject is feeling something twice as strongly; nor do we yet know what to do when one of our variables goes one way and the other goes another. But the hope that more specific patterns can eventually be delineated keeps many of us at work.

Dr. Notterman: I am sure that a scaling specialist would want to disagree with the implication that psychometric procedures cannot provide good intensity measures. Thurstonian methods go far in providing precisely this sort of information.

Dr. Mandler: If we really believe that the affective side—the subjective report of the subject that Dr. Ruff was talking about—and the physiological aspect, namely the measured physiological changes, are somehow related, then there ought to be some relatively straightforward ways of finding out *how* they are related. Dr. Korchin and I have tried, and so have others, but on the whole we are quite unsatisfied with the results. Our correlation coefficients are significant enough for us to publish our findings, but although accounting for

25 percent of the variance may be good enough for a journal, it isn't good enough for science! We have tried other things—to teach subjects to discriminate changes in heart rate of two beats per minute, for example (Mandler & Kahn, 1960)—and can't do it. We don't even know which physiological changes control behavior, what particular change in heart rate, for example, produces some particular differential reaction—overt, verbal, or otherwise (cf. Mandler, 1962). Obviously, we need finer indices, better research methods, etc.

I have always felt that, in principle, it ought to be possible to train people to give more discriminating reports on their physiological states—and changes in them—if we could find the appropriate training methods. I still believe that operant conditioning offers the best approach. Would Dr. Nowlis feel that this sort of thing is possible in light of the very fine nuances he finds in his mood studies?

Dr. Nowlis: Yes. You are referring to the important fact that we have very little knowledge about the relations between physiological changes and private events. Certainly the content of these private events depends very much on the same processes of social learning which are also involved in verbal behavior. Thus we would expect that operant conditioning could simultaneously lead to more discriminating private events and more relevant and accurate verbal reports. I am told that some Asian cultures foster these subtle discriminations much more than we do.

Kamiya (1962) has successfully taught subjects, already students of Zen, to identify the occurrence of their EEG alpha rhythm. Interestingly, it turns out to be that learning to identify the alpha rhythm gives the subject some degree of control over its occurrence.

Dr. Lazarus: I think there are two questions here: first, whether people can discriminate bodily states; and, secondly, the quite independent question of whether psychological states that people report are directly associated with physiological changes. It seems to me that one of the difficulties with physiological measurement is that, except for the underdeveloped area of response patterning and its psychological meaning, we are generally dealing with a single dimension of reaction, as in the concept of arousal or activation. But affects or moods are multi-dimensional. A person can report high levels of anxiety and at the same time increases in pleasantness, depression, or anger. When we ask subjects to report the amount of distress they feel in watching a movie and we simultaneously record skin conductance and heart rate, the ups and downs in a roughly-scaled dimension of subjective distress do indeed correspond with the events portrayed in the film. They also correspond to a degree with the autonomic measurements. The two questions, correspondence between experience and physiological reactions and the perception of physiological reactions, are quite different. I would concur, certainly, that the scaling of affect, particularly multidimensional affect, is a prime methodological research problem with which psychologists haven't spent sufficient time.

Dr. Back: I would suggest that training to report these physiological events might produce other problems. Linguists have shown that perception can change if subjects are using more detailed names and labels. Thus, if you train a subject to be a very sensitive reporter of emotions, you really change his perception of his emotions, and he is not a representative of untrained subjects any more.

Dr. Nowlis: This is one reason we tried to base the *MACL* on operant verbal items which vary in probability of occurrence with mood rather than on verbal descriptions of private events. As I said earlier, however, private events do influence how one checks the *MACL,* and it is fully legitimate, if difficult, to design better ways of studying them and using them in psychophysiological research.

Dr. Ax: I think you are getting discouraged too soon. We are trying to translate a language which is probably as different as English to Korean, namely the introspective or conscious information to a physiological language. These are extremely different and we have about 1/10 of 1 percent of a dictionary—because you are only conscious of a small part of the potentially conscious process that is going on—and we are only measuring an extremely small percentage of the total physiology going on. So we are arguing that maybe there is dissociation—or at least no real correlation—here. I don't have the slightest doubt that there's absolutely perfect correlation! We are just measuring such small parts of both that they don't very often happen to match up.

Dr. Mechanic: We have had some experience in trying to record mild morbidity through intensive measurement at very frequent intervals. Some of our subjects have refused to participate any further because they felt that focusing on their symptoms in such detail made them feel less well. I believe that such extreme focus on personal physical and intrapsychic states may make a person so sensitive to his feelings that the feelings themselves become exaggerated and change, as I believe Dr. Back indicated they might. If you persist in asking a person to indicate all of the pains he might possibly have at the moment, he can produce a lot of pains he wouldn't ordinarily think about had you not attempted to record them so precisely.

Chairman's summary

RICHARD TRUMBULL: Dr. Weybrew, facing the problem of translation of research results into application, serves to focus attention on a discrepancy between quantity and quality in stress research. A user must have special criteria and his impatience is understandable. It is evident that the user, to whom Dr. Weybrew responds, tends to want answers for specific situations in a field where the answers available are in other specific situations. The generalizable theory and the basic knowledge of man as opposed to subjects are not appearing. On the other hand, the researcher in the military structure seems to be working so close to the generational problem that he does not have the time to build a translating bridge from the basic side. In this instance, the basic side must include multiple stressors approximating the operational setting and the problem becomes proportionately more difficult.

Further, Dr. Weybrew reminds us that there is an additional "meaning" demanded of his research-prediction. He cannot afford to stop with observation of relationships between stressors and adaptation but must ask how these mechanisms allow an individual to maintain integrity and functional competence in a predictable way. His needs, too, remind us that simple one-time measures are deceptive as related to both the individual and the stressor situation. The individual always is in some phase of on-going processes, even moods, and the stressors to which he is subjected are sequential as well as multiple, with an ebb and flow, summation or cancelling, occurring through their interactions. This leads to a requirement for some evaluation of relative strengths of stressors and such interactions.

The models presented by both Drs. Weybrew and Nowlis are very helpful in showing these relationships. The latter gives us encouragement that the phenomenological, mediating, and physiological processes can be assayed through verbal behavior, as it plays a role in expression of both *pre*disposition and disposition or postaffect. Verbal behavior, then, takes its place as "a legitimate and potentially indispensable component" in stress theory development. The discussion of quantification and establishment of functional relationships between the three intra-organismic processes produced both enthusiasm for a return to consideration of "private events" (Dr. Korchin), recognition of problems related to individual meaning of such report (Dr. Ruff), and the question of training in the Titchenerian tradition to sensitize perception of bodily state.

There are translation problems here as well, as the subject becomes influenced by the very process of report, but the feeling persists that the correlation is there if procedures can be found for measuring it. The value of such measures in operations which cannot be interrupted by more common blood pressure, EEG, and other physiological techniques is evident. Once again, Dr. Weybrew's indication of the constraints and needs in operational settings must be recognized.

The perspective provided by such an orientation as operational needs impose is necessary to remind those doing the bulk of the research reported in the numbers quoted by Dr. Weybrew that there is such an end requirement for their product. We can share his concern over the military setting for sounder basic research and the hope that the scope and rationale of other basic research will provide some of the bridge required before psychology makes a contribution to operations as well as to knowledge *per se*.

WILLIAM W. HAYTHORN

IRWIN ALTMAN

13

Personality factors in
isolated environments

Although there appears to be no unequivocal way of distinguishing the responses to one kind of stress from those to another, it nonetheless seems the better part of caution to restrict discussion in this paper to one broad class of stress-inducing situations: that of isolated environments. In deference to the Weltanschauung of the 1960's, the stress of isolation will be examined in a systems context. That is, stress is regarded as an *intra-organismic* concept with both physiological and psychological components, largely environmentally initiated, and exercising determining influences on organismic behavior.

The stress of isolation may, in extreme conditions, impair the viability of the individual or group, impair or enhance performance effectiveness, or impose emotional adjustment difficulties leading to psychiatric and/or interpersonal problems. Although stress will be examined here as an intervening variable between environmental conditions and behavior, it is regarded as only one of many such intervening variables and, therefore, not likely to account for all of the variance in any specific situation. In this examination of isolation stress, attention will be given to individual differences in reaction to isolation and the role of personality variables in determining such differences.

In particular, this paper will present the results of a recently completed study of isolated pairs of men, selected and matched to test several hypotheses regarding the degree to which composition of such dyads on the basis of personality variables might modify the effects of isolation and confinement. The study represents an attempt to trace the effects of isolation on subjective stress and emotional symptomatology, as modified by interpersonal need satisfactions, and in turn, the effects of these intervening processes upon performance.

There have been several highly competent reviews of the literature on isolation (cf. Kubzansky & Leiderman, 1961; Zubek, 1964), particularly as defined in sensory and perceptual deprivation studies, but perhaps some useful additional order can be obtained by casting the mainstreams of the literature in a conceptual framework of the independent-intervening-dependent variable type, shown in Figure *13-1.* Among the inde-

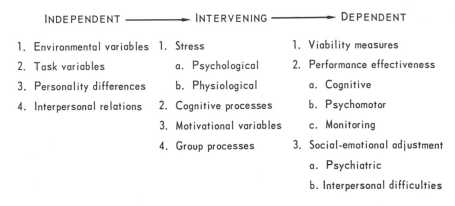

INDEPENDENT ⟶ INTERVENING ⟶ DEPENDENT

1. Environmental variables
2. Task variables
3. Personality differences
4. Interpersonal relations

1. Stress
   a. Psychological
   b. Physiological
2. Cognitive processes
3. Motivational variables
4. Group processes

1. Viability measures
2. Performance effectiveness
   a. Cognitive
   b. Psychomotor
   c. Monitoring
3. Social-emotional adjustment
   a. Psychiatric
   b. Interpersonal difficulties

FIGURE 13-1.   Conceptual framework of key social isolation research variables.

pendent variables which are germane to isolation research, one can distinguish four classes: (1) aspects of the physical environment, such as sensory versus perceptual deprivation, social isolation, and confinement [1]; (2) aspects of the task environment, such as cognitive versus psychomotor, and group versus individual tasks [2]; (3) personality differences, such as field dependent versus independent, active versus passive, and anxious versus calm individuals [3]; and (4) interpersonal relations—compatible versus incompatible, homogeneous versus heterogeneous backgrounds, and so on.[4]

Although stress is the primary intervening variable of concern here, one must bear in mind that cognitive and motivational variables also intervene, as do various interpersonal or group processes. Among

[1] *Cf.* Lilly (1956*a*); Hebb (1955*b*); Myers (1964); Myers et al. (1962); Zubek (1964); Mullin and Connery (1959); Kinsey and Murphree (1955); Gaito et al. (1958); Wexler et al. (1958); Gunderson (1963).

[2] *Cf.* Adams and Chiles (1961); Hartman et al. (1962); Myers et al. (1962); Vernon and McGill (1961); Vernon et al. (1959); Myers (1964); Wexler et al. (1958); Zubek (1964).

[3] *Cf.* Nardini et al. (1962); Rohrer (1961); Mullin (1960); Mullin and Connery (1959); Eilbert and Glaser (1959); Nelson and Gunderson (1962, 1964); Myers (1964); Zubek (1964); Hull and Zubek (1962).

[4] *Cf.* Rohrer (1961); Eilbert and Glaser (1959); Mullin (1960).

dependent variables, it seems helpful to discriminate among *viability measures,* i.e., how long people can endure in isolation; *performance effectiveness,* which must at least distinguish among monitoring, cognitive, and psychomotor performance; and *social-emotional adjustment,* which includes personal reactions of a psychiatrically-significant nature, subjective stress responses, and difficulties in interpersonal relations.

The links between independent and dependent variables in this framework are of course complicated and diverse. In a complex system of relationships, science typically proceeds by seeking to identify comparatively simpler links. Emphasizing stress as the intervening variable of primary interest, one can identify several specific links in the chain of relationships by which the conditions of isolation result in predictable patterns of behavior. These include—but are not limited to—the relationships between isolation and performance effectiveness, isolation and social-emotional adjustment, the conditions of isolation and the stress induced thereby, the interactions of personality variables with isolation in producing stress, interpersonal incompatibilities and stress, interactions between incompatibility and isolation in producing stress, and the longer chain of interaction effects between isolation and personality in producing stress, which in turn affects both performance effectiveness and adjustment. The majority of studies in the literature deal with individual links in these chains, or treat relationships that leave out the intervening variables. The study described below attempted to focus on the entire chain of relationships, emphasizing the importance of subjective stress and emotional symptomatology as variables mediating the relationships between isolation and task performance.

The literature presents a variety of conditions under the labels of isolation, confinement, stimulus deprivation, stimulus reduction, and perceptual deprivation. For purposes of the following discussion, the essential ingredients of isolation are (1) reduced access to valued stimuli, particularly social stimuli; (2) limited freedom of movement; and (3) reduced variety of stimulation. Extreme stimulus deprivation was of less relevance to isolated military duty (and therefore to the research reported herein) than were the effects of loss of ordinary social psychological stimulation, general confinement, and separation from valued stimuli (Kinsey & Murphree, 1955; Gaito et al., 1958; Wexler et al., 1958). In addition, the modifying effects of group composition (Haythorn, 1957) on the interpersonal friction often arising in socially isolated groups was of interest.

The logic of the study

The focus in the study to be described below has been on the effects of variations in the *physical environment, task environment,* and *interpersonal characteristics* on individual and group functioning. Effects of *physical environment* were studied through comparison of matched isolation and control groups. Isolation groups consisted of pairs of men socially isolated from the outside world, who lived and worked in a small room for a ten-day period. They were not in a sensory or perceptually deprived environment in the classical sense. They were in a situation of social isolation and confinement with limited access to recreation materials, normal facilities regarding food, sleeping, and work schedule. Controls followed a similar schedule but had more access to the outside world.

Effects of the *task environment* were studied through individual and group functioning on three tasks. Because little isolation research has been done using group *qua* group tasks, these were emphasized in this study.

Effects of variations of *interpersonal characteristics* on individual and group functioning were studied by manipulation of interpersonal compatibility and incompatibility. Of primary concern were variations in group composition characteristics on dogmatism, need achievement, need affiliation, and need dominance.

The aims of this study were to assess the simple and interactive effects of these independent variables on several classes of intervening and dependent variables and, where possible, to identify intervening processes associated with independent-dependent relationships. On the dependent variable side, one primary concern was with *performance effectiveness.* With respect to *social-emotional adjustment,* clinical test and interview data were collected on pre- and post-test bases. Similarly, *interpersonal adjustment* was assessed by several sociometric instruments. Finally, a crude measure of *viability* (i.e., the ability of a group to complete the experimental period voluntarily) was available. Discussion will be restricted to dependent measures of performance on group tasks.

To assess some of the intervening dynamics which may link independent variables to changes in group functioning, data were collected on *problem-solving processes* and *psychological state characteristics* (stress and emotional symptomatology). In addition, intervening processes concerned with *interpersonal relationships* were obtained through observation of free time interaction behavior and interpersonal exchange and self-disclosure. No data concerning physiological states were collected. Because of space limitations, the emphasis here will be on intervening processes concerned with psychological states, as reflected in subjective reports of experienced stress and emotional symptomatology.

To summarize, the following discussion will deal with the relationship chain shown opposite.

It is recognized that behavioral dynamics to be accounted for certainly include more complex combinations of independent, intervening,

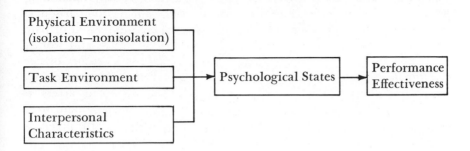

and associated dependent variable classes, but it has nevertheless seemed important to explore even these relatively simple sequential linkages between antecedent events and consequent outcomes in order to provide an empirical basis for further development of a conceptual model of the behavior of isolated groups.

Hypotheses

The following general hypotheses were tested in the present study.

Hypothesis I.   Pairs of men socially isolated from society will exhibit greater subjective stress, will report more emotional symptomatology, and should perform less effectively on several tasks than nonisolated pairs.

Hypothesis II.   Groups composed of individuals with compatible personality characteristics will exhibit less subjective stress and less emotional symptomatology, and would function better as a work team, and perform more effectively than groups composed of individuals with personality characteristics which predispose them to conflict.[5]

Hypothesis III.   Properties of the physical environment and group composition were expected to have interactive effects on psy-

[5] The detailed logic of these predictions and qualifications to them are spelled out elsewhere (Haythorn, Altman, & Myers, 1966; Altman & Haythorn, 1965) and need not concern us here, except that composition predictions were not based on a simple homogeneous-heterogeneous congruence logic, nor on a complementarity basis alone. That is, for certain personality characteristics, (e.g., need affiliation) similarity at either the high or low end of the continuum was presumed to be associated with compatibility, and heterogeneity with incompatibility. For others (e.g., need dominance), on the other hand, homogeneity at the low end of the continuum, as well as heterogeneity, were hypothesized to be associated with compatibility, whereas high-dominance homogeneity was hypothesized to be associated with incompatibility.

chological states and performance effectiveness. Specifically, it was hypothesized that the effects of interpersonal incompatibility would be accentuated and most salient in a socially isolated environment.

Experimental procedure

Subjects.   Ss were volunteer sailors recruited early in boot training from the Great Lakes Naval Training Center, Illinois. The volunteer rate was approximately 85 percent. Based on personality testing, Ss satisfying design requirements reported to the Naval Medical Research Institute, Bethesda, Maryland, at the completion of training, five weeks later. Eighteen pairs were selected to meet specific personality composition criteria on need affiliation, need achievement, need dominance, and dogmatism. Nine matched pairs were assigned to isolation and nonisolation control conditions. Assignment of Ss to dyads also depended on several other criteria: that they came from different boot camp companies and were relative strangers; that they were 17–21 years of age; that they had GCT scores between 46–59, with a mean of 49.9 (IQ equivalent of about 100); and that within a dyad they were matched as closely as possible on age, education, religion, family size, birth order, and size of home town.

Isolation control conditions and general procedure.   The day prior to the experiment, Ss were told of their assignments, were trained on tasks, and completed tests and questionnaires.

The isolation area was a 12 × 12 foot laboratory room, equipped with double decker bunks, chemical toilet, storage cabinet, table, two chairs, and a lamp. The room had loudspeakers to present task inputs and instructions. Observation was conducted through a one-way mirror and audio system. Supplies were sent into the room by a portable closet rolled up to the door. For recreation, Ss had a deck of cards, checker game, cribbage board, and religious reading matter. They were allowed to take in one magazine and one book on Day 1 and were provided additional self-selected reading material on the fourth, seventh, and tenth days. Isolation Ss received no mail or communication with the outside and were not permitted to have radios, watches, or calendars, although they were told that a regular work schedule with reveille at 7:30 a.m. and taps at 11:00 p.m. would be followed. Neither isolation nor control groups were informed of the length of the experiment (which was to be ten days). Because their military orders specified an approximate two-week stay at the Research Institute, most Ss adopted this as an anchor, although they were told that this was only approximate and could vary considerably. All groups worked two hours in the morning, three hours in the afternoon, and one hour in the evening on three tasks, to be described below.

Controls followed the same schedule but lived in barracks, ate meals at the base mess, and had ten-minute breaks between tasks. After work, they were free to use base recreation facilities. Thus, while restricted and spending approximately twelve hours a day together, controls had considerable access to outside stimulation.

Personality composition of groups.   The test battery used to select Ss was the Rokeach Dogma Scale (1960) and a shortened Edwards' Personal Preference Schedule (1959). High and low Ss were selected, i.e., those who were approximately in the upper or lower tertiles on the variable under consideration.

Personality composition effects were assessed within a Greco-Latin square experimental design (Figure *13–2*). Each cell of the 3 × 3 square

NEED ACHIEVEMENT

	HOMOGENEOUS HIGH	HETEROGENEOUS	HOMOGENEOUS LOW
HOMOGENEOUS HIGH	αC	βA	γB
HETEROGENEOUS	γA	αB	βC
HOMOGENEOUS LOW	βB	γC	αA

(DOGMATISM — left vertical axis label)

NEED AFFILIATION
α Homogeneous high
β Heterogeneous
γ Homogeneous low

NEED DOMINANCE
A Homogeneous high
B Heterogeneous
C Homogeneous low

FIGURE 13-2.   Greco-Latin square experimental design.

represents a dyad defined by the personality characteristics of the two members. For example, the upper left cell represents a pair of men homogeneously high with regard to dogmatism, need achievement, and need affiliation, and homogeneously low with regard to need dominance.

The design was repeated under conditions of isolation and nonisolation, yielding a total of eighteen dyads.

Tasks.   During the ten-day experiment, groups worked on three tasks which varied in several respects, e.g., perceptual-motor versus abstract reasoning, high requirements for cooperation versus optional cooperation requirements versus a one-man task. The tasks also differed somewhat in realism, with one being part of a combat information center operation and one an artificial, abstract reasoning task.

1. *Monitoring or vigilance task.* This one-man, perceptual task required a S to monitor an eight-light console. When a light flashed on, he was to press a button below the light to put it out. The task was routine and required little skill. Each work session was composed of three eight-block trials and lasted an hour. Within each trial block four time intervals between lights were greater and four intervals were less than 120 seconds (range: ten seconds to four minutes). Reaction time was measured in fifteenths of a second.

2. *Syllogistic reasoning task (Decoding).* This abstract reasoning task required cooperation between Ss. The dyad had to reach a joint decision as to the truth or falsity of statements, based upon a set of premises. Each S had a set of premise statements needed to determine the truth of a statement of relationship between nonsense syllables. Neither S had sufficient information to arrive at a decision alone. They had to exchange information verbally and identify a chain of reasoning between terms to evaluate the problem statement. Ss worked on thirteen problems of varying difficulty during each one-hour session. The basic performance measure was number of correct solutions on easy, medium, and difficult problems.

3. *Combat information center task (CIC).* This group task was designed to simulate realistically part of a Navy combat information center. Reports of direction, range, and depth of alleged sonar targets were presented over the loudspeaker system, and Ss plotted these on a plotting board and were to determine which formed tracks of vehicles moving in the underwater environment and which were simply random noise. (The majority of reports were random noise, while a small number represented tracks moving in curving or straight line patterns.) Using specified rules of permissible speed and depth changes, teams were to identify real tracks. At the end of thirty reports or five minutes, Ss applied these rules and reported the position of any real tracks they found. Following this, another series of reports was presented. This sequence was repeated six-to-seven times and required an hour.

Each problem had six real tracks, although Ss were unaware of the number. There were several hard and several easy tracks, which differed in terms of amount and nature of information they contained.

Each task was presented an equal number of times at each of the scheduled work periods during a day, to balance time of day effects. Each was begun at the scheduled time employing a set of standard instructions, either prerecorded or read by the observer. The completion of a task period was also indicated by instruction.

Measures of subjective stress and emotional symptomatology. On the tenth day, at the time Ss would normally begin afternoon work, they were informed that the experiment was over. E entered the room shortly thereafter and administered the *Subjective Stress Scale* (*SSS*), developed by Kerle and Bialek (1958). The scale consists of fifteen adjectives to which scale values were assigned by a Thurstone scaling procedure. The adjectives range from "wonderful" and "fine," with low scale values, to "in agony" and "scared stiff," with high scale values. In addition to validation data provided by the authors, the usefulness of the instrument has been reported by Berkun et al. (1962) and Myers (1964). Ss were asked to select one adjective on the list which best described how they felt at the time of testing (*now*); how they felt during the time they were in the experimental rooms (*then*); and how they normally feel (*normal*).

Following this, Ss completed other questionnaires and were interviewed. One instrument of relevance here was a subjective symptomatology questionnaire, developed and reported by Myers et al. (1962), consisting of 240 items from 23 content areas (e.g., visual sensations, dreams, sex, inefficiencies of thought, worry and fright, and physical symptoms).

Results

Analysis rationale. The basic analysis design was a Greco-Latin square to assess composition effects, replicated under conditions of isolation and control and with repeated measures on two to six variables. The monitoring task analysis was a $2 \times 9 \times 3 \times 3 \times 2 \times 2$ design with 1943 degrees of freedom. The variables were Isolation-Control $\times$ Dyads (the Greco-Latin square) $\times$ Time of day (morning, afternoon, and evening) $\times$ Period-within-task-session (blocks of eight trials) $\times$ Time interval between lights (short versus long) $\times$ Days. Two Ss within dyads provided the additional degrees of freedom. In this design, repeated measures were obtained on all variables except isolation-control, dyads, and Ss within dyads.

Analysis of syllogistic reasoning (Decoding) performance followed the same general logic. In addition to the Greco-Latin square and the isolation-control variable, repeated measures were obtained on difficulty level (hard, medium, easy), five two-day blocks, and two different times of day (morning and afternoon). Thus, the analysis design was a $2 \times 9 \times 3 \times 5 \times 2$ paradigm with 539 degrees of freedom.

Two main analyses were done on the CIC task, both of which made comparisons between isolation-control groups and among different compositions of the Greco-Latin square design. They also included repeated measures over three three-day blocks and on different CIC problems. For the case of *unweighted report scores,* it was possible to examine performance as a function of difficulty level, yielding a $2 \times 9 \times 3 \times 5 \times 3$ design with 809 degrees of freedom. Analysis of weighted CIC report scores involved the same design except for the absence of difficulty level comparisons.

The *SSS* and emotional symptomatology data analyses followed the same pattern, i.e., a Greco-Latin square design replicated under isolation and control conditions. For the *SSS,* a third factor, instructional set (*now, then, normal*), was also involved. To facilitate interpretation, analyses were done on all combinations of pairs of instructional sets. A separate analysis of variance was conducted for each of 23 content areas covered by the emotional symptomatology questionnaire.

Detailed results of these analyses are described elsewhere (Haythorn, Altman, & Myers, 1966; Altman & Haythorn, 1965); here we shall only highlight findings in order to describe the characteristics of one sequential chain.

To facilitate exposition, relationships between the independent variables of isolation-control and group composition, and dependent measures of subjective stress and emotional symptomatology will be considered first, and, following this, findings with respect to performance. Subsequently, the set of findings will be integrated into a general conceptual model.

Subjective stress and emotional symptomatology: Isolation versus control

Analysis of *SSS* responses indicated significant differences between isolation and control conditions, but only under the set "How do you feel *now?*" There were no differences between isolation and control conditions for *normal* and *then* sets, although the elevation from *normal* to *then* was significant in both conditions. The absence of an isolation-control $\times$ set (*normal* versus *then*) interaction indicated that Ss in these different environmental conditions reported equivalent stress elevations under the *then* set. For the *now* set, however, the isolations were higher than controls, suggesting a lack of recovery from stresses occurring during isolation. Thus, the hypothesis that isolation Ss would exhibit more subjective stress than controls was supported. Nevertheless, the absolute magnitude of experienced stress was *mild to moderate,* rather than severe—as reflected in a mean response scale value somewhere between "indifferent" and "didn't bother me" under the *then* set.

Although isolation Ss exhibited higher emotional symptomatology on sixty percent of the 23 scales of the questionnaire, differences were significant in only one case, contrary to hypothesis. In view of the previously demonstrated usefulness of this questionnaire, results were compared with those obtained in an earlier study involving 96-hour dark-quiet isolation (Myers et al., 1962). In almost all areas, isolation *and* control Ss in the present study reported more symptomatology than controls in the earlier study, suggesting that our control dyads were under some stress. This is consonant with the SSS results reported above.

In summary, the data partially support the hypothesis that isolation Ss would exhibit greater levels of emotional stress and symptomatology than control Ss, although it appears that the absolute size of the elevation was only of a mild-moderate degree. The elevated SSS scores for the controls suggest that the attempt to make the situation and schedule generally equivalent may have led to some level of stress in our control conditions. (Because of the work schedule and their peculiar status as transients to the naval base, controls also were effectively restricted to each other's company for a considerable portion of the waking day.)

That the stress was real for isolated dyads is indicated not only by these data but by the fact that two of the nine isolated dyads aborted—asked to be released from isolation—before the ten-day period had elapsed. In addition, members of two of the remaining seven groups displayed serious overt hostility toward each other. None of the control dyads gave evidence of this degree of trouble.

Subjective stress and emotional symptomatology for various group compositions

Dogmatism. Ss homogeneously high and homogeneously low on dogmatism were predicted to be more compatible and to exhibit less stress than heterogeneous groups. There were no overall SSS or symptomatology differences among compositions, contrary to hypothesis. On the emotional symptomatology questionnaire, however, there were several dogmatism $\times$ isolation-control interactions which confirmed the hypothesis that isolated incompatible groups would exhibit more emotional symptomatology than isolated compatible groups and that such differences would be less evident for control groups. Isolated hetero-dogmatism dyads, theoretically incompatible, reported more visual sensations, more concern with self-appraisal, more hunger, and more temporal disorientation than other dogmatism conditions in isolation, and more than their matched control counterparts.

Need achievement.   Dyads heterogeneous on need achievement were expected to be more incompatible and to exhibit more stress and symptomatology than dyads homogeneously high or low on this variable. On the *SSS,* heterogeneous dyads reported more stress under the *then* set than low achievement dyads but were not different from the high dyads. On the emotional symptomatology questionnaire, the hypothetically incompatible heterogeneous need achievement dyads reported having more dreams; no other differences were obtained. Thus, partial support for the hypothesis that incompatible need achievement groups will exhibit more subjective stress and emotional symptomatology than compatible groups was obtained.

The expectation that composition effects would be more evident in social isolation received stronger support. Although the *SSS* did not yield any significant isolation-control $\times$ achievement interactions, a number were obtained for the emotional symptomatology questionnaire. The incompatible dyads in isolation differed from their control counterparts more than did either of the compatible compositions. They reported more novelty and surprise, inefficiency of thought, hunger, and regret regarding participation in the experiment, than their control counterpart or the other isolated achievement composition conditions. In addition, they reported more concern with the tedium of time passage, more thoughts of religion, and more reminiscence and memory than the isolated compatible achievement composition conditions.

Thus, the data lend reasonable support to the hypothesis that incompatibility on need achievement produces greater emotional disturbance than compatibility, for isolated dyads only.

Need affiliation.   The hypothesis that incompatible need affiliation groups would exhibit more subjective stress and emotional symptomatology than compatible groups was not supported. In addition, the hypothesis that the effects of compatibility and incompatibility would be more pronounced under conditions of isolation, was only weakly supported.

On the *SSS,* groups incompatible on need affiliation exhibited an elevation in stress from the *normal* to the *now* set, but this was equally true of the compatible compositions. More importantly, there were no differences in amount of *then* stress experienced by the incompatible versus compatible conditions, nor were there any main effect differences on the emotional symptomatology instrument.

Although a number of isolation-control $\times$ affiliation interactions were significant on the symptomatology questionnaire, most results appeared to be associated with differences between low need affiliation dyads in isolation versus control, or in the relatively low level of symptomatology reported by low affiliation dyads in the control condition.

Need dominance.   The prediction that dyads homogeneously high on need dominance would be more incompatible and exhibit more subjective stress and emotional symptomatology than heterogeneous and homogeneous low dominance dyads was not consistently supported by *SSS* responses but was by the emotional symptomatology questionnaire. The maximally compatible dominance dyads—heterogeneous—reported fewer dreams, less concern for passage of time, less anger, less regret regarding participation in the experiment, and a greater feeling of well-being than the other dominance compositions.

The results also confirmed the prediction that composition effects would be more pronounced in isolation. The compatible hetero-dominance dyads showed no elevation in *SSS* scores under either isolation or control conditions. The compatible low dominance dyads exhibited elevated stress from *normal* to *then* sets, but recovered, as indicated in a stress decline under the *now* set. The controls exhibited a complete recovery to normal levels, whereas the isolated dyads exhibited only a partial recovery. For the incompatible groups, however, both isolation and control conditions showed elevations in stress from *normal* to *then* sets, and the isolations did not show a recovery from *now* to *normal* sets. They also exhibited greater stress than either compatible composition. The emotional symptomatology data are partly in line with these results, although the primary differences appear to be between compatible heterogeneous dominance dyads and other compositions.

Summary.   Taken together, the results generally confirm the hypothesis that a condition of social isolation is associated with increased stress and emotional symptomatology. In addition, results suggest that compatibility differences are associated with stress and symptomatology, although not to the extent anticipated. The results strongly indicate that composition is a significant determinant of subjective response to the stress of isolation and confinement—with compatibility and incompatibility factors being most evident under conditions of isolation. This appeared most true for need dominance and need achievement, perhaps indicating the salience of these characteristics for the population and situation studied.

Performance effectiveness of isolation versus control

As indicated earlier, groups worked on three tasks during the ten-day period—two group tasks and a one-man perceptual-monitoring task. To summarize the results of several analyses, the expectation that socially-isolated groups would perform less effectively than non-isolated groups was not confirmed. In fact, results were in the opposite direction, with isolation dyads performing significantly more effectively than control groups, particularly as days of the experiment progressed.[6]

There are, of course, a multiplicity of potential *post hoc* explanations for these findings. For example, some literature suggests that any stimulation in a sensory-reduced environment may minimize performance deterioration (Suedfeld et al., 1964; Zubek, 1963; Zubek & Wilgosh, 1963). It may also be that the lack of a wide range of stimulation permitted or perhaps forced isolated Ss to focus on the immediate task environment more than nonisolated individuals.

In addition, it may be that isolated individuals came to know and depend on one another to a greater extent than controls. One outcome of this may have been more effective teamwork and performance. This is consistent with other results in the present study, indicating that isolates disclosed greater amounts and more intimate information to one another than controls (Altman & Haythorn, 1965).

The obtained results may also be partly due to the somewhat curious condition of controls in the present experiment. Since they worked on the same schedule as isolation groups, they were restricted to a laboratory room for a considerable portion of the day. As transients to the military base, they also were somewhat separate from the regular Navy complement. These conditions may have generated a state of boredom and poor motivation.

Performance effectiveness for various group compositions

Dogmatism. Contrary to hypotheses, groups incompatible with respect to dogmatism performed more effectively than the other compositions, but this was true only in the control condition. In isolation, there were no differences among compositions. Thus, isolation appeared to be an equalizer of compatibility differences, the advantage of the incompatible groups in the control condition having been eliminated or offset by other effects.

Interestingly, there was an indication that compatible dogmatism groups performed better in isolation than in the control condition. The overall picture indicates performance of incompatible groups was de-

---

[6] The issue becomes even more intriguing if one examines the performance of individual groups. Two isolation groups aborted; one was terminated on the sixth day, and the other on the eighth. In both cases, it was apparent that one or both Ss were having difficulty remaining in isolation. Two other groups had a great deal of interpersonal trouble, but completed the ten-day period. These data are not incongruent with those reported elsewhere, which show no difference in performance of individuals who are unable to complete sensory deprivation experience compared with those who do (Zubek, 1964; Myers, 1964). It may be that individuals who had obvious difficulty in isolation devoted more energy to their work as a way of attempted adjustment to the situation.

graded under conditions of social isolation compared to nonisolation, whereas the performance of compatibly composed groups was enhanced in isolation.

Need achievement.   A similar pattern was obtained for need achievement. Again, the data are contrary to the hypothesis, with incompatible achievement dyads outperforming the compatible achievement dyads. However, these findings did not apply equally to isolation and control conditions, as evidenced by significant isolation-control $\times$ achievement interactions. The superiority of the incompatible groups appeared only in the control condition. In isolation, incompatible groups either performed less effectively or equal to compatible groups. In short, incompatible groups in isolation performed worse than their matched controls, while compatible achievement isolation groups performed better than their controls. The net result was an equality in performance among isolation conditions. As before, whatever advantage was associated with incompatibility for control groups was not evident in a more isolated situation.

Need dominance.   Results for this variable showed a similar pattern to those obtained for need achievement and dogmatism. Again, contrary to prediction, incompatible dominance dyads performed better than compatible dominance dyads. However, significant isolation control $\times$ dominance interactions showed that the better performance by incompatible dominance groups did not hold in isolation. Furthermore, compatible isolation groups performed better than their matched controls. Thus, while there was some tendency for the incompatible dominance groups to exhibit reasonably good performance compared to other compositions, there was the suggestion that in isolation this difference was no longer as evident.

Need affiliation.   Results for need affiliation were more in line with original hypotheses, although they were somewhat inconsistent with findings for the other composition variables. As predicted, dyads incompatible on need affiliation generally performed less effectively than compatible affiliation dyads. This effect was more apparent under isolation than control conditions. Finally, isolated incompatible affiliation dyads performed worse than their control counterparts.

A GENERAL CONCEPTUAL MODEL

In attempting to understand the sometimes confirming, sometimes disconfirming and sometimes unclear results concerning performance, subjective stress, and symptomatology, the following general facts are to be faced: Isolates reported more subjective stress and somewhat more emotional symptomatology than controls. On the other hand, they performed more effectively.[7] Second, incompatible groups reported more stress than compatible groups (on two of the four personality variables). Yet, they performed better. Finally, both compatible and incompatible groups exhibited more stress than their similarly composed controls. However, composition effects on performance were less evident in isolation, as compared to the control condition.

If the two sets of data are integrated, there appears to be a positive relationship between situationally-induced stress and performance, between composition-induced stress and performance, and a somewhat cloudier link between stress induced by the interactive effect of situation $\times$ composition and performance. Thus, if one assumes that a moderate level of stress has a facilitating effect on performance, then much of the data of the present study falls reasonably into place. Now one can examine results separately for achievement, dominance, affiliation, dogmatism, and isolation/control and generate unique plausible *post hoc* hypotheses for each cluster. We attempted to develop a more parsimonious set of concepts to help account for the findings. Figures *13-3* through *13-5* illustrate such a general model which appears to integrate the stress findings and performance data reasonably well. Figure *13-3a* proposes a simple sequential link between situational factors and performance, with stress as a mediator. In general, it is inferred that social isolation in this study generated a moderate amount of stress, which facilitated group functioning. As shown, both the stress and performance data are in accord with this conceptualization.

Figure *13-3b* proposes another conceptual chain congruent with other data. As shown, incompatibility among group members on need achievement and need dominance was associated with elevated stress, which, in turn, was associated with enhanced performance.

As Figure *13-3c* indicates, another sequential chain occurs for need affiliation and dogmatism. These data indicate no elevation in stress as a function of either need affiliation or dogmatism incompatibility. However, the *compatible* affiliation and *incompatible* dogmatism compositions performed better than their opposite members. Thus, the data suggest that if incompatibility does not generate interpersonal stress, then *compatibility* may be associated with either better or worse performance,[8] depending perhaps on the nature of the compatibility.

[7] Hereafter, the term *stress* will be used in a general sense to indicate physical, physiological, intra-individual and interpersonal psychological states of a debilitating type. The latter can include anxiety, perceptions of inability to function normally, fright, feelings of malaise, etc. We use the term with trepidation, especially in view of the multitude of distinctions concerning stress that have been made by others.

[8] The question naturally arises as to why incompatibility on need affiliation did

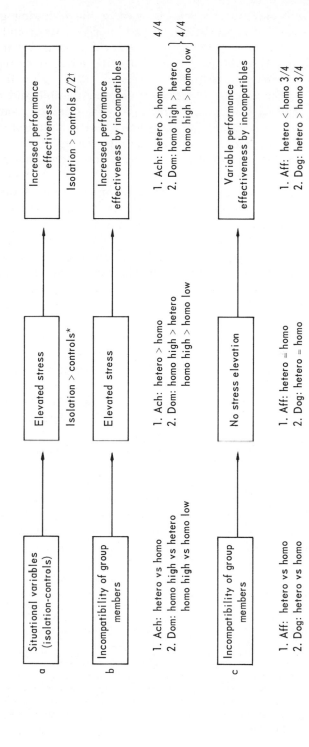

* Indicates the general stress and emotional symptomatology (see Haythorn, Altman, & Myers, 1966).
† Indicates the general performance results reported in this paper. The ratio indicates the number of comparisons in the direction shown in the flow diagram relative to the total number of comparisons made.

FIGURE 13-3. Conceptual model of simple sequential links between situational variables and composition variables, stress and group performance.

The data and conceptual models discussed to this point indicate that one must not only understand situational and interpersonal compatibility links with performance via an intervening set of stress dynamics but that an understanding of the relevance of the particular composition variable to the behavior of interest is critical.

The foregoing considers the operation of situation and composition factors as they separately relate to stress and performance. Interaction terms in the analyses indicate that situational and composition factors also *jointly* operate to affect performance via intervening stress dynamics. Figure *13-4* shows three separate cases of composition $\times$ situation $\longrightarrow$ stress $\longrightarrow$ performance linkages.

Case I represents a composition-stress-performance chain involving *compatibility* between group members. The comparison is between isolation and control groups with the same composition. It can be seen that compatibles in isolation generally tended to exhibit more stress than their matched controls. Thus, isolation generated stress even where interpersonal compatibility was high. For cases where stress was elevated, seven out of ten comparisons showed the isolated compatible groups significantly outperforming their controls. That is, enhanced performance was associated with elevated stress for compatible groups. This conceptual chain is congruent with those discussed earlier.

Case II and Case III of these more complex sequential chains do not show the same pattern, but suggest that beyond a certain point, increased stress does not facilitate performance. Case II shows incompatible groups in isolation versus incompatible groups in the control condition. Here, two types of stresses are operative—one attributable to social isolation and another attributable to interpersonal incompatibility. As the figure indicates, the stress level for incompatible groups in isolation is generally higher than for matched control groups. Yet, their performance is no longer consistently better. In only one comparison did incompatible isolations perform more effectively, while in all other cases they either performed equal to or worse than their matched controls. It appears that as the sources of stress mount, performance is no longer enhanced. While there is no clear evidence of deterioration, there does appear to be a

---

not generate stress whereas the other personality characteristics did, at least for isolation groups. Two alternatives seem compelling. First, it may be that need affiliation characteristics are more "remote" or less directly relevant to task functioning than the other characteristics. Second, it may be that need achievement and need dominance differences were important to much of the isolated group's total functioning, including cleanup and housekeeping activities, sharing of responsibilities, etc., whereas need affiliation differences may be less tangibly linked to interpersonal functioning or may only become evident at later stages of a relationship.

With respect to dogmatism, it may be that heterogeneity is a stimulant to problem-solving effectiveness, in spite of its assumed incompatibility (cf. Triandis et al., 1965). Thus, it appears that one must consider more than the question of compatibility, but also the relevance of a personality characteristic and varying composition to task demands and requirements.

tapering off in advantage. Were the sources and intensity of stress elevated further, performance might actually begin to deteriorate.

This chaining is further suggested in Case III, involving comparisons among isolation compositions. Again, two types of stress are presumably operative—situational and interpersonal. Incompatible isolation groups showed higher stress levels than compatible ones, but did not demonstrate a decided advantage in performance. Again, it appears that the performance enhancement that accrued from only a single source of stress—reflected in the simple sequential chains—was no longer apparent.

Within the constraints of the present experiment, it appears that a reasonable proportion of the data falls into the general composition $\times$ situation $\longrightarrow$ stress $\longrightarrow$ performance model discussed above. While it is incomplete and *post hoc,* the model incorporates the results within a fairly parsimonious set of concepts. Equally important, it appears to have the potential advantage of providing one set of concepts which may prove useful in ordering the somewhat contradictory findings that exist both in the group composition literature and in the isolation research field.

Heretofore, the analysis has been separately concerned with relationships between independent variable classes and stress measures, and between independent variable classes and performance measures. In order to extend and evaluate the logic of this qualitative integration, the relationship between stress and performance measures was examined directly. Figure *13-5* shows one such relationship—between CIC task performance scores and stress response to the *now* set (solid lines), and summarized findings from a study by Berkun et al. (1962) using the same stress measure in a different performance situation (dotted lines). As shown, the combination of points 1, 2, and 3, and points 1, 2, and 3 describes the sequential chains discussed earlier fairly well, e.g., isolated dyads show more stress and better performance than controls, incompatible dyads in isolation perform less effectively than incompatibles in control groups and show somewhat more stress, etc. The puzzling aspect of Figure *13-5* is represented by the point 4—point 1 comparison, i.e., the incompatible versus compatible controls. The sequential chains discussed earlier did not cover this case. The incompatible controls far outperformed the compatible controls but surprisingly did not show greater stress. It is possible that the incompatible control dyads experienced initial incompatibility but were able to minimize stress experiences through energy dissipation via the task, and restricted much of their interaction with one another to the task. The incompatible isolation Ss may not have been able to sublimate completely their interpersonal conflicts via the task. The occurrence of less exchange of personal information by controls supports the idea of their engaging in more limited interaction (Altman & Haythorn, 1965).

The dotted lines of Figure *13-5* represent a rough summary of results

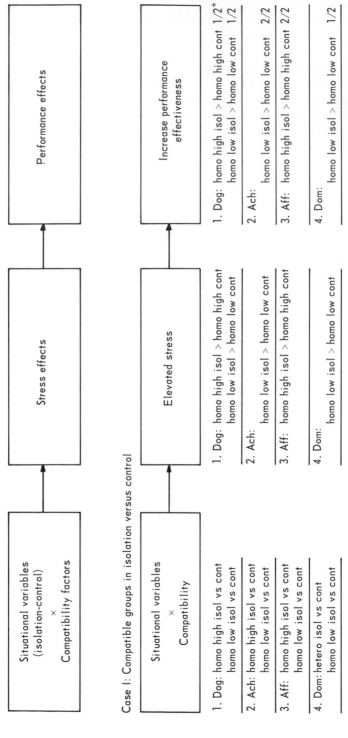

Case I: Compatible groups in isolation versus control

382

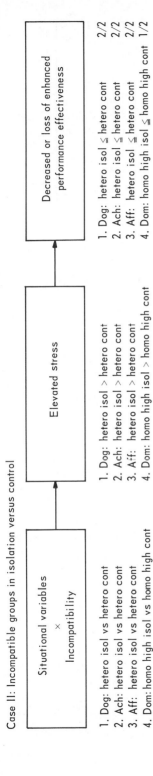

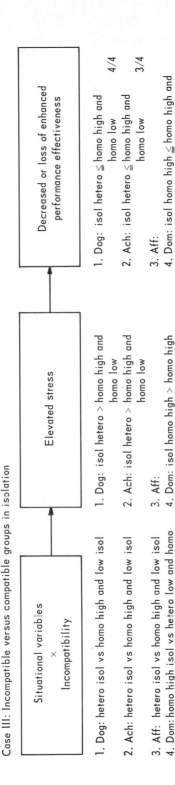

Case II: Incompatible groups in isolation versus control

Situational variables × Incompatibility	Elevated stress	Decreased or loss of enhanced performance effectiveness

1. Dog: hetero isol vs hetero cont
2. Ach: hetero isol vs hetero cont
3. Aff: hetero isol vs hetero cont
4. Dom: homo high isol vs homo high cont

1. Dog: hetero isol > hetero cont
2. Ach: hetero isol > hetero cont
3. Aff: hetero isol > hetero cont
4. Dom: homo high isol > homo high cont

1. Dog: hetero isol ≤ hetero cont   2/2
2. Ach: hetero isol ≤ hetero cont   2/2
3. Aff: hetero isol ≤ hetero cont   2/2
4. Dom: homo high isol ≤ homo high cont   1/2

Case III: Incompatible versus compatible groups in isolation

Situational variables × Incompatibility	Elevated stress	Decreased or loss of enhanced performance effectiveness

1. Dog: hetero isol vs homo high and low isol
2. Ach: hetero isol vs homo high and low isol
3. Aff: hetero isol vs homo high and low isol
4. Dom: homo high isol vs hetero low and homo low isol

1. Dog: isol hetero > homo high and homo low
2. Ach: isol hetero > homo high and homo low
3. Aff:
4. Dom: isol homo high > homo high and homo low

1. Dog: isol hetero ≤ homo high and homo low   4/4
2. Ach: isol hetero ≤ homo high and homo low   3/4
3. Aff:
4. Dom: isol homo high ≤ homo high and homo low   3/4

* Indicates the general performance results reported in this paper. The ratio indicates the number of comparisons in the direction shown in the flow diagram relative to the total number of comparisons made.

FIGURE 13-4.   Conceptual model of joint effects of situation and composition on stress and group performance.

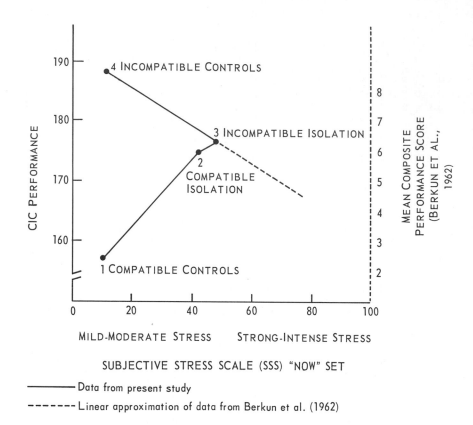

MILD-MODERATE STRESS   STRONG-INTENSE STRESS

SUBJECTIVE STRESS SCALE (SSS) "NOW" SET

———— Data from present study

- - - - - - Linear approximation of data from Berkun et al. (1962)

FIGURE 13-5.   **Relationship between stress and performance.**

obtained by Berkun et al. (1962), who studied performance as a function
of the stressfulness of situations. As is evident, the situations used in
their study evoked higher subjective stress levels (using the same dependent measure of stress as employed here). In addition, it can be seen that
when the stress of the situation was above that of the present study,
performance began to show deterioration. Thus, the combined findings
suggest that, up to a point, increased levels of stress are associated with
enhanced functioning. Beyond that, elevated stress may be associated with
degraded performance output. In the present study, it appears that as
the number of sources of stress was increased, e.g., social isolation and
incompatibility, a point was approached where the enhancing effect of
stress on performance began to level off. Had our situation gone further,
in terms of induced and experienced stress levels, performance might
have begun to deteriorate. Extrapolating, one might hypothesize that

groups operating in a more extreme isolated environment—especially incompatible groups—will show significant performance decrement. Thus, the present results, combined with those of Berkun et al. (1962) and others (e.g., Lanzetta, 1955), provide an integrated set of findings which are consistent with the generally hypothesized inverted-U relationship between stress and performance. Of more specific interest are the hypothesized contributions of situational factors, such as isolation, and interpersonal factors of personality composition, to the characteristics of that general curvilinear function.

There are some obvious qualifications and restrictions to the proposed situation $\times$ composition $\longrightarrow$ stress $\longrightarrow$ performance model. For one, the stress operative in the present experiment has not been defined as strictly and precisely as one might wish. Furthermore, the nature of stress which might be relevant to the phenomena at hand, with regard to number, kind, and intensity, has not been fully identified. As earlier suggested, there are a number of potential sources of stress, e.g., environment, interpersonal characteristics, task characteristics, etc. In spite of these limitations, the model—though admittedly *post hoc*—appears to account for a great deal of data and seems worthy of further experimental research.

General conclusions

The present experiment led to the following general conclusions:

1.   Variations in group personality composition and a situational factor of social isolation have an effect on group and individual performance effectiveness, but understanding their contribution appears to require an understanding of intervening stress levels they may generate. Mild degrees of stress appear to be associated with enhanced performance, whether they derive from the situation or from group composition characteristics. Combining or adding separate sources of stress does not lead to further performance advantage but is associated with a leveling or impairment of performance effectiveness.

2.   Further research appears necessary to validate the Situation $\times$ Composition $\longrightarrow$ Stress $\longrightarrow$ Performance model hypothesized in the present study, which, in turn, may have important implications for existing research on isolation effects and group composition. One key aspect of such research is that it attempts to establish links between isolation and composition characteristics and performance via sequential mediating processes.

The attempt to establish simple bivariate relationships is apt to lead to confusion, for performance outcomes depend not only on initial inputs but also on the nature and characteristics of intervening events. A second desirable aspect of further research in this area is that it attempts to develop sensitive measures and means of experimentally controlling the variety of stresses operative in isolation which are generated within groups as a function of interpersonal compatibility. Furthermore, work is required to identify other types of stresses that develop as a function of task characteristics (e.g., difficulty, overload, etc.) and to integrate these into a general model of the type proposed here.

Invited commentary

PHILIP E. KUBZANSKY: I think that Drs. Haythorn and Altman's paper is very interesting and important from a number of points of view. One of the key issues they raise is one that might be worth a symposium of its own— namely, the strategy in the study of stress. Looking at research today, it is interesting to see the increase in number of real life situations that have come under concern and that have become the focus for attempts at the development of laboratory paradigms. Where we cannot develop adequate laboratory paradigms, we have attempted to look at the situations themselves in as rigorous a way as possible.

It seems to me that as a general strategy in the research on stress, we ought to make more room in our methodological or strategic armamentarium for the natural observation of events that are so difficult to replicate in the laboratory. Good careful observations on situations that occur only once or that are difficult to recapture can make some very worthwhile contributions. For example, I know that Dr. Trumbull and the ONR have supported research on a mountain-climbing group that went out to Everest not too long ago, in an attempt to make some careful observations of the interactions and events on this expedition. As scientists, we recognize, however, the desirability of bringing many of these phenomena under rigorous experimental control where possible. What we attempt then to do is to simulate these procedures in the laboratory, retaining as many of the essential elements in the situation as is feasible. One of the important contributions of the Haythorn-Altman program of research then is its attempt to bring into the laboratory a situation which, to my knowledge, has not been so studied before in quite the same way. They are attempting to study two things: ways of selecting people to be isolated for a prolonged period of time, and secondly, the group interaction and group formation in a meaningful and prolonged exchange between the members of the groups.

The comment was made earlier that much of the social psychological research on small groups consists of artificially constituted groups that get together for very brief periods and rapidly dissolve where we have no information about the evolution or life history of the process. These prolonged periods in the present study—even if very expensive and requiring elaborate instrumentation—do have the virtue of making possible so much more careful and precise observations of the kinds of interactions that take place and the ways in which they change over time.

The Haythorn-Altman approach to the problem is in direct response to the question of the military. "How do we put men together to face difficult environments and to do difficult tasks for a long period of time?"

In attempts to simulate real life stresses and difficult life situations, one has to ask the questions: "What is it that one is attempting to simulate?" and "How can it best be done?" Of course, in the laboratory, the very notion of simulation implies the necessity of compromises all the time. We compromise with the types of tasks with which we confront our subjects, and we compromise with the types of motivational conditions that we impose upon them. If, let's say, our intent is indeed to simulate motivational conditions of severe stress, then it would seem that the consequences of inadequate performance ought perhaps to be more serious than some of our experimental conditions make them. That is, if our subjects fail to solve a given problem, or if they are inadequate in it, perhaps we should reduce the oxygen content in the air or make some other really serious consequence follow upon failure to perform. In this way, we would be coming closer to simulation of the motivational conditions that are essential in the evaluation of performance under these circumstances.

In the same way the simulation of this group-in-isolation situation is one which requires that the experimenter make a whole series of more-or-less arbitrary choices. Let's examine this study closer for some of these choice points. What personality theory does one start from that leads to the selection of the variables of dominance, achievement, affiliation, etc., as relevant "personality" or group composition variables to examine? What conceptions of personality lead us to a definition of compatibility and incompatibility? Do we simply accept patterns of scores on a paper-and-pencil instrument, or do we have some more thorough-going conceptual specification of what is compatibility and incompatibility? This is not so much to argue with the choices made by Drs. Haythorn and Altman as to point out the questions which in our present state of knowledge can lead to a very wide range of choices. The kinds of choices that get made are dictated in part by the extent to which one is trying to simulate some kind of real life conditions and the extent to which one has some kinds of theoretical precommitments which guide the selection of variables.

We might add that the decision to look at dyads is one that has the virtue of considerable simplicity relative to the extraordinary complexity posed by the field commanders' questions, e.g. "Should we put twenty or thirty men in an optimal group?" Given the latter context the dyad offers a very restricted sampling of what is possible. We can't hold the experimenters here responsible for getting answers to everything at one time. We raise this as a way of coming to the question of the strategy of research. Does one choose to approach this problem from the point of view of dyadic interactions, or should one perhaps work with substantially larger groups. A number of other choices that were made in the present study reflect a particular set of guiding concerns that these investigators have had and are not necessarily the choices that others involved in the same research concern would have made.

A second question that is raised concerns the appropriate control group to use in a study of this kind. When one is studying sensory deprivation using single individuals, one is able to define the experimental condition with some precision, at least descriptively. At the conceptual level it becomes very much more difficult to describe of just what the individual has been deprived. Until one offers such a description it becomes very difficult to decide on relevant controls. Or, putting the question another way, "For what is one controlling?" Again, if we look at the present study the members of the control population were recent "immigrants" from Great Lakes Naval Training Station who had just finished boot camp and were new to the NMRI installation. From one point of view, these sailors were not isolated in that they had access to the entire base and to its ample recreational facilities and opportunities. On the other hand, one might argue that two new recruits arriving at a base for the first ten days are very much isolated in some very important respects, and from that point of view, may not be very different from the ones in the experiment proper. They may simply be in a different kind of isolation. Indeed, one can maintain that this is as much a relevant instance of isolation as is the isolation in the chamber itself.

Two other comments bear repeating even if they were made earlier. The first is on the relevance of duration in studying stress. There is much to be gained from an examination of the problem of stress with this perspective in mind in two ways. One of these concerns the impact of, or response to stress at different stages of development. The description by Dr. Lacey (see p. 35) of the different correlations between stress indicators in the child as opposed to the patterns of these autonomic correlations in the adult bears upon the early learning of response to stress; such discrepancies ought to be examined more closely than they have been until now. The consequences of differential stress exposure early in the life of the organism have only fairly recently come under systematic investigation. In addition, a closer examination of the temporal evolution of various stress indicators in a given situation has been emphasized in this symposium several times and perhaps need not be elaborated further.

One final point concerns the reference by Drs. Haythorn and Altman to the facilitation of performance under moderate degrees of stress. It is interesting that the conception of stress that many of us hold, at least in theory, calls for the possibility of behavioral facilitation under conditions of stress. Yet it is relatively rare that we hear much reference to the facilitation issue in this series of papers. In fact, when Dr. Ruff (Chapter 11) made reference to the fact that astronauts seem to be quite facilitated in much of what they did in coping with their mission assignments, the point was raised as to whether, if they were so successful, their situation could be considered to be stressful at all. It seems that in our usual conceptions of stress, we are surprised and taken aback when we find behavior facilitated under what we consider stressful conditions.

Having been a baseball fan for a long time, I frequently think in this connection of Tommy Henrich—an outfielder for the New York Yankees. He was known among ball players as a "money ball player." What made Henrich a money ball player was that while he had only a .260 to .270 batting average—which is acceptable but not outstanding or unusual for a baseball player—if there were men on base, you wanted Henrich at bat because he could be counted upon to get a disproportionate share of hits under these pressuring conditions. The pressure consisted of the pitcher bearing down and the crowd yelling its loudest, but Henrich apparently had the capacity to respond under these circumstances with some facilitation of his performance. This facilitation phenomenon is one to which we have given insufficient attention. We don't know that the correlation between degree of stress and degree of facilitation is a simple or a linear one, but it is reassuring to hear of research making reference to the facilitation question and to see us perhaps giving it more attention.

Discussion

Dr. Ruff: The NMRI study is a fine start on a problem that we can expect to become increasingly important as long-term confinement missions become more frequent—either under the sea or up in space. I wonder if part of the reason that the incompatibility problem isn't more striking is that we don't have a measure of whether there was incompatibility. All that can really be said is that a potentiality for incompatibility was built into the experiment. If it were possible—though I think it would be difficult—to show what degree of incompatibility actually existed, and use this as the independent variable, you might begin to see other kinds of changes.

Dr. Sells: I seriously question whether one can even discuss incompatibility on the basis of scores on tests such as we have here. You might speak of incompatible profiles, but I think incompatibility needs to be tested in terms of interactions between people. A few years ago, when I was working for the Air Force, we were asked by the Training Command if we could match instructors with students in order to get compatible matchings for the purpose of improving the output in flight training schools. We considered using tests at that time and rejected it, but tried another procedure which involved asking instructors, without any guidance as to terms, to indicate what *kinds* of students they wanted, and then asking students what kinds of instructors they wanted. The instructors' answers were rather revealing. Some instructors said they didn't want any students who were taller than 5'5", some preferred no college graduates, others rejected foreign students, and so on. The students' answers were similarly largely related to their interests, such as in instructors who would be more in the category of a peer, or a father-figure, and the like.

There might be some advantage in doing what you actually did, Dr. Haythorn, when you were at Randolph Field where you wrote a paper on crew assembly (1957), based on self-selection of compatibles or rejection of incompatibles.

This comment also leads to the question of the use of the term *group*. When we think of groups we think of stable interaction patterns, etc. These certainly have not been achieved here, nor in most other military situations. This matter was referred to earlier by Dr. Ruff when he mentioned that Slayton was finally assigned as the captain of the astronaut team . . . the question of a person in charge and a mission, etc. I have always expressed myself as being dissatisfied with the use of artificial conditions for this sort of investigation. I feel a much higher degree of realism could be achieved.

In real life, we deal with compatibility among submariners of an elite crew or of astronauts. It might be quite different for others. I think one of the most important kinds of realism that should be considered in this kind of research is to use as subjects people who are at least in the same category and frame of reference of the situation upon which the research is focused.

Dr. Haythorn: I certainly agree with many of the points you made, though many are generated from the basic question asked by the field commander "How can I improve my selection of people in the situation?" We were not directly attacking that problem. We were rather attacking a more general question as to what kinds of interpersonal need structures promote mitigation of stress in a closed environment. We don't regard this as our last study in the area but expect to continue studying additional variables.

Going back to the question of whether we were dealing with compatibility or just with an independent variable manipulation, we were obviously doing the latter. If you define compatibility as a dependent measure, growing out of interaction, then we haven't told you anything about that. We do have the data but we haven't thoroughly analysed that aspect. I think you have to recognize that, given the independent variable manipulation that we initiated, based on the crew composition literature, we did get rather pronounced effects in two particular variables—the need for achievement and the need for dominance. I think the reason that these two came out is that these are salient in this situation for this population of people. In another situation, another population of people, other things might be more salient. If we had had a heterogeneous need achievement situation, within a couple of days the high need achievement individual would begin to criticize the other man for being lazy, not carrying his share of the work, and this would escalate. If they were both dominance-oriented—our observers rated dominance very high at the beginning of the ten day period and this dropped off—apparently they came to grips with the dominance situation by trying to establish a dominance relationship and were not able to do so. We did get the fighting, in fact one attempted knifing. We got a considerable amount of verbal abuse. We had one pair of men simply walk out without asking permission. They just opened the door and walked out. I think there is no doubt that whether these are the best measures or not, we did get some significant facts.

Dr. Altman: I think Dr. Sells', Dr. Ruff's, and Dr. Kubzansky's statements are really getting at a very basic strategic problem concerning research in this area. Studies like this are methodological nightmares in the sense that you make tremendous commitments of resources in terms of money, people, time, and psyche, and you necessarily make decisions that, to a great extent, are based on some degree of guesswork. There is a history of research that you can draw on—but this is a very serious question. For instance, there is the use of the Edwards scale. It is an instrument that has difficulties. It is probably not giving you a detailed picture of an individual, but you are faced with the problem of screening hundreds of people to fit a design. The actual design is artificial in the sense that you are not dealing with interactions among these personality characteristics, or ones like them. The concept of control groups, as Dr. Kubzansky pointed out, is a major problem; I am not sure that there is an appropriate control group, or rather that there are a whole host of control groups. The question is how long should one study a group for such effects to occur? These are relatively arbitrary at this point.

Dr. Lazarus: Dr. Haythorn, you have made stress an intervening variable in your analysis. I wonder what the nature of this intervening variable is. For example, did you speculate about or have some evidence about what accounts for the change in performance as a function of incompatibility and stress?

Dr. Haythorn: Not anything except in an anecdotal kind of way. On the decoding task, for example, a task which requires a lot of communication and a fair amount of very tight back and forth give and take. When we had a pair of men who didn't get along, who disliked each other, who grew literally to hate each other, they would deliberately not tell each other things that they should have. They would have a piece of information that they would deny the other man in order to be the one who came up with the solution. It became not a matter of "this is a team task that we are trying to solve," but "here is a chance for me to demonstrate my control of the situation." So they would hold back or one man would ask for information too fast—"What do you have about so and so," and before the man had an answer—"What do you have about something else," and obviously be using the task behavior as a way of achieving dominance. The other man would back off and this would definitely impair their performance. It was this kind of thing that I think was taking place. The way stress is an intervening variable here is that the tension between them led to use of the task situation as something other than just a task situation. It was an attempt to work out an interpersonal relationship.

Dr. Weybrew: Speaking of interpersonal processes as they relate to stress adjustment, a year or so ago we were asked to plan a selection program for two- to four-man minisubmarine crews. Now these vehicles are very compact exploratory or rescue subs that are designed to go to very dangerous depths. At that time, I felt, and I still do, that one of the best ways to handle this particular screening problem would be to bring the subject "pool" together during the training or orientation procedures, then to implement some sort of a peer nomination or rating technique to obtain data upon which, in part at least, the selection decisions are based. We have used this technique in matching officer and enlisted study groups and in terms of obtaining small groups that function cohesively; this technique seems to work rather well for us. While I am not at all sure of the mechanisms underlying these peer evaluations, I feel the method has considerable merit for selecting small groups to be exposed to stressful situations.

While on the subject of interpersonal processes in peer groupings, I would like to mention some unpublished data suggesting that rather obvious physiognomical cues may be involved. Prior to the launching of the Nautilus in 1954, we were assigned the task of selecting 23 men out of a population of 100 volunteers to be confined in a sealed submarine for two months. Before these 23 men were allowed to become acquainted, we asked each man to rank order passport-size, face-on photos of the remaining 22 men in terms of the likelihood that they will become friendly during the experiment. We were amazed at the correspondence between the rank ordering of the photos and the peer preferences following the sixty-day confinement period.

Dr. Haythorn: I would like to say something with regard to the self-selection procedure because I think it is an illusion to look too far in that direction. The reason is in the following. If you are dealing with two-man groups, there is literature indicating that if people know each other and you give them a chance to choose each other as work partners, they can probably do a better job than we are going to do by any other technique for a long time to come. But you are frequently faced with a situation where men do not know each other very well, and you bring them together for a little while and try to have them mutually choose each other. What evidence I know on this indicates that the choices under these conditions are first of all not very reliable, secondly not very much given to mutuality—which is sort of a basic condition required for a self-selection procedure—and thirdly, if you are dealing with more than a two-man group self-selections are not transitive. That is, if you find that A chooses B and B chooses C, but C rejects A, then you have a problem. I think that we don't know how to resolve this yet. There is a need, I believe, to develop a theory of what sort of personality or individual characteristics are conducive to an effectively operating group, directed towards the eventual goal of trying to assemble crews rationally, even though we may think now that for two-man groups you can do it better by a self-selection procedure.

Dr. Haggard: I would like to return to the comments made earlier about the importance of the time dimension, and especially the importance of the individual's prior life history with respect to interpreting the data in the literature on isolation experiences. A great deal depends upon what the individual has become used to and skilled at doing (Haggard, 1964). In connection with a study of the effects of social isolation, I have seen isolates (persons reared on isolated farms in Norway) show remarkable perceptual acuity—in a world they are used to and comfortable in. But on some standardized perceptual tests, such as one involving imbedded figures, they did not do particularly well. Also, with respect to the phenomena usually associated with the sensory deprivation experiments, we exposed isolates and urbanites to five hours in an "isolation chamber." The urbanites from Norway, like the college students from Canada and the United States, showed the typical range of disturbances during and following the isolation experience. However, the isolates, who had spent a large part of their life alone in the forests or fields, seemed to breeze through the experience with few if any of the usual disturbances. One isolate, when asked if he saw or heard anything unusual during the experiment, replied, "Oh, nothing more than I see or hear in the forest."

Dr. Appley: Dr. Haythorn seemed to suggest that either isolation stress or some type of social interaction stress produced an improvement in performance but that there was a significant decrease in performance when the two were combined. Is that correct?

Dr. Haythorn: Either a decrease or no improvement. We thought that when we got both the stresses operating together we were either at the peak of the curve or approaching the downward side of curvilinear relationship.

Dr. Appley: I was trying to determine where your situations would fall on a stress intensity continuum. For example, you point out that Berkun's continuum started where yours left off. Where then, should we start talking about stress? Is the improvement in performance you noted a function of a kind of mild exhilaration at being in the strange situation? Is it stress? Is it the same thing that happened when you combined the two and you got a shift in the performance curve? In short, we don't know which condition "really" represents stress.

Dr. Haythorn: This is a problem. There have been many comments that imply that stress is a "go no-go" kind of situation, and I don't think it is. As I use the term, it implies a condition under which the organism is faced with a stimulus situation to which it is difficult to respond adequately. I think that a certain amount of difficulty facilitates performance—an individual tries harder—and this is maybe an arousal or activation kind of phenomenon. But if it is too difficult so that his responses are utterly inadequate, you get a breakdown and a performance decrement. Now if you want to limit the concept *stress* to the point at which the decrement starts, then I think we only had three dyads in the "truly stress" area of the continuum.

Dr. Pepitone: I would like to throw in a counterweight in favor of more laboratory experimentation. It seems to me that this study does illustrate something that perhaps could be improved if we had a greater manipulatory control of the situation. For example, the problem of the self-selection of the subjects and the problem of interpreting statistical interaction effects could be overcome by manipulating and generating the incompatibility. For fifteen years now we have had a technique—invented by Professor Back and known appropriately as the Back technique—for experimentally inducing compatibility, congeniality, cohesiveness—call it what you will. It seems that the use of this technique would be the obvious way to determine the effects of such a variable.

Dr. Haythorn: Do we know whether that kind of manipulation persists for any length of time? Would it carry over ten days, for example?

Dr. Pepitone: To my knowledge we don't, but the way to find out is to try it.

Dr. Altman: I don't think that is the answer. We must either take the position advocated by Dr. Sells—that one should observe groups primarily in their natural environment without imposing any kind of manipulative input—or assume that the solution to understanding these phenomena resides at the other end and examine only one segment of behavior at a time in a carefully controlled and rigorously studied environment. I think these are complex phenomena—as are all phenomena that we are interested in—and I would take the position that what we need to do very systematically is to employ a spectrum of methods, all the way from naturalistic observation to tight laboratory control. A study like this represents one point on a continuum and a very incomplete one.

Dr. Pepitone: I don't want to be misunderstood as to the value of field and especially naturalistic research. I am simply suggesting that if one wants to find out the effects of incompatibility, the best way to do it is to generate this kind of social relationship.

Dr. Opler: I have a compromise suggestion. Maybe it grows out of listening to Dr. Lazarus' paper, noting that he said something in his title about cognitive and personality factors operating, and then recalling that Dr. Sells talked about the importance of realistically getting these personality factors into the picture. I agree with Dr. Pepitone that we should have tight research design. Now it seems astounding to me that if one is going to do research on stress, one does not screen people.

The merest suggestion would be to think from psychiatric cases back to normals. In psychiatric cases I find people who love stress. Like Dr. Kubzansky's examples, they operate well under stress, they are masochistic people who like pain. Sometimes they like to inflict it, too. If this is so, I don't know why things like MMPI subscales can't be used to determine who these individuals are, in some kind of profiling sense, and then subject them to these kinds of stresses, whether they are the incompatibles or the something else, to see how these *already* patterned models of behavior and personality are going to operate under certain circumstances. Otherwise there is again a kind of assumption about human beings in our society viewed as if they were men from Mars upon whom we impose laboratory conditions. They come into the laboratory, we assume, as free souls. I just don't think there is this amount of free will and undetermined personality in existence.

Dr. Lucas: I was very interested in Drs. Haythorn and Altman's compatibility idea because in our study of the 1958 Nova Scotia mine disaster, a real life problem under real life stress, involving the choice of living or dying and the decision to drink urine in order to survive, the question of compatibility just didn't arise. What did arise (see Beach & Lucas, 1960) was a structuring, a division of labor, a social organization that made it possible for a group of interacting miners to be able to survive for a week entombed in a mine without food, water, or contact with the outside. I have listened to the kinds of problems discussed in the other papers and have found that few of them arose in the rather detailed accounts of each man's week trapped in the mine. My feeling is that the kind of stress arising from a natural mine disaster—am I going to live or die?—is so very different from the electric shock or other types of laboratory-induced stress that the problems experienced by the men involved are also different.

Now, without any question, I was amazed at the number of experimental laboratory findings that we were able to support from the real life evidence of the Minetown study. This is impressive. I was not completely convinced of the validity of laboratory findings until we found the number of small group research conclusions which were verified in the mine disaster study. But, it remains that under the kind of all-pervading stress of impending death experienced by the miners, the conscious preoccupation was not with the kinds of problems discussed today. Instead, it was simply how to maintain life. One crucial problem was: "Can I behave like a 'man' in this situation?" To act and, if necessary, die like a man and a miner was very important, and from this simple point a whole set of social controls over behavior developed.

One interesting point was that some miners who were judged by psychiatrists as badly mentally damaged performed very well while trapped in the mine. This supports Dr. Opler's point, a point made several times before, that people who do not cope too well with the world on a day-to-day basis perform extraordinarily well in certain kinds of stress situations.

Dr. Haythorn: Perhaps if we place our particular laboratory studies in the larger Navy context, the problem of field versus laboratory studies will go away! We were set up at Bethesda specifically as a laboratory-oriented group because the Navy already had Dr. Wilkins' group at San Diego, and Dr. Weybrew's group at New London dealing with field situations, and ONR, who are supporting all kinds of laboratory research in that medium. We were conceived, in any case, as a kind of in-between group that would try to scan what was being done in the field situations, in Wilkins' and Weybrew's areas, keep in touch with what research is coming out of ONR, try to provide a focus for funnelling or identifying research problems relevant to confinement and conducting laboratory research where it was needed, but also leaning heavily on both of these other wings of the spectrum, if you wish. So I think that what everyone has said is certainly in our overall philosophy. You need field studies, you need laboratory studies, and something we don't have much of at all, I think, we need computer models.

Dr. Arnold: I don't quite know just what kind of computer model is being suggested, but I was going to say that, of course, our aim as scientists surely is to provide the kind of laboratory design that is going to refine the natural situation. But all the same it seems to me we should start with a natural situation, for instance in this compatibility selection it would be a good thing to start with a naturally compatible group, however you can—you can select them out by sociometric techniques or the techniques that Dr. Weybrew suggested— and then find out whether in these really compatible people or groups you can see any personality differences or personality factors that you do not find in your incompatible groups. It seems to me extremely dangerous to commit yourself to any theory, no matter how beguiling, in devising tests for compatibility. The safest way is always to start from empirical determinations. Find a compatible group and an incompatible group and then find out what the personality characteristics are.

Dr. Haythorn: I quite agree with the need to look to empirical data, but I would like to point out that our concepts of what are compatible and incompatible did not spring from whole cloth. There is quite a bit of research on crew composition and on compatibility—much of it having to do with marital relationships to be sure, but also much of it having to do with group cohesiveness. We looked to that literature, which I have been reviewing off and on for several years. From that we identified these four dimensions as four which had a reasonable amount of empirical support. They were not the only ones with empirical support, but they were four that—if one were to limit himself to four—most people I think would come up with.

Dr. Nowlis: Was there any positive affect shown, particularly in the isolation groups? Did they have fun? Did they play? Did they goof-off in vigorous ways that were somehow satisfying and tension reducing?

Dr. Haythorn: Some of them certainly did, yes. The pairs that were compatible on dominance, by our definition, seemed to enjoy themselves a great deal. We have one pair in particular that developed, for reasons that were completely irrelevant to our design, a very compatible relationship. This was because they both had high interest in hot rods, and one of them was an artist. They knew their cars well enough so that they could talk along such lines as—"Could you put the hood from a '54 Chevy on a '52 Ford?" And they knew enough to answer the question whether it could be done, and then the artist would draw a car like that. They would put the picture up and decide whether they liked it, and then they would go on to other similar considerations. They spent all of their spare time during the ten days doing this. Any time one picked up the earphones and listened in on them they were talking about cars. When we interrupted them—and interrupted is the word—to announce that the period was over, they were genuinely disappointed—they were having a ball!

Dr. Mandler: If the question to be answered is—What does incompatibility do?—obviously you manipulate compatibility and find out. But I don't think this is what this project was about. The question was: What produces lasting compatibility for two subjects? How can we produce a group that will be lastingly compatible? The question of what incompatibility does was, in a sense, already answered before the experiment ever started, namely it is going to be bad, we won't like it. In other words, if the question had been the one that you raised, then manipulation obviously would have been the answer. What bothers me about the way we have gone about this problem of group compatibility is that we are now getting into a field which is very, very tired, namely the field of personality theory. We still pursue some classical concepts and try to make the inherited theories work. Even the best of the lot, the Murray-McClelland theory and typology (see McClelland et al., 1953), hasn't lived up to its promise. During the past ten years some fields in psychology have been reawakened—social psychology, psychophysiology, verbal learning—and maybe personality theory is going to be reawakened one of these days. Right now, it all seems static and old hat. This is not a reflection at all on the people who are doing the research. After all, I am not asking Dr. Haythorn or Dr. Altman to come up with a brand new personality theory that is going to throw over current notions. We must work with what we've got, but what we've got hasn't worked too well and I see no reason to expect that it will.

Now, how are we going to break out, how can we wake up the field? Dr. Arnold suggested essentially empirical research. You find out which groups work and which groups don't work and measure their personality characteristics. I would be all in favor of that strategy if we knew what we were looking for in the first place. I don't think we will find out by going back to the classical variables that haven't produced much in twenty years, and we're not going to get there even with purely empirical research to find a compatible group. Unless you know what variables you're going to look for in that compatible group, it isn't going to do a thing for you.

Dr. Appley: One problem that emerges is that one decides to use or study certain variables and then begins to treat them as if they were the same variable that everyone else using similar terms is treating. I particularly come back to stress and ask if we are using the same base lines? Are we in the same range at all when we talk of *stress* in the ten-day isolation room at Bethesda, as compared to sixty days in a submarine in midocean, as compared to an astronaut in space? We ought to be very careful to report the range *within* the variable that we expect we are considering. In Dr. Haythorn's setting, for example, we may have an anxiety situation and maybe an approach to a stress situation. The two are quite different—and yet we meld the data without recognizing this. We lose something in translation from a field study to a laboratory study and back again. I think it's a point we must constantly keep in mind.

Dr. Haythorn: I would like to agree with that and suggest that, since we have been trying to find physiological versus psychological relations, the subjective stress scale (*SSS*) that was developed by HUMMRO (Kerle & Bialek, 1958), has been validated in a variety of situations, has been correlated with physiological measures, and stands up reasonably well, might be a good instrument by which we could share some evidences as to where we are on the scale.

Dr. Nowlis: A number of references have been made to the fact that high levels of physiological arousal do not necessarily require the presence of a stressor, a cognitive appraisal of threat, the contending emotions of anger and fear (as Dr. Arnold calls them), or the occurrence of negative affect. Following Dr. Kubzansky's reference to the ball player who hits best in the clutch, we might take time to consider as model a situation which regularly provides high arousal, unusual performance, and pleasure—that of sex behavior. Even though many of the physiological indices of sex arousal are similar to those of anger and of fear, most people do enjoy sexual activity and often perform with unusual vigor and often find that they have better muscular coordination than usual. The model suggests that in training for the performance of any task which may have to be performed under conditions which elicit high levels of activation, we should try to build some positive affect into the performance as soon as possible. If the bodily signs of arousal in performing the task are regularly accompanied by positive cognitive appraisal and by pleasure, performance might improve rather than deteriorate when situations leading to very high levels of arousal are encountered, whether deliberately or inadvertently.

Dr. Mandler: I don't find anything particularly surprising about the high level of physiological activity in sexual arousal. Another example of an activity that produces high physiological arousal *and* pleasure is the roller coaster phenomenon. I am sure that if you get people on the roller coaster and take their heart rate and GSR on the downturn of the roller coaster, you are going to get the usual signs of autonomic arousal, yet some people continue to seek out this stimulus week after week. I think sex and the roller coaster situations have two aspects to them. First of all, the variable that Schachter (1962) has stressed, namely that arousal is one thing but the conditions under which the arousal occurs determine the tone of the emotion, determine the affect. The other one is that in neither of those two situations—either sexual arousal or the roller coaster—is there any problem as to what you are going to do next. Presumably, you are going to get off the roller coaster, you know where the roller coaster is going to go, you have every belief that it is going to get there at the end. The analogy to sexual behavior I leave to your imagination. In other words, there is no helplessness, there is no disorganization, and under those conditions arousal produces positive affects. It only produces the negative affect if there is in fact helplessness.

Dr. Arnold: Since there seems to be so much difficulty in determining whether one type of stress is the equivalent of another, would it not be better, as I have suggested in my paper, to start from stress emotion rather than to find a criterion for stress? Dr. Haythorn has described a situation that aroused boredom, and boredom surely is an emotion, but an emotion quite different from fear of death among the miners and different also from the confidence felt by the astronauts who seemed to strive for mastery in a challenging situation. This confidence, even audacity, is perhaps also the emotion felt by people on the roller coaster who seem to accept the challenge despite their natural fear.

Chairman's summary

RICHARD TRUMBULL: Experience has taught us that environment has a social aspect, the nature of which has strong implications for tolerance to other stressors and the level, type, and duration of performance of those involved. The NMRI research program describes attempts to determine the social factors and their influence. The isolation setting is dictated by Navy requirements for and concern over protracted submerged operations. The choice of criteria and personality measures reflects the interests of the investigators. As indicated, the situation is complex, and many other approaches could have been employed. Deliberate matching and mismatching of subjects (pairs) on dogmatism, need achievement, need affiliation, and need dominance did not produce the level of stress differences anticipated, although incompatible dyad interactions and performance do lend support to the basic hypothesis. Some of the differences might have been decreased due to the presence of a more stressful situation for the control group than had been anticipated. Another consideration is whether other measures of incompatibility might not be required. There is evidence of social exchanges as well as strong affect with some pairs. The problem of sampling this behavior in some objective and reliable manner remains.

While this study began with dyads to keep the design simple, it is possible that such reduction invites techniques too refined for present technology. Transition from observational and report methods of large group interactions to this level of understanding is not easy to accomplish when so many variables still are uncontrolled. Salience of measures for the situation and type of subjects is mentioned by Dr. Haythorn. It is one area demanding more attention but only to be predicated upon a more thorough acquaintance with both situation and subject than is current practice. Dr. Mandler suggests that this will involve a new look at personality theory itself. Dr. Appley desires another definition for this type of situation if isolation is to be the sole determinant of *stress*. His comment about the experimenter's assumption of stress because he so structured the situations reminds us once again of the *subject's* perception of the situation. This applies, too, to their perception of each other in this situation.

Comment was made earlier about the Everest expedition, and I would note two observations made by Lester in the report of that study, relevant to others made here. Lester believed that the size of the team was one of the things which saved it. He had a definite feeling that you have to have a certain number of people involved so that you have more interactions available or outlets. One could talk about social deprivation as well as sensory or perceptual deprivation. There is the problem of number—and we have run into number before in decision-making groups, etc. It opens a whole different complex of things. With respect to rating, Lester reported that these men rated each other before they started—while they were still relatively unacquainted with each other—and the same ratings obtained all the way through the experience. He speculated as to the meaning of these findings—does this mean that once you rate somebody you then look for the characteristics in him which substantiate your original rating? Or are we really that good in our preliminary judgments, or estimates, of other people's personalities on first meeting them?

RICHARD TRUMBULL

MORTIMER H. APPLEY

41

Some pervading issues

The preceding chapters have dealt with some focal issues in research in one of the most active areas of investigation in this past decade. Interest in and need for stress research have been enhanced by the programmatic extensions of man's operating environment that are taking place today as he explores outer space and the ocean floor. The accelerated pace of these developments has given rise to an increasing number and variety of investigations and has led to an ever-broadening use of the concept of stress to cover a wide range of phenomena, situations, stimuli, reactions, and effects.

The theories, techniques, and interpretations of results presented in the foregoing chapters represent the applications of various disciplines to the analysis of stress. We have indicated the early origins of man's awareness of the balances by which he maintains himself in hostile environments and outlined the more specific recent developments given impetus by the work of Selye and his associates.

We have reviewed stressful situations which were imposed, (e.g., captivity), assigned (e.g., submarine duty), chosen (e.g., Space and Antarctic missions), and devised (e.g., experimental settings), wherein the personal and situational variables believed to be relevant to the impact or successful duration of periods of exposure are evaluated. This is a spectrum of stress situations—from the natural to the simulated or experimental to the unnatural. What is studied varies from reactions of systems within man to reactions of man as an individual, man in groups, and man in society, as he fails or succeeds in dealing with various parts of that spectrum.

The problems inherent in attempts at translation of the concept of stress from one discipline to another and, especially, in attempts to refine it beyond a very general level are apparent from the reading. One must agree with Dr. Cohen's observation that "stress is one of those peculiar terms which is understood by everyone when used in a very general context but understood by few when an operational definition is desired which is sufficiently specific to enable the precise testing of certain relationships" (p. 78).

Since each paper was discussed and each chapter summarized, no further attempt at summary will be made here. This final chapter will, however, examine some of the pervading issues which have emerged from the papers and discussions on which this volume is based. We do not expect that all of the participants will agree with the way we have structured these issues, but we do hope that this effort will allow the reader to depart with at least a partial sense of closure or satisfaction that the picture is becoming clearer and that the areas where efforts still are demanded are beginning to appear.

A man is not a man . . .

In the beginning, one must accept that a man is not a man is not a man! Too many studies start like a recipe which says "take an egg." A good cook knows that the egg makes a difference. A good research man knows that the history of his subject makes a difference. This is particularly true of research in the stress field. The society and the culture from which a man comes form important parts of his history. Dr. Opler has observed that society defines stress for the individual while it is itself being subjected to stress in its own evolution. That evolution and resultant stress are often precipitated by acceleration. Time, pacing, and temporal patterning, then, become variables with which we must deal from the beginning.

Cultural patterns establish the limits which define the stressfulness of events and even the acceptable modes of reaction in voice, gesture, grimace, and, to some extent, physiological output. The standards thus set are often so strong as to override very basic needs. This may result in unusual tolerances for some stressors, on the one hand, and in loss of life due to social inhibitions (e.g., food taboos) or selective sensitivities, on the other. Dr. Back suggests that this is almost a "social reductionism," in that the adaptation even of our physiological system follows societal definition of what "ought" to disturb, disgust, or distress us and the kinds of loads we are "supposed to" be able to take.

The problems posed for an experimenter, then, who does not share or understand the norms that govern the particular cultural or social substratum to which his subject belongs, are many. Cultural determinants are brought into the "testing" situation by the subject and are often so potent as to mask the effects of any experimental manipulations. In stress research, therefore, there is a very real need for cultural normative data in order to identify response repertoires of groups within and across cultures and societies. Only by comparison with such norms can we hope to interpret meaningfully changes (or lack of change) observed in our studies.

The subject also brings genetic, biochemical, and neurophysiological histories along with him. It is increasingly clear that baseline data and longer periods of testing are required to assure oneself that deviations in neurophysiological measures represent responses beyond the normal fluctuations of the system(s) involved. The cyclic nature of cardiac, respiratory, and other system operation, for example, and the demonstrated differences in responses elicited by stimulus imposition at various times within these cycles, makes such histories most relevant to an understanding of phenomena occurring at a given moment. The experiment begins, in effect, many minutes, hours, days, or years before we undertake specific manipulation of the subject or his environment to study his stress responses.

Dr. Stern reminds us, further, that the cardiac system may have both specific and nonspecific responses. Dr. Bovard focuses our attention on the neurological systems, with capability of reciprocal inhibition and facilitation, as the mediator of all responses. Drs. Oken and Cohen point to adaptive and/or permissive roles for the adrenal cortex, also a system with a history. These observations make more evident our need for better understanding of the functioning of these systems under normal circumstances as a basis for appreciating their roles in stress reactions.

A measure is not a measure . . .

Although somatic (and specifically autonomic) response measures are widely used to index stress, Dr. Lazarus reminds us that the maximum correlation between various indicators of autonomic nervous system reaction is probably only modest under the most favorable conditions, while Schnore (1959) finds such correlation only in direction but not in degree. A number of persons in the past have expressed concern over the lack of correlation among physiological measures and between such indices and feelings of emotion or stress reactions on motor or other levels. Inadequate measurement techniques have been blamed for the "failure" to find better relations. On the other hand, it should be emphasized that the poorly correlating indices provide the major basis for the study of response patterning. We have yet to find the real key to an understanding of such patterning. It may lie in some form of real time, auto-correlation, stereotyped situations, personal history, or other framework not yet considered. It may be that conditioning or cultural patterns constrain some or all of the expressions of response available. There is further no reason for assuming that the psychobiological system has but a limited number or variety of responses available to it, or that all ages, sexes, and cultures must exhibit the same pattern. Too much data show differences within the individual related to time of day, momentary emotional state, set, anticipation, the physiological learning mentioned by Dr. Ax (see p. 38), and so forth, to promise a simple answer.

Dr. Korchin finds value in the lack of correlation, in that it forces us to examine the conditions under which correlations might not exist. (In the case of novelty, as an example, there might well be physiological response but no affective response.) Dr. Lazarus agrees that we should focus on "just those instances where our response measures *don't* agree" (p. 179). He points out that response divergence has always been an important basis for inferences about intervening psychological processes (e.g., in clinical diagnosis) and that the psychodynamics of stress will be best understood if we concentrate here.

Accumulating evidence appears to point to differential patterning *within* the sympathetic nervous system itself. Electromyography indicates that the neuromuscular system exhibits individual response specificity just as does the autonomic system. Further, personality variables play a role in determining muscle tension both at rest and in stressful situations. One certainly should expect discrepancies then at some levels.

The conviction that correlations should exist among electrocortical, autonomic, and behavioral arousal systems persists, Dr. Lacey suggests, because they *"in general* occur simultaneously." However, he is convinced that they are "different forms of arousal, each complex in itself," forming "imperfectly coupled, complexly interacting systems." He concludes that ". . . one cannot easily use one form of arousal as a highly valid index of another" (p. 15). If these are indeed different arousal systems, as is suggested, they should be functionally and anatomically separable by appropriate experimental means. This in turn would help clarify the meaning of the measures we typically obtain in stress research.

Those who share Dr. Lacey's opinion that continued search on the present path is unprofitable can show that there has in fact been a shift in emphasis in psychophysiological research away from the use of physiological variables to index psychological events and toward the treatment of physiological and psychological variables as independent dimensions reflecting integrative CNS activity. As a result, more careful consideration is being given to individual differences in both resting and stimulated response patterns in the various systems; and more attention is being paid to the effects of varying levels of CNS activity on the various systems and to the influence of initial level of activity on later response patterns.

Our need to focus on initial levels, cycles, and integrative processes is further emphasized when the question of "psychological mediation" of adrenal and other endocrine stress responses is taken into consideration (see Discussion in Chapter 3).

Laboratory versus life . . .

Dr. Lacey's concept of *situational stereotypy* provides us with a natural bridge to our next issue—the experimental versus real life stress situation. While we have indicated that the subject's history might account for idiosyncratic patterning of responses, it is Dr. Lacey's impression that individual history differences will be overwhelmed by environmental factors and that *classes* of stressor situations will become our point of interest. The subject-situation interaction may account, for example, for the specific versus nonspecific cardiac patterns mentioned by Dr. Stern. As Dr. Lacey reports, the cardiac system is "particularly responsive to the intention of the subject to note and detect external stimuli" (p. 33).

As we set up our stress experiments, we must be mindful, too, that other kinds of behavior, e.g., internalized problem-solving activity, may affect the degree to which we will get the external attention which our design or instructions demand. Man, as has been emphasized, is not just a passive participant in his environment or the experimental situation we wish to structure. His active participation is colored by the histories of which we have been speaking, by his previous experience with situations similar to the one to which he is exposed, and by his ability to recognize those similarities (whether the "recognition" is overt or covert). There is good experimental evidence, for example, that the *anticipation* of the re-occurrence of dreaded events that a person previously experienced will produce physiological changes as great as or greater than those that would occur if exposed to the events themselves. Finally, Dr. Sells reminds us that even the mere posture assumed by a subject represents some hypothesis concerning the nature of the environment or experimental situation. He cites the influence of ongoing activity upon the effects of drugs, for example, wherein exactly opposite reactions can be obtained from a same treatment, depending on the subject's activity state (p. 39). How meaningful can results of studies be if experimenters fail to take account of or control for possible masking variables which happen not to be the ones they are concerned with manipulating?

The circumstances under which the subject is recruited, the orientation he receives, the setting in which the experiment takes place, the instructions, both explicit and implicit, he is given, the nature of the stimulus (both as intended by the experimenter and as perceived by the subject), etc., may introduce variables not explicitly being manipulated or studied that would influence results in unknown or unknowable ways. Obviously, as many of these situational factors as well as subject condition and history factors need to be controlled as is possible. It is further obvious that age, as well as specific previous experience (and these are not necessarily correlated), plays a role.

Witkin et al. (1954) have demonstrated that children are initially field-dependent, becoming less so as they mature. This suggests that field-dependency may be associated with a more primitive, less mature, less integrated, or less organized perceptual apparatus or CNS, especially as it concerns integration of external and internal signals and the formation of a stable internal norm. Thus, Culver (1964) reports that field-oriented subjects perform more poorly than body-oriented subjects on three tests of spatial-perceptual ability (tactile localization, embedded figures, and laterality discrimination). These findings, together with his somatosensory and autonomic response findings, suggest that differences in integrative CNS functions might be related to (or correlates of) perceptual mode differences. A number of findings of variability in drug responsivity related to psychological differences in subjects (as measured by the MMPI and psychiatric interviews) have also been reported. Lasagna et al. (1954) note that placebo reactors were more anxious and more dependent on outside stimulation than upon their own mental processes (similar to field-dependent subjects). Notterman and Trumbull (1959) call attention to subjects who are active searchers for inputs from the environment. Other studies have emphasized the influences of subjects' expectations interacting with conditions of experiments in determining responses to drugs, as has earlier been noted.

For Dr. Opler there is ample evidence that different cognitive preparations for the same stimuli result in different physiological responses. This cognitive level of meaning and symbolic interaction in humans is the very level on which anthropologists begin their inquiries into conditions under which culture operates and human beings adapt, strive, cope, and develop (or fail to). Immediate interaction is discussed by Dr. Stern, who points out that marked differences in physiological responses, as well as subjective reports, are obtained in reaction to a same objective stimulus if subjects are led to expect a shock versus the experience of a tingling sensation. Grings, Carlin, and Appley (1962) showed that subjects could be led to report they had received a shock and to give galvanic skin responses reflecting this even when no shock was administered under conditions in which a series of unrelated expectancies were consistently confirmed and shock delivery was at least perceived by the subject to be feasible in the situation. Berkun et al. (1962) found that real life (military training) stressors did not act as such if subjects refused to accept them as threatening.

Finally, with regard to the stressfulness of the testing situation, it may be noted that some conditions may provide a distraction or welcome relief rather than being the stressful exposure intended, if introduced in a context that is itself stressful. Dr. Ruff acknowledged that this was likely the case in the brief sensory deprivation exposure given the astronauts, for example, during a week of hectic activity (see p. 313). This introduction of tests to ascertain level of vigilance or of performance degradation during an exposure will be discussed later as a problem of research methodology in this field.

The social context

One final category of variables is introduced when subjects are placed in stressful environments in pairs or groups. The resultant social stress conditions of competition, pressure to conform, achievement, etc., significantly affect the subject as he strives for self-evaluation, self-improvement, and/or self-validation, in Dr. Pepitone's terms (see Chapter 7), and enormously complicate the task of the investigator. Dr. Mechanic suggests that many other socially-derived goals and motives come into play as well (p. 200), while Drs. Haythorn and Altman enumerate the complexities encountered when dealing even with simple pairs or dyads (Chapter 13).

Social conditions can set behavioral and physiological norms, as was earlier noted, which carry over into subsequent experience. Some measures now employed are sensitive to these social conditions and the order in which they occur, while others appear to reflect relatively stable characteristics of the individual. The latter, in turn, may influence coping behavior directly or through the mediating process of appraisal. As an example of direct influence of a personality trait, Dr. Lazarus points out that social constraints may be ineffective in inhibiting the expression of coping impulses in individuals who characteristically lack impulse control (Block & Block, 1952). Such an "act now, regret later" pattern does not involve a mediating evaluative appraisal process.

Finally, there would appear to be a need for further structuring of the social aspects of stress to find the social counterparts of the many systems indicated on the more psychophysiological level. Dr. Mechanic properly decries the emphasis which has so far been given in stress research to *intra*psychic dynamics to the neglect of attention to studying "the ways in which people use their abilities, skills, strategies, and information in approaching threatening situations" (p. 201). He feels that man's skills in actively molding, structuring, selecting, pacing, energy mobilizing, and directing, etc., in dealing with the environment are neglected and that the extent of a stress experience is a direct reflection of these as well as "the extent to which the individual has social and environmental supports" (p. 202).

Interaction with the stimulus

Let us turn now from discussions of cultural and biological history, previous experience, the interaction of the subject with the testing environment, and the effects of social context to a consideration of the interplay between subject and stimulus. There is no question that we strive to attain as much objectivity as possible in the measurable aspects of stimuli and responses, such as myography, adrenal productivity, EEG, EKG, motor response, and even mood and subjective state. But Dr. Arnold reminds us (Chapter 5) that although we may be successful in such measurement, our data do not provide a picture of the underlying processes which are set in motion by the stimulus. She suggests that a series of appraisals, actions, reappraisals, and reactions goes on before a subject finds some means for reducing the actual or perceived value of the stimulus where the latter is negative. She believes that such an intervening process must be posited if we are to account for the perceptual and response variability that is typically encountered.

Past exposure and experiences of success or failure in dealing with the same or similar situations provide the setting against which neurophysiological, biochemical, and endocrinological reactions are set into motion. Her elaboration implies that appraisal, recall, and imagination are not unitary functions but are modality-specific, just as are sense experiences. Her experiments, limited to single sensory modalities, are designed to test hypotheses about brain function in this appraisal sequence. There is little question that cognitive control over response to stressful situations can be complete. Misperception, illusion, and delusion are cognitive products and are all capable of destroying the value of a stimulus.

Dr. Lazarus (Chapter 6) believes that behavior is organized by these cognitive processes leading to emotion and not by the emotions themselves. These processes are the intervening elements in psychological stress analysis and serve as precursors of stress reaction, though the way in which they function is yet to be understood. Dr. Lazarus denies that cognitive appraisal implies awareness, good reality testing, or adaptiveness. He argues only that thought processes ("beliefs, expectations, perceptions, and their motivations") must be involved both in determining threat production and perception and in coping. He further points out that identification of the conditions which precipitate the former does not, by itself, lead to prediction of the nature of the reaction.

Dr. Pepitone suggests that appraisal likely involves at least five assessment steps: (1) of the relevance of the event to the individual's existing state, (2) of the degree of danger, (3) of the resources available to one, (4) of whether fight or flight is indicated, and (5) of how to structure the defense or escape. Dr. Lazarus reminds us that there will be specific appraisals which lead to each form of coping with its observable behavioral and physiological response pattern. The same will be true for each form of defense. Identification of these relationships is a major task before us. For clarification, Dr. Mechanic (p. 201) suggests that coping and defense be defined and maintained separately, with coping referring to instrumental behavior and capacities for meeting life's demands and goals, and defense referring to the manner in which one manages his emotional and affective states when discomfort is aroused or anticipated. Dr. Appley (p. 170 ff.) offers an even more detailed breakdown of the possible steps involved in threat production and perception and in coping and defense. In any event, these appraisals are shaped by the stimulus configuration and personality as they interact.

"Private events"

The by-products of subject-stimulus interaction have been the major items of interest in stress literature and have called upon many measurement techniques of physiology, biochemistry, psychophysiology, personology, and other disciplines. The intercorrelations of these measures and the problems associated with limited time samples, temporal patterning, etc., have been discussed above. Less is known or appreciated about another method of assessment of stress effects—that of verbal report or the "private events" which, as Dr. Korchin observes, are so often lost in the shuffle of behavioral and physiological measurements. This interplay takes one back to earlier James-Lange theories of emotions and the relationships between "feelings" and response.

Dr. Nowlis provides us with a schematic representation of the three levels of processes—physiological, mediating, and phenomenological (see p. 356). He suggests that as functional relationships are established for any one of the sets of intra-organismic processes and events, an attempt be made to assess the degree of articulation between relationships at that level and those at either or both of the other levels for a given environmental input. Such a procedure could tell us whether we indeed do need information about private events if we are to be able to predict, control, or understand behavior. Dr. Nowlis is certain that the content of these private events depends very much upon the same processes of social learning which are involved in verbal behavior. Thus, techniques which allow evaluation of the one should have some value for the other.

Subjects have different capabilities for reporting physical events or those related to their physiological states, but such reports can be important data to the extent that they are or can be made consistent and reliable. Dr. Nowlis suggests that we have tended to restrict the concept of *subjective response* to private events and reports of same and that efforts to obtain dependable verbal reflections of psychophysiological and other intraorganic processes and events would be worthwhile. Dr. Lazarus notes some of the complexities of such analyses, however. Affects and moods, he points out, are multidimensional, whereas our typical treatment of psychophysiological measures is unidimensional. He acknowledges the significant exception of ". . . the underdeveloped area of response patterning and its psychological meaning" (p. 360), which when developed along with improved techniques for scaling of affect, may reveal the kinds of relationships which one suspects exist but which elude the present-day investigator. Needless to say, when affect is roughly scaled along a single dimension—as in Dr. Lazarus' scale of subjective distress (see Chapter 6), relationships can be obtained between degree of felt distress and of autonomic displacement.

Dr. Ruff reminds us that in regard to mood and affect, as well as in relation to cardiac and other physiological reactions (as previously mentioned), one is faced with cyclic baseline patterns which have to be understood if stimulus-related responses are to be distinguished from normal variations. Once again, one is in the position of the proverbial blind men and the elephant—we can make reasonably good particular assessments but lack sufficient knowledge of the overall relationships to put our observations in their proper perspective.

Further to the above is Dr. Back's concern about the effects of feedback from reporting processes. He believes that training to report such feelings might so sensitize the subject-observer as to make his observations unrepresentative of others similarly exposed. Focusing upon such personal, physical, and intrapsychic states might produce a reflection of presumed experimenter interest rather than the subject's perceptions of his own ongoing processes in their "true" sequence and importance. Direct questions may, under some circumstances, however, better serve the purposes of an investigation than more sophisticated or devious techniques designed to outwit the subject. Verbal report, then, comes as a mixed blessing as a technique and must be understood in that light.

With the above in mind, it is interesting to note that Dr. Nowlis' *Mood Adjective Check List* relies on operant verbal items of known probability of occurrence with mood and not on verbal descriptions of private events, although he concedes that "private events do influence how one checks the *MACL*" (p. 357). The HUMRRO *Subjective Stress Scale,* it may be noted, too, has been validated in a variety of situations and has stood up fairly well in correlations with physiological measures. There have been other efforts as well to add measurements of subjective states to the complete description of the stress response. We must obviously continue to seek ways of independently assessing subjective response, for, as Dr. Oken points out, it cannot be assumed from the nature of the stimulus. We are already aware that one cannot assume objective responses of the other systems any more accurately.

SOME PROBLEMS, PERSPECTIVES, AND PERSUASIONS

There can be little doubt that stress research will continue as an important interdisciplinary field of investigation for some time to come. New theory and new data will be added; new researchers will join those now in the field. Hopefully, there has been guidance for them in the chapters of this book. Their designs should be better, their variables more clearly identified, their errors fewer. To this end some especially relevant issues will be emphasized here once more.

Time

It has become increasingly apparent that time, in its many aspects, is an important factor in stress research and design. A stressor has to act over time. Too long an exposure and adaptation will occur as a function of the system involved. Temporal relationships between the introduction of a stressor and the ongoing phases of systems are not adequately appreciated. Innate system rhythmicity, pacing, the role of pace-setters and of temporal conditioning are too little understood. Differential time delays in various response systems make difficult the interpretation of simultaneous recordings. Such temporal phenomena as *warm up, incubation, let down,* and *end spurt,* their sensitivity to mood, to anticipations, to experience, to orientation, etc., and their shaping by inadvertent time cues are all factors which must be carefully assessed and regulated in planning stress research and taken into account in interpreting results of stress studies. Averaging of responses across trials and/or subjects may hide effects of these phenomena. They must obviously be understood in themselves and as factors affecting response if we are ever to predict stress behavior.

Life situations

Much has been said and written about the differences between laboratory and life situations and the relative advantages and disadvantages of studying stress under both conditions. Most stressors which are employed in research have their counterparts in real life and most life stressors have been duplicated, in part at least, in experimental settings. Observations, if not deliberate manipulations, have been made in a number of extreme conditions—in starvation, extreme thirst, pain, long isolation, freezing, heat, sleeplessness, sustained effort, etc. But several major considerations limit quite severely the generality of stress research findings. First, only rarely do we have the opportunity directly to observe extreme conditions in actual life emergencies. Moral and ethical reasons preclude the simulation of such situations. Yet the absence of the full context of life threat conditions of necessity limits conclusions about stress reactions from any situation less intense. The few reports of social and biological scientist teams sent to disaster areas or on frontier-type missions have been most valuable but tend further to cause us to be uneasy about results from less severe conditions.

Secondly, the laboratory focus on hunger or heat or cold or some other specific type of deprivation or stressor has denied us the opportunity to appraise interaction. Thus, a stressor might be more tolerable *in context* rather than as a single laboratory-imposed stimulus. Thirdly, there are many instances where total adjustment is satisfactory but the introduction of a test situation shows degradation. Conversely, one may find that the introduction of a test situation into a stressful experience brings enough change or challenge to provide an improvement in performance. And fourthly, the inevitable uncertainty of the subject's interpretation of both stressor and context, his mood, his aspirations, hopes, fears, etc., and the influence these have on behavior, remain problems which the stress researcher must somehow resolve before he can meaningfully interpret or generalize from his findings.

The looking glass

Both natural situations and laboratory experiments are projective devices, in a manner of speaking, and the researcher must guard against seeing himself or his discipline or profession to the exclusion of objectivity. Dr. Biderman has warned against reading into reactions "things that never would have been so interpreted in everyday life with the same variables obtaining" (p. 269). Prisoner "apathy" and mortality rates, for example, might be the same for a group of chronically ill persons in any hospital where general physical debility levels were as low. The same criticism may be levelled at social scientists who accept social dislocation, frustration, and destruction of personal values as determinants of loss of "will to live," overlooking a host of biological factors which may be directly responsible instead.

The same type of projective error also often applies to selection of stressors and determination of the stressfulness of certain events. Because the researcher thinks a situation *should be* stressful does not make it so. Enough has already been said about the subject-relatedness of stressors to make caution here self-evident.

Selection of measurements or instruments also often reflects personal bias (or convenience), a limited appreciation of the whole sequence of responses and their relationships, and a lack of understanding of response-measure interactions. The historical treatments throughout this book will have shown how selective perceptions guided (and misguided) early stress research. The regrettable noncomparability of stressors, of measures, of samples, of situations, of variables, and of results makes it imperative that we replace the independent, arbitrarily defined study with more comprehensive, systematic, interdisciplinary efforts that give due consideration to the kinds of problems here described. It is especially critical where simulation studies are planned that careful examination of the variables to be simulated and their translatability be made.

A raison d'être

There are many returns for the research undertaken in stress. Discovering the limits of man and of men is a goal in itself. Extensions of the habitable and operational world depend upon such knowledge. For selection purposes we need to know about the consistency of reactions and the value of life history variables for predicting potential for stress resistance. Drs. Ruff and Korchin emphasized the "history of success" pattern they found in the astronauts and which they believed to be relevant to their performance. In this regard, one may note the value of stressful experiences as amplifiers of the personality traits of the individual, thus making them more available for detailed analysis—an avenue only partly explored in traditional psychodiagnostic procedures.

The use of controlled stress experience has significant implications for training, a fact known to any parent or school teacher. The fine line between enough exposure to provide familiarity and permit development of coping behavior and traumatic exposure with potentially damaging effects can hopefully be drawn more carefully as wisdom accumulates in further stress research. Many suggestions of devices and controls for training purposes can already be compiled from the existing stress literature. Information is also available that can be useful for selection on the basis of motivation and experience and for situation structuring to minimize stressfulness and maximize stress resistance. Man's potential is yet undetermined. Research on stress directly addresses the question of limits. Its pursuit may bring us closer to the realization of that potential.

Bibliography-author index

ABEL, T., 1951. The sociology of concentration camps. *Soc. Forces, 30,* 150–155.
246, 247

ADAMS, J. S., 1963. Toward an understanding of inequity. *J. abn. soc. Psychol.,
67,* 422–436. **192**

ADAMS, J. S., & JACOBSEN, PATRICIA, R., 1964. Effects of wage inequity on work
quality. *J. abn. soc. Psychol., 69,* 19–25. **192**

ADAMS, O. S., & CHILES, W. D., 1961. *Prolonged human performance as a function of the work-rest cycle.* Marietta, Ga.: ORD 273, Lockheed Aircraft
Corp. (May). *Human performance as a function of the work-rest ratio during
prolonged confinement.* ASD Tech. Rep. 61-720 (Contract No. AF 33(616)-
6050, Aeronautical Systems Div., Aerospace Med. Lab., Wright-Patterson
AFB, Ohio), Lockheed-Georgia Co. (November). **348, 364**

ADLER, H. G., 1958. Ideas toward a sociology of the concentration camp. *Amer. J.
Sociol., 63,* 513–522. **251**

AHLQUIST, R. P., 1948. A study of the adrenotropic receptors. *Am. J. Physiol.,
153,* 586–600. **53**

ALEXANDER, A. A., ROESSLER, R., & GREENFIELD, N., 1963. Ego strength and
physiological responsivity. *Arch. gen. Psychiat., 9,* 142–145. **56**

ALEXANDER, F., 1950. *Psychosomatic medicine.* New York: Norton. **47**

ALEXANDER, F., FLAGG, G., FOSTER, S., CLEMENS, T., & BLAHD, W., 1961. Experimental studies in emotional stress. I. Hyperthyroidism. *Psychosom. Med., 23,*
104–114. **47**

ALTMAN, I., & HAYTHORN, W. W., 1965. Interpersonal exchange in isolation.
Sociometry, 28, 411–426. **367, 372, 376, 381**

AMIN, F., 1958. Fatal effects of heat on man. *J. Tropical Med., 61,* 280–281. **254**

ANDERSON, C. L., BOYSEN, A. M., ESENTEN, S., LAMB, G., & SHADISH, W. R., 1954.
Medical experiences in Communist POW camps in Korea: Experiences and
observations of five American medical officers who were prisoners of war.
J. Amer. Med. Ass., 156, 120–122. **249, 253**

ANDERSON, R. C., 1947. The motivations of the flyer and his reactions to the
stresses of flight. *J. aviat. Med., 18,* 18–30. **344**

ANOKHIN, O. K., 1961. Electroencephalographic analysis of cortico-subcortical relations in positive and negative conditioned reflexes. *Ann. Acad. Sci., 2,* 799–938. **101, 108**

APPLEY, M. H. (Ed.), 1957a. *Psychological stress and related concepts: A bibliography.* Proj. NR 172–288, Contr. Nonr 996(02), New London, Conn.: Connecticut College. **1**

APPLEY, M. H., 1957b. Psychological stress. (Appendix II of *A study of operational safety requirements in the submarine polaris missile system*). Groton, Conn.: Electric Boat Div., General Dynamics Corp. (February), dittoed. **1**

APPLEY, M. H., 1961. Neuroendocrine aspects of stress. In B. E. FLAHERTY (Ed.), *Psychophysiological aspects of space flight.* New York: Columbia, pp. 139–157. **3**

APPLEY, M. H., 1962. Motivation, threat perception and the induction of psychological stress. *Proc. Sixteenth Internat. Congr. Psychol., Bonn, 1960.* Amsterdam: North Holland Publ., pp. 880–881 (Abstract). **7, 170**

APPLEY, M. H., 1964. On the concept of psychological stress. Paper presented at Psychology Colloquium, Buffalo: State University of New York, (December). **327, 345**

APTER, N., 1958. Aging and conditioned reflexes. In W. H. GANTT (Ed.), *Physiologic basis of psychiatry.* Springfield, Ill.: Charles C Thomas, pp. 22–38. **101**

ARMINGTON, J. C., & MITNICK, L. L., 1959. Electroencephalogram and sleep deprivation. *J. appl. Physiol., 14,* 247–250. **336**

Army Medical Service School, 1953. *Symposium on stress.* Washington, D.C.: Walter Reed Army Med. Center. **324**

ARNOLD, MAGDA B., 1960. *Emotion and personality,* 2 vols. New York: Columbia. **125, 130, 131, 133, 153, 160, 161**

ARNOLD, MAGDA B., 1962. *Story sequence analysis.* New York: Columbia. **292**

ARNOTT, P., 1965. Personal communication to Dr. Prescott. **114**

AUGUST, J. T., NELSON, D. H., & THORN, G. W., 1958. Medical progress: Aldosterone. *N. E. J. Med., 259,* 917–923, 967–971. **51**

AX, A. F., 1953. The physiological differentiation between fear and anger in humans. *Psychosom. Med., 15,* 433–442. **25, 37, 55, 57, 127**

AX, A. F., BECKETT, P. G. S., FRETZ, N. A., & GOTTLIEB, J. S., 1965. *Development of a selection test for motivational aptitude.* Contract No. NAS 2-1031. Detroit, Mich.: Lafayette Clinic. **354**

AXELROD, S., & COHEN, L., 1961. Senescence and embedded figure performance in vision and touch. *Percept. Mot. Skills, 12,* 283–288. **101**

AZIMA, G., & CRAMER, F. J., 1956. Effects of partial isolation in mentally disturbed individuals. *Dis. nerv. Sys., 17,* 117–121. **107**

BACCELLI, G., GUAZZI, M., LIBRETTI, A., & ZANCHETTI, A., 1965. Pressoceptive and chemoceptive aortic reflexes in decorticate and decerebrate cats. *Am. J. Physiol., 208,* 708–714. **28**

BACK, K. W., & BOGDONOFF, M. D., 1964. Plasma lipid responses to leadership, conformity, and deviation. In P. H. Leiderman and D. Shapiro (Eds.), *Psychobiological approaches to social behavior.* Stanford, Calif.: Stanford, pp. 24–42. **208**

BACK, K. W., HOOD, T. C., & BREHM, MARY L., 1964. The subject role in small group experiments. *Social Forces, 43,* 181–187. **208**

BACK, K. W., & SARAVAY, JUDITH, 1966. From bright ideas to social research: A study of the Kennedy assassination. *Public Opinion Quart.,* in press. **205**

BAINES, R. D., GEURKINK, N. A., & SCHOTTSTAEDT, W. W., 1962. Renal clearances of insulin and PAH associated with the stress of mental concentration. *Psychosom. Med., 24,* 584–589. **52**

BAKER, G. W., & CHAPMAN, D. W. (Eds.), 1962. *Man and society in disaster.* New York: Basic Books. **235**

BALDWIN, M., LEWIS, S. A., & FROST, L. L., 1957. Perceptual interference after cerebral ablation. *Percept. Mot. Skills, 7,* 47–48. **82**

BARBER, T. X., 1959. Toward a theory of pain: Relief of chronic pain by prefrontal leucotomy, opiates, placebos, and hypnosis. *Psychol. Bull., 56,* 430–460. **337**

BARD, P., 1928. A diencephalic mechanism for the expression of rage with special reference to the sympathetic nervous system. *Amer. J. Physiol., 84,* 490–515. **337**

BARKER, R. (Ed.), 1963. *The stream of behavior.* New York: Appleton-Century-Crofts, 352 pp. **277**

BARTON, A. H., 1963. *Social organization under stress: A sociological review of disaster studies.* Disaster Study Number 17. Washington, D.C.: National Academy of Sciences—National Research Council **235**

BARTORELLI, C., BIZZI, E., LIBRETTI, A., & ZANCHETTI, A., 1960. Inhibitory control of sinocarotid pressoceptive afferents on hypothalamic autonomic activity and sham rage behavior. *Arch. Ital. Biol., 98,* 308–326. **28**

BASOWITZ, H., KORCHIN, S. J., OKEN, D., GOLDSTEIN, M. S., & GUSSACK, H., 1956. Anxiety and performance changes with a minimal dose of epinephrine. *AMA Arch. Neurol. & Psychiat., 76,* 98–108. **359**

BASOWITZ, H., PERSKY, H., KORCHIN, S. J., & GRINKER, R. R., 1955. *Anxiety and stress.* New York: McGraw-Hill. **7, 45, 47, 299, 314, 319, 343, 345**

BASTIAN, A., 1881. *Der Volkergedanke im Aufbau einer Wissenschaft vom Menschen und seine Begründung auf ethnologische Sammlungen.* Berlin. **211**

BAUST, W., NIEMCYSK, H., & VIETH, J., 1963. The action of blood pressure on the ascending reticular activating system with special reference to adrenaline-induced EEG arousal. *Electroenceph. clin. Neurophysiol., 15,* 63–72. **29**

BEACH, F. A., 1950. Discussion. In H. G. Wolff (Ed.), *Life stress and bodily disease. Res. Publ. Ass. Nerv. Ment. Dis.,* vol. *29,* Baltimore, Md.: Williams & Wilkins, pp. 1048–1049. **123**

BEACH, H. D., & LUCAS, R. A. (Eds.), 1960. *Individual and group behavior in a coal mine disaster.* Washington, D.C.: Publication 834, National Academy of Sciences—National Research Council. **394**

VON BECKH, J. R., 1959. Human reaction during flight to acceleration preceded by or followed by weightlessness. *Aerospace Med., 30,* 391–409. **333**

BECKMAN, E. L., COBURN, K. R., CHAMBERS, R. M., DeFOREST, F. E., AUGERSON, W. S., & BENSON, V. G., 1961. Physiologic changes observed in human subjects during zero G simulation by immersion in water up to neck level. *Aerospace Med., 32,* 1031–1041. **88**

BENEDICT, RUTH, 1934. *Patterns of culture.* Boston: Houghton Mifflin. **218**

BENEDICT, RUTH, 1946. *The chrysanthemum and the sword.* Boston: Houghton Mifflin. **157**

BENNETT, P. B., & GLASS, A., 1961. Electroencephalographic and other changes induced by high partial pressures of nitrogen. *EEG clin. Neurophysiol., 13,* 91–98. **333, 334**

BERGSMAN, M., 1959. The urinary excretion of adrenaline and noradrenaline in some mental diseases. *Acta Psychiat. et Neurol. Scand.,* Suppl. 133, *34.* Copenhagen: E. Munksgaard. **100**

BERKOWITZ, L., 1962. *Aggression.* New York: McGraw-Hill. **163, 164**

BERKUN, M. M., BIALEK, H. M., KERN, R. P., & YAGI, K., 1962. Experimental studies of psychological stress in man. *Psychol. Monogr., 76,* No. 15. (Whole No. 534) **343, 344, 346, 349, 351, 371, 381, 384, 385, 405**

BERNARD, C., 1859. *Leçons sur les proprietes physiologiques et les alterations pathologiques des liquides de l'organisme.* Vols. I and II. Paris: Balliere. **3**

BERNSTEIN, A. S., 1965. Race and examiner as significant influences on basal skin impedance. *J. pers. soc. Psychol., 1,* 346–349. **157**

BETTELHEIM, B., 1943. Individual and mass behavior in extreme situations. *J. abn. soc. Psychol., 38,* 417–452. **258**

BETTELHEIM, B., 1960. *The informed heart—Autonomy in a mass age.* New York: Free Press. **246, 250, 255, 267**

BEVAN, W., 1963. The pooling mechanism and the phenomena of reinforcement. In O. J. HARVEY (Ed.), *Motivation and social interaction.* New York: Ronald, pp. 18–34. **117**

BEVAN, W., & ADAMSON, R., 1961. Internal referents and the concept of reinforcement. In N. F. WASHBURNE (Ed.), *Decisions, values and groups.* Vol. II. New York: Pergamon, pp. 453–472. **117**

BEXTON, W. H., HERON, W., & SCOTT, T. H., 1954. Effects of decreased variation in the sensory environment. *Canad. J. Psychol., 8,* 70–76. **77, 78, 79, 88, 342**

BIDERMAN, A. D., 1959. Effects of Communist indoctrination attempts: Some comments on an Air Force prisoner-of-war study. *Soc. Prob., 6,* 304–313. **247**

BIDERMAN, A. D., 1960a. The relevance of studies of internment for the problems of shelter habitability. In G. W. BAKER & J. H. ROHRER (Eds.), *Symposium on human problems in the utilization of fallout shelters.* Washington, D.C.: National Acad. of Sci.—National Research Council, *Publ. 800,* pp. 31–50. **252, 254**

BIDERMAN, A. D., 1960b. Social psychological needs and "involuntary" behavior as illustrated by compliance in interrogation. *Sociometry, 23,* 120–147. **247**

BIDERMAN, A. D., 1963. *March to calumny*. New York: Macmillan. **206**

BIDERMAN, A. D., 1964. Captivity lore and behavior in captivity. In G. H. GROSSER, H. WECHSLER, & M. GREENBLATT (Eds.), *The threat of impending disaster*. Cambridge, Mass.: M.I.T., pp. 223–250. **246**

BIDERMAN, A. D., LOURIA, MARGOT, & BACCHUS, JOAN, 1963. *Historical incidents of extreme overcrowding*. Washington, D.C.: Bureau of Social Science Research (March), BSSR 354–355. **244, 250, 254, 274**

BIRKET-SMITH, K., 1936. *The Eskimos*. London: Methuen. **221**

BIRREN, J. E., CARDON, P. V., & PHILLIPS, S. L., 1963. Reaction time as a function of the cardiac cycle in young adults. *Science, 140,* 195–196. **32**

BLISS, E. L., MIGEON, C. J., BRANCH, C. H. H., & SAMUELS, L. T., 1956. Reaction of the adrenal cortex to emotional stress. *Psychosom. Med., 18,* 56–76. **45, 46**

BLOCH, H. A., 1946–7. The personality of inmates of concentration camps. *Amer. J. Sociol., 52,* 335–341. **246, 253, 255**

BLOCK, J., & BLOCK, JEANNE, 1952. An interpersonal experiment on reactions to authority. *Hum. Relat., 5,* 91–98. **163, 406**

BLUHM, HILDE O., 1948. How did they survive? Mechanisms of defense in Nazi concentration camps. *Amer. J. Psychother., 2,* 3–32. **249**

BOARD, F. A., PERSKY, H., & HAMBURG, D. A., 1956. Psychological stress and endocrine functions: Blood levels of adrenocortical and thyroid hormones in acutely disturbed patients. *Psychosom. Med., 18,* 324–333. **45, 46, 52**

BOARD, F. A., WADESON, R., & PERSKY, H., 1957. Depressive affect and endocrine functions: Blood levels of adrenal cortex and thyroid hormones in patients suffering from depressive reactions. *AMA Arch. Neurol. & Psychiat., 78,* 612–620. **46, 266**

BOGDONOFF, M. D., & ESTES, E. H., JR., 1961. Energy dynamics and acute states of arousal in man. *Psychosom. Med., 22,* 23–32. **54**

BOGDONOFF, M. D., KLEIN, R. F., BACK, K. W., NICHOLS, C. R., TROYER, W. G., & HOOD, C., 1964. Effect of group relationship and of the role of leadership upon lipid mobilization. *Psychosom. Med., 26,* 710–719. **54, 208**

BONDY, C., 1943. Problems of internment camps. *J. abn. soc. Psychol., 38,* 453–478. **253, 255**

BONVALLET, M., & ALLEN, M. B., 1963. Prolonged spontaneous and evoked reticular activation following discrete bulbar lesions. *Electroenceph. clin. Neurophysiol., 15,* 969–988. **27**

BONVALLET, M., & BLOCK, V., 1961. Bulbar control of cortical arousal. *Science, 133,* 1133–1134. **27**

BONVALLET, M., DELL, P., & HIEBEL, G., 1954. Tonus sympathique et activité électrique corticale. *Electroenceph. clin. Neurophysiol., 6,* 119–144. **27**

BONVALLET, M., DELL, P., & HUGELIN, A., 1954. Influence de l'adrénaline sur le contrôle réticulaire des activités corticale et spinale. *J. de Physiol., 46,* 262–265. **27**

BOVARD, E. W., 1961. A concept of hypothalamic functioning. *Perspect. Biol. Med., 5,* 52–60. **62, 64**

BOVARD, E. W., 1962. The balance between negative and positive brain system activity. *Perspect. Biol. Med., 6,* 116–127. **62**

BRADY, J. V., 1958. Ulcers in "executive monkeys." *Scientific Amer., 199,* 95–103. **315**

BRADY, J. V., PORTER, R. W., CONRAD, D. G., & MASON, J. W., 1958. Avoidance behavior and the development of gastroduodenal ulcers. *J. exp. anal. Behav., 1,* 69–72. **271**

BRADLEY, P. B., 1958. The central action of certain drugs in relation to the reticular formation of the brain. In H. H. JASPER, L. D. PROCTOR, R. S. KNIGHTON, W. C. NOSHAY, & R. T. COSTELLO (Eds.), *Reticular formation of the brain.* Boston: Little, Brown. **17**

BRATTGARD, S. O., 1952. The importance of adequate stimulation for the chemical composition of retinal ganglion cells during early post-natal development. *Acta Radiolog.,* Suppl. 96. **119**

BRAUN, J. R., & SELLS, S. B., 1962. *Military small group performance under isolation and stress. III. Environmental stress and behavior ecology.* Fort Wainwright, Alaska: Aeromedical Laboratory. AAL-TDR 62–33. **279, 284**

BREHM, MARY L., BACK, K. W., & BOGDONOFF, M. D., 1964. A physiological effect of cognitive dissonance under stress and deprivation. *J. abn. soc. Psychol., 69,* 302–310. **208**

BRIDGER, W., 1964. The neurophysiological accompaniments of sensory and sleep deprivation and their role in the production of psychological disturbances. In J. WORTIS (Ed.), *Recent advances in biological psychiatry, 6,* pp. 105–110. **106**

BROWN, A. M., 1965. Mechanoreceptors in or near the coronary arteries. *J. Physiol., 177,* 203–214. **26**

BRUCE, R. H., 1941. An experimental analysis of the social factors affecting the performance of white rats. I. Performance in learning a simple field situation. *J. comp. Psychol., 31,* 363–377. **338**

BRUCE, W., 1960. *Man and his thermal environment.* Ottawa, Can.: National Research Council. Division of Building Research, (February), *Technical Paper,* No. 84. **250**

BRUNER, J. S., 1961. The cognitive consequences of early sensory deprivation. In P. SOLOMON et al. (Eds.), *Sensory deprivation.* Cambridge, Mass.: Harvard, pp. 195–207. **106, 107, 111**

BUNNEY, W. E., JR., MASON, J. W., & HAMBURG, D. A., 1963. Correlations between behavioral variables and urinary 17-hydroxycorticosteroids in depressed patients. *Psychosom. Med., 25,* 488. (Abstract) **46**

BURCH, N. R., & GREINER, T., 1960. Drugs and human fatigue: GSR parameters. *J. Psychol., 45,* 3–10. **90**

BURNEY, C., 1946. *The dungeon democracy.* New York: Duell, Sloan & Pearce. **247**

BURNEY, C., 1952. *Solitary confinement.* New York: Coward-McCann. **78**

BURNS, N. M., CHAMBERS, R. M., & HENDLER, E. (Eds.), 1963. *Unusual environments and human behavior.* New York: Collier-Macmillan. **12, 78**

BURNS, N. M., & KIMURA, D., 1963. Isolation and sensory deprivation. In BURNS, N. M., CHAMBERS, R. M., & HENDLER, E. (Eds.), *Unusual environments and human behavior.* New York: Collier-Macmillan, pp, 167–192. **341, 342, 343**

BURTON, A. C., & EDHOLM, O. G., 1955. *Man in a cold environment.* London: Edward Arnold. **335**

BUTLER, R. A., 1953. Discrimination learning by rhesus monkeys to visual exploration motivation. *J. comp. physiol. Psychol., 46,* 95–98. **114**

BUTLER, R. A., 1957. The effect of deprivation of visual incentives on visual exploration in monkeys. *J. comp. physiol. Psychol., 50,* 177–179. **114**

BUTLER, R. A., & ALEXANDER, H. M., 1955. Daily patterns of visual exploratory behavior in the monkey. *J. comp. physiol. Psychol., 48,* 247–249. **114**

BYRD, R. E., 1938. *Alone.* New York: Putnam. **78, 342**

CALLAWAY, E., 1965. *Some effects of respiratory and cardiac cycles.* Washington, D.C.: ONR Progr. Rep., NONR 2931 (00), (January). **32**

CALLAWAY, E., & BRUXBAUM, M., n.d. *Autonomic afferent influence on voluntary activity.* ASTIA Report, 439–302. **111**

CALLAWAY, E., & LAYNE, R. S., 1964. Interaction between the visual evoked response and two spontaneous biological rhythms: The EEG alpha cycle and the cardiac arousal cycle. In R. KATZMAN (Ed.), *Sensory evoked response in man. Ann. N.Y. Acad. Sci., 112, Art. I.* **32**

CANNON, W. B., 1915. *Bodily changes in pain, hunger, fear and rage.* (2nd ed., 1929) New York: Appleton-Century-Crofts. **53, 127**

CANNON, W. B., 1932. *The wisdom of the body.* (2nd ed.) New York: Norton. **3, 335**

CANNON, W. B., 1942. Voodoo death. *Amer. Anthropologist, 44,* 169–181. **209, 266**

CANNON, W. B., & ROSENBLEUTH, A., 1937. *Autonomic neuro-effector systems.* New York: Macmillan. **53**

CASON, H., 1930. Common annoyances: A psychological study of everyday aversions and irritations. *Psychol. Monogr.* (Whole No. 182). **316**

CATTELL, R. B., 1960. The dimensional (unitary-component) measurement of anxiety, excitement, effort, stress and other mood reaction patterns. In L. UHR & J. G. MILLER (Eds.), *Drugs and behavior.* New York: Wiley, pp. 438–462. **355**

CHAMBERS, R. M., 1963. Operator performance in accelerated environments. In N. M. BURNS, R. M. CHAMBERS, & E. HENDLER (Eds.), *Unusual environments and human behavior.* New York: Collier-Macmillan, pp. 193–319. **333**

CHOW, K. L., RIESEN, A. H., & NEWELL, F. W., 1957. Degeneration of retinal ganglion cells in infant chimpanzee in darkness. *J. comp. Neurol., 107,* 27–42. **119**

CHRISTIAN, J. J., & DAVIES, D. E., 1964. Endocrines, behavior and population. *Science, 146,* 1550–1560. **265, 267**

CILIGA, A., 1940. *The Russian enigma.* London: Labour Book Service. **243, 247**

CLARK, B., & GRAVELINE, D. E., 1957. The break-off phenomenon: A feeling of separation from the earth experienced by pilots at high altitudes. *J. aviat. Med., 28,* 121–126. **88**

CLYDE, D. J., 1959. *Manual: Clyde Mood Scale.* Bethesda, Md.: National Institute of Mental Health. **302**

CODDINGTON, R. D., SOURS, J. A., & BRUCH, HILDE, 1964. Electrogastrographic findings associated with affective changes. *Am. J. Psychiat., 121,* 41–44. **56**

COERMANN, R. R., 1938. *The effect of vibration and noise on the human organism.* Transl. by G. L. Davies. Washington, D.C.: Dept. of Commerce, Publ. 24679T. **340**

COFER, C. N., & APPLEY, M. H., 1964. *Motivation: Theory and research.* New York: Wiley. **1, 3, 8, 11, 171, 205**

COHEN, E. A., 1953. Human behavior in the concentration camp. New York: Norton. **250, 252, 255, 258**

COHEN, L. D., KIPNIS, D., KUNKLE, E. C., & KUBZANSKY, P. E., 1955. Observations of a person with congenital insensitivity to pain. *J. abn. soc. Psychol., 51,* 333–338. **337**

COHEN, S. I., & SHMAVONIAN, B. M., in press. Catechol amines, vasomotor conditioning and aging. In L. GITMAN, (Ed.), *Endocrines and aging.* Springfield: Charles C Thomas. **100**

COHEN, S. I., SILVERMAN, A. J., BRESSLER, B., & SHMAVONIAN, B. M., 1961. Problems in isolation studies. In P. SOLOMON et al. (Eds.), *Sensory deprivation.* Cambridge, Mass.: Harvard, pp. 114–129. **89, 100**

COHEN, S. I., SILVERMAN, A. J., & SHMAVONIAN, B. M., 1962a. Neurophysiological, humoral and personality factors in the response to sensory deprivation. *Proc. 3rd World Congr. Psychiat., 2.* Toronto: University of Toronto, pp. 1004–1009. **85, 89, 90, 96, 99**

COHEN, S. I., SILVERMAN, A. J., & SHMAVONIAN, B. M., 1962b. Psychophysiological studies in altered sensory environments. *J. Psychosom. Res., 6,* 259–281. **85, 89, 90, 96, 99, 101**

COHEN, W., & CADWALLADER, R. C., 1958. Cessation of visual stimulation under prolonged uniform visual stimulation. *Am. Psychol., 13,* 410 (Abstract). **82**

COLEMAN, J. C., 1956. *Abnormal psychology and modern life.* New York: Scott, Foresman. **344**

COLLINS, W., & O'LEARY, J. L., 1954. Somatic evoked responses recorded from the protecto-thalamic region of the cat. *Trans. Am. Neurol. Ass., 79,* 183–184. **129**

COLQUHOUN, W. P., 1960. Temperament, inspection efficiency, and time of day. *Ergonomics, 3,* 377–378. **342**

CONANT, J. B., 1951. *Science and common sense.* New Haven: Yale. **215**

CONN, J. W., & LOUIS, L. H., 1956. Primary Aldosteronism, a new clinical entity. In H. SELYE & G. HEUSER (Eds.), *Fifth Annual Report on Stress,* 1955–56, New York: MD Publications, pp. 104–116. **51**

CONN, L. K., & CROWNE, D. P., 1964. Instigation to aggression, emotional arousal and defensive emulation. *J. Pers., 32,* 163–179. **167**

COOK, E. B., & WHERRY, R. J., 1950. The urinary 17-ketosteroid output of Naval Submarine enlisted candidates during two stressful situations. *Human Biol.*, *22*, 104–124. **329, 344, 346**

CORSO, J. F., 1952. *The effects of noise on human behavior.* WADC Tech. Rep. 53–81, State Coll., Pa.: Pennsylvania State Coll. (December). **340**

COURTER, R., WALTANMAKER, R., & AX, A., 1965. Physiological concomitants of psychological differentiation. *Psychophysiology, 1,* 282–290. **104**

CRESSEY, D. L., & KRASSOWSKI, W., 1957. Inmate organization and anomie in American prisons and Soviet labor camps. *Soc. Prob., 5,* 217–230. **247**

CULVER, C., COHEN, S. I., SILVERMAN, A. J., & SHMAVONIAN, B. M., 1964. Cognitive structuring, field dependence-independence and the psychophysiological response to perceptual isolation. *Recent Advances in Biologic. Psychiatry, 6,* 119–128. **90, 91, 94, 95, 96, 97, 98, 99, 100, 405**

DAMASER, ESTHER C., SHOR, R. E., & ORNE, M. T., 1963. Physiological effects during hypnotically requested emotions. *Psychosom. Med., 25,* 334–343. **47**

D'AMATO, H. E., & HEGNAUER, A. H., 1953. Blood volume in hypothermic dog. *Am. J. Physiol., 173,* 100–102. **335**

DARROW, C. W., 1929a. Differences in the physiological reactions to sensory and ideational stimuli. *Psychol. Bull., 26,* 185–201. **34**

DARROW, C. W., 1929b. Electrical and circulatory responses to brief sensory and ideational stimuli. *J. exp. Psychol., 12,* 267–300. **34**

DARROW, C. W., & HENRY, C. E., 1949. Psychophysiology of stress. In D. B. LINDSLEY et al., *Human factors in undersea warfare.* Washington, D.C.: National Research Council, pp. 417–439. **331, 346, 347, 348**

DARROW, C. W., JOST, H., SOLOMON, A. P., & MERGENER, J. C., 1942. Autonomic indications of excitatory and homeostatic effects on the electroencephalogram. *J. Psychol., 14,* 115–130. **31**

DAVIS, J. F., 1959. *A manual of surface electromyography.* Montreal: Allen Memorial Institute of Psychiatry, McGill. **56**

DAVIS, J. O., CARPENTER, C. C. J., & AYERS, C. R., 1962b. Relation of renin and angiotensin II to the control of Aldosterone secretion. *Circulation Res., 11,* 171–181. **51**

DAVIS, J. O., MORRILL, R., FAWCETT, J., UPTON, V., BONDY, P. K., & SPIRO, H. M., 1962a. Apprehension and elevated serum cortisol levels. *J. psychosom. Res., 6,* 83–86. **48**

DAVIS, R. C., 1957a. Response patterns. *Trans. N.Y. Acad. Sci. Ser. II, 19,* 731–739. **25, 49, 55**

DAVIS, R. C., 1957b. *Electromyographic factors in aircraft control: Muscular tension when task requirements are changed.* Rept. 55–131, Randolph AFB, Texas: USAF Sch. Av. Med. (January). **340**

DAVIS, R. C., 1959. Somatic activity under reduced stimulation. *J. comp. physiol. Psychol., 116,* 309–314. **83**

DAVIS, R. C., & BERRY, F., 1963. Gastrointestinal reactions during a noise avoidance task. *Psychol. Rep., 12,* 135–137. **56**

DAVIS, R. C., BUCHWALD, A. M., & FRANKMANN, R. W., 1955. Autonomic and muscular responses, and their relation to simple stimuli. *Psychol. Monogr., 69* (Whole No. 405, No. 20). **25, 33**

DAVIS, S. W., ELMADJIAN, N., et al., 1952. *A study of combat stress: Korea 1952.* Chevy Chase, Md.: Operations Research Office, Johns Hopkins. **344, 349**

DELL, P., BONVALLET, M., & HUGELIN, A., 1954. Tonus sympathique, adrénaline et contrôle réticulaire de la motricité spinale. *Electroenceph. clin. Neurophysiol., 6,* 599–618. **27**

DEUTSCH, M., 1949. The effects of cooperation and competition upon group process. *Hum. Rel., 2,* 129–152. **186, 187**

DOANE, B. K., MAHATOO, W., HERON, W., & SCOTT, T. H., 1959. Changes in perceptual function after isolation. *Canad. J. Psychol., 13,* 210–219. **105**

DOLE, G., & CARNEIRO, R. (Eds.), 1960. *Essays in the science of culture.* New York: Crowell. **236**

DOMANSKI, T. J., 1954. *Physiological recognition of strain in flying personnel: Eosinopenia in B-29 training operations.* Rep. No. 4 (Proj. 21-1208085) Randolph Field, Texas: USAF Sch. Av. Med. (April). **337**

DOUST, J. W., 1962. Consciousness in schizophrenia as a function of the peripheral microcirculation. In R. ROESSLER & N. S. GREENFIELD (Eds.), *Physiological correlates of psychological disorder.* Madison: University of Wisconsin, pp. 61–96. **56**

DRYER, A. S., 1954. Aspiration behavior as influenced by expectation and group comparison. *Hum. Rel., 7,* 175–190. **192**

DUFFY, ELIZABETH, 1962. *Activation and behavior.* New York: Wiley. **15, 22**

DUREMAN, I., & EDSTRÖM, R., 1964. *EEG and time perception.* 22nd Report from the Department of Psychology, University of Uppsala, Sweden (December). **18**

DURKHEIM, E., 1951 (1st ed., 1897). *Suicide.* Transl. by J. A. SPAULDING & G. SIMPSON. Glencoe, Ill.: Free Press, Book II. See also H. MORSELLI, 1882. *Suicide.* New York: D. Appleton Century, pp. 388. **239, 240**

DYKMAN, R. A., CORSON, S. A., REESE, W. G., & SEAGER, L. D., 1962. Inhibition of urine flow as a component of the conditional defense reaction. *Psychosom. Med., 24,* 177–186. **52**

DYKMAN, R. A., REESE, W. G., GALBRECHT, R., & THOMASSON, J., 1959. Psychophysiological reactions to novel stimuli: Measurement, adaptation, and relationship of psychological and physiological variables in the normal human. *Ann. N.Y. Acad. Sci., 79,* 43–107. **22**

EAD, H. W., GREEN, J. H., & NEIL, E., 1952. A comparison of the effects of pulsatile and non-pulsatile blood flow through the carotid sinus on the reflexogenic activity of the sinus baroceptors in the cat. *J. Physiol., 118,* 509–519. **29**

EBERSOLE, J. H., 1960. The new dimensions of Submarine Medicine. *New Engl. J. Med., 262,* 599–610. **339**

EDELBERG, R., & BURCH, N., 1962. Skin resistance and galvanic skin response. AMA *Arch. Gen. Psychiat., 7,* 163–169. **90**

EDWARDS, A., & COHEN, S., 1965. Persistence of an evaluative response conditioned under LSD and sensory deprivation. In J. WORTIS (Ed.), *Recent Advances in Biological Psychiatry, 7,* 23–36. **99**

EDWARDS, A. L., 1959. *The Edwards Personal Preference Schedule.* New York: Psychological Corporation. **369**

EDWARDS, W., 1950. Recent research in pain perception. *Psychol. Bull. 47,* 449–474. **337**

EGDAHL, R. H., 1962. Further studies on adrenal cortical function in dogs with isolated pituitaries. *Endocrinology, 71,* 926–935. **50**

EGDAHL, R. H., 1964. Adrenal cortical function in dogs with central nervous system ablations. In L. MARTINI & E. PECILE (Eds.), *Hormonal steroids, biochemistry, pharmacology and therapeutics: Proceedings of the First International Congress on Hormonal Steroids.* New York: Academic, *1,* 209–216. **50**

EILBERT, L. R., & GLASER, R., 1959. Differences between well and poorly adjusted groups in an isolated environment. *J. appl. Psychol., 43,* 271–274. **279, 364**

EINSIEDEL, H., 1953. *I joined the Russians.* New Haven: Yale. **247, 264**

EISDORFER, C., 1960. Rorschach rigidity and sensory decrement in a senescent population. *J. Geront., 15,* 118–190. **101**

EISENBERG, L., 1963. Drug therapy of overactivity in children. *Clin. Proc. Children's Hosp.* The Johns Hopkins School of Medicine, 1963, *19,* 253–255. **115**

ELKES, J., 1957. Effects of psychosomimetic drugs in animals and man. In H. ABRAMSON (Ed.), *Neuropharmacology.* Transact. 3rd Conf. New York: Josiah Macy, Jr. Foundation, pp. 205–295. **99**

ELKES, J. 1958. Drug effects in relation to receptor specificity within the brain. Some evidence and provisional formulations. In G. E. W. WOLSTENHOLME & C. M. O'CONNOR (Eds.), *Neurological basis of behavior.* (Ciba Foundation Symposium), Boston: Little, Brown, pp. 303–336. **99**

ELLIOTT, R., 1964. Physiological activity and performance: A comparison of kindergarten children with young adults. *Psychol. Monogr., 78* (Whole No. 587, No. 10). **20, 22**

ELLIOTT, R., 1966. Effects of uncertainty about the nature and advent of a noxious stimulus (shock) upon heart rate. *J. personal. soc. Psychol., 3,* 353–356. **308**

ELMADJIAN, F., 1962a. Aldosterone excretion in behavioral disorders. In S. R. KOREY, A. POPE, & E. ROBINS (Eds.), *Ultrastructure and metabolism of the nervous system. Ass. Res. nerv. ment. Dis., 40,* Baltimore: Williams & Wilkins, pp. 414–419. **51, 52**

ELMADJIAN, F., 1962b. Adrenaline and noradrenaline. In R. I. DORFMAN (Ed.),

Methods in hormone research, Vol. I. Chemical determination. New York: Academic, pp. 337–349. **52, 53**

ELMADJIAN, F., 1962c. Epinephrine and norepinephrine. In R. I. DORFMAN (Ed.), *Methods in hormone research Vol. 2, Bioassay.* New York: Academic, pp. 371–383. **53**

ELMADJIAN, F., 1963. Excretion and metabolism of epinephrine and norepinephrine in various emotional states. *Editorial Sesator,* Lima, Peru, pp. 341–370. **53, 54**

ELMADJIAN, F., HOPE, J. M., & LAMSON, E. T., 1958. Excretion of epinephrine and norepinephrine under stress. In G. PINCUS (Ed.), *Recent progress in hormone research.* New York: Academic, 513–545. **54**

ENGEL, B. T., 1960. Stimulus-response and individual-response specificity. *AMA Arch. gen. Psychiat., 2,* 305–313. **22, 55**

ENGEL, F., & FREDERICKS, JOAN, 1957. Contribution to understanding of mechanism of permissive action of corticoids. *Proc. Soc. Exp. Biol. & Med., 94,* 593–596. **69**

ENGEL, G., 1963. Toward a classification of affects. In P. H. KNAPP (Ed.), *Expression of the emotions in man.* New York: International Universities, pp. 266–294. **266**

ENRIGHT, J., & JAECKLE, W. R., 1963. Psychiatric symptoms and diagnoses in two subcultures. *Internat. J. soc. Psychiat., 9,* 12–17. Cf. J. C. FINNEY, 1963. Psychiatry and multiculturality in Hawaii. *Internat. J. soc. Psychiat., 9,* 5–11. **221**

EPSTEIN, S., 1962. The measurement of drive and conflict in humans: Theory and experiment. In M. R. JONES (Ed.), *Nebraska symposium on motivation: 1962.* Lincoln: University of Nebraska, pp. 83–125. **318**

ERIKSON, E. H., 1950 (rev. ed., 1963). *Childhood and society.* New York: Norton. **164, 220**

VON EULER, U. S., 1951. The nature of adrenergic nerve mediators. *Pharm. Rev., 3,* 247–277. **52**

VON EULER, U. S., 1955. Relationship between cortical hormones and the catecholamine output in urine. *Ciba Colloquia Endocrinol., 8,* 268–274. **52**

VON EULER, U. S., 1956a. Stress and catechol hormones. In H. SELYE & G. HEUSER (Eds.), *Fifth annual report on stress.* New York: MD Publications, pp. 125–137. **54**

VON EULER, U. S., 1956b. *Noradrenaline.* American lecture series. Springfield, Ill.: Charles C Thomas. **54**

VON EULER, U. S., & HELLNER, S., 1952. Noradrenaline excretion in muscular work. *Acta. physiol. Scandinav. 26,* 183–191. **54**

VON EULER, U. S., LUFT, R., & SUNDIN, T., 1951. Noradrenaline output in urine after infusion in man. *Brit. J. Pharmacol., 6,* 286–288. **53**

VON EULER, U. S., LUFT, R., & SUNDIN, T., 1953. Excretion of urinary adrenaline in normals following intravenous infusion. *Acta physiol. Scandinav., 30,* 249–257. **53**

EVARTS, E. V., 1962. A neurophysiologic theory of hallucinations. In L. J. WEST (Ed.) *Hallucinations.* New York: Grune & Stratton, pp. 1–14. **105**

Experimental studies of human avoidance behavior, 1957. Washington, D.C.: Committee on Disaster Studies, National Research Council. **74**

EYSENCK, H. J., 1957. *The dynamics of anxiety and hysteria.* New York: Praeger. **114**

FANTL, B., & SHIRO, J., 1959. Cultural variables in the behavior patterns and symptom formation of Irish and Italian. *Internat. J. soc. Psychiat., 4,* 245–253. **229**

FARBER, I. E., HARLOW, H. F., & WEST, L. J., 1957. Brainwashing, conditioning and DDD (debility, dependency, and dread). *Sociometry, 20,* 271–285. **337, 338**

FAUCETT, R. E., & NEWMAN, P. P., 1953. *Operation Hideout: Preliminary report.* U.S.N. Med. Res. Lab. Rep. No. 228. New London, Conn.: U.S. Navy Submarine Base. **334, 337, 341, 347**

FELDMAN, S. M., & WALLER, H. J., 1962. Dissociation of electrocortical activation and behavioral arousal. *Nature, 196,* 1320–1322. **17**

FERREIRA, A. J., & WINTER, W. D., 1963. The palmar sweat print: A methodological study. *Psychosom. Med., 25,* 377–384. **56**

FESTINGER, L., 1954. A theory of social comparison process. *Hum. Rel., 7,* 117–140. **188**

FESTINGER, L., SCHACHTER, S., & BACK, K. W., 1950. *Social pressures in informal groups: A study of human factors in housing.* New York: Harper & Row. **274**

FINESINGER, J. E., & BRAZIER, MARY, A. B., 1946. *Studies on the physiological basis of the EEG changes found in hypoxia and their comparison with changes induced by other agents.* Washington, D.C.: ONR Proj. order XIV 05-664 Contract N5 ori-76, pp. 1–16. **335**

FINNEY, J. C., 1963. Psychiatry and multiculturality in Hawaii. *Internat. J. soc. Psychiat., 9,* 5–11. **214**

FIORICA, V., & MUEHL, S., 1962. Relationship between plasma levels of 17-hydroxycorticosteroids (17-OH-CS) and a psychological measure of manifest anxiety. *Psychosom. Med., 24,* 596–599. **49**

FISHER, S. (Ed.), 1959. *Child research in psychopharmacology.* Springfield: Charles C Thomas. **115**

FISHMAN, J. R., HAMBURG, D. A., HANDLON, J. H., MASON, J. W., & SACHAR, E., 1962a. Emotional and adrenal cortical responses to a new experience. *AMA Arch. gen. Psychiat., 6,* 271–278. **45, 47, 49**

FISHMAN, J. R., MUELLER, P. S., & STOEFFLER, V., 1962b. Changes in emotional state and in plasma-free fatty acids induced by hypnotic suggestion. *Psychosom. Med., 24,* 522 (Abstract). **54**

FLORY, W. E. S., 1942. *Prisoner of war: A study in the development of international law.* Washington, D.C.: Amer. Counc. Publ. Aff. **251**

FOLKOW, B., & VON EULER, U.S., 1954. Selective activation of noradrenaline and adrenaline producing cells in the cat's suprarenal gland by hypothalamic stimulation. *Circ. Res., 2,* 191–195. **52**

FOREMAN, P. B., 1959. Buchenwald and modern POW policy. *Soc. Forces, 37,* 289–297. **255**

FORTIER, C., 1962. Adenohypophysis and adrenal cortex. *Ann. rev. Physiol., 24,* 223–258. **51**

FOX, S. S., 1962. Self-maintained sensory input and sensory deprivation in monkeys; a behavioral and neuropharmacological study. *J. comp. physiol. Psychol., 55,* 438–444. **343**

FRANK, L. K., 1948. *Society as the patient.* New Brunswick, N.J.: Rutgers. **212**

FRANKL, V., 1959. *From death camp to existentialism.* Boston: Beacon Press. **257**

FRASER, D. C., 1954. *The study of fatigue.* London: Royal Air Force Inst. Aviation Med. **347**

FRASER, T. M., HOOVER, G. N., & ASHE, W. F., 1961. Tracking performance during low frequency vibration. *Aerospace Med., 32,* 829–835. **341**

FREEDMAN, S. J., GRUNEBAUM, H. U., & GREENBLATT, M., 1961. Perceptual and cognitive changes in sensory deprivation. In P. SOLOMON et al. (Eds.), *Sensory deprivation.* Cambridge, Mass.: Harvard, pp. 58–71. **106**

FREEDMAN, S. J., GRUNEBAUM, H. U., STARE, F. A., & GREENBLATT, M., 1962. Imagery in sensory deprivation. In L. J. WEST (Ed.), *Hallucinations.* New York: Grune & Stratton, pp. 108–117 **106**

FREEMAN, G. L., 1948. *The energetics of human behavior.* Ithaca: Cornell. **352**

FREUD, S., 1959. *Collected papers.* Vols. 1–5. New York: Basic Books. **213**

FREYRE, G., 1963. *The masters and the slaves.* New York: Knopf. See also FREYRE, G., 1963. *The mansions and the shanties.* New York: Knopf. **268**

FRIEDMAN, P., 1949. Some aspects of concentration camp psychology. *Amer. J. Psychiat., 105,* 601–605. **338**

FROST, J. W., DRYER, R. L., & KOHLSTAEDT, K. G., 1951. Stress studies on auto race drivers. *J. lab. clin. Med., 38,* 523–525. **45**

FUHRER, M. J., 1964. Differential verbal conditioning of heart rate with minimization of changes in respiratory rate. *J. comp. physiol. Psychol. 58,* 283–289. **33**

FUNKENSTEIN, D. H., KING, S. H., & DROLETTE, M. E., 1957. *Mastery of stress.* Cambridge, Mass.: Harvard. **25, 55**

GAITO, J., HANNA, T. D., BOWE, R., & GRECO, S., 1958. *Environmental effects of sealed cabins for space and orbital flights. Part 3. Performance habitability aspects of extended confinement.* Philadelphia: Naval Air Material Center. **364, 365**

GALAMBOS, R., 1961. Psychological testing of subjects undergoing acceleration stress. In *Reports on human acceleration.* Publ. No. 901, Washington, D.C.: Nat'l. Acad. Sci.—Nat'l. Res. Council, pp. 13–54. **334**

GALIN, D., 1964. Effects of conditioning on auditory signals. In W. S. FIELDS & B. R. ALFORD (Eds.), *Neurological aspects of auditory and vestibular disorders.* Springfield, Ill.: Charles C Thomas, pp. 61–76. **29**

GANONG, W. F., & FORSHAM, P. H., 1960. Adenohypophysis and adrenal cortex. *Ann. rev. Physiol., 22,* 579–614. **50**

GEER, J. H., 1964. Measurement of the conditioned cardiac response. *J. comp. physiol. Psychol., 57,* 426–433. **33**

GELLHORN, E., 1943. *Autonomic regulations.* New York: Interscience Publ. **336**

GELLHORN, E., 1957. *Autonomic imbalance and the hypothalamus.* Minneapolis: University of Minnesota. **334, 352**

GELLHORN, E., & LOOFBOURROW, G. N., 1963. *Emotions and emotional disorders.* New York: Hoeber. **51**

Geneva Convention Relative to the Treatment of Prisoners of War of August 12, 1949, 1950. *Geneva conventions of August 12, 1949, for the protection of war victims.* Photographic reproduction Dep. of State Publ. 3938. Washington, D.C.: Govt. Print. Off. No. 6004 **251**

GIBSON, W., 1953. *The boat.* Boston: Houghton Mifflin. **78, 338**

GLADWIN, T., 1958. Canoe travel in the Truk area: Technology and its psychological correlates. *Amer. Anthropologist, 60,* 893–899. **287**

GLASSER, R. L., & TIPPETT, J. W., 1965. Dissociation of facilitatory mechanisms in the midpontile decerebrate cat. *Nature, 205,* 810–811. **18**

GLICKSTEIN, M., CHEVALIER, J. A., KORCHIN, S. J., BASOWITZ, H., SABSHIN, M., HAMBURG, D. A., & GRINKER, R. R., 1957. Temporal heart rate patterns in anxious patients. *AMA Arch. neurol. Psychiat., 78,* 101–106. **158, 174, 175**

GOFFMAN, E., 1957. *Asylums.* Chicago: Aldine. **247**

GOLDBERGER, L., & HOLT, R. R., 1958. Experimental interference with reality contact (perceptual isolation): Method and group results. *J. nerv. ment. Dis. 127,* 99–112. **90, 107**

GOLDFRIED, M. R., 1960. A psychoanalytic interpretation of sensory deprivation. *Psychol. Rev., 10,* 211–214. **107**

GOLDMAN, D. E., 1948. *A review of subjective responses to vibratory motion of the human body in the frequency range 1 to 70 cycles per second.* Navy Med. Res. Inst. Rep. 1, Proj. NM 004001. Bethesda, Md.: Naval Medical Research Institute (March). **341**

GOLDSTEIN, I. B., 1964. Role of muscle tension in personality theory. *Psychol. Bull., 61,* 413–425. **56**

GOLDSTEIN, I. B., GRINKER, R. R., HEATH, H. A., OKEN, D., & SHIPMAN, W. G., 1964. A study in the psychophysiology of muscle tension: I. Response specificity. *AMA Arch. gen. Psychiat., 11,* 322–330. **56**

GOLLWITZER, H., 1953. *Unwilling journey.* Philadelphia: Muhlenberg. **264**

GORBOV, F. D., & MYASNIKOV, Y., 1963. Stress and fatigue under isolation conditions. *Zhur, Vysshey Nervnoy Deyatel'noti, 8,* 585–592. **108**

GRAHAM, D. T., KABLER, J. D., & GRAHAM, F. K., 1962a. Physiological response to the suggestion of attitudes specific for hives and hypertension. *Psychosom. Med., 24,* 159–169. **25**

GRAHAM, D. T., LUNDY, R. M., BENJAMIN, L. S., KABLER, J. D., LEWIS, W. C., KUNISH, N. O., & GRAHAM, F. K., 1962b. Specific attitudes in initial interviews with patients having different "psychosomatic" diseases. *Psychosom. Med., 24,* 257–266. **25**

GRAHAM, D. T., STERN, J. A., & WINOKUR, G., 1960. The concept of a different specific set of physiological changes in each emotion. *Psychiatric Res. Rep., 12,* 8–15. **25**

GRANIT, R., 1955. *Receptors and sensory perception.* New Haven: Yale. **105**

GRANT, L. B., n.d. *Operation Big Switch: Medical intelligence processing.* Unpublished mimeographed document. **254, 255**

GRAVELINE, D. E., 1963. *Sleep and altered proprioceptive input as related to weightlessness in water immersion studies.* USAF Tech. Doc. Rep. No. AMRL-TDR-62-63 (August), (ASTIA, 286-022). **88**

GREENWOOD, M., & WEYBREW, B. B., 1964. *Behavioral periodicity: I. Bibliography of literature pertaining to human beings.* U.S. Navy Med. Res. Lab. Rep. No. 421. New London, Conn.: U.S. Navy Submarine Base. **341**

GRINGS, W. W., CARLIN, S., & APPLEY, M. H., 1962. Set, suggestion and conditioning, *J. exp. Psychol., 63,* 417–422. **405**

GRINKER, R. R., 1959. Anxiety as a significant variable for a unified theory of human behavior. *AMA Arch. gen. Psychiat., 1,* 537–546. **46**

GRINKER, R. R., 1961. The physiology of emotions. In A. SIMON, C. C. HERBERT, & R. STRAUS (Eds.), *The physiology of emotions.* Springfield, Ill.: Charles C Thomas, pp. 1–25. **46**

GRINKER, R. R., KORCHIN, S. J., BASOWITZ, H., HAMBURG, D. A., SABSHIN, M. A., PERSKY, H., CHEVALIER, J., & BOARD, F. A., 1956. A theoretical and experimental approach to problems of anxiety. *AMA Arch. neurol. Psychiat., 76,* 420–431. **46**

GRINKER, R. R., & SPIEGEL, J., 1945. *Men under stress.* Philadelphia: Blakiston. **344**

GRODZINS, M., 1946. *Loyal and disloyal: Social boundaries of patriotism and treason.* Chicago: University of Chicago. **244, 247**

GROSSMAN, M. I., 1955. Integration of current views in the regulation of hunger and appetite. *Annals N.Y. Acad. Sci. 63,* Art. 1, 76–89. **339**

GROSSMAN, S. P., 1960. Eating or drinking elicited by direct adrenergic or cholinergic stimulation of hypothalamus. *Science, 132,* 301–302. **339**

GUIGNARD, J. C., 1959. *The physical response of seated men to low-frequency vertical vibration: Some preliminary studies.* Farnborough, Engl.: Inst. of Aviation Med., Royal Air Force, FPRC Rept. 1062. **341**

GUNDERSON, E. K. E., 1963. Emotional symptoms in extremely isolated groups. *AMA Arch. gen. Psychiat., 9,* 362–368. **287, 291, 364**

GUNDERSON, E. K. E., 1964. Personal history characteristics of Antarctic volunteers. *J. soc. Psychol. 64,* 325–332. **286**

GUNDERSON, E. K. E., & NELSON, P. D., 1965. Biographical predictors of performance in an extreme environment. *J. Psychol., 61,* 59–67. **286**

GUNDERSON, E. K. E., NELSON, P. D., & ORVICK, J. M., 1964. *Personal history cor-*

relates of military performance at a large Antarctic station. San Diego, Calif.: U.S. Navy Medical Neuropsychiatric Research Unit, Unit Report No. 64-22 (August). **280, 286**

GUSTAFSON, J. E., WINOKUR, G., & REICHLIN, S., 1963. The effect of psychic-sexual stimulation on urinary and serum acid phosphatase and plasma nonesterified fatty acids. *Psychosom. Med., 25,* 101–105. **54**

GYLLENSTEIN, L., MALMFORS, T., & NORRLIN, M. L., 1965. Effect of visual deprivation on the optic centers of growing and adult mice. *J. comp. Neurol., 124,* 149–160. **119**

HABER, H., 1952. Problems of space travel. *Science News Letter, 62,* 180 (September). **339**

HAGGARD, E. A., 1943. Some conditions determining adjustment during and re-adjustment following experimentally induced stress. In S. S. TOMKINS (Ed.), *Contemporary psychopathology: A source book.* Cambridge, Mass.: Harvard, pp. 529–532. **308**

HAGGARD, E. A., 1949. Psychological causes and results of stress. In D. B. LINDSLEY et al., *Human factors in undersea warfare.* Washington, D.C.: National Research Council, pp. 441–461. **8, 320, 345**

HAGGARD, E. A., 1964. Isolation and personality. In P. WORCHEL & D. BYRNE (Eds.), *Personality change.* New York: Wiley, pp. 433–469. **320, 392**

HALBERG, F., 1961. Circadian rhythms: A basis of human engineering for aerospace. In B. E. FLAHERTY (Ed.), *Psychophysiological aspects of space flight.* New York: Columbia, pp. 166–194. **13**

HALBERG, F., 1962a. Physiological 24-hour rhythms: A determinant of response to environmental agents. In K. E. SCHAEFER (Ed.), *International symposium on submarine and space medicine, Vol. 1: Man's dependence on the earthly atmosphere.* New York: Macmillan, pp. 48–96. **13, 342**

HALBERG, F., 1962b. Circadian temporal organization and experimental pathology. *The seventh conference of the Society for Biological Rhythm including a section on basimetry.* Torino, Italy: Panminerva Medica, pp. 52–69. **115, 116**

HALL, E. T., 1959. *The silent language.* New York: Doubleday. **273**

HAMBURG, D., 1961. Relevance of recent evolutionary changes to human stress biology. In S. WASHBURN (Ed.), *Social life of early man.* Viking Fund Series in Anthropology, Chicago: Aldine. **45**

HAMBURG, D. A., SABSHIN, M. A., BOARD, F. A., GRINKER, R. R., KORCHIN, S., BASQWITZ, H., HEATH, H., & PERSKY, H., 1958. Classification and rating of emotional experiences. Special reference to reliability of observation. *AMA Arch. neurol. Psychiat., 79,* 415–426. **46**

HANDLON, J. H., 1962. Hormonal activity and individual responses to stresses and easements in everyday living. In R. ROSSLER & N. S. GREENFIELD (Eds.), *Physiological correlates of psychological disorder.* Madison: University of Wisconsin, pp. 157–170. **49**

HANDLON, J. H., WADESON, R. W., FISHMAN, J. R., SACHAR, E. J., HAMBURG, D. A., & MASON, J. W., 1962. Psychological factors lowering plasma 17-hydroxycorticosteroid concentration. *Psychosom. Med., 24*, 535–542. **49**

HANNA, T. D., 1962. A physiologic study of human subjects confined in a simulated space vehicle. *Aerospace Med., 33*, 175–182. **343**

HARDY, J. D., WOLFF, H. G., & GOODELL, H., 1952. *Pain sensation and reactions.* Baltimore: Williams & Wilkins. **338**

HARLOW, H. F., SCHRIER, A. M., & SIMONS, D. G., 1956. Exposure of primates to cosmic radiation above 90,000 feet. *J. comp. Physiol., 49*, 195–200. **339**

HARLOW, H. F., 1958. The nature of love. *Amer. Psychol., 13*, 673–685. **114**

HARLOW, H. F., 1959. Love in infant monkeys. *Scientific Amer., 200*, No. 6, 68–74. **214**

HARLOW, H. F., & HARLOW, MARGARET K., 1962. Social deprivation in monkeys. *Scientific Amer. 207*, No. 5, 136–146. **214**

HARRIS, W., MACKIE, R. R., & WILSON, C. L., 1956. *Performance under stress: A review and critique of recent studies.* Tech. Rep. VI, Los Angeles, Calif.: Human Factors Research Corp. (July), (ASTIA AD No. 103779). **1, 9**

HARTMAN, B. O., McKENZIE, R. E., & WELCH, B. E., 1962. Performance effects in 17-day simulated space flights. *Aerospace Med., 33*, 1098–1102. **364**

HARTMAN, B. O., FLINN, D. E., EDMUNDS, A. B., BROWN, F. D., & SCHUBERT, J. E., 1964. *Human factors aspects of a 30-day extended service ability test of the Minuteman missile.* Brooks Air Force Base, Texas: USAF School of Aerospace Medicine, Tech. Doc. Rep. No. 64-62 (October). **279**

HAUTY, G. T., 1962. Periodic desynchronization in humans under outer space conditions. In W. WOLF (Ed.), *Rhythmic functions in the living system. Annals N.Y. Acad. Sci., 98*, Art. 4, 1116–1125. **116, 292**

HAUTY, G. T., 1963. Relationships between operator proficiency and effected changes in biological circadian periodicity. *Aerospace Med., 34*, 100–105. **341, 342**

HAUTY, G. T., PAYNE, R. B., & BAUER, R. O., 1957. *Effects of oxygen and dextroamphetamine upon work decrement.* Randolph AFB, Texas: USAF Sch. Av. Med., Rep. 56-127. **348**

HAYTHORN, W. W., 1957. *A review of research on crew assembly.* Lackland Air Force Base, Texas: Air Force Personnel and Training Research Center (May), Res. Rep. AFPTRC-TR-57-62. **365, 389**

HAYTHORN, W. W., ALTMAN, I., & MYERS, T. I., 1966. Emotional symptomatology and stress in isolated groups. *J. exp. res. Personal.* (in press). **367, 372, 379**

HEATH, HELEN A., & OKEN, D., 1965. The quantification of "response" to experimental stimuli. *Psychosom. Med., 27*, 457–471. **56**

HEBB, D. O., 1946a. Emotion in man and animal: an analysis of the intuitive processes of recognition. *Psychol. Rev., 53*, 88–106. **144**

HEBB, D. O., 1946b. On the nature of fear. *Psychol. Rev., 53*, 259–276. **144**

HEBB, D. O., 1955a. The mammal and his environment. *Amer. J. Psychiat., 11*, 826–831. **77**

HEBB, D. O., 1955b. Drives and the C.N.S. (Conceptual nervous system.) *Psychol. Rev., 62,* 243–254. **282, 364**

HEIN, P., COHEN, S. I., & SHMAVONIAN, B. M., 1965. Perceptual mode and Pavlovian typology. In J. WORTIS (Ed.), *Recent advances in biological Psychiatry.* New York: Plenum Press, 7, 71–78. **101, 102, 103, 104, 111**

HELPER, M. M., 1957. *The effects of noise on work output and physiological activation.* Fort Knox, Ky.: Army Med. Res. Lab. **340**

HELSON, H., 1959. Adaptation level theory. In S. KOCH (Ed.), *Psychology: A study of a science.* Vol. 1. New York: McGraw-Hill, pp. 565–621. **117**

HELSON, H., 1964. *Adaptation level theory.* New York: Harper & Row. **117**

HENDLER, E., 1963. Temperature effects on operator performance. In N. E. BURNS, R. M. CHAMBERS, & E. HENDLER (Eds.), *Unusual environments and human behavior.* New York: Collier-Macmillan, pp. 321–353. **335, 336**

HENRY, A., & SHORT, J., JR., 1954. *Suicide and homicide.* New York: Free Press. **239**

HERON, W., 1957. The pathology of boredom. *Scientific Amer., 196,* 52–56. **77**

HERON, W., 1961. Cognitive and physiological effects of perceptual isolation. In P. SOLOMON et al. (Eds.), *Sensory deprivation.* Cambridge, Mass.: Harvard, pp. 6–33. **77, 82**

HERON, W., BEXTON, W. H., & HEBB, D. O., 1953. Cognitive effects of a decreased variation in the sensory environment. *Amer. Psychologist, 8,* 366 (Abstract). **77, 78**

HERON, W., DOANE, B. K., & SCOTT, T. H., 1956. Visual disturbances after prolonged perceptual isolation. *Canad. J. Psychol., 10,* 13–18. **343**

HERRICK, C. G., 1924. *Neurological foundations of animal behavior.* New York: Holt. **3**

HETZEL, B. S., SCHOTTSTEADT, W. N., GRACE, W. J., & WOLFF, H. G., 1955. Changes in urinary 17-hydroxycorticosteroid excretion during stressful life experiences in man. *J. clin. Endocrinol., 15,* 1057–1068. **45**

HEYERDAHL, T., 1950. *Kontiki.* Chicago: Rand McNally. **278**

HEYMANS, C., & NEIL, E., 1958. *Reflexogenic areas of the cardiovascular system.* Boston: Little, Brown. **26, 27**

HILL, S. R., GOETZ, F. C., FOX, B. J., MURAWSKI, B. J., KRAKAUER, L. J., REIFENSTEIN, R. W., GRAY, S. J., REDDY, W. J., HEDBERG, S. E., ST. MARC, J. R., & THORN, G. W., 1956. Studies on adrenocortical and psychological responses to stress in man. *AMA Arch. int. Med., 97,* 269–298. **45**

HINES, M., 1958. *The effects of intense vibration. II. Physiology and pathology.* Fort Knox, Ky.: U.S. Army Med. Res. Lab., Rep. 358. **341**

HINKLE, L. E., JR., 1961. The physiologic state of the interrogation subject as it affects brain function. In A. D. BIDERMAN & H. ZIMMER (Eds.), *The manipulation of human behavior.* New York: Wiley, pp. 19–50. **252**

HINKLE, L. E., JR., & WOLFF, H. G., 1956. Communist interrogation and indoctrination of "Enemies of the State." Analysis of methods used by the Communist state police. (Special report.) *AMA Arch. neurol. Psychiat., 76,* 115–174. **247**

HOAGLAND, H., 1961. Some endocrine stress responses in man. In A. SIMON, C. C. HERBERT, & R. STRAUS (Eds.), *The physiology of emotions.* Springfield, Ill.: Charles C Thomas, pp. 40–76. **51**

HOFER, M. A., & HINKLE, L. E., JR., 1964. Conditioned diuresis in man: Effects of altered environment, subjective state, and conditioning experience. *Psychosom. Med., 26,* 108–124. **52**

HOFF, E. C., & GREENBAUM, L. J., JR., 1954. *A bibliographical source book of compressed air, diving and submarine medicine. Vol. 2.* Washington, D.C.: Office of Naval Research & USN Bureau of Medicine and Surgery. **335**

HOFFMAN, P., FESTINGER, L., & LAWRENCE, D., 1954. Tendencies toward group comparability in competitive bargaining. *Hum. Rel., 7,* 141–160. **189**

HOLMES, T. H., & HAWKINS, N. G., 1956. *Psychosocial and psychophysiologic studies of tuberculosis.* Alaska: Ladd Air Force Base, Arctic Aero-medical Lab., Proj. 8-7951 (February). **337, 338**

HOLT, R. R., & GOLDBERGER, L., 1959. *Personological correlates of reactions to perceptual isolation.* Wright-Patterson Field, Ohio: WADC Report No. TR-59-735. **89**

HOLTZMAN, W. H., & BITTERMAN, M. E., 1952. *Psychiatric screening of flying personnel. VI. Anxiety and reactions to stress.* Randolph AFB, Texas: USAF School of Aviat. Med. Proj. No. 21-37-002, Rep. No. 6. **337, 344**

HOLTZMAN, W. H., & BITTERMAN, M. E., 1956. A factorial study of adjustment to stress. *J. abn. soc. Psychol., 48,* 179–185. **350**

HORD, D. J., JOHNSON, L. C., & LUBIN, A., 1964. Differential effect of the Law of Initial Value (LIV) on autonomic variables. *Psychophysiology, 1,* 79–87. **56**

HOWARD, A., & SCOTT, R. A., 1965. A proposed framework for the analysis of stress in the human organism. *Behav. Science, 10,* 141–160. **353**

HULL, J., & ZUBEK, J., 1962. Personality characteristics of successful and unsuccessful sensory isolation subjects. *Percept. Mot. Skills, 14,* 231–240. **364**

HUNT, H. F., & DIAMOND, I. T., 1959. Some effects of hippocampal lesions on conditioned avoidance behavior in the cat. *Acta Psychologica, 15,* 203–204. **135**

HUNT, J. McV., 1961. *Intelligence and experience.* New York: Ronald. **114**

HUNTER, E., 1952. *Brainwashing in Red China.* Tokyo: Tuttle. **78**

HUTT, M. L., 1947. A clinical study of "consecutive" and "adaptive" testing with the revised Stanford-Binet. *J. consult. Psychol., 11,* 93–103. **9**

INGLE, D., 1954. Permissibility of hormone action. A review. *Acta Endocrinol., 17,* 172–186. **69**

Institut de Médecine et de Chirurgie Expérimentales, 1964. Montreal: Université de Montréal, Faculté de Médecine. **3, 4**

JACOBSON, EDITH, 1949. Observations on the psychological effects of imprisonment on female political prisoners. In K. R. EISSLER (Ed.), *Searchlights on delinquency.* New York: International Universities. **247**

JACKSON, C. W., JR., & KELLY, E. L., 1962. Influence of suggestion and subjects' prior knowledge in research on sensory deprivation. *Science, 132,* 211–212. **85, 107**

JACKSON, C. W., JR., & POLLARD, J. C., 1962. Sensory deprivation and suggestion. A theoretical approach. *Behav. Sci., 7,* 332–342. **85, 107**

JANIS, I. L., 1958. *Psychological stress.* New York: Wiley. **71, 163**

JANIS, I. L., 1965. Psychodynamic aspects of stress tolerance. In S. Z. KLAUSNER (Ed.), *The quest for self-control.* New York: Free Press, pp. 215–247. **71**

JENKS, R. S., & DEANE, G. E., 1963. Human heart rate responses during experimentally induced anxiety: A follow-up. *J. exp. Psychol., 65,* 109–112. **33**

JERISON, H. J., 1955. *Effect of a combination of noise and fatigue on a complex counting task.* WADC Tech. Rep. 55-360, Dayton, Ohio: Wright-Patterson AFB. **340**

JERISON, H. J., 1958. *Experiments on vigilance: Duration of vigil and the decrement function.* WADC Tech. Rep. 58-369. Dayton, Ohio: Wright-Patterson AFB. **347**

JOHN, R., 1962. Some speculations on the psychophysiology of mind. In J. M. SCHER (Ed.), *Theories of mind.* New York: Free Press. **147**

JOHNSON, C. R., 1941. *Prisoner of war.* Los Angeles, Calif.: Univ. of Southern Calif., Soc. Sci. Series 22. **247**

JOHNSON, L. C., 1962. *Spontaneous autonomic activity, autonomic reactivity and adaptation.* San Diego, Calif.: Rep. 62-7, USN Med. Neuropsychiat. Res. Unit. **342**

JOHNSON, L. C., & CORAH, N. L., 1963. Racial differences in skin resistance. *Science, 139,* 766–767. **157**

JOHNSON, L. C., SLYE, ELAINE, & DEMONT, W., 1964. Electroencephalographic and autonomic activity during and after prolonged sleep deprivation. Prepublication mimeographed form. San Diego, Calif.: U.S. Navy Neuropsychiat. Res. Unit. **336**

JONES, B. F., FLINN, R. H., & HAMMOND, E. C., et al., 1941. *Fatigue and hours of service of interstate truck drivers.* Public Health Bull. No. 265. Washington, D.C.: Govt. Printing Office. **347**

JOY, R. J. T., POE, R. H., BERMAN, F. R., & DAVIS, T. R., 1962. Some physiological responses to Arctic living. *Arch. environ. Health, 4,* 22–26. **335**

KAGAN, J., & LEWIS, M., 1965. Studies of attention in the human infant. *Merrill-Palmer Quart., 11,* 95–127. **35**

KAGAN, J., & ROSMAN, B. L., 1964. Cardiac and respiratory correlates of attention and an analytic attitude. *J. exp. Child Psychol., 1,* 50–63. **35**

KAMIYA, J., 1962. Conditioned discrimination of the EEG alpha rhythm in humans. Paper presented to Western Psychological Association. **360**

KAPLAN, H. B., 1963. Social interaction and GSR activity during group psychotherapy. *Psychosom. Med., 25,* 140–145. **54**

KARDINER, A., LINTON, R., DUBOIS, C., & WEST, J., 1945. *Psychological frontiers of society.* New York: Columbia. **220**

KATCHMAR, L., 1953. *Indicators of behavior decrement: 22. The effects of stress, anxiety, and ego involvement on "shift" task performance.* Proj. DA-49-007-MD-222, Tech. Rep. 22. College Park, Md.: University of Maryland, Army Med. Res. & Devel. Bd.   **9**

KATZ, C. J., 1946. Neuropathologic manifestations found in Japanese prison camp. *J. nerv. ment. Dis., 103,* 456–465.   **253**

KATZ, C. J., 1950. Experiences in a prison camp as a background for therapy. *Ment. Hygiene, 34,* 90–96.   **253**

KAYSER, C., 1957. Physiological aspects of hypothermia. *Ann. rev. Physiol., 19,* 83–120.   **335**

KEHOE, M., & IRONSIDE, W., 1963. Studies on the experimental evocation of depressive responses using hypnosis. II. The influence of depressive responses upon the secretion of gastric acid. *Psychosom. Med., 25,* 403–419.   **47**

KELLEHER, R. T., & MORSE, W. H., 1964. Escape behavior and punished behavior. *Fed. Proc., 23,* 808–817.   **39**

KELLEY, H. H., CONDRY, J. C., DAHLKE, A. E., & HILL, A. H., 1965. Collective behavior in a simulated panic situation. *J. exp. soc. Psychol., 1,* 20–54.   **165**

KERLE, R. H., & BIALEK, H. M., 1958. *The construction, validation, and application of a subjective stress scale.* (Staff Memorandum, Fighter IV, Study 23). Presidio of Monterey, Calif.: Human Resources Research Office (February).   **371, 397**

KESSEN, W., & MANDLER, G., 1961. Anxiety, pain, and the inhibition of distress. *Psychol. Rev., 68,* 396–404.   **309**

KETY, S. S., 1960. A biologist examines the mind and behavior. *Science, 132,* 1861-1870.   **318**

KEYS, A., BROZEK, J., HENSCHEL, O. M., & TAYLOR, H. L., 1950. *The biology of human starvation. Vol. II.* Minneapolis: University of Minnesota.   **338**

KIMBLE, D. P., 1963. The effects of bilateral hippocampal lesions in rats. *J. comp. physiol. Psychol., 56,* 273–283.   **137, 138**

KINKEAD, E., 1959. *In every war but one.* New York: Norton.   **249, 260**

KINSEY, A. C., POMEROY, W. B., & MARTIN, C. E., 1948. *Sexual behavior in the human male.* Philadelphia: Saunders.   **277**

KINSEY, A. C., POMEROY, W. B., MARTIN, C. E., & GEBHARD, P. H., 1953. *Sexual behavior in the human female.* Philadelphia: Saunders.   **277**

KINSEY, J. L., & MURPHREE, H. B., 1955. *Claustrophobic reactions to some stresses of the submarine service.* New London, Conn.: U. S. Navy Submarine Base, Med. Res. Lab.   **364, 365**

KLEITMAN, N., 1939; rev. and enlarged, 1963. *Sleep and wakefulness.* Chicago: University of Chicago.   **13**

KLEITMAN, N., 1949. The sleep-wakefulness cycle of submarine personnel. In D. B. LINDSLEY et al., *Human factors in undersea warfare.* Washington, D.C.: National Research Council, pp. 329–341.   **341**

KLEITMAN, N., 1960. Discussion. In G. E. WOLSTENHOLME & MAEVE O'CONNOR (Eds.), *Ciba Foundation symposium on the nature of sleep.* Boston: Little, Brown, pp. 336–337.   **336, 342**

KLEITMAN, N., 1961. Physiological cycling. In B. E. FLAHERTY (Ed.), *Psychophysiological aspects of space flight.* New York: Columbia, pp. 158–165. **342**

KLERMAN, G. L., DiMASCO, A., GREENBLATT, M., & RINKEL, M., 1959. The influence of specific personality patterns and the reactions to phrenotropic agents. In J. MASSERMAN (Ed.), *Biological psychiatry.* New York: Grune & Stratton, pp. 224–241. **93**

KLING, A., 1963. Plasma 17-hydroxycorticosteroid levels to reward and punishment in the brain-operated monkey. *Psychosom. Med., 25,* 489 (Abstract). **50**

KOGON, E., 1950. *The theory and practice of hell.* New York: Farrar, Straus. **247, 253, 255, 258, 261**

KORCHIN, S. J., & BASOWITZ, H., 1956. The judgment of ambiguous stimuli as an index of cognitive functioning in aging. *J. Personal., 25,* 81–95. **174**

KORCHIN, S. J., BASOWITZ, H., GRINKER, R. R., HAMBURG, D. A., PERSKY, H., SABSHIN, M. A., HEATH, HELEN, & BOARD, F. A., 1958. Experience of perceptual distortion as a source of anxiety. *AMA Arch. neurol. Psychiat., 80,* 98–113. **45**

KORCHIN, S. J., & HERZ, M., 1960. Differential effects of "shame" and "disintegrative" threats on emotional and adrenocortical functioning. *AMA Arch. gen. Psychiat., 2,* 640–651. **47**

KORCHIN, S. J., & RUFF, G. E., 1964. Personality characteristics of the Mercury Astronauts. In G. H. GROSSER, H. WECHSLER, & M. GREENBLATT (Eds.), *The threat of impending disaster: Contributions to the psychology of stress.* Cambridge, Mass.: M.I.T., pp. 197–207. **300, 310**

KRAUSE, M. S., 1961. The measurement of transitory anxiety. *Psychol. Rev., 68,* 178–189. **179**

KRECH, D., ROSENZWEIG, M., & BENNETT, E., 1963. Effects of complex environment and blindness on rat brain. *AMA Arch. Neurol., 8,* 403–412. **81**

KROEBER, A. L., & KLUCKHOHN, C., 1952. *Culture: A critical review of concepts and definitions.* Cambridge, Mass.: Papers of the Peabody Museum, Harvard, Vol. XLVII, No. 1. **236**

KROPOTKIN, P. A., 1887. *In Russian and French prisons.* London: Ward and Downey. **243**

KUBIE, L., 1961. Theoretical aspects of sensory deprivation. In P. SOLOMON et al. (Eds.), *Sensory deprivation.* Cambridge, Mass.: Harvard, pp. 208–220. **107**

KUBZANSKY, P. E., 1961. The effects of reduced environmental stimulation on human behavior: A review. In A. D. BIDERMAN & H. ZIMMER (Eds.), *The manipulation of human behavior.* New York: Wiley, pp. 51–95. **79, 80**

KUBZANSKY, P. E., & LEIDERMAN, P. H., 1961. Sensory deprivation: An overview. In P. SOLOMON et al. (Eds.), *Sensory deprivation.* Cambridge, Mass.: Harvard, pp. 221–238. **364**

LACEY, J. I., 1950. Individual differences in somatic response patterns. *J. comp. physiol. Psychol., 43,* 338–350. **21**

LACEY, J. I., 1956. The evaluation of autonomic responses: Toward a general solution. *Ann. N.Y. Acad. Sci., 67,* 123–164. **21, 56, 213**

LACEY, J. I., 1959. Psychophysiological approaches to the evaluation of psycho-therapeutic process and outcome. In E. A. RUBINSTEIN & M. B. PARLOFF (Eds.), *Research in psychotherapy.* Washington, D.C.: American Psychological Association, pp. 160–208. **21, 22, 25, 31, 33, 49, 55**

LACEY, J. I., BATEMAN, D. E., & VANLEHN, R., 1952. Autonomic response specificity and Rorschach color responses. *Psychosom. Med., 14,* 256–260. **21**

LACEY, J. I., BATEMAN, D. E., & VANLEHN, R., 1953. Autonomic response specificity: An experimental study. *Psychosom. Med., 15,* 8–21. **21, 22**

LACEY, J. I., KAGAN, J., LACEY, BEATRICE, C., & Moss, H. A., 1963. The visceral level: Situational determinants and behavioral correlates of autonomic response patterns. In P. H. KNAPP, (Ed.), *Expression of the emotions in man.* New York: International Universities, pp. 161–196. **25, 34, 55, 89, 97, 111, 160, 161**

LACEY, J. I., & LACEY, BEATRICE C., 1958a. Verification and extension of the principle of autonomic response stereotypy. *Amer. J. Psychol., 71,* 50–73. **21, 89, 97, 111**

LACEY, J. I., & LACEY, BEATRICE C., 1958b. The relationship of resting autonomic activity to motor impulsivity. *Res. Publ. Ass. Nerv. Ment. Dis., 36,* 144–209. **49, 55, 56, 350**

LACEY, J. I., & LACEY, BEATRICE C., 1962. The Law of Initial Value in the longitudinal study of autonomic constitution: Reproducibility of autonomic responses and response patterns over a four-year interval. *Ann. N.Y. Acad. Sci., 98,* 1257–1290; 1322–1326. **21**

LACEY, J. I., & VANLEHN, R., 1952. Differential emphasis in somatic response to stress. *Psychosom. Med., 14,* 73–81. **21**

LAMBO, T. A., 1955. The role of cultural factors in paranoid psychosis among the Yoruba tribe. *J. mental Sci., 101,* 239–266. **209**

LANG, P. J., & HNATIOW, M., 1962. Stimulus repetition and the heart rate response. *J. comp. physiol. Psychol., 55,* 781–785. **33**

LASAGNA, L., MOSTELLER, F., VONFELSINGER, J. M., & BEECHER, H. K., 1954. The study of the placebo response. *Amer. J. Med., 16,* 770–779. **93, 405**

LANSING, A., 1959. *Endurance: Shackleton's incredible voyage.* New York: McGraw-Hill. **279**

LANZETTA, J. T., 1955. Group behavior under stress. *Hum. Relat., 8,* 20–53. **385**

LASHLEY, K. S., 1929. *Brain mechanisms and intelligence.* Chicago: University of Chicago. **132, 140**

LAZARUS, R. S., 1963. A laboratory approach to the dynamics of psychological stress. *Admin. Sci. Quart., 8,* 192–213. **346**

LAZARUS, R. S., 1965a. Psychophysiological reactions during emotional stress. Mimeographed preprint, Symposium, Karolinska Hospital, Stockholm, Sweden (in press). **23**

LAZARUS, R. S., 1965b. An inspirational view of response patterning. Paper given at the Western Psychological Association Meetings in a symposium entitled, The dynamics of emotion: Autonomic and behavioral effects, Honolulu (June 17). **154**

LAZARUS, R. S., 1966. *Psychological stress and the coping process.* New York: McGraw-Hill. **151, 155**

LAZARUS, R. S., & ALFERT, ELIZABETH, 1964. The short-circuiting of threat, *J. abn. soc. Psychol., 69,* 195–205. **7, 154, 161, 214**

LAZARUS, R. S., DEESE, J., & OSLER, SONIA F., 1952. The effects of psychological stress upon performance. *Psychol. Bull., 49,* 293–317. **7, 8, 9, 345**

LAZARUS, R. S., SPEISMAN, J. C., & MORDKOFF, A. M., 1963. The relation between autonomic indicators of psychological stress: Heart rate and skin conductance. *Psychosom. Med., 25,* 19–30. **23**

LAZARUS, R. S., SPEISMAN, J. C., MORDKOFF, A. M., & DAVISON, L. A., 1962. A laboratory study of psychological stress produced by a motion picture film. *Psychol. Monogr., 76* (Whole No. 553), p. 35. **46, 154**

LAZARUS, R. S., TOMITA, M., OPTON, E. M., JR., & KODAMA, M., 1966. A crosscultural study of stress reaction patterns in Japan. *J. personal. soc. Psychol.,* in press. **154**

LEAVITT, W., 1958. Man in space. *Air Force, 41,* 108–123. **339**

LEIDERMAN, P., 1962. *Imagery and sensory deprivation.* Washington, D.C.: U.S.A.F. Techn. Doc. Rep. No. MRL-TDR-62-28 (May). **82, 87, 90, 105**

LEIGHTON, A. H., 1945. *The governing of men: General principles and recommendations based on experiences at a Japanese relocation camp.* Princeton, N.J.: Princeton. **244**

LESSA, WILLIAM A., 1964. The social effects of typhoon *Ophelia* (1960) on Ulithi. *Micronesica, 1,* 1–47. **218**

LESTER, J. T., JR., 1964. Men to match Mount Everest. *Naval Res. Reviews, 17* (12), 7–14. **279**

LEVI, L., 1961. A new stress tolerance test with simultaneous study of physiological and psychological variables: A preliminary study. *Acta Endocrinol., 37,* 38–44. **54**

LEVI, L., 1965. The urinary output of adrenalin and noradrenalin during pleasant and unpleasant emotional states. A preliminary study. *Psychosom. Med., 27,* 80–85. **54**

LEVITT, E. E., & BRADY, J. P., 1963. Psychophysiology of hypnosis. In J. M. SCHNECK (Ed.), *Hypnosis in modern medicine.* (3rd ed.) Springfield, Ill.: Charles C Thomas, pp. 314–362. **49**

LEVITT, E. E., PERSKY, H., BRADY, J. P., 1964. *Hypnotic induction of anxiety.* Springfield, Ill.: Charles C Thomas. **47**

LEWIN, K., 1935. *A dynamic theory of personality.* New York: McGraw-Hill. **308**

LEWIS, G. C., & MEWHA, J., 1955. *History of prisoner of war utilization by the United States Army 1776–1945.* Pamphlet No. 20-213. Washington, D.C.: Dept. of Army. **247**

LEWIS, M., KAGAN, J., CAMPBELL, HELEN, & KALAFAT, J., 1966. The cardiac response as a correlate of attention in infants. *Child Develop., 37,* 63–71. **35**

LEWIS, P. R., & LOBBAN, M. C., 1957. Dissociation of diurnal rhythms in human subjects living on abnormal time routines. *Quart. J. exp. Physiol., 42,* 371–386. **342**

LIDDELL, H. S., 1950. The role of vigilance in the development of animal neurosis. In P. H. HOCH & J. ZUBIN (Eds.), *Anxiety.* New York: Grune & Stratton, pp. 183–196. **66**

LIFTON, R. J., 1961. *Thought reform and the psychology of totalism: A study of "brainwashing" in China.* New York: Norton. **247**

LILLY, J. C., 1956a. Mental effects of reduction of ordinary levels of physical stimuli on intact, healthy persons. Washington, D.C.: American Psychiatric Association, *Psychiat. res. Rep., 5,* 1–28. **77, 79, 364**

LILLY, J. C., 1956b. Effects of physical restraint and of ordinary levels of physical stimuli on intact, healthy persons. In *Illustrative strategies for research on psychopathology in mental health.* Group for the Advancement of Psychiatry, Symposium No. 2, New York: GAP Publications, 13–22. **257**

LINDSLEY, D. B., 1951. Emotion. In S. S. STEVENS (Ed.), *Handbook of experimental psychology.* New York: Wiley, pp. 473–516. **15**

LINDSLEY, D. B., 1961. Are there common factors in sensory deprivation, sensory distortion and sensory overload? In P. SOLOMON et al. (Eds.), *Sensory deprivation.* Cambridge, Mass.: Harvard, pp. 174–194. **110**

LIPTON, E. L., STEINSCHNEIDER, A., & RICHMOND, J. B., 1961a. Autonomic function in the neonate. III. Methodological considerations. *Psychosom. Med., 23,* 461–471. **56**

LIPTON, E. L., STEINSCHNEIDER, A., & RICHMOND, J. B., 1961b. Autonomic function in the neonate. IV. Individual differences in cardiac reactivity. *Psychosom. Med., 23,* 472–484. **56**

LIVANOV, M. N., & KONDRATEVA, I. N., 1960. *Sensitivity of the nervous system to low level radiation.* (Translation: AEC TR-4090) Moscow, USSR: Academy of Medical Sciences. **339**

LIVINGSTON, R. B., 1958. Central control of afferent activity. In H. H. JASPER, L. D. PROCTOR, R. S. KNIGHTON, W. C. NOSHAY, & R. T. COSTELLO (Eds.), *Reticular formation of the brain.* Boston: Little, Brown, pp. 177–185. **29**

LIVINGSTON, R. B., 1959. Central control of receptors and sensory transmission systems. In J. FIELD, H. W. MAGOUN, & V. E. HALL (Eds.), *Handbook of physiology, Section 1: Neurophysiology.* Vol. 1. Washington, D.C.: American Physiological Society, pp. 741–760. **29**

LOFCHIE, S. H., 1955. The performance of adults under distraction stress: A developmental approach. *J. Psychol., 39,* 109–116. **9**

LOFTUS, J. P., JR., & HAMMER, LOIS R., 1963. *Weightlessness.* In N. BURNS, R. CHAMBERS, & E. HENDLER (Eds.), *Unusual environments and human behavior.* New York: Collier-Macmillan, pp. 353–377. **333**

LUBY, E. D., FORHMAN, C. E., GRISELL, J. L., LANZO, J. E., & GOTTLIEB, J. S., 1960. Sleep deprivation: Effects on behavior, thinking, motor performance and biological energy transfer systems. *Psychosom. Med., 22,* 182–192. **336**

LUND, A., 1951. Elimination of adrenaline and noradrenaline from the organism. *Acta. Pharmacol. et Toxicol.,* 7, 297–308. **53**

LYMAN, R. S., KUPALOV, P. S., & SCHOLZ, W., 1933. Effects of roentgen rays on the central nervous system. *AMA Arch. neurol. Psychiat., 29,* 56–87. **339**

McCUBBIN, J. W., & PAGE, I. H., 1963. Neurogenic component of chronic renal hypertension. *Science, 139,* 210–215. **51**

McDONALD, D. G., STERN, J. A., & HAHN, W. W., 1963. *Studies of classical heart rate conditioning in the rat.* Bethesda, Md.: U.S. Navy Medical Neuropsychiat. Res. Unit, Rep. No. 63-3 (January). **33**

McFARLAND, R. A., 1953. *Human factors in air transportation.* New York: McGraw-Hill. **347**

McGUIRE, F., & TOLCHIN, S., 1961. Group adjustment at the South Pole. *J. mental Sci., 107,* 954–960. **282**

McGOUGH, W. E., SILVERMAN, A. J., & BOGDONOFF, M., 1965. Patterns of fat mobilization in field-dependent and field-independent subjects. *Psychosom. Med., 27,* 245–256. **100**

McCLELLAND, D. C., ATKINSON, J. W., CLARK, R. A., & LOWELL, E. L., 1953. *The achievement motive.* New York: Appleton-Century-Crofts. **396**

McMICHAEL, J., 1965. The role of fear in the retention of a conditioned avoidance response. Paper delivered at Eastern Psychological Assoc. (April 1). **206**

MACKWORTH, N. H., 1952. Some recent studies of human stress from a Marine and Naval viewpoint. *Trans. Inst. Mar. Engrs., 64,* 123–132. **328**

MACKWORTH, N. H., 1956. Vigilance. *Nature, 178,* 1375–1377. **106**

MacLEAN, P. D., 1958. Contrasting functions of limbic and neocortical systems of the brain and their relevance to psychophysiological aspects of medicine. *Am. J. Med. 25,* 611–626. **50**

MAGOUN, H. W., 1954. The ascending reticular system and wakefulness. In J. F. DELAFRESNAYE (Ed.), *Brain mechanisms and consciousness.* Springfield, Ill.: Charles C Thomas, pp. 1–20. **129**

MALMO, R. B., 1959. Activation: A neuropsychological dimension. *Psychol. Rev., 66,* 367–386. **15, 22, 84, 85, 343, 348**

MALMO, R. B., 1961. Slowing of heart rate after septal self-stimulation in rats. *Science, 133,* 1128–1130. **64**

MALMO, R. B., 1966. Cognitive factors in impairment: A neuropsychological study of divided set. *J. exp. Psychol., 71,* 184–189. **19**

MALMO, R. B., & SURWILLO, W. W., 1960. Sleep deprivation: Changes in performance and physiological indicants of activation. *Psychol. Monogr., 74,* No. 15. **336**

MANDELL, A. J., CHAPMAN, L. F., RAND, R. W., WALTER, R. D., 1963. Plasma corticosteroids: Changes in concentration after stimulation of hippocampus and amygdala. *Science, 139,* 1212. **50**

MANDLER, G., 1962. Emotion. In R. W. BROWN et al. *New directions in psychology*. New York: Holt, Rinehart and Winston, pp. 163–219. **308, 309, 360**

MANDLER, G., 1964. The interruption of behavior. In D. LEVINE (Ed.), *Nebraska symposium on motivation: 1964*. Lincoln: University of Nebraska, pp. 267–343. **307, 309**

MANDLER, G., & KAHN, M., 1960. Discrimination of changes in heart rate: Two unsuccessful attempts. *J. exp. anal. Behav., 3,* 21–25. **360**

MANDLER, G., & KREMEN, I., 1958. Autonomic feedback: A correlational study. *J. Personal, 26,* 388–399. **359**

MANDLER, G., & MANDLER, JEAN M., 1962. Associate behavior and somatic response. *Canad. J. Psychol., 16,* 331–343. **42**

MANDLER, G., MANDLER, JEAN, M., & UVILLER, ELLEN T., 1958. Autonomic feedback: The perception of autonomic activity. *J. abn. soc. Psychol., 56,* 367–373. **359**

MANDLER, G., MANDLER, JEAN M., KREMEN, I., & SHOLITON, R. D., 1961. The response to threat: Relations among verbal and physiological indices. *Psychol. Monogr., 75,* Whole No. 513. **346**

MANDLER, G., & WATSON, D. L., 1966. Anxiety and the interruption of behavior. In C. D. SPIELBERGER (Ed.), *Anxiety and behavior*. New York: Academic, pp. 263–290. **307, 308**

MARCHBANKS, V. H., HALE, H. B., & ELLIS, J. P., 1962. *Stress responses of pilots flying 6-hour overwater missions in F-100 and F-104 aircraft*. SMA-TDR-62-112, Brooks AFB, Texas: School of Aerospace Med. **337**

MARSHALL, S. L. A., 1947. *Men against fire*. Wash., D.C.: The Infantry Journal; and New York: Morrow. **165**

MARTIN, B., 1961. The measurement of anxiety by physiological-behavioral measures. *Psychol. Bull., 58,* 234–255. **179**

MASON, J. W., 1958. The central nervous system regulation of ACTH secretion. In H. H. JASPERS et al. (Eds.), *Reticular formation of the brain*. Boston: Little, Brown, pp. 645–670. **45, 50**

MASON, J. W., 1959a. Visceral functions of the nervous system. *Ann. rev. Physiol., 21,* 353–380. **45, 47**

MASON, J. W., 1959b. Psychological influence on the pituitary-adrenal cortical system. In G. PINCUS (Ed.), *Recent progress in hormone research*. Proceedings of the Laurentian Hormone Conf., Vol. XV, New York: Academic, pp. 345–389. **45, 47, 50, 348**

MAYER, W. E., 1956. Why did many GI captives cave in? *US News and World Rep., 38,* 56–62. **253**

MECHANIC, D., 1962. *Students under stress*. New York: Free Press. **164, 200, 207**

MELZACK, R., & SCOTT, T. H., 1957. The effects of early experience on the response to pain. *J. comp. physiol. Psychol., 50,* 155–161. **114**

MELZACK, R., & THOMPSON, W. R., 1956. Effects of early experience on social behavior. *Canad. J. Psychol., 10,* 82–90. **114**

MENDELSON, J. H., KUBZANSKY, P. E., LEIDERMAN, P. H., WEXLER, D., & SOLOMON, P., 1961. Physiological and psychological aspects of sensory deprivation—a case analysis. In P. SOLOMON, et al. (Eds.), *Sensory deprivation*. Cambridge, Mass.: Harvard, pp. 91–113. **88**

MERTON, R. K., WEST, PATRICIA S., JOHODA, MARIE, & SELVIN, H. C. (Eds.), 1951. Social policy and social research in housing. *J. Soc. Issues, 7,* Nos. 1 and 2. **274**

MEYERS, W. J., VALENSTEIN, E. S., & LACEY, J. I., 1963. Heart rate changes after reinforcing brain stimulation in rats. *Science, 140,* 1233–1234. **33**

MILES, W. R., 1919. The sex expression of men living on a lowered nutritional level. *J. nerv. ment. Dis., 49,* 208–224. **338**

MILLER, D. S., 1962. Effects of low-level radiation on audiogenic convulsive seizures in mice. In T. J. HALEY & R. S. SNEIDER (Eds.), *International symposium on the response of the nervous system to ionizing radiation.* Northwestern Medical School, New York: Academic, pp. 513–531. **339**

MILLER, G. A., GALANTER, E. H., & PRIBRAM, K., 1960. *Plans and the structure of behavior.* New York: Holt, Rinehart and Winston. **308, 355**

MILLER, J. G., BOUTHILET, LORRAINE, & ELDRIDGE, CARMEN, 1953. *A bibliography for the development of experimental stress-sensitive tests for predicting performance in military tasks.* PRB Tech. Rep. 1079, Res. Note 22, Washington, D.C.: Psychological Research Associates. **7, 324**

MILNER, BRENDA, 1959. The memory defect in bilateral hippocampal lesions. In D. E. CAMERON & M. GREENBLATT (Eds.), *Recent advances in neurophysiological research.* Washington, D.C.: Amer. Psychiat. Ass., pp. 43–52. **137**

MILNER, BRENDA, & PENFIELD, W., 1955. The effect of hippocampal lesions on recent memory. *Trans. Am. Neurol. Ass.,* 42–48. **137**

MINTZ, A., 1951. Non-adaptive group behavior. *J. abn. soc. Psychol., 46,* 150–159. **165, 186, 187**

MIRSKY, A. F., & CARDON, P. V., 1962. A comparison of the behavioral and physiological changes accompanying sleep deprivation and chlorpromazine administration in man. *Electroenceph. clin. Neurophysiol. 14,* 1–10. **18, 19**

Misconduct in the prison camp: A survey of the law and an analysis of the Korean cases. (A student note), *Columbia Law Rev.,* 1956, *56,* 709–794. **247, 262**

MOELLER, G., & CHATTIN, C. P., 1962. The palmar perspiration index and pursuit tracking. *Percept. Mot. Skills, 15,* 463–473. **348**

MOLONEY, J. C., & BIDDLE, C. R., 1945. Psychiatric observations in Okinawa Shima; Psychology of the Okinawan. *Psychiatry, 8,* 391–399. **234**

MORAN, L. J., & MEFFERD, R. B., JR., 1959. Repetitive psychometric measures. *Psychol. Rep., 5,* 269–275. **302, 304**

MORDKOFF, A. M., 1964. The relationship between psychological and physiological response to stress. *Psychosom. Med., 26,* 135–149. **23, 156**

MORGAN, C. T., & STELLAR, E. 1950. *Physiological psychology.* (2nd. ed.) New York: McGraw-Hill. **338**

MOWRER, O. H., & VIEK, P., 1948. An experimental analogue of fear from a sense of helplessness. *J. abn. soc. Psychol., 43,* 193–200. **308**

MULLIN, C. S., 1960. Some psychological aspects of isolated Antarctic living. *Amer. J. Psychiat., 117, 323–325.* **364**

MULLIN, C. S., & CONNERY, H. J. M., 1959. Psychological study at an Antarctic IGY station. *U.S. Armed Forces Med. J., 19,* 290–296. **364**

MURPHY, C. W., GRAFTON, J. P., & CLEGHORN, R. A., 1954. Effect of long range flights on eosinophil level and corticoid excretion. *J. aviat. Med., 25,* 242–248. **337, 347**

MURPHY, W. B. M., 1955. Refugee psychoses in Great Britain: Admissions to mental hospitals. In W. B. M. MURPHY (Ed.), *Flight and resettlement.* (Series: United Nations Educational, Scientific & Cultural Organization, Population and Culture, 2), Paris: UNESCO, pp. 173–194. **244**

MURRAY, E. J., 1959. *The psychological effects of adverse environmental conditions and their implications for adjustment in fallout shelters.* Washington, D.C.: Disaster Research Group, National Academy of Sciences for OCDM. **340**

MYERS, T. I., 1964. Sensory and perceptual deprivation. Presented to Symposium on Medical Aspects of Stress in the Military Climate. Washington, D.C.: Walter Reed Army Institute of Research (April 22). **313, 364, 371**

MYERS, T. I., MURPHY, D. B., SMITH, S., & WINDLE, C., 1962. Experimental assessment of a limited social and sensory environment: Summary results of the HUMMRO program. *Research Memorandum* U.S. Army Leadership Human Res. Unit (February). **364, 371, 373**

NADEL, A. B., 1963. Vibration. In N. E. BURNS, R. M. CHAMBERS, E. HENDLER (Eds.), *Unusual environments and human behavior.* New York: Collier-Macmillan, pp. 379–394. **340, 341**

NAKAO, H., BALLIM, H. M., & GELLHORN, E., 1956. The role of the sino-aortic receptors in the action of adrenaline, noradrenaline, and acetylcholine on the cerebral cortex. *Electroenceph. clin. Neurophysiol., 8,* 413–420. **27**

NARDINI, J. E., 1952. Survival factors in American prisoners of war of Japanese. *Amer. J. Psychiat., 109, 241–248.* **253, 270, 338**

NARDINI, J. E., HERRMANN, R. S., & RASMUSSEN, J. E., 1962. Navy psychiatric assessment program in the Antarctic. *Amer. J. Psychiat., 119,* 97–105. **364**

NAUTA, W. J. H., 1960. Limbic system and hypothalamus: Anatomical aspects. *Physiol. Rev., 40,* Suppl. #4, 102–104. **50**

Navy Bureau of Medicine and Surgery, Department of Navy, 1956. *Submarine medical practice.* Washington, D.C.: NAVMED-P 5054. **334**

NEIL, E., & HEYMANS, C., 1962. Cardiovascular and pulmonary reflexes. In A. A. LUISADA (Ed.), *Cardiovascular functions.* New York: McGraw-Hill, pp. 103–123. **26, 32**

NELSON, P. D., 1964a. *Compatibility among work associates in isolated groups.* San Diego Calif.: U.S. Navy Med. Neuropsychiat. Res. Unit, Unit Rep. No. 64-13 (July). **284**

NELSON, P. D., 1964b. *Structural change in small isolated groups.* San Diego, Calif.: U.S. Navy Medical Neuropsychiatric Research Unit, Unit Rep. No. 64-24 (September). **284**

NELSON, P. D., & GUNDERSON, E. K. E., 1962. *Analysis of adjustment dimensions in confined groups.* San Diego, Calif.: U.S. Navy Med. Neuropsychiat. Res. Unit, Unit Rep. No. 62-3. **364**

NELSON, P. D., & GUNDERSON, E. K. E., 1963. *Personal history correlates of performance among military personnel in small Antarctic stations.* San Diego, Calif.: U.S. Navy Med. Neuropsychiat. Res. Unit, Unit Rep. No. 63-20 (November). **280**

NELSON, P. D., & GUNDERSON, E. K. E., 1964. Analysis of adjustment dimensions in small confined groups. *Bulletin L'Etudes Recherche de Psychologie, 13*(2), 111–126. **364**

NELSON, P. D., & ORVICK, J. M., 1964. *Personal history correlates of performance among civilian personnel in small Antarctic stations.* San Diego, Calif.: U.S. Navy Med. Neuropsychiat. Res. Unit, Unit Rep. No. 64-4 (April). **280**

NICHOLS, B. L., JR., 1961. The role of antidiuretic hormone in corticotrophin release. *Yale J. Biol. Med., 33,* 415–434. **50**

NIKI, H., 1962. The effects of hippocampal ablation on the behavior in the rat. *Jap. Psychol. Res., 4,* 139–153. **137**

NORDHOFF, C., & HALL, J., 1934. *Men against the sea.* Boston: Little, Brown. **278**

NOTTERMAN, J. M., SCHOENFELD, W. J., & BERSH, P. J., 1952. Conditioned heart rate response in human beings during experimental anxiety. *J. comp. physiol. Psychol., 45,* 1–8. **40**

NOTTERMAN, J. M., & TRUMBULL, R., 1959. Note on self-regulating systems and stress. *Behav. Sci., 4,* 324–327. **122, 405**

NOWLIS, V., 1965. Research with the Mood Adjective Check List. In S. TOMKINS & E. IZARD (Eds.), *Affect, cognition and personality.* New York: Springer, pp. 352–389. **357**

NOWLIS, V., & NOWLIS, HELEN H., 1956. The description and analysis of mood. *Ann. N.Y. Acad. Sci., 65,* 345–355. **357**

OBRIST, P. A., 1963. Cardiovascular differentiation of sensory stimuli. *Psychosom. Med., 25,* 450–459. **25, 35**

OBRIST, P. A., WOOD, D. M., & PEREZ-REYES, M., 1965. Heart rate during conditioning in humans: Effects of UCS intensity, vagal blockade, and adrenergic block of vasomotor activity. *J. exp. Psychol., 70,* 32–42. **33**

OKEN, D., 1960. An experimental study of suppressed anger and blood pressure. *AMA Arch. gen. Psychiat., 2,* 441–456. **46, 175, 176**

OKEN, D., 1962. The role of defense in psychological stress. In R. ROESSLER & N. S. GREENFIELD (Eds.), *Physiological correlates of psychological disorder.* Madison: University of Wisconsin, pp. 193–210. **48**

OKEN, D., GRINKER, R. R., HEATH, HELEN A., SABSHIN, M. A., & SCHWARTZ, N.

1960. Stress response in a group of chronic psychiatric patients. *AMA Arch. gen. Psychiat., 3*, 451–466.   **48**

OKEN, D., GRINKER, R. R., HEATH, HELEN A., HERZ, M., KORCHIN, S. J., SABSHIN, M. A., & SCHWARTZ, N., 1962. Relation of physiological response to affect expression: Including studies of autonomic response specificity. *AMA Arch. gen. Psychiat., 6*, 336–351.   **46, 47, 55, 59**

OKEN, D., & HEATH, HELEN, A., 1963. The Law of Initial Values: Some further considerations. *Psychosom. Med., 25*, 3–12.   **56**

OLDS, J., 1956. A preliminary mapping of electrical reinforcing effects in the rat brain. *J. comp. physiol. Psychol., 49*, 281–285.   **132, 149**

OPLER, M. K., 1940. The Southern Ute Indians of Colorado. In R. LINTON (Ed.), *Acculturation in seven American Indian tribes*. New York: Appleton-Century-Crofts, pp. 119–203.   **213, 217**

OPLER, M. K. (Ed.), 1956. *Culture, psychiatry and human values*. Springfield, Ill.: Charles C Thomas (Rev. Ed., New York: Atherton, 1966).   **212, 215, 221, 229**

OPLER, M. K., 1957. Schizophrenia and culture. *Scientific Amer., 197*, 103–110.   **229, 238**

OPLER, M. K., 1958*a*. Dilemmas of Two Puerto Rican Men. In GEORGENE SEWARD (Ed.), *Clinical studies in culture conflict*. New York: Ronald, 223–244.   **229, 230**

OPLER, M. K., 1958*b*. In GEORGENE SEWARD (Ed.), *Clinical studies in culture conflict*. New York: Ronald. Cf. OPLER, M. K., 1957. Also cf. OPLER, M. K., & SINGER, J., 1956.   **224, 229**

OPLER, M. K., 1959. Dream analysis in Ute Indian therapy. In M. K. OPLER (Ed.), *Culture and mental health: Cross-cultural studies*. New York: Macmillan, pp. 97–117.   **238**

OPLER, M. K., 1960. Cultural evolution and the psychology of peoples. In G. DOLE & R. CARNEIRO (Eds.), *Essays in the science of culture*. New York: Crowell.   **220**

OPLER, M. K., 1966. Social and cultural influences on the psychopathology of family groups. In G. H. ZUK & I. BOSZORMENYI-NAGY (Eds.), *Family therapy and disturbed families*. Palo Alto, Calif.: Science & Behavior Books, in press.   **231**

OPLER, M. K., & SINGER, J., 1956. Ethnic behavior and psychopathology: Italian and Irish. *Internat. J. soc. Psychiat, 2*, 11–23. Cf. same authors, 1956. Contrasting patterns of fantasy and motility in Irish and Italian schizophrenics. *J. abn. soc. Psychol., 53*, 42–47.   **215**

ORNE, M. T., 1959. The nature of hypnosis: Artifact and essence. *J. abn. soc. Psychol., 58*, 277–299.   **47**

ORNE, M., & SCHEIBE, K., 1964. The contribution of non-deprivation factors in production of sensory deprivation effects. *J. abn. soc. Psychol., 68*, 3–12.   **107**

OSWALD, I., 1962. *Sleeping and waking*. Amsterdam: Elsevier.   **336**

function in three emotional states. Paper presented to American Psychosomatic Society, Philadelphia (April). **89**

PETERS, H. N., 1963. Affect and emotion. In M. H. MARX (Ed.), *Theories in contemporary psychology*. New York: Collier-Macmillan, pp. 435–454. **153**

PETERSON, L. H., 1962. The mechanical properties of the blood vessels and hypertension. In J. H. CORT, V. FENCL, Z. HEJL, & J. JIRKA (Eds.), *The pathogenesis of essential hypertension*. Prague: State Medical Publishing House, pp. 295–313. **29**

PETERSON, L. H., FEIGL, E., & GOURAS, P., 1960. Properties of the carotid sinus mechanism. *Fed. Proc., 19,* 40 (Abstract). **29**

PETRIE, A., 1960. Some psychological aspects of pain and the relief of suffering. *Annals N.Y. Acad. Sci., 86,* Art. 1, 13–27. **114**

PETRIE, A., COLLINS, W., & SOLOMON, P., 1960. The tolerance for pain and for sensory deprivation. *Amer. J. Psychol., 73,* 80–90. **81**

PETTIT, J., COHEN, S. I., & SILVERMAN, A. J., 1958. *Multiple psychophysiologic measures during gradual onset acceleration*. Dayton, Ohio: Wright-Patterson Air Force Base, WADC TN 57-234. **329, 333**

PINNEO, L. R., 1961. The effects of induced muscle tension during tracking on level of activation and on performance. *J. exp. Psychol., 62,* 523–531. **348**

POLLARD, J. C., UHR, L., & JACKSON, C. W., JR., 1963. Studies in sensory deprivation. *AMA Arch. gen. Psychiat. 8,* 435–454. **107**

PLUTCHIK, R., 1959. The effects of high intensity intermittent sound on performance, feeling and physiology. *Psychol. Bull., 56,* 133–151. **340**

PRESCOTT, J. W., 1965. Neural timing mechanisms, conditioning, and the CS-UCS interval. *Psychophysiology, 2,* 125–131. **117**

PRIBRAM, K. H., 1960. A review of theory in physiological psychology. *Ann. rev. Psychol., 11,* 1–40. **50**

PRIBRAM, K. H., & FULTON, J. 1954. An experimental critique of the effects of anterior cingulate ablation in monkey. *Brain, 77,* 34–44. **139**

PRICE, D. B., THALER, MARGARET, & MASON, J. W., 1957. Preoperative emotional states and adrenal cortical activity: Studies in cardiac and pulmonary surgery patients. *AMA Arch. neurol. Psychiat., 77,* 646–656. **45, 46, 337**

QUARANTELLI, E. L., 1954. The nature and conditions of panic. *Amer. J. Sociol., 60,* 267–275. **165**

QUAY, H., 1966. Psychopathic personality as pathological stimulation-seeking. *Amer. J. Psychiat., 122,* 180–183. **119**

RAHN, H. Personal communication to Dr. Opler. **218**

RAPAPORT, D., 1958. The theory of ego autonomy: A generalization. *Bull. Menninger Clin., 22,* 13–35. **107**

RASMUSSEN, J. E., & WAGNER, C. M., 1962. *Studies of the Bureau of Yards and*

Docks: Protective shelter. I. Winter trails. Washington, D.C.: Naval Res. Lab. Rep. No. 5882. **284**

RECKLESS, J. R., & COHEN, S. I., 1964. A psychophysiologic technique for the evaluation of individual differences in humans using central nervous system active drugs. *J. new Drugs, 4*(4), 226–227 (Abstract). **96**

RECKLESS, J. R., COHEN, S. I., SILVERMAN, A. J., & SHMAVONIAN, B. M., 1962. The influence of perceptual mode and controlled environment conditions on the response to drugs. *Psychosom. Med., 24,* 520 (Abstract). **91, 96**

REINARTZ, E. G., 1943. Some mental aspects of aviation medicine. *J. aviat. Med., 14,* 75–83. **340**

RICHTER, C., 1957. On the phenomenon of sudden death in animals and man. *Psychosom. Med., 19,* 191–198. **266, 269**

RICKENBACKER, E., 1943. *Seven came through.* New York: Doubleday. **278**

RIESEN, A. H., 1961. Excessive arousal effects of stimulation after early sensory deprivation. In P. SOLOMON et al. (Eds.), *Sensory deprivation.* Cambridge, Mass.: Harvard, pp. 34–40. **114**

RIESMAN, D. et al., 1950. *The lonely crowd.* New Haven: Yale. **114**

RIGG, R. B., 1951. *Red China's fighting hordes.* Harrisburg, Pa.: Military Service Publ. Co. **264**

RIHL, J., 1926. Die Frequenz des Herzschlages. In A. BETHE, G. VON BERGMANN, G. EMBDEN, & A. ELLINGER (Eds.), *Handbuch der Normalen und Pathologischen Physiologie. 7–1* (Blutzirkulation) Berlin: Julius Springer, pp. 449–522. **34**

RITTER, C. E., 1954. *A woman in the Polar night.* New York: Dutton. **78**

ROBY, T. B., 1956. *Sociometric index measures as predictors of medium-bomber crew performance.* Lackland Air Force Base, Texas: AFPTC Res. Rep. TN-56 (April). **284**

ROESSLER, R., GREENFIELD, N., & ALEXANDER, A., 1964. Ego strength and response stereotypy. *Psychophysiology, 1,* 142–150. **22**

ROGLER, L. H., & HOLLINGSHEAD, A. B., 1965. *Trapped: Families and schizophrenia.* New York: Wiley. **237**

ROHRER, J. H., 1959. *Studies of human adjustment to submarine isolation and implications of these studies in fallout shelters.* Washington, D.C.: Disaster Research Group, National Research Council, Working paper. **345**

ROHRER, J. H., 1961. Interpersonal relationships in isolated small groups. In B. E. FLAHERTY (Ed.), *Psychophysiological aspects of space flight.* New York: Columbia, pp. 263–271. **282, 294, 364**

ROKEACH, M., 1960. *The open and closed mind.* New York: Basic Books, Inc., pp. 71–80. **369**

ROTH, J. A., 1963. *Timetables.* New York: Bobbs-Merrill. **296**

RUCKMICK, C. A. (Ed.), 1936. *The psychology of feeling and emotions.* New York: McGraw-Hill. **33**

RUFF, G. E., 1961. Psychological effects of space flight. *Aerospace Med., 32,* 639–642. **79**

RUFF, G. E., 1963. Psychological and psychophysiological indices of stress. In

N. E. Burns, R. Chambers, & E. Hendler (Eds.), *Unusual environments and human behavior.* New York: Collier-Macmillan, pp. 33–59. **231**

Ruff, G. E., & Korchin, S. J., 1964. Psychological responses of the Mercury Astronauts to stress. In G. H. Grosser, H. Wechsler, & M. Greenblatt (Eds.), *The threat of impending disaster: Contributions to the psychology of stress.* Cambridge, Mass.: M.I.T., pp. 208–220. **300**

Ruff, G. E., & Levy, E. Z., 1959. Psychiatric evaluation of candidates for space flight. *Am. J. Psychiat., 116,* 385–391. **300**

Ruff, G. E., Levy, E. Z., & Thaler, V. H., 1959. Studies of isolation and confinement. *Aerospace Med., 30,* 599–604. **343**

Ryle, G., 1949. *The concept of mind.* London: Hutchinson. **356**

Sabshin, M. A., Hamburg, D. A., Grinker, R. R., Persky, H., Basowitz, H., Korchin, S. J., & Chevalier, J., 1957. Significance of pre-experimental studies in the psychosomatic laboratory. *AMA Arch. neurol. Psychiat., 78,* 207–219. **45, 47–48, 174**

Sachar, E. J., Fishman, J. R., & Mason, J. W., 1964. The influence of the hypnotic trance on plasma 17-hydroxycorticosteroid concentration. *Psychosom. Med., 26,* 635 (Abstract). **48**

Sachar, E. J., Mason, J. W., Kolmer, H. S. Jr., & Artiss, K. L., 1963. Psychoendocrine aspects of acute schizophrenic reactions. *Psychosom. Med., 25,* 510–537. **46**

Sapir, E., 1937. The contribution of psychiatry to the understanding of behavior in society. *Amer. J. Sociol., 42,* 862–870. **219**

Sawyer, W. H., Munsick, R. A., & van Dyke, H. B., 1960. Antidiuretic hormones. *Circulation, 21,* 1027–1037. **50**

Schachter, J., 1957. Pain, fear and anger in hypertensives and normotensives: A psychophysiologic study. *Psychosom. Med., 19,* 17–29. **25, 37, 55**

Schachter, S., 1965. Personal communication to Dr. Cohen. **147**

Schachter, S., & Singer, J. E., 1962. Cognitive, social, and physiological determinants of emotional state. *Psychol. Rev., 69,* 379–399. **54, 153, 167, 213, 308, 337, 398**

Schaefer, K. E., 1959. Experiences with submarine atmospheres. *J. aviat. Med., 30,* 350–359. **334, 341**

Schaefer, K. E., Clegg, D. R., Carey, G., & Weybrew, B. B., 1965. Effects of isolation in a constant environment on periodicity of physiological functions and performance. Paper read at 36th Annual Scientific Meeting, Aerospace Med. Ass., New York (April). **342**

Scheibel, M. E., & Scheibel, A. B., 1962. Hallucinations and brain stem reticular core. In L. J. West (Ed.), *Hallucinations.* New York: Grune & Stratton, pp. 15–35. **105**

Schein, E. H., 1956. The Chinese indoctrination program for prisoners of war; a study of attempted "brainwashing." *Psychiat., 19,* 149–172. **260**

SCHEIN, E. H., 1957. Reaction patterns to severe, chronic stress in American Army prisoners of war of the Chinese. *J. soc. Issues, 13,* 21–30. **247**

SCHEIN, E. H., 1959. Brainwashing and totalitarianism in modern society. *World Politics, 2,* 430–443. **260**

SCHEIN, E. H., 1960. Interpersonal communication, group solidarity, and social influence. *Sociometry, 23,* 148–161. **247**

SCHEIN, E. H., SCHNEIER, I., & BARKER, C. H., 1961. *Coercive persuasion.* New York: Norton. **284**

SCHIMKE, R. T., 1959. Effects of prolonged light deprivation for the development of retinal enzymes in the rabbit. *J. biol. Chem., 234,* 700–703. **119**

SCHMIDT, C. F., 1962. Editorial. (Second annual supplement on hypertension.) *Circ. Res., 11,* 2. **51**

SCHNEIDER, D. M., 1957. Typhoons on Yap. *Human Organization, 16*(2), 10–15. **235**

SCHNEIDER, R. C., CROSBY, E. C., & KAHN, E. A., 1963. Certain afferent cortical connections of the rhinencephalon. In W. BARGMANN & J. P. SCHADE (Eds.), *The rhinencephalon and related structures. Progr. in Brain Res., 3,* 191–217. New York: Elsevier. **140**

SCHNORE, M. M., 1959. Individual patterns of physiological activity as a function of task differences and degree of arousal. *J. exp. Psychol., 58,* 117–128. **22, 402**

SCHOCK, G. J. D., 1960. Airborne GSR studies. *Aerospace Med., 31,* 543–546. **333**

SCOTT, E. L., 1952. *Perceptions of organization and leadership behavior: A study of perceptions of organization structure and their social correlates in a submarine squadron of the U.S. Navy.* ONR Contr. N6ori-17. Columbus, Ohio: Ohio State University. **271, 345**

SCOTT, J. M., 1953. *Portrait of an ice cap with human figures.* London: Chatto & Windus. **338**

SCOTT, T. H., BEXTON, W. H., HERON, W., & DOANE, B. K., 1959. Cognitive effects of perceptual isolation. *Canad. J. Psychol., 13,* 200–209. **77**

SEATON, R. W., 1964. Deterioration of military work groups under deprivation stress. In M. JANOWITZ (Ed.), *The new military: Changing patterns of organization.* New York: Russell Sage Foundation, pp. 225–249. **284**

SEGAL, J., 1956. *Factors related to the collaboration and resistance behavior of U.S. Army P.W.'s in Korea.* HUMRRO Tech. Rep. No. 33. Washington, D.C.: HUMRRO, George Washington University (December). **247**

SELLS, S. B., 1963. An interactionist looks at the environment. *Amer. Psychol., 18,* 696–702. **240**

SELLS, S. B., 1965. *Ecology and the science of psychology.* Special Report, Contr. No. Nonr 3436 (00) Fort Worth: Texas Christian University, Institute of Behavioral Research. **240**

SELYE, H., 1950. *The physiology and pathology of exposure to stress.* Montreal: Acta, Inc. **1, 3, 43, 49, 128, 172**

SELYE, H., 1951–1956. *Annual report on stress.* Montreal: Acta, Inc., 1951,

SELYE, H., & HORAVA, A., 1952, 1953, SELYE, H., & HEUSER, G., 1954. M. D. Publicat. (New York), 1955–1956. **1**

SELYE, H., 1952. *The story of the adaptation syndrome.* Montreal: Acta, Inc. **3, 160**

SELYE, H., 1955. Stress and disease. *Science, 122,* 625–631. **3**

SELYE, H., 1956. *The stress of life.* New York: McGraw-Hill. **3, 352**

SELYE, H., 1959. Perspectives in stress research. *Perspect. Biol. Med., 2,* 403–416. **2, 3**

SELYE, H., & HEUSER, G., 1956. See SELYE, H., 1951–1956. **1**

SELYE, H., & HOROVA, A., 1953. See SELYE, H., 1951–1956. **2**

SEM-JACOBSEN, C. W., 1963. *Brain and consciousness: intracerebral depth electrographic studies in the human brain.* Final Report, Grant No. 61-236. New Haven, Conn.: The Foundations' Fund for Research in Psychiatry. **64, 317**

SHAPIRO, D., & LEIDERMAN, P. H., 1965. *The influence of different task roles on autonomic and subjective response.* Washington, D.C.: Office of Naval Research, Tech. Rep. No. 12, Contr. Nonr-1866 (43) NR 170–518. **346**

SHAPIRO, D., LEIDERMAN, P., & MORNINGSTAR, M., 1963. *Social isolation and social interaction.* Washington, D.C.: Office of Naval Research, Tech. Rep. No. 5 (January), HR 170–518. **87, 99**

SHELLEY, W. B., & HURLEY, H. J., 1953. The physiology of the human axillary apocrine sweat gland. *J. Invest. Dermatol., 20,* 285–296. **336**

SHILS, E. H., & JANOWITZ, M., 1948. Cohesion and disintegration in the Wehrmacht in World War Two. *Public Opinion Quart., 12,* 280–315. **199**

SHIPMAN, W. G., OKEN, D., GOLDSTEIN, I. B., GRINKER, R. R., & HEATH, HELEN, 1964. Study in psychophysiology of muscle tension. *AMA Arch. gen. Psychiat., 2,* 330–345. **56**

SHURLEY, J. T., 1960. Profound experimental sensory isolation. *Am. J. Psychiat., 117,* 539–545. **79, 90**

SIDMAN, M., MASON, J. W., BRADY, J. V., TACH, J., JR., 1962. Quantitative relations between avoidance behavior and pituitary-adrenal cortical activity. *J. exp. anal. Behav., 5,* 353–362. **48**

SIEGEL, A. I., & WOLF, J. J., 1963. Computer simulation of man-machine systems. In N. E. BURNS, R. M. CHAMBERS, & E. HENDLER (Eds.), *Unusual environments and human behavior.* New York: Collier-Macmillan, pp. 61–86. **354**

SILVERMAN, A. J., COHEN, S. I., & SHMAVONIAN, B. M., 1959. Investigations of psychophysiologic relationship with skin resistance measures. *J. Psychosom. Res., 4,* 65–87. **90**

SILVERMAN, A. J., COHEN, S. I., SHMAVONIAN, B. M., & KIRSHNER, N., 1961. Catechol amines in psychophysiologic studies. *Recent Advances Biol. Psychiat., 3,* 104–118. **54, 90**

SIMONS, D. G., 1958. Survival 20 miles up! *Science Digest, 44,* 43–47. **335, 339**

SIMONS, D. G., FLINN, D. E., & HARTMANN, B., 1963. Psychophysiology of high-altitude experience. In N. E. BURNS, R. M. CHAMBERS, & E. HENDLER (Eds.), *Unusual environments and human behavior.* New York: Collier-Macmillan, pp. 127–164. **326, 337**

SINGER, MARGARET T., & SCHEIN, E. H., 1958. Projective test responses of prisoners of war following repatriation. *Psychiat., 21,* 375–385. **247**

SKINNER, B. F., 1953. *Science and human behavior.* New York: Macmillan. **356**

SKINNER, B. F., 1957. *Verbal behavior.* New York: Appleton-Century-Crofts. **356**

SLOCUM, J., 1900. *Sailing alone around the world.* New York: Centray (Blue Ribbon Books, 1943). **78, 342**

SMALL, M. H., 1900. On some physical relations of society and solitude. *Pedag. Seminary, 7,* 13–69. **257, 258**

SMELSER, N. J., 1963. *Theory of collective behavior.* New York: Free Press. **164, 165**

SMITH, R. W., & ALTMAN, J. W., 1961. *Space psychology: Some considerations in the study of Astronauts' behavior.* Pittsburgh: American Institute for Research. **340**

SOKOLOV, E. N., 1960. Neuronal models and the orienting reflex. In MARY A. B. BRAZIER (Ed.), *Central nervous system and behavior.* Madison, N.J.: Madison Printing, pp. 187–276. **101, 111**

SOLOMON, P., LEIDERMAN, P. H., MENDELSON, J., & WEXLER, D., 1957. Sensory deprivation: A review. *Am. J. Psychiat., 114,* 357–363. **342**

SOUPAULT, P., 1946. *Age of assassins: The story of Prisoner No. 1234.* New York: Knopf. **25**

SPAIGHT, J. M., 1918. *War rights on land.* London: MacMillan. **251**

SPEISMAN, J. C., LAZARUS, R. S., DAVISON, L. A., & MORDKOFF, A. M., 1964a. Experimental analysis of a film used as a threatening stimulus. *J. consult. Psychol., 28,* 23–33. **179**

SPEISMAN, J. C., LAZARUS, R. S., MORDKOFF, A. M., & DAVISON, L. A., 1964b. The experimental reduction of stress based on ego-defense theory. *J. abn. soc. Psychol., 68,* 367–380. **154, 214**

SPEISMAN, J. C., OSBORNE, J., & LAZARUS, R. S., 1961. Cluster analyses of skin resistance and heart rate at rest and under stress. *Psychosom. Med., 23,* 323–343. **22**

SPICER, E. R., OPLER, M. K., LUOMALA, K., & HAMSEN, A., 1946. *Impounded people.* Washington, D.C.: U.S. Gov't. Printing Office, War Relocation Authority, Interior Department. **224, 244**

SPIRO, M. E., 1959. Cultural heritage and mental illness in a South Sea culture. In M. K. OPLER (Ed.), *Culture and mental health: Cross-cultural studies.* New York: Macmillan, pp. 141–171. **222**

SPITZ, R. A., & WOLF, K. M., 1946. The smiling response. *Genet. psychol. Monogr., 34,* 57–125. **143**

STEFANSSON, V., 1913. *My life with the Eskimos.* New York: Macmillan. **221**

STEFANSSON, V., 1922. *Hunters of the Great North.* New York: Macmillan. Cf. BIRKET-SMITH, 1936. *The Eskimos.* London: Methuen. **221**

STEINKAMP, G. R., HAWKINS, W. R., HAUTY, G. T., BURWELL, R. R., & WARD, J. E., 1959. *Human experimentation in the space cabin simulator: Development of life support systems and results of initial seven-day flights.* Brooks AFB, Texas: USAF Sch. Aviat. Med. SAM 59–101. **341**

STENNETT, R. G., 1957. The relationship of alpha amplitude to the level of palmar conductance. *Electroencephal. clin. Neurophysiol., 9,* 131–138. **24**

STERN, J. A., STEWARD, M., & WINOKUR, G., 1961. An investigation of some relationships between various measures of galvanic skin response. *J. Psychosom. Res., 5,* 215–223. **103**

STERN, J. A., & WORD, T. J., 1962. Heart rate changes during avoidance conditioning in the male albino rat. *J. Psychosom. Res., 6,* 167–175. **67**

STERN, R. (n.d.). *Electrophysiologic effects of short-term sensory deprivation.* Washington, D.C.: ASTIA Rep. 437-810. **84, 96, 99**

STERNBACH, R. A., 1960. Two independent indices of activation. *Electroencephal. clin. Neurophysiol., 12,* 609–611. **23, 24**

STERNBACH, R. A., 1962. Assessing differential autonomic patterns in emotions. *J. Psychosom. Res., 6,* 87–91. **47**

STOPOL, M. S., 1954. The consistency of stress tolerance. *J. Personal. 23,* 13–29. **9**

STRODTBECK, F. L., 1951. Husband-wife interaction over revealed differences. *Amer. sociol. Rev., 16,* 468–473. **202**

STRUGHOLD, H., 1952. *The physiological day-night cycle in global flights.* Special Report. Randolph Field, Texas: School of Aviat. Med. **341**

Study of space effects, 1958. *Science News Letter, 74,* 339. **340**

SUEDFELD, P., GRISSOM, R. J., & VERNON, J., 1964. The effects of sensory deprivation and social isolation on the performance of an unstructured cognitive task. *Amer. J. Psychol., 77,* 111–115. **376**

SURWILLO, W. W., 1965. The relation of amplitude of alpha rhythm to heart rate. *Psychophysiology, 1,* 247–252. **24**

SYMINGTON, T., CURRIE, A. R., CURRAN, R. C., & DAVIDSON, J. N., 1955. The reaction of the adrenal cortex to the conditions of stress. In G. E. W. WOLSTENHOLME & M. P. CAMERON (Eds.), *Ciba Foundation colloquia on endocrinology, Vol. 8. The human adrenal cortex.* Boston: Little, Brown, pp. 70–91. **69**

TEITELBAUM, P., & EPSTEIN, A. N., 1962. The lateral hypothalamic syndrome: Recovery of feeding and drinking after lateral hypothalamic lesions. *Psychol. Rev., 69,* 74–90. **338**

TEUBER, H. L., 1959. Some alterations in behavior after cerebral lesions. In A. D. BASS (Ed.), *Symposium on evolution of nervous control from primitive organisms to man.* Washington, D.C.: Amer. Assoc. Adv. Science, pp. 157–194. **91, 101**

TEUBER, H. L., 1961. Sensory deprivation, sensory suppression and agnosia: Notes for a neurologic theory. *J. nerv. ment. Dis., 132,* 32–40 **91**

THOMAS, G. J., & SLOTNICK, B. M., 1963. Impairment of avoidance responding by lesions in cingulate cortex in rats depends on food drive. *J. comp. physiol. Psychol, 56,* 959–964. **140**

THOMPSON, J. D., & HAWKES, R. W., 1962. Disaster, community organization, and

validation by psychological and psychiatric criteria. Randolph Field, Texas: Sch. Aviat. Med. Proj. No. 21-37-002 Rep. No. 4. **349**

U.S. Congress, Senate, 1957. (Committee on Government Operations, Permanent Subcommittee on Investigations.) *Communist interrogation, indoctrination and exploitation of American military and civilian prisoners.* 84th Congr., 2nd Sess., Senate Report No. 2832, Dec. 31, 1956. Washington, D.C.: Govt. Print. Off. **253**

U.S. Department of Defense, 1955. *POW: The fight continues after the battle. The report of the Secretary of Defense's Advisory Committee on Prisoners of War.* Washington, D.C.: Govt. Print. Off. **255**

UTTERBACK, R., & LUDWIG, G., 1949. *A comparative study of schedules for standing watches aboard submarines, based on body temperature cycles.* Bethesda, Md.: USN Med. Res. Inst. Proj. NM 004003, Rep. No. 1. **341**

VALINS, S. Manipulated heart rate feedback and emotional arousal. Unpublished manuscript. **65, 66**

VANNING, E. H., DRYENFURTH, I., & BECK, J. C., 1957. Effect of anxiety upon Aldosterone excretion in man. *J. clin. Endocrinol. Metab. 17,* 1005–1007. **52**

VERNON, J. A., & HOFFMAN, J., 1956. Effects of sensory deprivation on learning rate in human beings. *Science, 132,* 1074–1075. **78**

VERNON, J. A., & MCGILL, T. E., 1961. Sensory deprivation and pain thresholds. *Science, 133,* 330–331. **364**

VERNON, J. A., MCGILL, T. E., GULICK, W., & CANDLAND, D., 1959. Effect of sensory deprivation on some perceptual and motor skills. *Percept. Mot. Skills, 9,* 91–97. **364**

VOAS, R. 1964. Performance evaluation in the Mercury flights. In R. W. RUSSELL, V. J. BIELIAUSKAS, J. L. FULLER, E. H. GALANTER, J. P. ·GUILFORD, H. HARLOW, & S. B. SELLS (Eds.), *Frontiers in psychology.* Scott, Foresman, pp. 163–178. **312**

WALLACE, A. F. C., 1956. *Human behavior in extreme situations.* Washington, D.C.: National Acad. Sci.—National Res. Council Publ. No. 390. **246**

WARD, A. A., JR., 1948. The anterior cingular gyrus and personality. *Res. Publ. Ass. Nerv. Ment. Dis., 27,* 438–445. **139**

WASHBURN, S. (Ed.), 1961. *Social life of early man.* Chicago, Ill.: Aldine. **214**

WEBB, M. G., JR., 1958. Some effects of acceleration on human subjects. *J. aviat. Med., 29,* 879–884. **333**

WEBB, W. B., & ADIS, H., 1964. Sleep tendencies: Effects of barometric pressures. *Science, 143,* 263–264. **335**

WEINER, H., SINGER, MARGARET T., & REISER, M. F., 1962. Cardiovascular responses and their psychological correlates: I. A study in healthy young adults and patients with peptic ulcer and hypertension. *Psychosom. Med.,* *24,* 477–498. **160**

WEISSBERG, A., 1951. *The accused.* New York: Simon and Schuster. **247**

WELCH, B. L., 1965. Psychophysiological response to the mean level of environmental stimulation: A theory of environmental integration. In D. McK. RIOCH (Ed.), *Symposium on medical aspects of stress in the military climate.* Washington, D.C.: Walter Reed Army Institute of Research, pp. 39–96. **322**

WELCH, B. L., & WELCH, C., 1966. Effects of grouping on the level of brain norepinephrine in White Swiss Mice. *Life Sciences,* in press. **266**

WENGER, M. A., Personal communication to Dr. Ax. **37**

WENGER, M. A., 1948. Studies of autonomic balance in Army Air Force personnel. *Comp. psychol. Monogr., 19,* No. 4. **344, 349, 350, 352**

WENGER, M. A., CLEMENS, T. L., COLEMAN, D. R., CULLEN, T. D., & ENGEL, B. T., 1961. Autonomic response specificity. *Psychosom. Med., 23,* 185–193. **22, 55**

WENZEL, B. M., 1961. Changes in heart rate associated with responses based on positive and negative reinforcement. *J. comp. physiol. Psychol., 54,* 638–644. **33**

WESSMAN, A. E., & RICKS, J. H., 1966. *Mood and personality.* New York: Holt, Rinehart and Winston. **355**

WEST, L. J., 1958. Psychiatric aspects of training for honorable survival as a prisoner of war. *Amer. J. Psychiat., 115,* 239–336. **247**

WEST, L. J., 1962. *Hallucinations.* New York: Grune & Stratton. **105**

WEXLER, D., MENDELSON, J., LEIDERMAN, P. H., & SOLOMON, P., 1958. Sensory deprivation. *AMA Arch. Neuropsychiat., 79,* 225–233. **105, 364, 365**

WEYBREW, B. B., 1957. *Psychological and psychophysiological effects of long periods of submergence. I. Analysis of data collected during a 265-hour, completely submerged habitability cruise of the USS Nautilus (SSN571),* U.S.N. Med. Res. Lab. Rep. No. 281. New London, Conn.: U.S. Navy Submarine Base. **326, 347**

WEYBREW, B. B., 1962. *Behavioral energetics: I. A factor analytical study of individual differences in modes of energy discharge resulting from experimentally-induced frustration.* U.S.N. Med. Res. Lab. Rep. No. 378. New London, Conn.: U.S. Navy Submarine Base. **346**

WEYBREW, B. B., 1963*a.* Psychological problems of prolonged periods of marine submergence. In N. E. BURNS, R. M. CHAMBERS, & E. HENDLER (Eds.), *Unusual environments and human behavior.* New York: Collier-Macmillan, pp. 85–125. **279, 335, 343, 351**

WEYBREW, B. B., 1963*b. Autonomic resiliency, subjective symptomatology and submarine stress.* U.S.N. Med. Res. Lab. Memo Rep. No. 63-13. New London, Conn.: U.S. Navy Submarine Base. **279, 351**

WEYBREW, B. B., 1964. *Prediction of adjustment to prolonged submergence aboard a Fleet Ballistic Missile Submarine. IV. Psychophysiological indices.* U.S.N. Med. Res. Lab. Rep. No. 416. New London, Conn.: U.S. Navy Submarine Base. **346, 349**

WEYBREW, B. B., 1965. *Selection of men for hazardous duty from indices of individual differences in autonomic nervous system reactivity.* Groton, Conn.: U.S.N. Submarine Med. Center, Memo Rep. No. 65-1. **352**

WEYBREW, B. B., GREENWOOD, M., & PARKER, J. W., 1964. *Psychological and psychophysiological effects of confinement in a high-pressure helium-oxygen-nitrogen atmosphere for 284 hours.* Groton, Conn.: U.S.N. Submarine Med. Center, Rep. No. 441. **325, 343**

WEYBREW, B. B., & PARKER, J. W., 1960. Bibliography of sensory deprivation, isolation, and confinement. *Armed Forces Med. J., 11,* 903–911. **342**

WHEATON, J. L., 1959. *Fact and fancy in sensory deprivation studies.* Brooks AFB, Texas: Sch. Aviat. Med. **342**

WHITE, ELNA, 1965. Autonomic responsivity as a function of level of subject involvement. *Behav. Sci., 10,* 39–50. **158**

WHITEHORN, J. C., 1953. Introduction and survey of the problems of stress. In Army Medical Service Graduate School (Walter Reed Army Medical Center), *Symposium on stress.* Washington, D.C.: Army Med. Serv. Gr. Sch., pp. 2–7. **6**

WIESEL, T. N., & HUBEL, D. H., 1963. Effects of visual deprivation on morphology and physiology of cells in the cat's lateral geniculate body. Single-cell responses in striate cortex of kittens deprived of vision in one eye. *J. Neurophysiol., 26,* 978–993; 1003–1017. **119**

WIKLER, A., 1952. Pharmacologic dissociation of behavior and EEG "sleep patterns" in dogs: Morphine, N-allylnormorphine, and atropine. *Proc. Soc. Exp. Biol. Med., 79,* 261–265. **17**

WILDER, J., 1957. The Law of Initial Value in neurology and psychiatry. *J. nerv. ment. Dis., 125,* 73–86. **353**

WILKINSON, R. T., 1960. Effects of sleep-deprivation on performance and muscle tension. In G. E. W. WOLSTENHOLME & MAEVE O'CONNOR (Eds.), *Ciba Foundation symposium on the nature of sleep.* Boston, Mass.: Little, Brown, pp. 329–336. **336**

WILLIAMS, J. G. L., 1964. Use of a resonance technique to measure muscle activity in neurotic and schizophrenic patients. *Psychosom. Med., 26,* 20–28. **56**

WILSON, R. S., 1964. Autonomic changes produced by noxious and innocuous stimulation. *J. comp. physiol. Psychol., 58,* 290–295. **33**

WISSLER, CLARK, 1938. *The American Indian.* London: Oxford. **211**

WITKIN, H. A., DYK, R. B., FATERSON, H. F., GOODENOUGH, D. R., & KARP, S. A., 1962. *Psychological differentiation.* New York: Wiley. **89, 90, 100, 106**

WITKIN, H. A., LEWIS, H. B., HERTZMAN, M., MACHOVER, K., MEISSNER, P. B., & WAPNER, S., 1954. *Personality through perception.* New York: Harper & Row. **89, 100, 106, 114, 405**

WOLBERG, L. R., 1947. Hypnotic experiments in psychosomatic medicine. *Psychosom. Med., 9,* 337–342. **213**

WOLF, A. V., 1958. *Thirst: Physiology of the urge to drink and the problem of water lack.* Springfield, Ill.: Charles C Thomas. **338**

WOLF, S., CARDON, P. V., SHEPARD, E. M., & WOLFF, H. G., 1955. *Life stress and essential hypertension: A study of cardiovascular adjustments in man.* Baltimore, Md.: Williams & Wilkins. **52**

WOLF, S., & RIPLEY, H. A., 1947. Reactions among Allied prisoners of war subjected to three years of imprisonment and torture by the Japanese. *Amer. J. Psychiat., 104,* 180–193. **261, 338**

WOLFF, C. T., FRIEDMAN, S. B., HOFER, M. A., & MASON, J. W., 1964a. Relationship between psychological defenses and mean urinary 17-hydroxycorticosteroid excretion rates: I. A predictive study of parents of fatally ill children. *Psychosom. Med., 26,* 576–591. **48, 166**

WOLFF, C. T., HOFER, M. A., & MASON, J. W., 1964b. Relationship between psychological defenses and mean urinary 17-hydroxycorticosteroid excretion rates. II. Methodologic and theoretical considerations. *Psychosom. Med., 26,* 592–609. **48**

WOLFF, H. G., 1950a. Life situations, emotions and bodily disease. In M. L. REYMERT (Ed.), *Feelings and emotions.* New York: McGraw-Hill, pp. 284–335. **127**

WOLFF, H. G. (Ed.), 1950b. *Life stress and bodily disease. Res. Publ. Assoc. Nerv. Ment. Dis., Vol. 29.* Baltimore, Md.: Williams & Wilkins. **324**

WOLFF, H. G., 1960. Every man has his breaking point. *Mil. Med., 2,* 85–104. **247**

WOLSTENHOLME, G. E. W., & CAMERON, M. P. (Eds.), 1955. *Ciba Foundation Colloquia on Endocrinology, Vol. 8. The human adrenal cortex.* Boston: Little, Brown. **45**

WRIGHT, J. C., 1962a. Consistency and complexity of response sequences as a function of schedules of noncontingent reward. *J. exp. Psychol., 63,* 601–609. **204**

WRIGHT, R. D., 1962b. Control of secretion of Aldosterone. *Brit. Med. Bull., 18,* 159–163. **51**

WUNDT, W. M., 1911–1920. *Völkerpsychologie: eine Untersuchung der Entwicklungsgesetz von Sprache, Mythus, und Sitte.* Vols. 1–10, Leipzig: Englemann. **211**

YAMAMOTO, T. (pseud), 1952. *Four years in Hell. I was a prisoner behind the Iron Curtain.* Tokyo: Asia. **264**

YOUNG, P. T., 1961. *Motivation and emotion.* New York: Wiley. **334**

ZINNER, P., 1963. Personal communication to Dr. Sells. **277**

ZISKIND, E., 1962. A second look at sensory deprivation. *J. nerv. ment. Dis., 138,* 223–232. **79**

ZOTTERMAN, Y., 1953. Electrophysiological investigations on afferent fibres from the carotid sinus region. *Rapport au XIX Congr. Internat. Physiol. (Montreal),* 59–66. **29**

ZUBEK, J. P., 1963. Counteracting effects of physical exercise performed during prolonged perceptual deprivation. *Science, 142,* 504–506.   **376**

ZUBEK, J. P., 1964. Effects of prolonged sensory and perceptual deprivation. *Brit. Med. Bull. 20,* 38–42.   **79, 82, 87, 88, 313, 364**

ZUBEK, J. P., AFTANAS, M., HASEK, J., SANSOM, W., SCHLUDERMANN, E., WILGOSH, L., & WINOCUR, G., 1962. Intellectual and perceptual changes during prolonged perceptual deprivation: Low illumination and noise level. *Percept. mot. Skills, 16,* 171–198.   **82**

ZUBEK, J. P., AFTANAS, M., KOVACH, K., WILGOSH, L., & WINOCUR, G., 1963. Effect of severe immobilization of the body on intellectual and perceptual processes. *Canad. J. Psychol., 17,* 118–133.   **81**

ZUBEK, J. P., PUSHKAR, D., SANSOM, W., & GOWING, J., 1961. Perceptual changes after prolonged sensory isolation (darkness and silence). *Canad. J. Psychol., 15,* 83–101.   **81**

ZUBEK, J. P., WELCH, G., & SAUNDERS, M. G., 1963. Electroencephalographic changes during and after 14 days of perceptual deprivation. *Science, 139,* 490–492.   **82**

ZUBEK, J. P., & WILGOSH, L., 1963. Prolonged immobilization of the body: Changes in performance and in the electroencephalogram. *Science, 140,* 306–308.   **83, 343, 376**

ZUCKERMAN, M., 1964. Perceptual isolation as a stress situation: A review. *AMA Arch. gen. Psychiat., 2,* 255–276.   **78, 83, 85, 96**

ZUCKERMAN, M., & COHEN, N. J., 1964a. Is suggestion the source of reported visual sensations in perceptual isolation? *J. abn. soc. Psychol., 68,* 655–660.   **104, 107**

ZUCKERMAN, M., & COHEN, N. J., 1964b. Sources of reports of visual and auditory sensations in perceptual isolation experiments. *Psychol. Bull., 62,* 1–20.   **104, 107**

ZUCKERMAN, M., LEVINE, S., & BIASE, D. V., 1964. Stress response in total and partial perceptual isolation. *Psychosom. Med., 26,* 250–260.   **108, 109**

ZUCKERMAN, S., 1932. *The social life of the monkeys and apes.* New York: Harcourt, Brace & World.   **214, 269**

ZUIDEMA, G. D., 1956. Human tolerance to prolonged acceleration. *J. aviat. Med., 27,* 469–481.   **333**

Subject index

Since this book is a joint product of a number of authors, representing different disciplines and traditions, the index reflects the use of different terms for the same or for similar phenomena, processes, and objects. Cross-referencing has been attempted, but the reader is nevertheless advised to search for cognates if he does not find the entry under the term with which he is familiar.

Section headings and major discussions of a topic are indicated by italicized numbers.